SECOND OPINION

Canadian Edition

SECOND OPINION
An Introduction to Health Sociology

John Germov
Jennie Hornosty

OXFORD

UNIVERSITY PRESS

Oxford University Press is a department of the University of Oxford. It furthers the University's objective of excellence in research, scholarship, and education by publishing worldwide. Oxford is a registered trade mark of Oxford University Press in the UK and in certain other countries.

Published in Canada by
Oxford University Press
8 Sampson Mews, Suite 204,
Don Mills, Ontario M3C 0H5 Canada

www.oupcanada.com

Library and Archives Canada Cataloguing in Publication

Germov, John

Second opinion : an introduction to health sociology / John Germov and Jennie Hornosty. —1st Canadian ed.

Includes bibliographical references and index.

ISBN 978-0-19-543198-8

1. Social medicine—Canada. 2. Health—Social aspects—Canada.

I. Hornosty, Jennie Mary, 1944– II. Title.

RA418.3.C3S43 2011   306.4'610971   C2011-904832-9

For my wonderful sons,
Jason Hornosty and Justin Hornosty,
with love.

Contents

Preface to the Canadian Edition

The first Canadian edition of *Second Opinion: An Introduction to Health Sociology* introduces readers to the sociology of health and illness through an accessible yet authoritative overview of key debates, research findings, and theories, with a particular emphasis on Canadian perspectives. Current Canadian material in the form of examples, research, and statistical information is integrated throughout the book. A distinctive feature of the book is its critical perspective on health-related issues and a running theme on the social determinants of health. Contributions of Canadian researchers in this area are highlighted. A second theme that unifies various chapters is a concern with health inequalities, and the text examines the role of both structure and agency in creating and maintaining societal arrangements. Because health sociology is a complex and diverse area, rather than attempting to cover the entire field the topics included in the book were chosen to reflect health-related issues that should be of special interest to Canadian students in the twenty-first century. In sum, this book provides students with a contemporary overview of health sociology in Canada from a critical perspective. A clear and straightforward writing style and special pedagogic features make the book student-friendly.

A growing number of scholars in the area of the sociology of health have examined the impact of various structural inequalities on the health outcomes of individuals. Research on the social determinants of health, such as income inequality, education, environment, gender, Aboriginal status, and poverty, describes how such factors influence mortality and morbidity rates as well as the distribution and experience of illness within society. In Canada, in addition to looking at these social determinants of health, critical researchers are looking at how economic and political inequalities both within the country and on a global scale affect health policy and the delivery of health services. A critical political economy approach situates health and illness within a historical context as well as examines how dominant values and ideologies influence decisions around health priorities at both a formal and informal level. These macro and structural perspectives have influenced my approach in putting together this Canadian edition. At the same time, I have not ignored important contributions of the social constructionist tradition.

I first taught an undergraduate course in the sociology of health and illness nearly two decades ago. At that time there were only a couple of sociology books available that considered health issues in a Canadian context. While more Canadian material is available today, each year I have continued to look for an undergraduate text that has a critical analytical focus, has strong Canadian content, provides an integrated approach including a discussion of theories and methodological approaches, and is written at a level that most students can readily understand. These are the key elements that I have tried to incorporate in writing and compiling this Canadian edition. Unlike some academics who purport neutrality, I reject the idea that our work can ever be value-free. The approaches we take or do not take, the questions we ask or do not ask, and the theories we choose to emphasize or ignore reflect our basic values and assumptions about how the world works. At the same time, as teachers we have a responsibility to present other perspectives and approaches, especially in books written for a student audience. It is my hope that this book successfully presents my and my co-writers' values and assumptions as well as those of other perspectives. In some chapters, though, my personal views will be quite apparent: for example, I passionately believe that equal access to health care is an unalienable right and that one of the biggest challenges we face today as Canadians is the threatened erosion of our system of Medicare. This does not presume that all students will share this view.

Three Canadian scholars who research health and health care from a critical perspective have contributed new chapters for this Canadian edition. Patricia Armstrong, holder of a Canadian Institutes of Health Research (CIHR) Chair in Health Services and Nursing Research, has written a chapter on women's health and gender issues using a feminist political economy theoretical framework. Joel Lexchin has contributed a new chapter on the pharmaceutical industry and its interactions with Health Canada, in which he explores how the profit motive affects the operations of the industry. Zelda Abramson, in her chapter on environmental links to health, examines this complex relationship, using Canadian and international examples to illustrate how our health is affected by the air we breathe and the foods we eat.

Structure and Content of the Book

Second Opinion: An Introduction to Health Sociology, first Canadian edition, assumes no prior knowledge of sociology and is intended for undergraduate students. The text is structured to provide a solid foundation in the sociology of health and illness and to map out the key dimensions of the social model of health. As such, the book is divided into the following parts:

- Introduction: Health Sociology and the Social Model of Health
- Part 1: The Social Production and Distribution of Health and Illness
- Part 2: The Social Construction of Health and Illness
- Part 3: The Social Organization of Health Care: Politics, Values, and Professions
- Conclusion

The introduction provides the foundation for understanding the sociological contribution of studying health and illness. First of all, Chapter 1 explains the development of the social model of health, reviews critiques of the biomedical model, and provides an overview of the sociological imagination and how it can be used to analyze health issues. Chapters 2 and 3 specifically address the main theoretical perspectives and methodological debates in health sociology. In Part 1, The Social Production and Distribution of Health and Illness, the focus is on social determinants of health and health inequalities in terms of class, gender, ethnicity, and Aboriginal status. Part 1 also includes a chapter on the environment as a factor in the production and distribution of health and illness. Part 2, The Social Construction of Health and Illness, covers the debates about changing conceptions of health and illness; this section looks at the medicalization of society, the ways in which disabilities and chronic illnesses are constructed, and at issues around aging, death, and dying. Then, the five chapters in Part 3, The Social Organization of Health Care: Politics, Values, and Professions, examine different aspects of the social organization of health care and health-care delivery, including, in Chapter 12, the dominant influence of the medical profession on other health professions and on health-care delivery. Chapter 13, on Canada's health-care experience, situates Medicare's development in a historical context. The role and values of the pharmaceutical industry in Canada is the subject of Chapter 14, while Chapters 15 and 16, respectively, explore the current problems faced by the nursing profession and reasons for the growth of alternative medicines today. Finally, the conclusion provides a summary of major themes in the book, outlines some future trends in health sociology, and provides two current health-related examples for critical sociological reflection.

Overview of Key Features

Pedagogic features, an important aspect of the book, are found in each chapter and provide students with important learning tools. All chapters and pedagogic features that were part of the Australian edition have been revised and updated with Canadian data. These features include the following:

- **A chapter overview** appears at the beginning of each chapter and includes a series of questions and a short summary of the chapter to encourage a questioning and reflective approach to the topic.
- **Key terms and concepts** are highlighted in bold in the text and defined in separate margin notes.
- **A summary of main points** appears at the end of each chapter to help students identify the important issues covered in the chapter.
- **Theory Links boxes** clearly cross-reference discussions in different chapters.
- **Sociological reflection exercises** include self-directed or class-based exercises that help students apply their learning and highlight the relevance of sociological analysis.
- **Discussion questions** allow students to revisit key themes and ideas raised throughout the chapter.
- **Further investigation questions** help students to prepare for examinations and other assignments.
- **Further reading** lists some key books to allow students to research topics of particular interest.
- **Recommended chapter-specific web resources** allow students to explore different subject areas further.

Acknowledgements

When I was first approached by Oxford University Press to compile a Canadian edition of *Second Opinion,* I was not fully aware of what shape this project would take or where the journey would lead. Over the course of this project, however, I have gained a lot from the people with whom I've worked. I am most appreciative of the guidance I received from two developmental editors at Oxford University Press: Andrea Kennedy helped shepherd the process through its first year, and Mary Wat has worked diligently with me during this past year. Many thanks to both of you for your editorial advice, your words of encouragement, and your patience.

I also want to acknowledge two sociology graduate students, Barbara Morrisey and Kyle Lewis, who provided research assistance for sections of this book. Kyle deserves special mention for his contributions, which included research, interviewing, and more mundane tasks, such as formatting references and integrating the bibliography. And, over the years, undergraduate students in my sociology of health and illness course have helped me crystallize my approach to the subject. As well, I want to thank members in the Department of Sociology at the University of New Brunswick for their moral support.

My suggestions about needed revisions for the Canadian edition included three new chapters. I was most fortunate that the three individuals I identified agreed to be part of this book. Thanks so much to Zelda Abramsom, Patricia Armstrong, and Joel Lexchin, both for their chapter contributions and their understanding during this process. I also want to thank two colleagues in particular, Vanda Rideout and Matthew Hayes, who frequently asked how things were going and provided timely encouragement, each in their own way.

Writing would be a lonely endeavour were it not for the support of close friends and family. I cherished my many walks with Katy and her dog, which always lifted my spirits. Francesca always was willing to listen to any concerns and provide words of support. Thanks to both of you for your friendship. Also thanks to Joyce, Joe, Debbie, and George for the many Saturday morning laughs and get-togethers. I also want to acknowledge Susan and John, long-time dear friends, who, despite our geographical distance, have always been there for me.

Most important, I want to acknowledge my family. I am especially fortunate to have two wonderful sons, Jason Hornosty and Justin Hornosty, who, during this process as always, have been supportive, loving, and encouraging. In a strange way, it is for them that I wanted to do this book.

I am also grateful for my wonderful stepchildren: Michael Richardson, his partner, Meaghan Charlebois, and son, Liam; and Rebecca Richardson, her partner, Phil Allen, and daughters, Gemma and Mika. As well, I want to acknowledge my late partner, C. James (Jim) Richardson, who played such an important role in my academic life and with whom I first developed a course on the sociology of health and illness. And I want to remember my brother, Roy Hornosty, also a sociologist, who passed away a few years ago.

I would like to thank the Australian contributors for giving me an opportunity to work with their material and bring it to a Canadian audience. Thank you also to the three anonymous reviewers who provided feedback on an earlier draft of this edition. And I want to thank Colleen Ste. Marie and Lisa Ball and others at Oxford University Press for their assistance at different stages of the book's production.

INTRODUCTION

Health Sociology and the Social Model of Health

> The health of the people is really the foundation upon which all their happiness and all their powers as a state depend.
>
> — *Benjamin Disraeli*

We live in a health-obsessed age. We are bombarded with messages from health authorities and professionals, fitness gurus, and newspapers and magazines advising us to do this but not that. Everywhere we turn we are urged to take responsibility for our health. Yet amid this torrent of information we hear very little about the social origins of disease or our social responsibility to address the living and working conditions that impact our health. This is where a sociological second opinion can help.

It is often wise to get a second opinion. We seek second opinions about a whole range of things, but why do we need a second opinion about health and illness? What could sociology have to offer? And what is sociology, anyway? This book sets out to answer these questions and show the relevance of sociology to the study of health and illness. We all have a basic idea of what a medical opinion entails, even if we do not always fully understand that opinion. A sociology of health and illness offers a different perspective—a second opinion—by focusing on the social determinants that make us well or unwell.

At the heart of health sociology is a belief that many health problems have social origins. Thus, the focus of health sociology is not medical treatment or individual cures. Health sociology asks you instead to step outside the square, to look beyond medical opinions to the way society is organized. When individuals suffer ill health and require health care, some of the causes and cures can lie in the social context in which they live and work. We can say, in fact, that health, illness, and the health-care system are by-products of the way a society is organized. This book shows you how the social, cultural, economic, and political features of society affect an individual's chance of health and illness.

This introductory part of the book provides an overview of health sociology: what it is, its major theoretical perspectives, and the types of health research it draws upon. Specifically, the Introduction consists of three chapters:

- Chapter 1 examines the social determinants of health, highlights the limitations of medical approaches, and introduces the social model of health. It also explains what is distinctive about the perspective of sociology and how it can be applied to explain health problems.
- Chapter 2 explores the main theoretical perspectives used in health sociology.
- Chapter 3 outlines key issues and debates sociologists encounter when researching health.

CHAPTER 1

Imagining Health Problems as Social Issues

John Germov & Jennie Hornosty

Overview

- What social patterns of health and illness exist?
- What is the social model of health and how does it differ from the medical model?
- What are the social determinants of health?
- What is sociology and how can it be used to understand health and illness?

This chapter introduces you to the sociological perspective and how we can use that perspective to understand a wide range of health issues. While conventional approaches to health and illness focus on the biology and behaviour of individuals, health sociology focuses on the social determinants of health and illness, such as income and education, the environment, and working conditions. Health sociologists look for social patterns of illness, such as the variation in health status between women and men, between the poor and the wealthy, between immigrants and native-born, or between the Aboriginal and non-Aboriginal populations. Then, health sociologists seek social rather than biological or psychological explanations for these differences. Throughout this chapter you are introduced to examples of how health and illness can be analyzed sociologically using a social model of health that views health problems as social issues.

Key Terms

agency
biological determinism
biomedical model
biopsychosocial model
Cartesian dualism
class (or social class)
ecological model
epidemiology/social
   epidemiology

ethnicity
gender/sex
health promotion
lifestyle choices/factors
political economy
public health/public health
   infrastructure
race
reductionism
risk factors

social construction/constructionism
social determinants of health
social institutions
social model of health
social structure
sociological imagination
specific etiology
state
structure–agency debate
victim blaming

Introduction: The Social Context of Health and Illness

If we are ill we tend to seek medical opinions and treatments to make us well. When we think of health and illness it is difficult not to conjure up images of doctors in white coats and of high-tech hospitals. Our personal experience of illness means that we tend to view it in an individualistic way—as a product of bad luck, poor lifestyle, or genetic fate. As individuals we all want quick and effective cures when we are unwell, and thus we turn to medicine for help. Yet this is only part of the story.

Health and illness are also social experiences. For example, even the highly individualized and very personal act of suicide occurs within a social context. In 2004, of 3613 suicide-related deaths in Canada 76 per cent were male, with the highest rates occurring in the 35–44 and 45–54 age groups (WHO, 2004). In fact, the social patterning of suicide was first highlighted in the late nineteenth century by the sociologist Émile Durkheim (1858–1917). While Durkheim acknowledged individual reasons for a person's committing suicide, he found that suicide rates varied between countries and between different social groups within a country.

The social context of health and illness is evident when we compare the life expectancy (LE) figures of various countries. As we all know, LE in the least developed countries is significantly lower than that in industrially developed and comparatively wealthy countries, such as Canada, Australia, and the US. For example, the average LE at birth of people living in the least developed countries of the world in 2006 was around 64 years, with the African regions registering the lowest LE at 51 years. This is 20 to 30 years less than the life expectancy for developed countries, such as Canada, which has an average LE of 81 years (WHO, 2008, World Health Statistics). As Table 1.1 shows, LE varies among developed countries as well as between developed and developing countries. Therefore, the living conditions of the country in which you live can have a significant influence on your chances of enjoying a long and healthy life. Table 1.1 also shows figures for health-adjusted life expectancy (HALE), which represents the number of years people can expect to live without chronic illness or disability; the figure for Canada is 70.0 and 74.0 for men and women, respectively.

By international standards, Canada ranks near the top of the LE and HALE scales, slightly below Japan and Sweden. However, this is not due to any biological advantage in the Canadian gene pool but is, rather, a reflection of our distinctive living and working conditions. We can make such a case for two basic reasons. First, LE can change in a short period of time and, in fact, did increase for most countries during the twentieth century. For example, LE in Canada has increased by more than 20 years since 1920, which is too short a timeframe for any genetic improvement to occur in a given population (Statistics Canada, 2010). Second, data compiled over decades of immigration show that the health of immigrants comes to reflect that of their host country over time, rather than their country of origin. The longer immigrants live in their new country, the more their health mirrors that of the local population (Beiser, 2005; Marmot, 1999; Newbold & Danforth, 2003; Veenstra, 2009). This tendency has been referred to as the 'healthy immigrant effect'.

Theory Link
See Chapter 6 for the 'healthy immigrant effect'.

TABLE 1.1   Life Expectancy and Health-Adjusted Life Expectancy, at Birth

Country	Life Expectancy (LE) 2006		Health-Adjusted Life Expectancy (HALE) 2002	
	Men	Women	Men	Women
Canada	78	83	70	74
Aboriginal Canadians Status First Nations 2001	70.4	75.5	Not available	Not available
Australia	79	84	71	74
China	72	75	63	65
Cuba	76	80	67	70
France	77	84	69	75
Germany	77	82	70	74
Denmark	76	81	69	71
Iraq	48	67	49	51
Italy	78	84	71	75
Japan	79	86	72	78
India	62	64	53	54
Sweden	79	83	72	75
United Kingdom	77	81	69	72
US	75	80	67	71

Source: Adapted from World Health Organization (WHO). (2008). *World health statistics.* Available from www.who.int/whosis/whostat/EN_WHS08_Full.pdf; Adapted from Human Resources and Skills Development Canada. (n.d.). *Health–life expectancy at birth.* Available from www4.hrsdc.gc.ca/.3ndic.1t.4r@-eng.jsp?iid=3#M_3

While the average Canadian LE figure is comparatively high, it is still important to distinguish between different social groups within Canada. Life expectancy figures are crude indicators of population health and actually mask significant health inequalities among social groups within a country. For example, in Canada those in the lowest socio-economic group have the highest rates of illness and premature death, use preventive services less, and have higher rates of illness-related behaviours such as smoking (McIntosh et al., 2009; Raphael, 2009b,c). As well, both Aboriginal Canadian men and women have an LE that is seven years less than the national average. Suicide rates among First Nations youth are five to seven times higher than for non-Aboriginal youth, while suicide rates for Inuit youth are among the highest in the world, at 11 times the national average (Health Canada, 2005, First Nations, Inuit and Aboriginal Health).

Health sociology concerns the study of such social patterns of health and illness. It provides a second opinion to the conventional medical view of illness, derived from biological and psychological explanations, by exploring the social context of health and illness—the social, economic, cultural, and political features of society that influence why some groups of people get sicker and die sooner than others. To find answers to why such health inequalities exist, we need to look beyond the individual and investigate the social origins of illness.

The History of the Social Origins of Illness: Social Medicine and Public Health

Recognition of the social origins of health and illness can be traced to the mid-nineteenth century with the development of 'social medicine' (coined by Jules Guérin in 1848) or what more commonly became known as **public health** (sometimes referred to as social health, community medicine, or preventive medicine). At this time, infectious diseases, such as cholera, typhus, smallpox, diphtheria, and tuberculosis, were major killers for which there were no cures and little understanding of how they were transmitted. During the 1800s, a number of people, such as Louis-René Villermé (1782–1863), Rudolf Virchow (1821–1902), John Snow (1813–58), Edwin Chadwick (1800–90), and Friedrich Engels (1820–95), established clear links between infectious diseases and poverty (Porter, 1997; Rosen, 1972).

Engels, Karl Marx's collaborator and patron, in *The Condition of the Working Class in England* (1958/1845), made a strong case for the links between disease and poor living and working conditions as an outcome of capitalist exploitation. He used the case of 'black lung', a preventable lung disease among miners, to make the point that

> the illness does not occur in those mines which are adequately ventilated. Many examples could be given of miners who moved from well-ventilated to badly ventilated mines and caught the disease. It is solely due to the colliery owners' greed for profit that this illness exists at all. If the coal owners would pay to have ventilation shafts installed the problem would not exist. (1958/1845, p. 281)

Engels also noted the differences in the death rates between labourers and professionals, claiming that the squalid living conditions of the working **class** were primarily responsible for the disparity and stating that 'filth and stagnant pools in the working class quarters of the great cities have the most deleterious effects upon the health of the inhabitants' (1958/1845, p. 110).

In 1854, a cholera epidemic took place in Soho, London. John Snow, a medical doctor, documented cases on a city map and investigated all of the 93 deaths that had occurred within a well-defined geographical area. After interviewing residents he was able to establish that people infected with cholera had sourced their water from the same public water pump in Broad Street. Snow came to the conclusion that the water from the pump was the source of cholera, and at his insistence the pump's handle was removed and the epidemic ceased (McLeod, 2000; Porter, 1997; Rosen, 1972; Snow, 1936/1855). This case is famous for being one of the earliest examples of the use of **epidemiology** to understand and prevent the spread of disease.

Rudolf Virchow, often remembered in medical circles for his study of cellular biology, also made a clear case for the social basis of medicine, highlighting its preventive role when he claimed

> [m]edicine is a social science, and politics nothing but medicine on a grand scale . . . if medicine is really to accomplish its great task, it must intervene in political and social life. The improvement of medicine would eventually prolong human life, but improvement of social conditions could achieve this result even more rapidly and successfully. (cited in Porter, 1997, p. 415; and Rosen, 1972, p. 39).

---

public health/public health infrastructure

Policies, programs and services designed to keep citizens healthy and to improve the quality of life. The focus is on enhancing the health status and well-being of the general population rather than just looking at the health of individual persons. *Public health infrastructure* refers specifically to the buildings, and equipment necessary to ensure healthy living conditions for the population.

class (or social class)

A position in a system of structured inequality based on the unequal distribution of power, wealth, income, and status. People who share a class position typically share similar life chances. Marx spoke of class in terms of one's relationship to the means of production.

epidemiology/social epidemiology

The statistical study of patterns of disease in the population. Originally focused on epidemics, or infectious diseases, the field now covers non-infectious conditions, such as stroke and cancer. Social epidemiology is a subfield aligned with sociology that focuses on the social determinants of illness.

state

A term used to describe a collection of institutions, including Parliament (the government and Opposition political parties), the public-sector bureaucracy, the judiciary, the military, and the police.

Virchow was a significant advocate for public health care and argued that the **state** should act to redistribute social resources, particularly to improve access to adequate nutrition. Therefore, social medicine and the public health movement grew from the recognition that the social environment played a significant role in the spread of disease (Porter, 1997; Rosen, 1972). In other words, the infectious diseases that afflicted individuals had social origins that necessitated social reforms to prevent their onset (see Rosen, 1972 and 1993, and Waitzkin, 2000, for informative histories of social medicine; Porter, 1997, for a very readable history of medicine in general; Bloom, 2002, for a history of medical sociology; and White, 2001).

The Social Origins of Health and Illness In Canada

Canadian health researchers have focused on the social origins of health and illness by examining how people's living conditions impact their health. These conditions are referred to as the **social determinants of health** (Raphael, 2009a,b). Contrary to the assumption that individuals have personal control over their living conditions, these factors are imposed upon individuals by the types of communities, housing situations, work settings, social service agencies, and educational institutions with which they interact (Mikkonen & Raphael, 2010).

social determinants of health

Social determinants of health refer to the social and economic environments in which people live that determine their health. Examples of social determinants include housing, job security, working conditions, education, income, social class, gender, Aboriginal status, and the social safety net. The quality of these determinants is a reflection of how society is organized and how it distributes its economic and social resources.

Theory Link
See Chapter 4 for more on the social determinants of health.

In Britain, Edwin Chadwick was a key figure in the development of the first Public Health Act (1848) based on his 'sanitary idea'—that disease could be prevented through improved waste disposal and sewerage systems, particularly by removing cesspools of decomposing organic matter from densely populated areas, as well as through the introduction of high-pressure flushing sewers and food hygiene laws to protect against food adulteration.

Although the Public Health Agency in Canada was established only in 2004, from Canada's beginning in 1867 Parliament had jurisdiction over certain aspects of health. The first Quarantine Act was adopted in 1872 and remained largely unchanged until the severe acute respiratory syndrome (SARS) outbreak in 2003. Today the social determinants of health approach has been taken up by various public health units in the country as well as by the Public Health Agency of Canada.

Despite the influence of social medicine and the success of public health measures in the 1800s, health care developed in an entirely different direction. The insights of social medicine were, in fact, cast aside for almost a century as the new science of biomedicine gained ascendancy.

The Rise of the Biomedical Model

specific etiology

The idea that there is a specific cause or origin for each specific disease.

In 1878, Louis Pasteur (1822–96) developed the germ theory of disease, whereby illness is caused by germs infecting organs of the human body: a model of disease that became the foundation of modern medicine. Robert Koch (1843–1910) refined this idea with the doctrine of **specific etiology** (meaning 'specific cause of disease') through 'Koch's postulates':

a set of criteria for proving that specific bacteria caused a specific disease (Capra, 1982; Dubos, 1959). The central idea was that specific micro-organisms caused disease by entering the human body through air, water, food, and insect bites (Porter, 1997). This mono-causal model of disease, which came to be known as the medical or **biomedical model**, became the dominant medical paradigm by the early 1900s. Throughout the twentieth century, medical research, training, and practice increasingly focused on attempts to identify and eliminate specific diseases in individuals, and thus moved away from the perspective of social medicine and its focus on the social origins of disease (Najman, 1980).

The biomedical model is based on the assumption that each disease or ailment has a specific cause that physically affects the human body in a uniform and predictable way, meaning that universal cures for people are theoretically possible. The model involves a mechanical view of the body as a machine made up of interrelated parts, such as the skeleton and circulatory system. The role of the doctor is akin to a body mechanic, identifying and repairing the broken parts (Armstrong & Armstrong, 2003, pp. 12–45).

While early discoveries led to the identification of many infectious diseases, there were few effective cures. However, one of the earliest applications of the scientific understanding of infectious disease was the promotion of hygiene and sterilization procedures, particularly in surgical practice, to prevent infection through the transmission of bacteria (Capra, 1982). Until the early 1900s, it had been common practice to operate on patients without a concern for hygiene or the proper cleaning and sterilization of equipment, resulting in high rates of post-operative infection and death following surgery.

Before the development of medical science, quasi-religious views of health and illness were dominant, whereby illness was connected with sin, penance, and evil spirits. Therefore, the 'body as machine' metaphor represented a significant turning-point away from religious notions toward a secular view of the human body. Until this time, the dominant view had been to conceive the body and soul as a sacred entity beyond the power of human intervention. However, the influence of scientific discoveries, particularly through autopsies that linked diseased organs with symptoms before death, as well as Pasteur's germ theory eventually caused people to endorse a belief in the separation of body and soul. In philosophical circles, this view came to be known as mind/body dualism and was sometimes referred to as **Cartesian dualism**, after the philosopher René Descartes (1590–1650). Descartes, famous for the saying 'I think, therefore I am', suggested that although the mind and body interacted with one another, they were separate entities. Therefore, the brain was part of the physical body, whereas the mind (the basis of individuality) existed in the spiritual realm and was apparent evidence of a god-given soul. Such a distinction provided the philosophical justification for secular interventions on the physical body in the form of medical therapies. Since the body was merely a vessel for the immortal soul or spirit, medicine could rightly practise on the body while religion could focus on the soul (Capra, 1982; Porter, 1997). The assumption of mind/body dualism underpinned the biomedical model, whereby disease was seen as located in the physical body, and thus the mind, or mental state of a person, was considered unimportant.

The Limits of the Biomedical Model

While the biomedical model represented a significant advance in understanding disease and resulted in beneficial treatments, it has come under significant criticism from both

biomedicine/ biomedical model
The conventional approach to medicine in Western societies, based on the diagnosis and explanation of illness as a malfunction of the body's biological mechanisms. This approach underpins most health professions and health services, which focus on treating individuals, and generally ignores the social origins of illness and its prevention.

Cartesian dualism
Also called mind/body dualism and named after the philosopher Descartes, it refers to a belief that the mind and body are separate entities. This assumption underpins medical approaches that view disease in physical terms and thus ignore the psychological and subjective aspects of illness.

within medicine and across a range of social and behavioural disciplines, such as sociology and psychology. The major criticism is that the biomedical model underestimates the complexity of health and illness, particularly by neglecting social and psychological factors (Armstrong & Armstrong, 2003). Features of the biomedical model that are subject to criticism can be grouped under the following terms and phrases:

- The fallacy of specific etiology
- Objectification and medical scientism
- **Reductionism** and **biological determinism**
- Interventionist bias
- **Victim blaming**

The Fallacy of Specific Etiology

The idea of a specific cause for a specific disease, referred to as specific etiology, applies only to a limited range of infectious diseases (Armstrong & Armstrong, 2003). As early as the 1950s, René Dubos (1959, p. 102) argued that 'most disease states are the indirect outcome of a constellation of circumstances rather than the direct result of single determinant factors'. Furthermore, Dubos noted that not all people exposed to an infectious disease contracted it. For example, we may all come into contact with someone suffering from a contagious condition like the flu, but only a few of us will get sick. Therefore, disease causation is more complex than the biomedical model implies and is likely to involve multiple factors, such as physical condition, nutrition, and stress, which affect an individual's susceptibility to illness (Dubos, 1959).

Objectification and Medical Scientism

The biomedical model, underpinned by mind/body dualism and a focus on repairing the 'broken' parts of the machine-like body, can lead to the objectification of patients. Since disease is viewed only in physical terms, as something that can be objectively observed, treating 'it' takes primacy over all other considerations, and patients may become objectified as 'diseased bodies' or 'cases' rather than treated as unique individuals with particular needs. This form of criticism often underpins claims of doctors' poor interpersonal and communication skills. Such a situation is also related to what Fritjov Capra (1982) calls 'medical scientism'—that is, a reverence for scientific methods of measurement and observation as the most superior form of knowledge about understanding and treating disease. Therefore, patients' thoughts, feelings, and subjective experiences of illness are considered 'unscientific' and are mostly dismissed.

Reductionism and Biological Determinism

A further criticism of the biomedical model is its reductionism and its mechanical conception of the body (Armstrong & Armstrong, 2003). The development of medical science has led to an increasing focus on smaller and smaller features of human biology for the cause and cure of disease—from organs to cells to molecules and most recently to genes. By reducing its focus on disease to the biological, cellular, and genetic levels, medicine has ignored or downplayed the social and psychological aspects of illness. In concentrating on the pathology within an individual body, patients and their suffering are divorced from their social environment, and the disease treated as if it occurred in a social vacuum. Not

reductionism
The belief that all illnesses can be explained and treated by reducing them to biological and pathological factors.

biological determinism
An unproven belief that individual and group behaviour and social status is an inevitable result of biology.

victim blaming
The process whereby social inequality is explained in terms of individuals being solely responsible for what happens to them in relation to the choices they make and their assumed psychological, cultural, and/or biological inferiority.

only does this marginalize the importance of social support networks, it also ignores the role played by social factors, such as poverty, poor working conditions, and discrimination, in affecting an individual's physical and mental health.

A related outcome of reductionism has been an ever-growing number of medical specialties, such as cardiology (heart specialty) and ophthalmology (eye specialty), based on the assumption that each body part and function can be treated almost in isolation from the others. Such an approach has fuelled the search for 'magic bullet' cures, resulting in huge expenditures on medical drugs, technology, and surgery. This approach has also led to a curative and interventionist bias in medical care, often at the expense of prevention and nonmedical alternatives.

 Theory Link
See Chapter 12 for more on medical specialization.

Reductionism can also lead to biological determinism: a form of social Darwinism that assumes people's biology causes or determines their inferior social, economic, and health status. Biological determinism underpins most elitist, racist, and sexist beliefs. For example, some people argue that the poor are poor because they are born lazy and stupid. Such views have often been used to justify slavery and exploitation of people of colour, of women, of children, and of workers in general; biological determinism is a convenient 'explanation', particularly when those at the top of the social ladder espouse such views. When people argue that social or health inequalities are biologically determined, the implication is that little can or should be done to change those inequalities. Although such beliefs have no scientific validity, they have not vanished from our society and are the basis of so-called commonsense views of the world.

Victim Blaming

A final criticism of the biomedical model is its tendency toward victim blaming through the individualization of health problems (Ryan, 1971) because it locates the cause and cure of disease as solely within the individual. As Capra states, '[i]nstead of asking why an illness occurs, and trying to remove the conditions that lead to it, medical researchers try to understand the biological mechanisms through which the disease operates, so that they can then interfere with them' (1982, p. 150). Therefore, the individual body becomes the focus of intervention, and health and illness become primarily viewed as an individual responsibility. A preoccupation with treating the individual has the potential to legitimate a victim-blaming approach to illness, either in the form of genetic fatalism (your poor health is the result of poor genetics) or as an outcome of poor **lifestyle choices**. By ignoring the social context of health and illness and locating primary responsibility for illness within the individual, there is little acknowledgment of social responsibility—that is, the need to ensure healthy living and working environments.

Our critique of the biomedical model has necessarily been a generalization and does not imply that all doctors work from within the confines of this model. In fact, many of the criticisms of the model have come from those within the medical profession itself. While it is now widely accepted that the causes of illness are multifactorial, it is still fair

lifestyle choices/ factors

The decisions people make that are likely to impact their health, such as diet, exercise, smoking, alcohol, and other drugs. The term implies that people are solely responsible for choosing and changing their lifestyle.

to claim that the biomedical model remains the dominant influence on medical training and practice to this day.

Rediscovering the Social Origins of Health and Illness

In the 1960s, Thomas McKeown (1979, 1988), a doctor and epidemiologist, was one of the earliest authors to expose the exaggerated role of medical treatment in improving population health. McKeown argued that the medical profession and governments had overestimated the influence of medical discoveries on improvements in life expectancy during the twentieth century. McKeown (1976, 1979) found that mortality (death) from most infectious diseases had declined *before* the development of effective medical treatments, meaning that improvements in life expectancy were not substantially due to medical intervention. Estimates reported by McKinlay and McKinlay (1977) are that only 10–15 per cent of increased longevity since 1990 is the result of improved health care. Raphael (2009b, p. 8) writes that in Canada dramatic declines in mortality had already happened by the time vaccines for major diseases, such as measles and polio, and treatments for scarlet fever, typhoid, and diphtheria appeared. The same general trend occurred in Great Britain, Australia, and the United States.

McKeown (1979) suggests that the major reasons for the increase in life expectancy were not due to medical treatments but, rather, to rising living standards, particularly improved nutrition, which increased people's resistance to infectious disease. While McKeown's work highlighted the importance of social, nonmedical interventions for improving population health, Simon Szreter (1988) provides a more complex argument. He suggests that rather than the '"invisible" hand of rising living standards' (p. 37) it was the state's redistribution of economic resources that increased life expectancy through improved working conditions and a range of public health measures, such as improved public housing, food regulation, education, and sanitation reforms. Canadian researchers such as Armstrong & Armstrong (2003), Coburn (2001), Raphael (2009b), Bryant (Bryant et al., 2010), and others make the same argument.

While it is impossible to determine the exact contribution of public health measures, rising living standards, and medicine to improving population health, the significance of McKeown's work and subsequent findings as well as research focusing on the social determinants of health has been to highlight the importance of addressing the social origins of health and illness. As McKeown (1979) states, 'there is need for a shift in the balance of effort, in recognition that improvement in health is likely to come in future—from modification of the conditions which lead to disease, rather than from intervention in the mechanism of disease after it has occurred' (p. 198). It is important to note that McKeown himself was not anti-medicine but wanted to reform medical practice so that it focused on prevention of what he saw were the new threats to health: personal behaviour, as evidenced through smoking, alcohol consumption, drug taking, diet, and lack of exercise. Therefore, he still viewed health care in individualistic terms, by focusing preventive efforts at the level of modifying the behaviour of individuals. Others who focus more on structural factors have argued that it is organization of society and how a society distributes its material resources that significantly determine the health of individuals and populations (Raphael, 2006, 2009a).

Lifestyle and Risk: From Risk-Taking to Risk-Imposing Factors

Since McKeown's work, there has been considerable growth in preventive efforts aimed at individuals, particularly in the form of identifying **risk factors**. While the notion of 'lifestyle diseases' or 'diseases of affluence' is a clear indication of the social origins of health and illness, many preventive efforts, in the form of **health promotion**, have tried to reform the individual rather than pursue wider social reform (ignoring the fact that diseases of affluence affect the least affluent much more). By solely targeting risk-taking individuals, there is a tendency to victim blaming by ignoring the social determinants that give rise to risk taking in the first place, such as stressful work environments, the marketing efforts of corporations, and peer group pressure. Individuals are told to control stress, for example, by exercising more, getting more sleep, and eating healthier foods. Such an approach assumes that individuals can control all the factors that determine their health. Medical researchers and public health workers frequently emphasize the importance of traditional risk factors, such as cholesterol, diet, and physical activity, in decreasing a person's risk of heart disease and stroke.

>
> **Theory Link**
> See also *primary health care* and *public health*, discussed in Chapter 12.

In comparison to social determinants, however, these are relatively poor predictors (Raphael, 2009b,c). More importantly, as Michael Marmot (1999, p. 1) incisively puts it, there is a need to understand the 'causes of the causes'. In other words, rather than just focusing on risk-taking individuals, there is also a need to address 'risk-imposing factors' and 'illness-generating social conditions' (Ratcliffe et al., 1984; Waitzkin, 1983)—the social, cultural, economic, and political features of society that create unhealthy products, habits, and lifestyles. Socio-demographic factors, such as unemployment rate, Aboriginal status, minority status, income, poverty, and education, are in fact better predictors of health status (Raphael, 2006, 2009a).

There is no denying the significant role medicine has played in the treatment of illness, particularly in trauma medicine, palliative care, and general surgery, as well as in the prevention of illness through immunization. Thus, the expertise of doctors lies in treating individuals once they are ill. Yet the reductionist focus of the biomedical model on individual pathology has obscured the social origins of illness. The World Health Organization (WHO) effectively acknowledged this limitation of the model in 1946, when it included in its constitution the now-famous holistic definition of *health* as 'a state of complete physical, mental and social well-being and not merely the absence of disease or infirmity' (WHO, 1946). This often-quoted definition implies that a range of biological, psychological, and social factors determine health. Furthermore, health is conceptualized as 'not merely the absence of disease' but, rather, in the positive sense of 'well-being'. While this definition has been criticized for its utopian and vague notion of 'complete well-being', it is of symbolic importance because it highlights the need for a broader approach to health than the biomedical model alone can deliver.

risk factors

Conditions that are thought to increase an individual's susceptibility to illness or disease, such as abuse of alcohol, poor diet, or smoking.

health promotion

Has recently become a goal of health policy in Canada. Any combination of education and related organizational, economic, and political interventions designed to promote individual behavioural and environmental changes conducive to good health, including legislation, community development, and advocacy. Draws attention to a variety of social determinants.

biopsychosocial model

This model is an extension of the biomedical model. It is a multifactorial model of illness that takes into account the biological, psychological, and social factors implicated in a patient's condition. As with the biomedical model, it focuses on the individual patient for diagnosis, explanation, and treatment.

ecological model

Derived from the field of human ecology, and when applied to public health, it suggests that an understanding of health determinants must consider the interaction of social, economic, geographic, and environmental factors.

social model of health

Focuses on social determinants of health, such as the social production, distribution, and construction of health and illness, and the social organization of health care. It directs attention to the prevention of illness through community participation and social reforms that address living and working conditions.

political economy

An approach that emphasizes the links between people's health and the political, economic, and ideological conditions of a society.

The widespread recognition of the biomedical model's limitations, from those within and outside the medical profession, has led to the development of a variety of multifactorial models, such as the **biopsychosocial model** (Cooper et al., 1996; Engel, 1977, 1980), the web of causation (MacMahon & Pugh, 1970), and the **ecological model** (Hancock, 1985). While these models represent a significant advance over the biomedical model in acknowledging the multiple determinants of health, to greater and lesser degrees they remain focused on health interventions aimed at the individual, particularly through lifestyle/behaviour modification and health education. An explicitly **social model of health** that focuses on people's living conditions is necessary to substantially highlight the social determinants of illness and to propose health interventions at the population and community level (Ashton & Seymour 1988; Baum 2002; Raphael, 2003, 2006, 2009; Waitzkin, 1983; World Health Organization, 2004).

A Sociological Second Opinion: The Social Model of Health

The 'social model of health', frequently referred to in Canada as the **social determinants of health** approach, focuses attention on the societal level of health determinants and health intervention. It is consistent with the new public health paradigm, which combines traditional health promotion that focuses on individual behaviour with health measures designed to mitigate the effects of social inequality. The social model approach is drawn primarily from the field of health sociology. Sociologists have criticized some new public health approaches arising from the health sciences for their over-reliance on individualistic solutions in practice (see Lupton, 1995; Petersen & Lupton, 1996).

However, there are significant examples of sociologically informed approaches that can make it problematical to draw distinctions between the social model of health and the new pubic health paradigm (see especially Baum, 2002; Baggott, 2000; Beaglehole & Bonita, 1997). Nonetheless, for our purposes we will keep the distinction between the two and use the term 'social model of health', as it better reflects the unique theories, research methods, and modes of analysis of health sociology discussed in this book.

The social model of health has been used as a general umbrella term to refer to approaches that focus on the social determinants of health and illness (see Broom, 1991; Gillespie & Gerhardt, 1995; Mikkonen & Raphael, 2010; Raphael, 2006, 2009a). As Dorothy Broom (1991) states, 'the social model locates people in social contexts, conceptualises the physical environment as socially organised, and understands ill health as a process of interaction between people and their environments' (p. 52). It is one of the aims of this book to map out the social model in more detail through a **political economy** lens to explain the underlying societal factors that give rise to the social determinants of health people experience. Table 1.2 contrasts the key features of the biomedical model with the social model, focusing on the various social determinants of health, to highlight the different focus, assumptions, benefits, and limitations of each model. It is important to emphasize that focusing on material conditions does not deny the existence of biological or psychological aspects of disease that manifest in individuals, or deny the need for medical treatment. Instead, this focus highlights that health and illness occur in a social

TABLE 1.2   Comparison of Biomedical and Social Models of Health: Key Characteristics

	Biomedical Model	**Social Model**
Focus	Individual focus: acute treatment of ill individuals	Societal focus: living and working conditions that affect health
	Clinical services, health education, immunization	Public health infrastructure, legislation, social services, community action, equity, access issues
Assumptions	Health and illness are objective biological states	Health and illness are social constructions
	Individual responsibility for health	Social responsibility for health
Key indicators of illness	Individual pathology	Social inequality
	Hereditary factors, sex, age	Social groups: class, gender, 'race', ethnicity, age, occupation, unemployment
	Risk factors	Risk-imposing/illness-inducing factors
Causes of illness	Gene defects and micro-organisms (viruses, bacteria)	Political/economic factors: distribution of wealth, income, power, poverty, level of social services
	Trauma (accidents)	Employment factors: employment and educational opportunities, stressful and dangerous work
	Risk-taking behaviour/lifestyle	Cultural factors (values, traditions), prejudice, discrimination (racism, sexism, homophobia)
Intervention	Cure individuals via surgery and pharmaceuticals	Public policy
	Behaviour modification (non-smoking, exercise, diet)	State intervention to alleviate health and social inequalities
	Health education and immunization	Community participation, advocacy and political lobbying
Goals	Cure disease, limit disability, and reduce risk factors to prevent disease in individuals	Prevention of illness and reduction of health inequalities to aim for an equality of health outcomes
Benefits	Addresses disease and disability of individuals	Addresses the social determinants of health and illness
	Prevention of disease through immunization	Highlights the need for preventive measures that often lie outside the scope of the health system
Criticisms	Disease focus leads to lack of preventive efforts	Utopian goal of equality leads to unfeasible prescriptions for social change
	Reductionist: ignores the complexity of health/illness	Over-emphasis on the harmful side effects of medical approaches
	Fails to take into account social origins of health/illness	Proposed solutions can be complex and difficult to implement in the short term
	Medical opinions can reinforce victim-blaming	Sociological opinions can underestimate individual responsibility and psychological factors

context and that effective health interventions, particularly preventive efforts, need to move beyond the medical treatment of individuals. Exposing the social origins of illness necessarily implies that a greater balance between individual and social interventions is required since the vast majority of health funding continues to be directed toward medical intervention. Therefore, the social model is not intended to replace the biomedical model but, rather, to coexist alongside it.

The biomedical model focuses on the level of the individual for the cause and cure of disease by attempting to address pathology and/or modify behaviour, assuming individuals are solely responsible for their health. The social model, on the other hand, assumes health is a social responsibility by examining the social determinants of individuals' health status and health-related behaviour. Therefore, while the biomedical model concentrates on treating disease and risk-taking among individuals, the social model focuses on societal factors that are risk-imposing or illness-inducing (for example, toxic pollution, stressful work, discrimination, peer pressure), and in particular highlights the health inequalities suffered by different social groups based on class, **gender**, **ethnicity**, **'race'**, and occupation, and so on. What should be clear from the comparison offered in Table 1.2 is that health issues have a number of dimensions.

A social model approach logically implies that any attempts to improve the overall health of the community need to address material conditions, such as poverty, employment opportunities, working conditions, and cultural differences. The social model gives equal priority to the prevention of illness along with the treatment of illness and aims to alleviate health inequalities. A critical political economy approach goes a step further in that it considers how forces such as globalization and neo-liberalism affect the way societies are organized. Such an approach can help challenge people's current perception and beliefs and encourage them to think critically about how things could be different (Coburn, 2006). The social model makes it clear that many of the causes of sickness lie outside the strict confines of the health system or individuals' control.

The Three Main Dimensions of the Social Model of Health

The social model arose as a critique of the limitations and misapplications of the biomedical model, such as its inability to effectively explain and address health inequalities experienced by various social groups (for example, Indigenous peoples, those living in poverty, etc.). Sociological research and theorizing that underpins the social model of health is comprised of three main dimensions or themes, which are reflected in the structure of this book:

1. The Societal Production and Distribution of Health and Illness

This dimension of the social model highlights that many illnesses that individuals suffer from are socially produced; that is, they are an outcome of people's material and living conditions. For example, illnesses arising from environmental contaminants, substandard housing, or unhealthy/unsafe workplaces are beyond an individual's control and therefore need to be addressed at a societal level. Furthermore, there is an unequal distribution of wealth and income in society, and both are important determinants of health. For example, those in the lower socio-economic quintiles suffer higher rates of morbidity and mortality. As well, income is a determinant of other experiences, such as education,

gender

This term refers to the socially constructed categories of feminine and masculine (the cultural values that dictate how men and women should behave), as opposed to the categories of biological sex (female or male).

ethnicity

Sociologically, the term refers to a shared cultural background, which is a characteristic of all groups in society. As a policy term, it is used to identify immigrants who share a culture that is markedly different from that of Anglo-Canadians. In practice, it often refers only to immigrants from non-English-speaking backgrounds (NESB migrants).

'race'

A term without scientific basis that uses skin colour and facial features to describe allegedly biologically distinct groups of humans. It is a social construction that is used to categorize groups of people and usually implies assumed (and unproven) intellectual superiority or inferiority.

food security, employment, and quality of early life (Raphael, 2009b, p. 9). A focus, therefore, on the social production and distribution of health examines the role that living and working conditions play in causing and alleviating illness.

2. The Social Construction of Health and Illness

This dimension refers to how definitions of health and illness can vary among cultures and change over time—what is considered a disease in one culture or time period may be considered normal and healthy elsewhere and at other times. For example, homosexuality was once considered a psychiatric disorder despite the lack of scientific evidence of pathology. It is no longer medically defined as a disorder but nonetheless is an example of how cultural beliefs, social practices, and social institutions shape or construct the ways in which health and illness are understood and experienced. Therefore, notions of health and illness are not necessarily objective facts or static states, but can be **social constructions** that reflect the culture, politics, and morality of a particular society at a given point in time.

3. The Social Organization of Health Care

This dimension of the social model concerns the way a particular society organizes, funds, and utilizes its health services. A central focus of study has been the dominant role of the medical profession, which has significantly shaped health policy and funding to benefit its own interests, largely to the detriment of nurses and to allied and alternative health practitioners. Unequal relationships between the health professions can prevent the efficient use of health resources and the optimal delivery of health care to patients. The state also plays a central role in shaping health-care delivery through public policy. For example, neo-liberal government policies put emphasis on the market and the private sector as the source of economic wealth and growth. This results in cutbacks in social programs and a growing gap between the rich and poor. In the health sector these policies mean a decrease in public expenditures for health, privatization of health services, and dismantling of public health infrastructure (Navarro, 2008, p. 153).

How Can Sociology Help? Using a Sociological Imagination

As individuals we are brought up to believe that we control our own destinies, especially our health. It is simply up to individuals to 'do what they wanna do and be what they wanna be'. However, this belief ignores the considerable influence of society. Sociology makes us aware that, individually, we cannot ignore the social conditions that influence our lives. We are social animals and are very much the product of our environment, from the way we dress to the way we interact with one another. We are all influenced by the social structure or the way social life is organized. **Social structure** is a key sociological concept that refers to the social patterns or recurring arrangements that we experience in our daily lives (from cultural customs to **social institutions**). The idea of social structure serves to remind us of the social or human-created aspects of life, in contrast to purely random events or products of nature (Lopez & Scott, 2000). In other words, the social structure is a product of human action and interaction.

The social structure can be likened to the human skeleton. The various parts of the body—the muscles, heart, lungs, and other organs—need the frame of the skeleton to exist

**social construction/
constructionism**

Refers to the socially created characteristics of human life based on the idea that people actively construct reality, meaning it is neither natural nor inevitable. Therefore, notions of normality/abnormality, right/wrong, and health/illness are subjective human creations that should not be taken for granted.

social structure

The recurring patterns of social interaction through which people are related to each other, such as social institutions and social groups.

social institutions

Formal structures within society—such as health care, government, education, religion, and the media—that are organized to address identified social needs.

and function. If we think of society as having a skeleton that links its parts together, we begin to understand the concept of social structure. Figure 1.1 is a 'social skeleton' and shows the basic features of the social structure of which we are all a part. It represents a way of conceptualizing the key elements of how our society is organized or structured. The various parts of the social skeleton are interrelated (as the two-way arrows indicate). For example, the type of economy we have has influenced our culture and our political system. Religion, through marriage and the family, has significantly influenced the structure of our personal relationships. Therefore, understanding the structure of society enables us to examine the social influences on our personal behaviour and our interactions with others.

Social institutions (such as the media, health care, government, and education) are formal structures within society that are set up to address identified social needs. Social groups form as a result of the way that these social institutions are structured. For example, social classes emerge from the economic system: culture, laws, and education influence male and female roles, and attitudes toward people whose appearance may vary

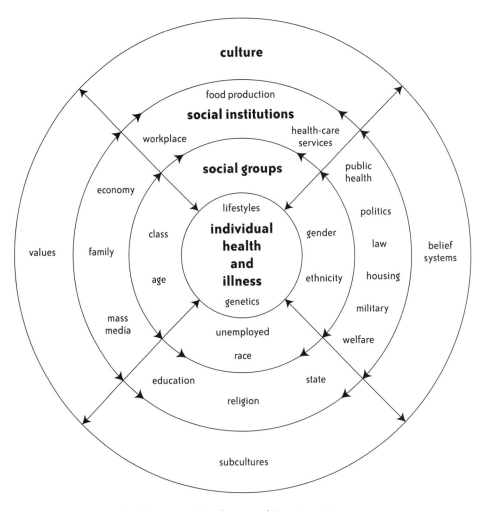

FIGURE 1.1 The Social Skeleton: Health, Illness and Structure–Agency

from the majority or who act differently from the majority (gay/lesbian and transsexual peoples, Indigenous peoples, and members of ethnic groups, for example). Other social relationships also form, such as those between doctors and patients, teachers and students, parents and children, or employers and employees. While the social structure has a great influence on us all, it is not fixed in one shape for eternity; in fact, recent history has shown it can be subject to significant change. The two-way arrows in Figure 1.1 are used to indicate that we exercise **agency** in our daily lives and in doing so can influence the way society is structured. The interplay between structure and agency along the various layers of the social skeleton are the subject matter of sociology.

agency

The ability of people, individually and collectively, to influence their own lives and the society in which they live.

Introducing the Structure–Agency Debate

To what extent are we products of society? How much influence do we have over our lives? Are we solely responsible for our actions or is society to blame? These questions represent a key debate in sociology, often referred to as the **structure–agency debate**. There is no simple resolution to this debate, but it is helpful to view structure and agency as interdependent—that is, humans shape and are simultaneously shaped by society. In this sense, structure and agency are not either/or propositions in the form of a choice between constraint and freedom but are part of the interdependent processes of social life. Therefore, the social structure should not automatically be viewed in a negative way—that is, as only serving to constrain human freedom—since in many ways the social structure enables us to live, by providing health care, welfare, education, and work. As C. Wright Mills (1916–62) maintained, an individual 'contributes, however minutely, to the shaping of this society and to the course of its history, even as he is made by society and by its historical push and shove' (1959, p. 6). Mills was clearly a product of the 'historical push and shove' of his social structure, as he uses the masculine he to refer to both men and women—a usage now seen as dated and sexist.

structure–agency debate

A key debate in sociology over the extent to which human behaviour is determined by social structure.

Peter Berger long ago warned against depicting people as 'puppets jumping about on the ends of their invisible strings' (1966, p. 140). If we use the 'all the world is a stage and we are mere actors' analogy, we could liken life to a theatre in which we all play our assigned roles (father, mother, child, labourer, teacher, student, and so on). Whether it is how we are dressed as we walk down the street or how we present ourselves at a funeral, customs and traditions dictate expected modes of behaviour. In this sense we are all actors on a stage. Yet we have the scope to consciously participate in what we do. We can make choices about whether simply to act or to modify or change our roles and even the stage on which we live our lives.

To paraphrase Karl Marx, people make history but not necessarily under the conditions of their choosing. Although we are born into a world not of our making and in countless ways our actions and thoughts are shaped by our social environment, we are not simply 'puppets on strings'. Humans are sentient beings—that is, we are self-aware and thus have the capacity to think and act individually and collectively to change the society into which we are born. Structure and agency may be in tension, but they are interdependent—that is, one cannot exist without the other. Sociology is the study of the relationship between the individual and society; it examines how 'we create society at the same time as we are created by it' (Giddens, 1986, p. 11).

The Sociological Imagination: A Template for Doing Sociological Analysis

What is distinctive about the sociological perspective? In what ways does it uncover the social structure that we often take for granted? How is sociological analysis done? The American sociologist C. Wright Mills answered such questions by using the expression **sociological imagination** to describe the distinctive feature of the sociological perspective. The sociological imagination is 'a quality of mind that seems most dramatically to promise an understanding of the intimate realities of ourselves in connection with larger social realities' (Mills, 1959, p. 15). According to Mills, the essential aspect of thinking sociologically, or seeing the world through a sociological imagination, is making a link between 'private troubles' and 'public issues'.

As individuals, we may experience personal troubles without realizing they are shared by other people as well. If certain problems are shared by groups of people, they may have a common cause and be best dealt with through some form of social or collective action. In the late 1960s, the phrase 'the personal is political' became popular in the women's liberation movement. The phrase encapsulates the sociological imagination by linking women's personal experiences to wider social and political issues. For example, issues of sexism, discrimination, domestic violence, and access to child care and contraception were traditionally regarded as 'personal troubles' and often considered taboo topics not fit for public discussion, leaving many women to suffer individually in silence. However, these personal problems were, and in some cases continue to be, shared by many women and can only be addressed through public debate and social reforms, such as pay equity, sexual harassment and sex discrimination legislation, and employment equity legislation. As Mills (1959, p. 226) states, 'many personal troubles cannot be solved merely as troubles, but must be understood in terms of public issues—public issues must be revealed by relating them to personal troubles'.

The sociological imagination can be viewed as consisting of four interrelated parts (Willis, 2004):

1. Historical factors: how the past influences the present
2. Cultural factors: how our culture impacts on our lives
3. Structural factors: how particular forms of social organization shape our lives
4. Critical factors: how we can improve on what exists

This four-part sociological imagination template is an effective way to understand how to think and analyze in a sociological way. Figure 1.2 represents the sociological imagination template as a diagram that is easy to remember. Anytime you want to sociologically analyze a topic, simply picture this diagram in your mind.

Sociological analysis involves applying these four aspects to the issues or problems under investigation. For example, a sociological analysis of why manual labourers have a shorter life expectancy would examine how and why the work done by manual labourers affects their health, by investigating the following:

1. Historical factors: to understand why manual workplaces are so dangerous
2. Cultural factors: such as the cultural value of individual responsibility and belief systems

---

sociological imagination

A term coined by C.W. Mills to describe the sociological approach to analyzing issues. We see the world through a sociological imagination, or think sociologically, when we make a link between personal troubles and public issues.

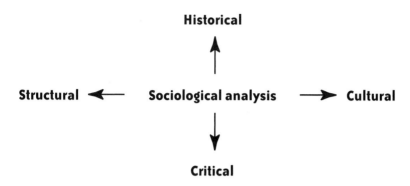

FIGURE 1.2 The Sociological Imagination Template

3. Structural factors: such as the way work is organized, the role of managerial authority, the rights of workers, and the role of the state
4. Critical factors: such as alternatives to the status quo (increasing the effectiveness of occupational health and safety legislation, for instance)

By using the four parts of the sociological imagination template, you begin to 'do' sociological analysis. It is worth highlighting at this point that the template simplifies the process of sociological analysis. When analyzing particular topics, it is more than likely that you will find that the parts overlap with one another, making them less clear-cut than the template implies. It is also probable that for some topics, parts of the template will be more relevant and prominent than others—this is all to be expected. The benefit of the template is that it serves as a reminder of the sorts of issues and questions a budding sociologist should be asking. In fact, it is the intention of the structure and content of this book to apply the sociological imagination to the three key dimensions of the social model of health outlined earlier.

Conclusion

A common accusation made of sociology is that it is just common sense dressed up in unnecessary jargon. The subject matter of sociology is familiar, and as members of society it is easy to think we should all be experts on the subject. It is this familiarity that breeds suspicion and sometimes contempt. All disciplines have specialist concepts to help classify their subject matter, and sociology is no different. Sociological concepts, such as those you have been introduced to in this chapter, are used to impose a sense of intellectual order on the complexities of social life; they are a form of academic shorthand to summarize a complex idea in a word or phrase.

As this chapter has shown, to understand the complexity of health and illness we need to move beyond biomedical approaches and incorporate a social model of health. Sociology enables us to understand the links between our individual experiences and the social context in which we live, work, and play. With a sociological imagination, seeing health problems as social issues can be a healthy way of opening up debate on a range of topics previously not discussed.

Summary of Main Points

- Much of health sociology has arisen as a critique of the dominance of the medical profession and its biomedical model.
- Health sociology examines social patterns of health and illness, particularly various forms of health inequality, and seeks to explain them by examining the influence of society. When groups of people experience similar health problems, there are likely to be social origins that require social action to address them.
- Health sociology challenges individualistic and biological explanations of health and illness through a social model of health that involves three key dimensions: the social production and distribution of health, the social construction of health, and the social organization of health care.
- The sociological imagination, or sociological analysis, involves four interrelated features—historical, cultural, structural, and critical—that can be applied to understand health problems as social issues.

 Sociological Reflection: A Sociological Autobiography

Apply the four parts of the sociological imagination template to explain the person you have become. In other words, write a short sociological autobiography by briefly noting the various things that have influenced you directly or indirectly in terms of your beliefs, interests, and behaviour.

- Historical factors: how has your family background, or key past events and experiences, shaped the person you are?
- Cultural factors: what role have cultural background, traditions, and belief systems played in forming your opinions and influencing your behaviour?
- Structural factors: how have various social institutions influenced you?
- Critical factors: have your values and opinions about what you consider important changed over time? Why or why not?

Repeat the sociological reflection, but this time apply the sociological imagination template to a health problem of interest to you. Briefly note any key points that come to mind under the four parts of the template. What insights can you derive by adopting a sociological imagination?

 Discussion Questions

1. How can illness have social origins? Refer to the social skeleton in Figure 1.1 and give examples in your answer.
2. What are the advantages and limitations of the biomedical model?

3. What have been some of the consequences of the dominance of biomedical explanations for our understanding of health and illness?
4. Why did the insights of social medicine/public health approaches have such a limited influence over the development of modern medicine?
5. What are the three key dimensions of the social model of health? Provide examples of each in your answer. What are the advantages and limitations of the model?
6. In 1946, the World Health Organization (WHO) defined health as a state of complete physical, mental, and social well-being and not merely the absence of disease or infirmity. Why might some groups regard this definition as radical and utopian? Who might these groups be? What do you think of the definition?

Further Investigation

1. 'The influence of the biomedical model is waning—the future belongs to public health.' Discuss.
2. 'Illness is simply a matter of bad luck, bad judgment, or bad genetics.' Critically analyze this statement by applying a sociological imagination to explore the social origins of illness.

Further Reading

Armstrong, P., & Armstrong, H. (2003). *Wasting away: The undermining of Canadian health care* (2nd ed.). Don Mills, ON: Oxford University Press.

Armstrong, P., Armstrong, H., & Coburn, D. (Eds.). (2001). *Unhealthy times (political economy perspectives on health and care in Canada)*. Don Mills, ON: Oxford University Press.

Bolaria, S., & Dickinson, H. (Eds.). (2009). *Health, illness, and health care in Canada* (4th ed.). Toronto, ON: Nelson Education Ltd.

Bryant, T. (2009). *An introduction to health policy.* Toronto, ON: Canadian Scholars' Press Inc.

Bryant, T., Raphael, D., & Rioux, M. (2010). *Staying alive: Critical perspectives on health, illness and health care* (2nd ed.). Toronto, ON: Canadian Scholars' Press Inc.

Chappell, N., & Penning, M. (2009). *Understanding health, health care and health policy in Canada.* Don Mills, ON: Oxford University Press.

Clark, J. (2008). *Health, illness and medicine in Canada* (5th ed.). Don Mills, ON: Oxford University Press.

Coburn, D., D'Arcy, C., & Torrance, G. (Eds.). (1998). *Health and Canadian society (sociological perspectives)* (3rd ed.). Toronto, ON: University of Toronto Press.

Conrad, P. (Ed.). (2005). *The sociology of health & illness (critical perspectives)* (7th ed.). New York, NY: Worth Publishers.

Freund, P., McGuire, M., & Podhurst, L. (2003). *Health, illness, and the social body: A critical sociology* (4th ed.). Englewood Cliffs, NJ: Pearson.

Marmot, M., & Wilkinson R.G. (Eds.). (2006). *Social determinants of health* (2nd ed.). Oxford, UK: Oxford University Press.

Navarro, V. (1976). *Medicine under capitalism.* New York, NY: Prodist.

Organisation for Economic Co-operation and Development. (2004). OECD *health data 2004.* Paris: OECD.

Raphael, D. (Ed.). (2009). *Social determinants of health* (2nd ed.). Toronto, ON: Canadian Scholars' Press Inc.

Usdin, S. (2007). *The no-nonsense guide to world health.* Toronto, ON: Between the Lines.

Waitzkin, H. (2000) *The second sickness: Contradictions of capitalist health care* (2nd ed.). Lanham, MD: Rowman & Littlefield.

Weiss, G., & Lonnquist, L. (2009). *The sociology of health, healing, and illness* (6th ed.). Upper Saddle River, NJ: Pearson Education Inc.

Wilkinson, R. & Marmot, M. (Eds.). (2003). *Social determinants of health: The solid facts* (2nd ed.). Copenhagen: World Health Organization.

Web Resources

Canadian Centre for Policy Alternatives (CCPA)
www.policyalternatives.ca

Canadian Community Health Survey, 2010, Annual Component (CCHS)
www.statcan.gc.ca/cgi-bin/imdb/p2SV.pl?Function=getSurvey&SDDS=3226&lang=en&db=imdb&adm=8&dis=2

Canadian Institute for Health Information (CIHI): Health Indicators, 2010
http://secure.cihi.ca/cihiweb/products/Healthindicators 2010_en.pdf

Canadian Policy Research Networks (CPRN)
www.cprn.org

American Sociological Association (ASA): Medical Sociology Section
www.asanet.org/sections/medical.cfm

Society for Social Medicine (SSM)
www.socsocmed.org.uk

Statistics Canada: Health Reports
www.statcan.gc.ca/ads-annonces/82-003-x/index-eng.htm

World Health Organization (WHO)
www.who.org

CHAPTER 2

Theorizing Health: Major Theoretical Perspectives in Health Sociology

John Germov & Jennie Hornosty

Overview

- What is theory?
- Why is theory necessary?
- What are the main theoretical approaches in health sociology?

This chapter provides an overview of some of the main theoretical perspectives and approaches in health sociology: functionalism, Marxism, Weberianism, symbolic interactionism, feminism, and post-structuralism/postmodernism. It draws out the key features, assumptions, and concepts of these different perspectives. The chapter aims to provide an appreciation of what theory is and the reasons it is important. Differences between theoretical perspectives are discussed, particularly with reference to the structure–agency debate and the different questions addressed by various perspectives. The chapter ends with a caution against confusing perspectives with specific theories.

Key Terms

agency	institutional ethnography (IE)	social construction/
biological determinism	McDonaldization	constructionism
biomedical model	medical-industrial complex	social control
capitalism	meta-analysis/meta-narratives	social determinants of health
class	patriarchy	social structure
commodification of health care	political economy	socialism/communism
deviance	rationalization	sociological imagination
emotional labour	relations of ruling	stigma
feminism/feminist	sexual division of labour	structure–agency debate
functional prerequisites	sick role	theory
gender	socialization	total institutions
ideal type	social closure	verstehen

Introduction: What Is Theory and Why Do We Need It?

A theory is an explanation of how things work and why things happen. Theories allow us to make sense of our world—they provide answers to the 'how' and 'why' questions of life—by showing the way certain facts are connected to one another. We often think of theory as somehow divorced from reality, but we actually make use of theories every day of our lives. For example, when some people suggest that violence on television or in the lyrics of popular music may lead to increased acts of violence in the wider community, they are espousing a theory of why things happen. Such explanations generally reflect people's fundamental beliefs and values.

It is not uncommon for people to voice their everyday opinions or theories on the differences between women and men, rich and poor, Black and White, heterosexuals and homosexuals, to name but a few. Such theories can influence how people relate to one another, how tolerant they are of others, and whether they support social policies and laws aimed at addressing various forms of discrimination and inequality. So, rightly or wrongly, people have opinions or theories about how and why social life is the way it is.

Perhaps because of our familiarity with the subject matter of sociology—the study of social life and human behaviour—it is not unusual to be a little skeptical of sociological theories. While many of us do not understand the theories of chemistry and physics, we tend to accept them because of their practical applications to such things as medicines and technologies. Sociological theories (or social theories for short), on the other hand, appear at first glance to be impractical and seem to complicate a world we already know much about (Craib, 1992). Everyday opinions such as those noted above, however, are usually based on unacknowledged prejudices and lack reliable supporting evidence. What sets social theories apart from everyday opinions is that they attempt to explain social life by presenting a logical, detailed, and coherent account derived from systematically researched evidence.

Theoretical Perspectives in Health Sociology: An Overview

> 'The Answer to the Great Question of ... Life, the Universe and Everything ... Is ... Forty-two.'
>
> — *Douglas Adams, The Hitchhiker's Guide to the Galaxy*

As the above quote implies, the search for a 'theory of everything' is likely to be a futile task. Even if we could construct a theory that explained every imaginable social problem, public issue, or human action, its complexity would likely be so great as to make it unusable. A theory attempts to simplify reality and generalize its common and related features relevant to the topic at hand. The sheer variety of social life and the diversity of human behaviour mean that there is no single sociological 'theory of everything.' As Fritjov Capra (1982) puts it, '[a]ll scientific theories are approximations to the true nature of reality ... each theory is valid for a certain range of phenomena. Beyond this range it no longer gives a satisfactory description of nature, and new theories have to be found to replace the old one, or, rather, to extend it by improving the approximation' (p. 93).

As you read the chapters of this book and consult the wider literature, you will quickly become aware that there are many different and sometimes opposing social theories on a topic. While the **sociological imagination** outlined in Chapter 1 is the core of a sociological approach, there are significant differences of opinion over how to put it into practice. Over the years, many social theories have been developed and advocated by sociologists, making it frustrating for those new to sociology to steer a course through the maze of theories that exist. One way to navigate through this theory maze is to start by grouping theories into the following theoretical perspectives or frameworks:

- Structural functionalism
- Marxism
- Weberianism
- Symbolic interactionism
- Feminism
- Post-structuralism/postmodernism
- Human rights and anti-racist approaches

Theoretical perspectives are a form of shorthand to group similar theories of society together. Within each perspective there exist many individual theories developed by different writers, but they all tend to share the core features of the particular perspective. Any attempt to group theories in this way necessarily involves simplification by focusing on the similarities within the one perspective, at the expense of the differences between specific theories. For example, many Marxist theorists today would disagree with some of Karl Marx's ideas, but they would nonetheless still share the core assumptions and principles of a Marxist perspective.

One of the main distinctions between perspectives is the purpose or the questions they address. For example, some authors are concerned with explaining social order, others with explaining social inequality, and others with understanding and promoting social change. While these concerns often overlap, they have caused considerable debate among sociologists about the appropriate uses of sociological knowledge. Some perspectives, such as functionalism, attempt to understand society as it currently exists and assert that they do not take part in advocating how social life ought to be. Other perspectives seek to use sociological knowledge to promote social change. For example, Marxist and feminist perspectives propose alternatives to present social arrangements to overcome social and economic inequalities.

Another distinction between theoretical perspectives is the level of analysis in relation to the **structure–agency debate**. Whereas we can imagine that the natural world exists without our presence, it is difficult to imagine that a society could exist without humans (Giddens, 1997). Therefore, humans collectively 'make' society through their daily social interactions and through the social institutions they create, support, reproduce, and reform. It is this interplay between **social structure** and human **agency** that sociologists seek to understand. Despite this common goal, continuing disagreement exists among sociologists over the extent to which individuals shape or are shaped by the social structure. Some theoretical perspectives lean more toward the structure side of the debate and others more toward the agency side.

Sociological perspectives can be depicted broadly along a structure–agency continuum, with structuralist approaches at one end and agency approaches at the other.

sociological imagination

A term coined by C.W. Mills to describe the sociological approach to analyzing issues. We see the world through a sociological imagination, or think sociologically, when we make a link between personal troubles and public issues.

structure–agency debate

A key debate in sociology over the extent to which human behaviour is determined by social structure.

social structure

The recurring patterns of social interaction through which people are related to each other, such as social institutions and social groups.

agency

The ability of people, individually and collectively, to influence their own lives and the society in which they live.

Structuralist approaches assume that social structures, such as the economic and political system, play a significant role in shaping individual and group behaviour—that is, basic societal structures are a determining factor in how you think, feel, and act, as well as in your chances of health, wealth, and happiness. Agency approaches, on the other hand, tend to focus on micro factors: they see society as the product of individuals' acting socially or collectively to make the society in which they live. Agency perspectives focus on small-scale aspects of social interaction or the meanings people give to their experiences. Functionalism and Marxism tend to focus more on societal structures, whereas Weberianism, symbolic interactionism, and postmodernism are more focused on the role of agency. Those working within a feminist perspective generally draw on either symbolic interactionism or structural approaches. For our purposes it is important to realize that most sociological theories fall somewhere between these two poles—indeed, many contemporary social theories attempt to integrate structure and agency. Few authors writing within any of the perspectives completely deny the roles that social structure or human agency play in any given social situation; nevertheless, these perspectives reflect different starting points for analysis and guide one's research questions.

Key Features of Major Theoretical Perspectives

Table 2.1 summarizes the key features of the major theoretical perspectives in health sociology and how, at a glance, they apply to health issues. The remainder of the chapter provides greater detail on each perspective.

Structural Functionalism

Émile Durkheim (1858–1917), Talcott Parsons (1902–79), and Robert Merton (1910–2003) are the key theorists of structural functionalism, more commonly referred to simply as functionalism. Once the dominant theoretical paradigm in the United States, this perspective studies the way social structures function to maintain social order and stability. Functionalism focuses on large-scale social processes and is based on the assumption that a society is a system of integrated parts, each of which have certain needs (or **functional prerequisites**) that must be fulfilled for social order to be maintained. Hence, functionalists study various parts of society to understand how they interrelate and function to promote social stability.

Functionalism is sometimes referred to as 'consensus theory' because of its concentration on how social order is reached and maintained in society. In viewing society as a social system of related parts, functionalism has been particularly influential in organizational studies and public-policy analysis, where it is often referred to as 'systems theory.' For example, it is not uncommon to find descriptions of the health system as consisting of inputs, outputs, processes, and roles.

While such an approach can be useful for describing the basic operation of the health system, it neglects the influence of political, economic, and ideological interests, all of which make the health system less consensual, ordered, or systematic than a functionalist perspective would depict. Critics of functionalism also highlight its conservative tendencies (due to its focus on social stability and consensus) and hence its difficulties in accounting for social conflict and social change (Ritzer, 1996). Since the 1980s,

functional prerequisites

A debated concept based on the assumption that all societies require certain functions to be performed for them to survive and maintain social order. Also known as functional imperatives.

TABLE 2.1 Main Theoretical Perspectives in Health Sociology

Theoretical Perspective	Key Theorists	Key Concepts	Focus of Analysis	Health Example
Structural Functionalism	Émile Durkheim Talcott Parsons Robert Merton	Value consensus Sick role Society as comprising interrelated parts	Structuralist focus: shows how various parts of society function to maintain social order	The sick role (social expectations of how doctors and patients should behave) exposes the management of illness as a social experience
Marxism (and Critical Political Economy Approach)	Karl Marx Friedrich Engels Vincente Navarro Pat and Hugh Armstrong David Coburn Howard Waitzkin	Class conflict Capitalism Medical-industrial complex Commodification of health care Social inequality	Structuralist focus: shows how the unequal distribution of scarce resources in a capitalist society is based on class division and highlights who benefits and who is disadvantaged	Analyzes the links between class and health status, and between class, medical power, and profit-maximization Concerned with social inequalities in health Looks at role of the state in health care
Weberianism	Max Weber George Ritzer Bryan Turner	Bureaucracy Ideal type Rationalization McDonaldization Verstehen	Combines a primary focus on agency, with structuralist tendencies: looks at how the increasing regulation of social life takes place and how this may stifle human creativity; considers forms of social inequality and conflict	Examines how health professionals are increasingly subject to regulation and managerial control, producing greater efficiency and uniformity in health-care delivery, but potentially decreasing the effectiveness of patient care
Symbolic interactionism	George H. Mead Erving Goffman Anselm Strauss Herbert Blumer	The self Labelling theory Stigma Total institutions Negotiated order	Agency focused: emphasizes how individual and small-group interaction construct social meaning in everyday settings to reproduce and change social patterns of behaviour	Uncovers how and why certain forms of behaviour are treated as deviance, exposing the stigma, negative consequences, and biased treatment of social groups whose behaviour is deemed abnormal (e.g., homosexuality) Looks at the meaning of illness for individuals
Feminism	Dorothy Smith Patricia Hill Collins Ann Oakley Meg Luxton Arlie Hochschild Nancy Hartsock	Patriarchy Gender Sexual division of labour The double day	Consists of a range of strands that are either structuralist or agency focused Concerned with gender inequalities; seeks to explain and change the unequal position of women in society	Exposes sexism, biological determinism, and gender inequality in health research, theory, and treatment Critique of the medicalization of women's lives
Post-structuralism/postmodernism	Michael Foucault Jacques Derrida Judith Butler	Discourse Panopticon Surveillance Performativity	Agency focused: critiques theories based on universal truths and structuralist assumptions Concentrates on subjectivity, diversity, and fragmentation	Examines how certain discourses of normality and panoptic effects serve to discipline and control various social groups

some theorists, such as Jeffrey Alexander (1947–), have attempted to address many of these criticisms through the development of the perspective of 'neo-functionalism' (see Alexander, 1985, 1998).

The functionalist analysis of health care has been primarily influenced by the work of Talcott Parsons (1951a), who viewed the health of individuals as a necessary condition of a stable and ordered society. He conceptualized illness as a form of **deviance**—that is, he viewed it as stopping people from performing various social roles, such as paid work and caring for children, which were essential to the functioning of society. In Parsons' terms, 'health is intimately involved in the functional pre-requisites of the social system . . . too low a general level of health, too high an incidence of illness, is dysfunctional . . . because illness incapacitates the effective performance of social roles' (1951b, p. 430). For Parsons, because illness disrupted the normal functioning of society, it was important that the sick were encouraged to seek expert help so that they returned to health and could perform their social roles. This was achieved through the **sick role**—that is, the social expectations that dictated how an individual sick person was meant to act and be treated.

According to Parsons, the sick role involves a series of rights and responsibilities. Once sick, individuals have the right to be exempted from their normal social roles, such as those of parent, employee, or student. This exemption from performing their duties is legitimated by medical diagnosis and treatment. For example, students regularly have to provide medical certificates to support their case for missing an exam or not submitting work on time. A further right of the sick person is that since illness is generally beyond individuals' control, they are not held personally responsible and should be able to rely on others to care for them while they are ill.

However, the sick also have certain responsibilities. For example, they are expected to seek medical assistance and comply with the recommended treatment. Moreover, they are obliged to recover and then resume their normal social duties. Alexander Segal argues that there should be a separation of the informal sick role from the formal patient role and that there is a need to recognize that one can enter and exit the sick role without seeking medical assistance (Segall, 1997, as cited in Segall & Chappell, 2000). He proposes a revision of the sick role to reflect the fact that everyday self-care behaviours include health maintenance activities as well as managing one's illness.

The sick role concept directs attention to the social nature of the illness experience and focuses attention on the doctor–patient relationship. However, the concept's importance also lies in the many critiques it has inspired as a result of its limited application to chronic, terminal, and permanently disabling conditions, as well as in its uncritical acceptance of the role of the medical profession and its neglect of the limitations of the **biomedical model**. Critics point out that one's ability to take on the sick role is shaped by such factors as ethnicity, class, age, occupation, and gender. According to Ivan Emke (2002), the sick role takes on a particular meaning in the 'New Economy' (characteristic of Canada and other Western societies today), whereby individuals are held responsible for the onset of illness (by not looking after themselves) and at the same time are instructed to use as few medical services as possible. He cites the example of a pilot project in 1994 by the Ontario government to discourage people from going to a doctor for minor complaints. 'In the New Economy, we are told that the government deficit is the

deviance

Behaviour or activities that violate social expectations about what is normal.

sick role

A concept used by Talcott Parsons to describe the social expectations of how sick people are expected to act and of how they are meant to be treated.

biomedical model

The conventional approach to medicine in Western societies, based on the diagnosis and explanation of illness as a malfunction of the body's biological mechanisms. This approach underpins most health professions and health services, which focus on treating individuals, and generally ignores the social origins of illness and its prevention.

fault of all of us, and that we must all do our part in reducing it. This includes reducing the extent to which we rely on medical assistance and the length of time we might spend as "unproductive" members of society' (p. 88).

Marxism

The term 'Marxism' refers to a wide body of theory and political policies based on the writings of Karl Marx (1818–83) and Friedrich Engels (1820–95). Marx was a philosopher, economist, and sociologist. He was also politically active, and since his death his writings have not only inspired many sociologists but have also laid the foundations for numerous political movements around the world. Marxism, sometimes referred to as 'conflict theory' or 'materialism', asserts that society is dominated by a fundamental conflict of interest between two social classes—the bourgeoisie (the capitalist class) and the proletariat (the working class)—that comprise the economic system of **capitalism**. The capitalist class expands its control by exploiting the labour power of the working class (Marx, 1967/1867, 1970/1845).

The influence and contribution of Marxism in sociology is widespread, but the perspective's core concern remains class analysis, especially its emphasis on class conflict as the defining feature of social life and the catalyst of social change (toward its goal of changing the social relations of production). Although Marxist analysis has a structuralist focus, Marx argued that it is conscious human action that changes society. For Marx, human beings are products of their society yet are capable of transforming their social conditions (Marx, 1964/1844, 1970/1845). Many working within the Marxist tradition are activists who are committed to fighting for social justice. For others, Marxism is an emotionally charged term because of its negative association with **socialism** and **communism**, both concepts that have been distorted by the media and by some conservative academics.

To add to the definitional confusion, some conflict theorists, such as Randall Collins (1975) and Ralf Dahrendorf (1959), while acknowledging a debt to Marx, no longer consider themselves Marxists since they have incorporated other forms of social conflict, such as that engendered in various organizational settings and among a range of social movements (such as youth, environmental, and anti-nuclear movements). Much of Marx's theory has been reinterpreted and modified and is now often referred to as neo-Marxism. Critical theory is one such neo-Marxist approach, in which a diverse group of theorists, such as Herbert Marcuse, Jürgen Habermas, Douglas Kellner, and Max Horkheimer, emphasized the importance of mass culture in comparison with the economy and merged psychoanalysis with Marxism (Ritzer, 1996). A critical political economy perspective whose focus is social inequality is another approach inspired by the works of Marx (Bourgeault, 2006). Here, the emphasis is on how material conditions directly and indirectly determine the health of individuals and communities (Raphael, 2006, 2009).

A Marxist perspective on health and illness is reflected in the contemporary writings of Pat and Hugh Armstrong (2003); David Coburn (2000, 2001); Howard Waitzkin (1983, 2000); Vincente Navarro (1976, 1986, 2004, 2008); and Bob Connell (1988). A primary focus of this perspective is on the impact of working and living conditions in capitalist society and how these contribute to illness, as well as on the role of the medical profession. In particular, Marxist perspectives have highlighted that the exploitation of workers

capitalism

An economic and social system based on the private accumulation of wealth.

socialism/communism

Socialism is a political ideology with numerous variations but generally refers to the creation of societies in which private property and wealth accumulation are replaced by state ownership and distribution of economic resources. *Communism* represents a vision of society based on communal ownership of resources, cooperation, and altruism to the extent that social inequality and the state no longer exist. Both terms are often used interchangeably.

and the pursuit of profit inherent in the structure of capitalism can create dangerous work environments and poor living conditions, resulting in higher mortality and morbidity rates among the working class.

Theory Link
See Chapter 4 for a discussion of the Marxist tradition.

Marxist analyses of health care also look at the professional power of doctors that serve class interests by placing profit maximization above access to optimal health care. Navarro, Armstrong & Armstrong, and Waitzkin have been strong critics of the medical profession's individualistic focus and its continued reliance on the biomedical model. By locating the cause and treatment of illness in individuals and ignoring what Waitzkin (1983, 2000) calls 'illness-generating social conditions', the medical profession is viewed as performing an ideological function by masking the real causes of illness and thereby supporting the capitalist system. According to Navarro (1986, p. 35), in capitalist societies the influence of work on health 'is of paramount importance' since workers 'have no control over their work and, thus, over their lives, including their health'. Canadian researchers Pat and Hugh Armstrong (2003) have examined how the drive for profits in the health-care sector leads to management strategies that intensify the work and creates additional stress on nurses. David Coburn (2001) shows the effect of neo-liberal policies on exacerbating socially determined health inequalities, while Joel Lexchin explains how the pharmaceutical industry's profit motive can lead to negative health outcomes for patients. Toba Bryant (2009) looks at the impact of economic globalization on health policy and health-care provision in Canada.

Theory Link
See Chapter 14 for Joel Lexchin's discussion of the pharmaceutical industry in Canada.

Australian sociologists Evan Willis (1989a, b) and Bob Connell (1988) have highlighted the profit-orientation and entrepreneurial ethos of the medical profession and its tendency to align itself with upper-class interests. This is evidenced in Canada where the previous two presidents of the Canadian Medical Association were in favour of more for-profit health care in Canada. Two historical doctors' strikes in the country also illustrate the self-interested orientation of the medical profession. Furthermore, fee-for-service, self-regulation, and the suppression of competition from other health practitioners (Coburn, Torrance, & Kaufert, 1983; Torrance, 1998) are indicative of medicine's alignment with 'the economic and ideological patterns of capitalism' (Connell, 1988, p. 214). According to Connell, this has resulted in a commonality of lifestyles and interests between doctors and the upper class so that 'doctors as a group . . . have particular political and economic interests they do not share with most of their patients: interests in maintaining a sharp division of labour in health care, in a substantial amount of public ignorance about health, and in seeing that self-help arrangements for health care remain marginal or ineffective' (p. 214).

Theory Link
See Chapter 13 for a further discussion of the doctors' strikes in Canada.

A further area of interest for Marxist authors has been the entry of large profit-oriented corporations, including pharmaceutical companies, into the health sector, often referred to as the **medical-industrial complex**, a term originally coined by Navarro and colleagues in 1967 (Navarro, 1998). The medical-industrial complex highlights the **commodification of health care**, whereby health is increasingly viewed as a commodity from which profit can be made, the pursuit of which may clash with the health needs of individuals and of the wider community. Connell (1988), among others, cautions against the vast growth and influence of profit-oriented medical enterprises, such as drug companies, pathology and radiology clinics, private health insurance companies, private nursing homes, and private hospitals. While Canadians have universal access to public health care through Medicare, some groups seek to undermine the system despite its overwhelming public support (Romanow, 2002). Joel Lexchin (2001, 2006, 2010; Lexchin & Wiktorowicz, 2009) has written extensively about the growing cost of medications, profit strategies utilized by pharmaceutical companies, and the Canadian government's willingness to turn regulatory decisions over to drug manufactures.

medical-industrial complex

The growth of profit-oriented medical companies and industries, whereby one company may own a chain of health services, such as hospitals, clinics, and radiology and pathology services.

commodification of health care

Treating health care as a commodity to be bought and sold in the pursuit of profit maximization.

Political Economy Approach

A **political economy** approach to health and health care characterizes much of the critical work being done in Canada. In Canada the political economy tradition goes back to the 1920s and 1930s and the writings of Harold Innis and the staples theory (1999/1930), which showed how staples, such as lumber, fish, and fur, shaped the economic and political structure of Canada. The more recent writings in Canadian political economy have been very much influenced by Marxism and take a critical materialist perspective that challenges the dominant beliefs about how society is structured and raises questions about how things could be different. Scholars such as Leo Panitch (1977) and Wallace Clement (1975) have looked at the interlinkages between economic, ideological, and political forces; feminists in that tradition, such as Pat Armstrong (2001; Andrew et al., 2003; Armstrong & Armstrong, 2010) and Meg Luxton (1987), introduced a tradition of feminist political economy that paid attention to women's work in the home and to gender relations. William Carroll (2004) has used a political economy perspective to consider the role of transnational forces, such as globalization and neo-liberalism in shaping corporate power in Canada. According to Armstrong, Armstrong, and Coburn (2001),

political economy

Focuses on how political, economic, and ideological factors influence the distribution of power and other resources in a society, which in turn shapes individual experience and state policies.

> Political economists grapple with the tensions between structure and agency, between ideas and material conditions, between class and gender, class and race, and between the tendency to separate aspects of these for the purposes of analysis and the need to unite them in order to understand the whole. (p. ix)

In the area of health, political economy provides a unique contribution in that it focuses on the links between health and the economic, political, and social lives of people in different regions and societies. Political economy asks questions such as the following:

- Why do some people have better health than others?
- Why do some countries have a publicly supported universal medicare system while others have for-profit health care?
- Why are there inequalities in access to health care?
- Why do social inequalities exist? (Coburn, 2006, pp. 59–61)

As well, a critical political economy approach to health is materialist—that is, greater explanatory emphasis is placed on how society is organized and on the way people live rather than on the ideas they produce. This type of analysis is illustrated in works by Canadian scholars such as David Coburn (2000, 2001, 2006); Dennis Raphael (2006, 2009b,c); Joel Lexchin (2001, 2006, 2010; Lexchin & Wiktorowicz, 2009); and Pat and Hugh Armstrong (2001, 2003). In addition, Navarro's and Muntaner's edited collection *Political and Economic Determinants of Population Health and Well-Being* (2004) provides an excellent overview of the current relationship between social inequalities and health worldwide. In another example of this type of analysis, all the contributors to *Unhealthy Times: Political Economy Perspectives on Health and Care in Canada* (2001), edited by Pat Armstrong, Hugh Armstrong, and David Coburn, use a critical political economy approach to view different facets of our health care system. For example, Peggy McDonough (pp. 195–222) examines how workers' health is affected by global pressures on labour markets to downsize and increase the use of casual labour. Paul Williams et al. (pp. 7–30) look at how current pressures of neo-liberalism and globalization are trying to reduce government's role in health-care services in favour of the private sector.

Weberianism

Max Weber (1864–1920) (pronounced *vay-ber*)[1] ranks along with Marx as one of the most influential theorists in sociology. Weber (1968/1921) like Marx produced a theory of society that acknowledges the way in which people both shape and are shaped by the social structure. Weber's writings are extensive, but his major contributions concern his concept of social action, his notion of **verstehen**, his analysis of bureaucracy, and his account of power and social inequality through the concepts of class, status, and party. Like Marx, Weber viewed class as important and believed that social conflict was a defining characteristic of increasingly complex societies. Unlike Marx, rather than two basic classes Weber also considered the middle classes as important, which he saw as consisting of those occupational groups with qualifications and skills that provided them with market advantages (higher wages, prestige, and better working conditions) over those in manual occupations. Not only did the diversity of social classes provide the basis for various forms of collective action to protect and expand group interests, thereby laying the basis for social conflict, Weber suggested that in addition to class inequality, status groups and parties were also a source of group formation and social inequality.

Status groups reflect cultural and sometimes legally conferred privileges, social respect, and honour. They are usually based on membership in specific professional, ethnic, and religious groups, and members tend to share common interests and lifestyles.

verstehen
Refers to a process of interpretative and empathetic understanding.

---

1. I would like to acknowledge a debt to Bessant and Watts (2002) for their insights in conveying the pronunciations of author surnames.

Status group membership is often restricted through what Weber termed a process of **social closure**. While class and social status tend to be closely related, they need not be. Moreover, other groups, or 'parties' in Weber's terms, could also serve as the basis for collective interests and social inequality. 'Parties' refer to groups attempting to wield power and include political parties, associations such as unions and professional bodies, as well as various interest/pressure groups.

Another strand of Weber's work concerned the process of **rationalization**, which he considered the overarching trend in society, epitomized by the growth of bureaucracy. Weber (1968/1921) predicted the 'future belongs to bureaucratisation' (p. 1401) and described an **ideal type** bureaucratic organization as having a highly specialized and hierarchical division of labour bounded by formal rules and regulations (see Weber 1968/1921, pp. 221–3). For Weber, bureaucracies were an effective response to social complexity and democracy by attempting to eliminate fraud, mismanagement, and inefficiency through conformity to standardized procedures. Despite what he saw as the significant benefits of bureaucracy, he feared that social life would be so governed by objective and informal rules that people would become entrapped by an 'iron cage' of regulations that would limit their creativity and individuality.

Weberian analyses of health tend to focus on health professions and the health bureaucracy. Prominent theorists include Magali Sarfati Larson (1977), Anne Witz (1992), Bryan Turner (1987), and George Ritzer (1993). Ritzer updates Weber's idea of rationalization and suggests that the fast-food industry (rather than bureaucracy) represents an intensified model of rationalization, which he terms **McDonaldization**. For example, medical practice is increasingly subject to regulations and performance indicators so that health care becomes predictable and uniform (just like a fast-food restaurant). Armstrong and Armstrong's (2003) work from a political economy perspective also illustrates the rationalization of health-care delivery (nursing work) and the implementation of quality assurance techniques and cost-saving measures as a consequence of neo-liberalism. Ritzer's argument extends Weber's concept of the 'iron cage', whereby the introduction of performance indicators that are motivated by cost factors alone may make health professionals more consistent in their treatment but may also dehumanize interaction with patients and lessen the flexibility and quality of care provided. In their study of nurses in Halifax, Beagan and Ells (2009) found that new managerial practices undermined nurses' professional values and reduced the quality of care. Nurses felt caught between their ethic of care and the institutions' demand for quantification.

social closure

A term first used by Max Weber to describe the way that power is exercised to exclude outsiders from the privileges of social membership (in social classes, professions, or status groups).

rationalization

The standardization of social life through rules and regulations. See *McDonaldization*.

ideal type

A concept originally devised by Max Weber to refer to the abstract or pure features of any social phenomenon.

McDonaldization

A term coined by George Ritzer to expand Weber's notion of rationalization; defined as the standardization of social life by rules and regulations, such as increased monitoring and evaluation of individual performance, akin to the uniformity and control measures used by fast-food chains. These principles are now applied to other sectors, both locally and globally.

Theory Link
See Chapter 15 for a discussion of nursing in the twenty-first century.

Symbolic Interactionism

Symbolic interactionism is considered by many to have its roots in Weber's ideas. It is associated with key theorists, such as George Herbert Mead (1863–1931), Charles Cooley (1864–1929), Howard Becker (1928–), Erving Goffman (1922–82), Anselm Strauss (1916–96), and Herbert Blumer (1900–87), who coined the term in 1937. The perspective arose as a reaction against structuralist approaches such as structural functionalism, which tends to view humans as simply responding to external influences. Instead, symbolic interactionists focus on agency and how people construct, interpret, and give meaning to their behaviour through interaction with others. The core philosophical assumption is that humans create reality through their actions and the meanings they give to them. Therefore, society is the cumulative effect of human action, interaction, and interpretation, and these are more significant than social structures—hence the focus of the perspective. Symbolic interactionism has a number of strands, such as ethnomethodology (see Garfinkel, 1967) and phenomenology (see Berger & Luckmann, 1967; Schutz, 1972/1933). Its emphasis on the **social construction** of reality has influenced many other perspectives, such as cultural studies and postmodernism (Ritzer, 1996).

Symbolic interactionism provides a theoretical bridge between sociology and psychology by concentrating on small-scale social interaction and how this impacts an individual's identity or image (often referred to as 'the self' or 'self-concept'). Cooley's (1964/1906) term 'the looking-glass self' encapsulates this approach, whereby the reactions of others influence the way we see ourselves and thus how we in turn behave. For example, if people regularly tell you that you are attractive and intelligent, this reaction can influence what you believe and how you behave.

Symbolic interactionism emphasizes that health and illness are perceived subjectively and are social constructions that change over time and vary between cultures. Therefore, what is considered an illness is socially defined and passes through a social lens that reflects the culture, politics, and morality of a particular society at a particular point in time. Such a viewpoint has been used to great effect by interactionist theorists to expose many medical practices and opinions that are based on social (or moral) rather than biological factors. Many interaction studies have also focused on patients' subjective experience of illness, interactions between patients and health professionals, and interactions among health professionals (especially between doctors and nurses). For example, Schneider and Conrad's work on epilepsy (1983) looks at the meaning of having a chronic illness from the perspective of those who live with it. How does it affect their everyday lives and the lives of those around them? Gareth Williams (2000) looks at how people's beliefs about the cause of their rheumatoid arthritis need to be understood as part of a large narrative process that they construct. Becker (1963) argues that deviance is created through social interaction when certain behaviours or groups of people are labelled as deviant by social institutions, such as the police, the courts, and mental health authorities. According to Becker, 'deviance is not a quality of the act a person commits, but rather a consequence of the application by others of rules and sanctions to an offender. The deviant is one to whom that label has successfully been applied; deviant behaviour is behaviour that people so label' (1963, p. 9).

social construction/ constructionism

Refers to the socially created characteristics of human life based on the idea that people actively construct reality, meaning it is neither 'natural' nor inevitable. Therefore, notions of normality/ abnormality, right/wrong, and health/illness are subjective human creations that should not be taken for granted.

Theory Link
See Chapter 10 on constructing disability and living with chronic illness.

Labelling theory examines the effect that being labelled deviant has for the individual concerned. Such an approach draws attention to how and why certain behaviours and groups of people are labelled deviant. Moreover, labelling theory exposes the way that medicine (especially psychiatry) could be used as an instrument of **social control** to constrain the actions of so-called difficult social groups (see Roach Anleu, 1999; Szasz, 2007).

Canadian-born sociologist Erving Goffman (1961, 1963) examined **stigma** and focused attention on what he termed **total institutions**, such as asylums. According to Goffman, a person becomes stigmatized when they possess an attribute that negatively affects social interaction. He identified three forms of stigma: physical deformity, individual characteristics (mental disorder), and 'tribal' factors (based on 'race', ethnicity, and religion). In his terms, these resulted in tainted or 'spoiled identities', whereby social interaction was affected by negative traits associated with the particular stigma. For example, people may react to someone with a physical disability through outright discrimination or may treat that person as if he or she were also mentally incompetent. A person diagnosed as having suffered from schizophrenia may be treated as (and often called) a 'schizophrenic', as if it was the sole characteristic of who he or she was. In such cases, the stereotype associated with the condition overrides the actual personality, actions, and achievements of the individual concerned. A person with HIV/AIDS is similarly stigmatized.

Goffman's (1961) analysis of institutionalization (the incarceration of people for some form of treatment or sanction) focused on the experience from the perspective of the 'inmates'. His observations of the interaction between inmates and institutional staff reflected the overt and covert forms of power relationships imbued in what he termed the 'total institution'. While such institutions served to impose highly regimented and authoritarian forms of conformity on inmates, often to the detriment of their personal and health needs, they also resulted in a hidden 'underlife' through which people kept a sense of their individual identity by resisting or undermining authority in secret ways (see also Scheff, 1966). Goffman's insights on the negative affects of institutionalization have had a wide impact, which can be seen in fictional works such as the film *One Flew Over the Cuckoo's Nest*. Excellent discussions of deviance can be found in Sharyn Roach Anleu's (1999) *Deviance, Conformity and Control* and Peter Conrad and John Schneider's (1992) *Deviance and Medicalization: From Badness to Sickness*.

Feminism

Feminist perspectives in sociology first arose in the 1960s and were primarily aimed at addressing the neglect of gender issues and in some cases the blatant sexism of traditional sociological theories, exposing that most mainstream sociology was in fact 'male-stream' (Smith, 1974, 1987; Sydie, 1987). Feminists have pointed out that some approaches perpetuated sexist assumptions about the role of women in society, such as Parsons's view of women as performing 'expressive roles' in society, fulfilling the 'function' of providing emotional care and support of men and families. Hence, feminist perspectives addressed the question 'What about the women?' and focused on social inequality between women and men. Feminists further pointed out that women's experiences as workers, partners, caregivers, or victims of abuse were rarely studied or theorized about. Feminists see the world as gendered such that women and men have different access to power. These differences, however, are not natural but are socially constructed.

One of the most eminent feminist theorists is Canadian sociologist Dorothy Smith (1926–), who made the important distinction between a sociology *of* women and a sociology *for* women. In *The Everyday World as Problematic: A Feminist Sociology* (1987) , Smith

social control

Mechanisms that aim to induce conformity, or at least to manage or minimize deviant behaviour.

stigma

A physical or social trait, such as a disability or a criminal record, that results in negative social reactions, such as discrimination and exclusion.

total institutions

A term used by Erving Goffman to refer to institutions, such as prisons and asylums, in which life is highly regulated and subjected to authoritarian control to induce conformity.

relations of ruling

A concept used by Dorothy Smith to refer to social relations in which people are involved that dominate them, to the rational forms of knowledge that are developed, and to the organizations that administer and mange these.

institutional ethnography (IE)

A feminist research strategy associated with Dorothy Smith combining theory and method. It begins from the standpoint of people in the actualities of their everyday world to show how people's social relations are organized by forces outside of them.

patriarchy

A system of power through which males dominate households. It is used more broadly by feminists to refer to society's domination by patriarchal power, which functions to subordinate women and children.

socialization

The process of learning the culture of a society (its language and customs), which shows us how to behave and communicate.

outlines the differences between men's standpoint and women's. According to Smith, men's standpoint is linked to the **relations of ruling** but has been represented as universal. However, 'the fulcrum of a sociology for women is the standpoint of the subject. A sociology for women preserves the presence of subjects as knowers and actors. It does not transform subjects into the objects of study. . . .' (p. 105). A sociology for women begins with the actualities of their everyday worlds and 'offers an understanding of how those worlds are organized and determined by social relations immanent in and extending beyond them' (p. 106). Smith's **institutional ethnography** (IE) approach is a way to examine the link between people's everyday experiences and the relations of ruling that coordinate and shape those lives as a means to help people understand how and why things happen (1987, 1993): 'Rather than taking up issues and problems as they have been defined by the discipline [sociology], the aim is to explicate the actual social processes and practices organizing people's everyday experience from a standpoint in the everyday world' (1987, p. 151) Smith developed the approach initially in a feminist context as a method that could produce a 'sociology for women'; however, she sees this approach as having much wider applications. Canadian researchers such as Janet Rankin and Marie Campbell (2006, 2009) have used institutional ethnography to examine the Canadian health-care system and the work of nurses. Christina Sinding (2010) employed institutional ethnography to explore health-care disparities in the context of study on cancer care in Ontario.

Feminism is a broad social and intellectual movement that addresses many issues from a range of academic disciplines. Sandra Harding (1991), Dorothy Smith (1987/1974, 1987, 1993), Patricia Hill Collins (2000), bell hooks (1984), Shulamith Firestone (1979/1970), Judith Butler (1990), Carol Gilligan (1993), Rosemary Pringle (1998), and Sandra Bartky (1998) are some of the many prominent feminist theorists. There are many 'feminisms' today, most of which can be grouped into four schools of thought:[2]

- Liberal feminism
- Radical feminism
- Socialist and Marxist feminism
- Post-structuralist/postmodern feminism

Alison Jaggar (1983), Rosemary Tong (1998), and Lorraine Code (1993) provide comprehensive introductions to the different feminist perspectives. Roberta Hamilton and Michele Barrett (1986) have edited an excellent collection of articles by Canadian feminist sociologists, primarily within the socialist feminist tradition.

Despite the diversity of approaches, feminist perspectives all highlight the importance of **patriarchy**. They argue that the social structure is patriarchal, with social institutions, such as the legal, health, and education systems, as well as the wider culture reflecting sexist values and supporting the privilege of men. Feminists challenge biological assumptions about women's nature, highlighting that gender is a social construction and identifying gender-role **socialization** and sex discrimination as keys to understanding inequality between the sexes. Black feminists, however, like Patricia Collins and bell hooks, have criticized much of feminism for its failure to recognize other forms of oppression. They

2. There are also other versions of feminism, such as ecofeminism, Freudian feminism, and psychoanalytic feminism, which focus on issues such as the environment, sexuality, 'race', and identity.

argue that cultural patterns of oppressions, such as race, class, ethnicity, and sexual orientation, are interrelated and bound together. Hence an understanding of intersectionality is vital to bringing about gender equality:

> All women may currently occupy the position 'woman' . . . but they do not occupy it in the same way. Women of colour in a white ruled society face different obstacles than do white women, and they may share more important problems with men of colour than with their white 'sisters' . . . consolidating all women into a falsely unified 'woman' has helped mask the operations of power that actually divide women's interests as much as unite them. (Poovey, 1988, p. 59)

Feminist perspectives on health care have underpinned the women's health movement and have drawn attention to how patriarchy has shaped the ideas and practices of medicine and how gender is a factor in every aspect of illness. Among the many topics feminists have addressed are the following:

Theory Link
Refer to Chapter 5, Women's Health in Context: Gender Issues.

- The medicalization of women's bodies and women's lives (Berenson et al., 2009); the medicalization of menopause (Ehrenreich & English, 1973; McCrea, 1983); unwarranted and sometimes harmful interventions in the management of pregnancy, childbirth, contraception, reproductive technology, and gynecological disorders (Annandale & Clarke, 1996; Kaufert & Gilbert, 1987; McCrea, 1983; Oakley, 1980; Riessman, 1983; Walters, 1992, 1994)
- The **sexual division of labour** in health care, particularly the historical role of women healers; the subordination of female-dominated professions, such as nursing; the performance of **emotional labour**; the role of women as informal carers outside the health system; and the effect of the increasing entry of women into the medical professions (Armstrong et al., 2009; Ehrenreich & English, 1973, 1974, 1979; Hothschild, 1979; Kirk, 1994)
- Sexism and **biological determinism** in health care, particularly medical research and treatment, according to which much health research has been conducted on men and extrapolated to women, and how women's specific health concerns have been under-researched or falsely assumed to be the result of their menstrual cycles—that is, women as 'helpless victims of their hormones' (Barrett & Roberts, 1978; Findlay & Miller, 2002; Mitchinson, 1993; Walters, 1994)
- The issues of sexuality, rape, and domestic violence as key health issues requiring the need for appropriate health policies and specialized training of health workers (Ford-Gilboe, et al., 2006, 2009; Varcoe, 2009; Wuest, et al., 2007)
- The impact of structures of social inequality on health (Denton & Walters, 1999)
- Body image and eating disorders (Bartky, 1998; Bordo, 1993; Berenson et al., 2009; Williams & Germov, 2004; Wolf 1991)

sexual division of labour

This refers to the nature of work performed as a result of gender roles. The stereotype is that of the male breadwinner and the female homemaker.

emotional labour

Refers to the use of feelings by employees as part of their paid work. In health care, a key part of nursing work is caring for patients, often by providing emotional support.

biological determinism

An unproven belief that individual and group behaviour and social status is an inevitable result of biology.

Today feminist perspectives and concerns are a central feature of sociology and health sociology in particular. Feminism has exposed the sexism and biological determinism of medical approaches and facilitated increasing attention on women's health rights in terms of health research, funding, and the provision of appropriate services (see Annandale, 2004, for a review of feminist theories applied to health).

Post-structuralism and Postmodernism

The terms *post-structuralism* and *postmodernism*[3] are often used interchangeably (Ritzer, 1997) even though distinctions can be made between the two. For our purposes we will focus on their similarities and treat them as one (and for simplicity only use the term *postmodernism*). Postmodernism arose in the 1980s and reflects a diverse range of social theories from many academic disciplines, making it difficult to categorize or treat systematically. However, to greater or lesser degrees, most social theorists who fall under the umbrella of postmodernism share the following key assumptions:

- The rejection of universal truths about the world, instead suggesting that reality is a social construction. Therefore, all theoretical perspectives (whether they be in the natural, health, or social sciences) reflect the vested interests of one group or another and thus all knowledge is merely a claim to truth, reflecting the subjectivity of those involved.
- The rejection of grand theories or **meta-narratives**: postmodernists dispute the existence or importance of unifying trends and structural determinants such as functional prerequisites, class conflict, patriarchy, or rationalisation.
- Since no perspective is neutral and there are no universal structural determinants of social life, postmodernists focus on how truth claims about the world are socially constructed. Thus, there is no single reality or ultimate truth, only versions or interpretations of what is 'real', 'true', 'normal', 'right', or 'wrong'. Such a perspective supports tolerance of diversity, but can imply that 'almost anything goes'.

meta-analysis and meta-narratives

The 'big picture' analysis that frames and organizes observations and research on a particular topic.

In sociology, the work of Michel Foucault (1926–84) has had the most influence, especially his historical work on asylums, prisons, and hospitals, which uncovered how knowledge and power are used to regulate and control various social groups. Foucault's (1979) conceptualization of the panopticon as a metaphor for his theory of surveillance and social control has been a key legacy of his work. The panopticon ('all-seeing place') was developed by Jeremy Bentham in the eighteenth century as an architectural design for a prison, consisting of a central observation tower surrounded by circles of cells so that every cell could be observed simultaneously. According to Foucault,

> All that is needed, then, is to place a supervisor in a central tower and to shut up in each cell a madman, a patient, a condemned man, a worker, or a schoolboy . . . [resulting in] a state of consciousness and permanent visibility that assures the automatic functioning of power . . . in short, that the inmates

---

3. The use of either term usually reflects a particular author's preference; however, some authors who are considered postmodern theorists dispute the validity of the term or any attempt to generalize about postmodernism. The spelling of the terms also varies slightly, with some authors preferring to use a hyphen: 'post-modernism'.

should be caught up in a power situation of which they themselves are the bearers. (1979, p. 200–1)

Therefore, control could be maintained by the assumption of being constantly under surveillance so that individuals subjected to the disciplinary gaze were 'totally seen without ever seeing, whilst the agents of discipline see everything, without ever being seen' (Foucault, 1979, p. 202). Bourgeault (2006, p. 49) writes that Foucault's work on how medical knowledge and discourse have been used to control the body through systems of surveillance in the supposed broader interest of society is a critical insight. For example, the wide promotion of the thin ideal of female beauty in Western societies results in panoptic effects whereby many women perceive themselves to be under constant body surveillance and undergo numerous disciplined activities in an attempt to conform to the pressure to be thin.

Postmodernism has significantly influenced diverse feminist perspectives, with the strand of postmodern feminism (or post-feminism) being developed by a diverse range of authors, such as Rosemary Pringle, Michele Barrett, Sandra Bartky, and Judith Butler.

Human Rights and Anti-Racism

A human rights approach while not a theory provides a framework for developing health programs and policies using human rights principles as the basis for design, implementation, and evaluation. Such an approach focuses on addressing health inequities at the local and global level. This approach suggests that the right to health must be understood in connection with other inalienable human rights: non-discrimination and equality, including women's reproductive rights; political and civil rights; economic, social, and cultural rights, including the right to an adequate standard of living, to education, and to cultural freedom; and the right of nations to development and economic autonomy (Rioux, 2006, pp. 85–110). A human rights approach interrogates health and health care from the perspective of social justice; it underscores the fact that poor health status is related to the exclusion and loss of human rights: 'The movement toward defining health as a human right requires a social injustice-based analysis of the relationships among health and social policy decisions, health and social service expenditures, population health outcomes, and the social determinants of health' (McGibbon, 2009, p. 319). McGibbon stresses the need for an intersectionality framework that recognizes that health and access to health care is influenced by an intersection of identities (gender, race, ethnicity, sexual orientation, [dis] ability, age) and social determinants of health, such as class, early childhood development, employment, education, as well as individuals' geographical location.

A growing number of scholars are recognizing that the structure and experiences of 'race' and racism are critical for understanding the health experiences of racialized groups. Canadian anti-racist scholar George Sefa Dei (1999, pp. 395–409) points out that 'race' is a socio-political construction by which dominant groups can exercise power and control over those defined as 'other'. Galabuzi (2009, pp. 252–79) reminds us that racialized groups encounter processes of marginalization in many spheres of life and that the experience of racism is a primary source of stress and hypertension in racialized communities. A recent study by the Women's Bureau of the Ontario Ministry of Health found that 'immigrant, racial minority and refugee women are discriminated against by the Ontario health care system' (cited in Egan & Gardner, 1999, p. 295). Anti-racist researchers have documented the various ways in which social determinants of health and institutionalized racism in the health-care system negatively impact the health status of racialized peoples. Dei argues that anti-racism praxis requires recognizing the saliency of 'race' and racial oppression in people's lives.

Theory Link
See Chapters 6 and 7 for a further discussion of 'race' and racism.

Conclusion

Despite the differences among the theoretical perspectives discussed here, the distinctions among specific social theories produced by individual authors are likely to be less clear-cut. While sociologists generally align themselves with particular perspectives, they tend to be in less disagreement than the differences between perspectives might imply. This is partly because sociologists attempt to incorporate the insights of a range of perspectives into their specific social theory.

While the existence of so many perspectives can be challenging, new theories and perspectives are likely to continue to emerge. Social theories change over time as society itself changes and new knowledge, ideas, and capabilities emerge. This is as true of natural sciences as it is of the social sciences. In response to social change and the development of new insights, theories are regularly modified, reinterpreted, and even rejected.

The theoretical perspectives presented in this chapter are more complex than can be discussed here. Furthermore, no attempt has been made to evaluate the theoretical perspectives, a feature beyond the scope of this introductory chapter. Rather, the aim has been to convey a basic understanding of some of the main assumptions, concepts, and approaches to explain the differences between perspectives and the insights they offer, and to help lay the foundations of understanding for various sociological theories you will encounter in this text and in the wider literature.

At this point it is important to sound a note of caution about the use and critique of sociological theories. When attempting to evaluate how well a specific social theory fits the evidence, there is a danger of making the mistake of critiquing the general perspective to which the theory belongs, rather than assessing the insights of the specific theory itself. This is not an argument to ignore the various limitations of theoretical perspectives that many authors have exposed but, rather, a warning against falling into the trap of dismissing a theory because of the perspective with which it is associated. A much healthier approach is to adopt a position of theoretical pluralism—that is, to accept that many theories have something to offer even though you may have a preference for a certain theoretical perspective. Indeed, these perspectives should be viewed as potentially complementary rather than automatically oppositional (Turner & Samson, 1995). It is up to you to judge how well a particular theory fits the researched evidence based on your reading and experience.

Summary of Main Points

- Sociologists seek to interpret their findings by offering a 'how' and/or 'why' explanation—a theory—for what they seek to understand.
- However, there is often disagreement over which 'how' and 'why' explanations, or social theories, best explain certain aspects of social life. Just as there are people with different opinions, there are sociologists who offer different theories to explain social life.
- One way to understand the range of social theories that exist is to group them into main theoretical perspectives: functionalism, Marxism, Weberianism, symbolic interactionism, feminism, and post-structuralism/postmodernism.
- Human rights and anti-racist approaches complement other theories.
- Differences between the theoretical perspectives are based on a range of philosophical assumptions and levels of focus, which direct attention to particular aspects of social life and how they should be investigated.
- The use of theoretical perspectives oversimplifies reality. Thus, sociologists may adopt different theoretical positions according to the topic under study or may incorporate the insights of other perspectives into their own social theory.
- While it is important to be aware of the underlying assumptions and limitations of theoretical perspectives, a specific social theory should always be evaluated on its own merit.

Sociological Reflection: What's Your Theory?

Sociological theories can help us to understand how and why certain health problems exist. As this chapter has shown, most theories can be grouped into different theoretical perspectives:

- Functionalism
- Marxism
- Political economy
- Weberianism
- Symbolic interactionism
- Feminism
- Post-structuralism/postmodernism
- Human rights and anti-racist approaches

Which theoretical perspective do you prefer? Why? Identify some of the key insights into understanding health and illness that your preferred perspective provides.

Discussion Questions

1. Which theoretical perspective do you most dislike? Why?
2. What are some of the limitations of adopting one theoretical perspective and ignoring others? (Provide examples in your answer.)
3. Which perspectives focus attention on health inequality?
4. What insights into health issues and health care have feminist perspectives provided?
5. What insights do political economists bring to the study of health and illness?
6. How might one reconcile macro and micro perspectives to get a better understanding of which factors impact one's health?

 Further Investigation

1. Choose two of the perspectives discussed in this chapter and examine the similarities and differences in their approach to studying health and illness.
2. 'The sick role is no longer applicable to the experience of illness and health care in a postmodern world.' Discuss.
3. Compare Marxist and symbolic interactionist perspectives on a health issue of your choice.

 Further Reading

Health Sociology Texts

Armstrong, P., Armstrong, H., & Coburn, D. (Eds.) (2001). *Unhealthy times: Political economy perspectives on health and care in Canada*. Toronto, ON: Oxford University Press.

Bolaria, S., & Dickinson, H. (Eds.). (2009). *Health, illness & health care in Canada* (4th ed.). Toronto, ON: Nelson Education Ltd.

Brown, P. (Ed.). (2000). *Perspectives in medical sociology* (3rd Ed.). Illinois: Waveland Press Inc.

Bryant, T., Raphael, D., & Rioux, M. (Eds.). (2010). *Staying alive: Critical perspectives on health, illness and health care* (2nd ed.). Toronto, ON: Canadian Scholars' Press Inc.

Chappell, N., & Penning, M. (2009). *Understanding health, health care and health policy in Canada*. Toronto, ON: Oxford University Press.

Clarke, J. (2008). *Health, illness and medicine in Canada* (5th ed.). Toronto, ON: Oxford University Press.

Coburn, D., d'Arcy, C., & Torrance, G. (Eds.). (1998). *Health and Canadian society: Sociological perspectives* (3rd ed.). Toronto, ON: University of Toronto Press.

Conrad, P. (Ed.). (2005). *The sociology of health and illness: Critical perspectives* (7th ed.). New York, NY: Worth Publishers.

Frankel, G., Speechley, M., & Wade, T. (1996). *The sociology of health and health care: A Canadian perspective*. Toronto, ON: Copp Clark.

Lorber, J., & Moore, L. (2002). *Gender and the social construction of illness* (2nd ed.). New York, NY: AltaMira Press.

Raphael, D. (Ed.). (2009). *Social determinants of health: Canadian perspectives* (2nd ed.). Toronto, ON: Canadian Scholars' Press.

Navarro, V. (1986). *Crisis, health & medicine: A social critique*. London, UK: Tavistock.

Segall, A., & Chappell, N. (2000). *Health and health care in Canada*. Toronto, ON: Prentice-Hall.

Turner, B., & Samson, C. (1995). *Medical power and social knowledge* (2nd ed.). London, UK: Sage.

General Social Theory Books

Beck, U. (1992). *Risk society: towards a new modernity*. Thousand Oaks, CA: Sage.

Berger, P., & Luckmann, T. (1967). *The social construction of reality*. Harmondsworth, UK: Penguin.

Craib, I. (1992). *Modern social theory* (2nd ed.). London, UK: Harvester Wheatsheaf.

Craib, I. (1997). *Classical social theory*. Oxford, UK: Oxford University Press.

Garner, R. (2000). *Social theory: Continuity and confrontation*. New York, NY: Broadview Press.

Jagger, A. (1983). *Feminist politics and human nature*. New Jersey: Rowman & Allanheld.

Oakely, A. (2002). *Gender on planet Earth*. Cambridge, UK: Polity Press.

Ritzer, G. (1997). *Postmodern social theory*. New York, NY: McGraw-Hill.

Ritzer, G. (Ed.). (2003). *The Blackwell companion to major classical social theorists*. Malden, MA: Blackwell.

Ritzer, G. (Ed.). (2005). *Encyclopedia of social theory* (Vols. 1–2). Thousand Oaks, CA: Sage.

Ritzer, G., & Goodman, D. J. (2004). *Sociological theory* (6th ed.). New York, NY: McGraw-Hill.

Seidman, S. (2004) *Contested knowledge: Social theory today* (3rd ed.). Malden, MA: Blackwell.

Smith, D. (1987). *The everyday world as problematic: A feminist sociology*. Toronto, ON: University of Toronto Press.

Smith, D. (1990). *The conceptual practices of power: A feminist sociology of knowledge*. Toronto, ON: University of Toronto Press.

Smith, D. (1993). *Texts, facts & femininity: Exploring the relations of ruling*. New York, NY: Routledge.

Sydie, R. A. (1987). *Natural women, cultured men: A feminist perspective on sociological theory*. Agincourt, ON: Methuen Publishers.

Tong, R. P. (1998). *Feminist thought: A more comprehensive introduction* (2nd ed.). Sydney, Australia: Allen & Unwin.

Walby, S. (1990). *Theorizing patriarchy*. Oxford, UK: Blackwell.

Weedon, C. (1997). *Feminist practice and poststructuralist theory* (2nd ed.). Cambridge, MA: Blackwell.

Web Resources

Feminist.com
www.feminist.com/resources/links/links_health.html

American Sociological Association: Medical Sociology
http://dept.kent.edu/sociology/asamedsoc/Section Homepage

Canadian Women's Health Network
www.cwhn.ca

Feminist Theory Website: Feminism in Canada
www.cddc.vt.edu/feminism/can.html

Feminist Majority Foundation
www.feminist.org

Sociosite: General theory
www.sociosite.net/topics/theory.php

Health related
www.sociosite.net/topics/health.php

CHAPTER 3

Researching Health: Methodological Traditions and Innovations

Douglas Ezzy & Jennie Hornosty

Overview

- What are the major approaches to researching health and illness?
- What are the limitations of the major research methods used in biomedical studies, such as evidence-based medicine, randomized control trials, and epidemiology?
- In what way do health sociologists address some of these limitations through qualitative approaches to the study of health and illness?
- What are some recent innovations in qualitative methods?

Health research includes a number of different methodologies. In this chapter we examine quantitative and qualitative methodologies and the limitations of the dominant research methods used in biomedical studies of health and illness, which tend to emphasize individualistic approaches to health. In contrast, epidemiological and qualitative methodologies informed by a sociological perspective recommend health policy responses that are more focused on social, cultural, and public health factors.

Key Terms

autoethnography

biomedicine/biomedical
   model

epidemiology/social
   epidemiology

ethnography

evidence-based medicine
   (EBM)

grounded theory

participatory action research

positivist research
   methodologies

purposive sampling

qualitative research

quantitative research

randomized control trials
   (RCTs)

research methods

risk factors

rigour

Introduction

As noted in the previous chapter there are a variety of theoretical perspectives in sociology that guide research in the areas of health and illness. Each perspective has certain basic assumptions that guide the methodology, questions, and focus of research. For example, scholars within a Marxist or political economy perspective often use historical and comparative data to look at macro issues; they ask questions about the structure of inequality and its impact on health and the health-care system. Researchers working in the symbolic interaction tradition, on the other hand, will focus on micro issues, such as people's experiences of illness and the meanings they attach to those experiences. Feminist sociologists research both macro and micro issues; in each case their primary concern is women's experience and the impact on women's health, and the aim of the research often is to empower women.

Broadly speaking, research methods can be categorized as either quantitative or qualitative, although many researchers use a combination of the two. Sociological research in the study of health and illness today is becoming more diverse with new methodologies. However, although the field of health sociology publishes its own journals and increasingly contributes to health policy debates, many of the **research methods** are still profoundly shaped by biomedical research. This is reflected by its dominance in the field of 'scientific' research, which covers nearly all aspects of health and illness. And although biomedical research methods, such as **randomized control trials** (RCTs), are not part of health sociology's research methods, it is essential that health sociologists understand their logic and the consequences of the theoretical and political baggage those research methods carry with them.

The first section of this chapter discusses positivist **quantitative research**, such as randomized control trials, evidence-based medicine, and the more public-health-oriented epidemiological research methods. The second section provides an overview of traditional **qualitative research**, introducing the distinctive logic of qualitative methods rather than discussing any particular tradition in detail. Finally, the chapter briefly outlines recent innovations in qualitative methods, pointing to the value of experimentation in methodologies.

Quantitative Research and the Positivist Tradition

Quantitative approaches and **positivist research methodologies** attempt to study the world through standardized procedures, uninfluenced by politics, subjectivity, or culture. These methodologies, including randomized control trials and epidemiological surveys, have proven to be very powerful methods for examining the efficacy of various treatments and identifying the risk factors associated with particular diseases. They have been used by government bodies such as Health Canada as a basis for health reform and determining health policy. However, positivist methodologies are not very useful for examining meanings, interpretations, and the experience of illness. Positivist research is typically considered to be more important than other forms of research and, as a consequence, the cultural and interpretative dimensions of social life are often inadequately researched and understood. Further, supporters of positivist methodologies pretend that politics does not influence the research process and, as a consequence, are often blind to the power of the particular interest groups that these research methodologies serve.

research methods
Procedures used by researchers to collect and investigate data.

randomized control trials (RCTs)
A biomedical research procedure used to evaluate the effectiveness of particular medications and therapeutic interventions. *Random* refers to the equal chance of participants being in the experimental or control group (the group to which nothing is done and is used for comparison); *trial* refers to the experimental nature of the method. RCTs are often mistakenly viewed as the best way to demonstrate causal links between factors under investigation but these procedures privilege biomedical over social responses to illness.

quantitative research
Research that focuses on the collection of statistical data.

qualitative research
Research that focuses on the meanings and interpretations of the participants.

positivist research methodologies
Research methods that attempt to study people in the same way that physical scientists study the natural world—by focusing on quantifiable and directly observable events. Such research methods focus on the collection of statistical data.

Randomized Control Trials (RCTs)

Randomized control trials are a powerful way of demonstrating the efficacy of drugs and other biomedical interventions for diseases. An excellent example is a double-blind study conducted in four Canadian centres over three winter seasons to study the effectiveness of light therapy compared to antidepressants to treat seasonal affective disorder. Randomized patients were assigned to eight weeks of either a 10 000-lux light treatment and a placebo capsule or a 100-lux light treatment (a placebo light) and 20 mg of fluoxetine (an antidepressant). The researchers found no significant difference between light therapy and antidepressant medication (Lam et al., 2006). The trial was randomized in the sense that whether a person received light therapy or an antidepressant was decided randomly. Randomized trials prevent doctors, for example, from choosing to give the medication to people that they think may be more likely to benefit. The trial was controlled in the sense that a comparison group of people, who did not receive the medication but who were drawn from the same social group, were included in the trial. The benefit of the treatment or medication was then assessed by comparing the two groups, in which the only difference was whether they received light therapy or medication. RCTs are important because they allow cherished beliefs to be disproved. For example, the drug clofibrate was initially thought to be beneficial because it significantly reduced the level of cholesterol in the blood. It was used extensively to treat high cholesterol until an RCT demonstrated that, on the contrary, it increased mortality (Sackett, 1981).

Richards (1988) provides an excellent account of the social and political nature of RCTs. She makes the strong claim that '[t]he randomised controlled clinical trial, no matter how tightly organized and evaluated, can neither guarantee objectivity nor definitively resolve disputes over contentious therapies or technologies' (p. 686). She also provides a detailed analysis of the use of RCTs to test the efficacy of vitamin C as a cancer treatment, involving two rival medical clinics. One clinic argued for the value of vitamin C, not as a drug to kill cancer cells but as a supplement to support the immune system's own suppression of the cancer tumours. However, the rival clinic was funded to conduct the trials, and it evaluated the therapeutic value of vitamin C using criteria drawn from comparable trials of cytotoxic drugs. Not surprisingly, vitamin C was found to be ineffective: 'They made no attempt to evaluate the efficacy of vitamin C . . . and ignored or were unaware of the available information on the physiology of vitamin C which should have been taken into account in the design of their study' (p. 672). Richards shows how the conduct of the published RCTs was clearly influenced by the theoretical and professional perspectives of the scientists involved.

However, as noted by Richards, the most telling criticism of the debate over vitamin C is that the clinic advocating the value of vitamin C was prevented from publishing further research and was not given the opportunity to comment on the existing studies already published; this points out the myth of disinterested and open scientific discussion. Richards (1988) concludes, 'If the orthodox claim of the inefficacy of vitamin C in cancer treatment prevails . . . it will *not* be as the result of agreement or consensus brought about by the disinterested application of impersonal rules of experimental procedure' (p. 672) (original emphasis). She provides a further analysis that suggests a direct, or indirect, influence of big business with vested interests in maintaining control over expensive treatments and preventing the use of widely available, relatively inexpensive alternatives: 'The institution of medicine has a great deal invested in the perpetuation of the myth of objective evaluation. It underpins the cognitive and social authority of its practitioners and legitimates powerful vested interests, not only in medicine, but in society at large' (p. 686).

David Healy (2003, 1997), a psychiatrist and once a consultant for such major pharmaceutical industries as Eli Lilly, Pharmacia, and Upjohn, also raises important questions about the objectivity of medical research. He points out that much of the medical-scientific research today is funded by big pharmaceutical companies. This raises important questions about conflict of interest in drug regulation and bias in the research process. Healey notes that there is often suppression of data on lethal side effects of drugs and that articles in prestigious medical journals are written by ghost writers employed by pharmaceutical companies. Linda Muzzin (2001) speaks of the pharmaceutical appropriation of science and how 'pharmaceutical scientists are increasingly prone to manipulation by the pharmaceutical industry' (p. 113).

Theory Link
See Chapter 14 on the pharmaceutical industry.

A criticism of one RCT does not, of course, demonstrate that all RCTs are unreliable. RCTs are important in that they allow for the assessment of the relative effectiveness of intervention and the assessment of various treatments. Physicians and scientists use them, for example, to determine the efficacy of new types of medications. And, as in the previously mentioned study of seasonal affective disorder, RCTs can show that non-drug modalities can be as effective as drugs for certain health issues. However, the criticisms made of RCTs do demonstrate that political and theoretical interests are inherent in the conduct of medical and health research. This is one of the central insights of the application of sociological theory to **biomedical** research methodology.

Evidence-based Medicine (EBM)

Evidence-based medicine (EBM) equates evidence with positivist research and clinical expertise. It is an extension of the privileging of RCTs, and proponents of EBM argue that clinical practice should be based on evidence from RCTs rather than on other forms of evidence that are thought to be potentially more biased and therefore less effective. However, both RCTs and EBM are not as universally applicable and objective as they are claimed to be. Both are infused with political and theoretical biases that are unavoidable. While they are useful and rigorous within the parameters for which they are designed, they become problematic when researchers forget or ignore that they cannot be used to assess all aspects of health and illness, particularly those relating to social, cultural, and interpretative dimensions of illness.

The underlying world view that privileges RCTs as the so-called gold standard against which all other methodologies must be assessed results in a failure to properly research or understand the dimensions of health and illness that cannot be studied utilizing RCTs. It is difficult and quite unusual, for example, to conduct randomized control trials of the effects of clean water, poverty, international debt repayments, or food security on the health of people. The focus of RCTs and EBM is on the individual. There is little analysis

biomedicine/ biomedical model

The conventional approach to medicine in Western societies, based on the diagnosis and explanation of illness as a malfunction of the body's biological mechanisms. This approach underpins most health professions and health services, which focus on treating individuals, and generally ignores the social origins of illness and its prevention.

evidence-based medicine (EBM)

An approach to medicine that maintains that all clinical practice should be based on evidence from randomized control trials (RCTs) to ensure treatment effectiveness and efficacy.

of the social, economic, and cultural variables that profoundly shape the distribution of disease in contemporary society. The social determinants of health or how the intersectionality of identities influence health and illness in populations are not factored in (McGibbon, 2009; Raphael, 2009b). As such, EBM and RCTs do not represent the radical paradigm shift that their advocates insist they do. Rather, both are an extension of the positivist, individualistic, politically driven model of science that has informed most of modern medical practice. Both treat people as a collection of bodily parts that can be quickly fixed, rather than using a more holistic approach that takes into account individuals' social, psychological, and physical needs (Armstrong & Armstrong, 2003).

Similarly, RCTs are not a particularly useful way of understanding, for example, how people maintain hope during illness or how people adjust to life after serious illness. The privileging of RCTs implicitly devalues the social and cultural aspects of the experience of illness. Can people be understood by studying only their bodies? The problematic nature of this somatic fundamentalism is clearest in the treatment of so-called diseases such as depression and mental illness, where huge sums of money are expended on new drugs, but by comparison relatively little research has been conducted on the social and cultural dimensions of such illnesses. It is not difficult to see the political interests of drug companies and doctors in producing this imbalance in research and, as a consequence, in treatment.

The diagnosis and treatment of attention deficit hyperactivity disorder (ADHD) is a case in point. Once thought to be a phase some young children go through, today in Canada ADHD is considered to be the most common childhood behavioural disorder: it occurs in 3–5 per cent of school-aged children. Boys are four times more likely than girls to be diagnosed with the condition (CIHR, 2006 Child Health). Since the early 1970s when Ritalin was approved for use in children and became the drug of choice for treating ADHD, there has been a dramatic increase in the use of prescription stimulants for treatment. In the 1990s, there was a rapid increase in the use of psychotropic medications, including stimulants, for children and adolescents (Conrad, 2007, pp. 126–1277). Rather than focusing on the cultural and social factors that might generate these differences, positivist- and RCT-inspired research would focus on the efficacy of various drug treatments or would search for the problem in an individual's biology (Reid et al., 1993).

Epidemiology and Public Health Research

In public health research, epidemiological surveys, which purport to be objective and value-neutral, have been used to perform a similar function as EBM, becoming the scientific standard. Conventional **epidemiology** examines the distribution of diseases and tries to identify the specific nature of the **risk factors** associated with the development of the disease. Epidemiological surveys are typically very large and aim to generate statistically representative samples that can be used to generalize the findings to the general population. The aim is to identify risk factors that can then be targeted in both prevention and treatment of the disease (Daly et al., 1997). A classic example is the work of Dr John Snow, widely referred to as the 'father of epidemiology', 150 years ago in England. Snow wanted to understand why so many people in London had become ill with cholera. Using statistical mapping methods, he found that the patterns of the disease could be linked with specific water supplies (Vachon, 2005).

epidemiology/social epidemiology

The statistical study of patterns of disease in the population. Originally focused on epidemics, or infectious diseases, it now covers non-infectious conditions, such as stroke and cancer. Social epidemiology is a subfield aligned with sociology that focuses on the social determinants of illness.

risk factors

Conditions that are thought to increase an individual's susceptibility to illness or disease, such as abuse of alcohol, poor diet, or smoking.

Epidemiological population surveys can be powerful tools for examining the distribution of a disease and planning the nature of the response to it. For example, epidemiology researchers may study patterns of cancer in a population to determine what factors distinguish people who develop or die from cancer and those who do not. Researchers at McGill University in Quebec found that although Canadians overall have a relatively low rate of cervical cancer, it takes a particularly heavy toll among the Canadian Inuit and Aboriginal Canadians in Saskatchewan. The latter have an age-standardization rate that is six times higher than the national average. Understanding the determinants of infection—that is, who is more likely to contract cervical cancer—facilitates the implementation of effective public health programs aimed to control cervical cancer (Franco et al., 2001). Researchers at the University of Windsor in Ontario used epidemiological data to determine whether socio-economic status had a different impact on cancer survival rates in Canadians and Americans diagnosed with cancer. Researchers found a strong correlation between socio-economic status and survival rates for the US cohort but no such correlation for Canadians, a factor they attribute to Canada's more equitable health care system (Gorey et al., 1997).

As we know today, HIV/AIDS is a global threat that knows no boundaries. However, AIDS is unevenly distributed, both within a country and among countries. According to the Public Health Agency of Canada (PHAC, 2008), at the end of 2005 an estimated 58 000 people were living with HIV infection (including AIDS), representing an increase of about 16 per cent from 2002. When the AIDS epidemic first came into public consciousness, prevention efforts were focused on the entire population, with the memorable and psychically scarring image of the grim reaper in television advertising to encourage people to practise safe sex. However epidemiological research has demonstrated that men who have sex with men, injecting drug users, and those in prison are at a much higher risk than the general Canadian population (PHAC). Furthermore, research indicates that Aboriginal injection drug users in Vancouver are becoming infected with HIV at twice the rate of non–Aboriginal injection drug users (CIHR, 2006, Research Findings). A study led by Dr. Calzavara at the University of Toronto found that the longer people at risk of HIV tested negative, the more likely they were to believe that their high-risk behaviour was safe (CIHR, 2006, Research Findings). Such findings illustrate the importance of prevention campaigns that target certain groups, making more effective use of resources, and, in the case of Aboriginal peoples, planning and implementing a public health strategy in partnership with the Aboriginal community.

Although highly useful and necessary for public health strategy, epidemiological research still privileges the aspects of social life that can be measured and statistically summarized. For example, there is an impressive array of statistical material that demonstrates that on virtually every health measure, the health of Aboriginal peoples in Canada is significantly worse than that of non-Aboriginal Canadians (Health Canada, 2003a). However, statistical data fail to examine how social-historical factors, such as colonization and racism, continue to play a role in Aboriginal peoples' daily lives to the detriment of their health. The study of these factors requires a different methodology that explicitly examines people's meanings and interpretations.

Theory Link
See Chapter 7 on Aboriginal Peoples' Health.

The Qualitative Tradition

The logic, theoretical framing, and practice of qualitative methods differ fundamentally from those of the statistical approach of the quantitative or positivist tradition. These differences are both the qualitative tradition's strength and its weakness. The strength lies in the qualitative method's ability to examine the meanings and interpretations of health-related issues that are inaccessible to traditional statistical methods. Its weakness is evident because positivist scientific methods and rhetoric still dominate in the spheres of policy making, research funding, and the publishing of academic journals. Consequently, qualitative research and many aspects of life that are only brought to light using qualitative methods are frequently ignored and undervalued.

Qualitative methods differ from quantitative methods in two ways. First, qualitative researchers examine meanings. They explicitly examine how people interpret or make sense of their illness experience. While statistics reduce interpretations and evaluations to scales and numerical values, much of qualitative research is exploratory in nature. Qualitative researchers are interested in the stories, in the ways that people make sense, and in the way social interaction and culture change these meanings. Second, qualitative methods typically use a very different sampling strategy. Good statistical studies attempt to draw representative samples so that if 10 per cent of the sample reports something, the researchers can be confident that 10 per cent of the wider population will experience the same thing. Statistical studies generally use random sampling, which allows the researcher to generalize the findings to the population at large. The objective of qualitative sampling, however, is not to make statistical generalization but to generalize about the nature of the experience. This is called **purposive sampling,** where the aim is to be able to describe the processes, meanings, and interpretations that lie behind the different aspects of the experience.

purposive sampling
Refers to the selection of units of analysis to ensure that the processes involved are adequately studied, and where statistical representativeness is not required.

For example, in Ezzy's qualitative study of mental health and unemployment, the focus was to understand why some people report feeling depressed after losing a job while other people report feeling much better about themselves (Ezzy, 2000b). Survey research had already established that about one-third of people who lose their job report feeling better, and two-thirds report feeling worse. A sample of unemployed people was not drawn randomly, that is, to ensure statistical representativeness, but purposively, to ensure that there were enough people to interview from both groups so that the processes that lead to depression or hope were clearly understood. That is to say, the sample was chosen purposively to ensure that the different types of meanings of unemployment were properly understood, rather than to ensure that they statistically represented the more general population of unemployed people.

Qualitative researchers also examine how individual meanings are shaped by people's cultural and social context. For example, obesity is considered a major health concern today in Canada. A recent Statistics Canada report cited by the CBC found that two-thirds of all Canadians were overweight, with 20 per cent clinically obese (CBC, 2011). In response, Canadians were admonished to make wiser food choices that are beneficial to maintaining a certain weight. However, what does being overweight mean, and does it have the same meaning for all Canadians? Using qualitative methodology, Ristovski-Slijepcevic et al. (2010) examined the social, cultural, and political contexts within which people make food choices and conceptualize issues of weight. Based on interviews with adult Black and White women and men living in Halifax, Nova Scotia, and in Vancouver, British Columbia, they found that although there was general acceptance of the discourse that weight gain is unhealthy, 'there was much diversity in how such discourses were taken up, leading to complex combinations of body image and weight understandings based on gender, ethnic and regional background' (p. 326). For example, Black women were more likely than White women and all men to reject the general assumption that being thin is equated with healthiness. Their conception of healthy and unhealthy weight was in contrast to the medically defined standard. The authors concluded that interpretations of body image, weight, and health must be understood within the larger social, cultural, and political contexts in which people make choices. Survey research, like that produced by Statistics Canada, provides a general snapshot of the percentage of people considered overweight; however, qualitative research can look at the meaning that obesity discourse has for different individuals and social groups.

Similarly, Kathy Charmaz (1994) takes the basic statistical observation that men contract more serious and life-threatening chronic illnesses than women and then looks into what it is that is distinctive about the experience of illness for men. She is not interested in the statistical distribution of the illness of the men she studies. Rather, she examines the meanings, interpretations, and identity dilemmas that are characteristic of the men's illness experiences. The focus is on describing the social processes, not the statistical distributions. Charmaz asks her research questions in this way:

> What is it like to be an active, productive man one moment, and a patient who faces death the next? What is it like to change one's view of oneself accordingly? Which identity dilemmas does living with continued uncertainty pose for men? How do they handle them? When do they make identity changes? When do they try to preserve a former self? (p. 271)

Notice the structure of the questions. They are not about the distribution of illness experience but about the process of making sense of illness; they explore meanings and interpretations. Only qualitative methods can answer these sorts of questions.

Charmaz (1994) shows how masculine identities tend to be active and problem solving, emphasizing personal power, autonomy, and bravery in the face of danger. When dealing with illness, these masculine identity strategies allow men to develop some distinctive coping strategies but also prevent them from developing others. The emphasis on active problem solving facilitates the re-creation of new identities to replace those lost as a consequence of chronic illness. However, if it proves difficult to find a new active identity, the men find it difficult to develop and feel comfortable with identities that are less autonomous and less active. If satisfying alternative identities cannot be found, this can increase the likelihood of depression. Whereas survey research documents the distribution of an illness in a population, qualitative research focuses on the context in which the illness occurs and the meaning this has for the people concerned.

An excellent example of the tension between statistical methods and qualitative methods is provided by Boston's (1999) study of palliative care nurses. In Canada, nursing administrators had implemented a workload-measurement statistical system. Under this system, all aspects of the nurses' work were quantified in an attempt to plan nursing requirements and to increase efficiency of services. Based on a qualitative study using 50 long interviews, Boston showed that this attempt to objectively quantify and systematize nurses' work failed to deal with the nature of nursing care required in a multicultural environment. The problem that Boston identified was not simply that the workload measurement system has insufficient categories to cover the wide range of tasks that nurses consider part of their work. Rather, Boston argued that it is impossible to quantify many aspects of nursing practice that involve intuitive and personalized ways of dealing with patients in a culturally complex environment. In particular, dealing with patients from diverse cultural backgrounds requires taking time to learn, understand, and accommodate culturally distinct responses to terminal illness, diagnosis, and rituals associated with death and dying. These processes are extremely difficult to quantify. As a consequence, 'that subjective "inner" knowledge, which necessarily involves prioritizing cultural concerns, is left to "fall between the cracks"' (p. 151). In short, statistical, categorical, and deductive methodologies for assessing and studying nursing practice miss many of the central tasks that nurses perform.

Evaluating the Quality of Qualitative Research

The criteria for what constitutes good research also significantly change between quantitative and qualitative methods. In survey research, studies are designed to be valid (to accurately reflect what is being studied) and reliable (or repeatable, and subsequently verifiable). In contrast, qualitative researchers typically prefer to describe good research as 'rigorous'. Surely, you might ask, qualitative research should also aim to be valid and reliable? However, the problem with these terms is that they ignore the way in which social life is a product of interpretative processes. Qualitative researchers tend to prefer to use the term **rigour** to avoid the positivist overtones of the terms *validity* and *reliability*. The aim of rigorous research is to closely scrutinize the meanings and interpretations of the people being studied (Lincoln, 1995). People's meanings change with time and depending on who they are talking to. Qualitative methods try to explicitly engage with the fluidity of meanings and interpretations rather than avoiding them, as is attempted by quantitative research. Often this requires examining the social context in which an illness or behaviour occurs.

rigour
A term used by qualitative researchers to describe trustworthy research that carefully scrutinizes and describes the meanings and interpretations given by participants.

For example, Hornosty and Doherty's research on family violence in farm and rural communities found that meanings of family violence and people's willingness to report family violence are influenced by the values, environments, and familial relationships characteristic of rural communities (2003, 2004). Using qualitative research methods, Hornosty and Doherty, through their interviews with abused women in rural New Brunswick, found that structural and cultural factors—such as geographic and social isolation, the lack of anonymity and confidentiality, patriarchal attitudes, community values, and rural identity—presented barriers to rural women's both naming and reporting abuse. Farm women, they found, had additional barriers, such as concerns with the survival of the family farm and their attachment to farm animals. They were concerned that their leaving the farm could lead to its demise and hence to a lack of economic security for their children. The researchers concluded that to fully understand the subjective experiences of abused women as well as to design appropriate and effective programs for helping abused women it is essential to examine the social and cultural context in which abuse occurs. Although there are similarities in the nature of family violence in both urban and rural environments, one cannot generalize from data gathered in urban areas.

Making sense of the data involves using inductive strategies that are sensitive to the social context in which behaviour occurs. In according authenticity to women's experiences in their everyday lives, the researchers gave voice to those whose views have historically been marginalized. In other words, an aim of qualitative research is to examine the contexts in which meanings and interpretations are constructed. Unlike quantitative studies that are concerned more with issues of frequency and distribution, the goal of qualitative studies is to grasp the subjective aspects of social life. Meaning and the interpretative process are integral to qualitative methods, and rigorous research explicitly engages with the interpretative process.

Kavanagh and Broom (1997) provide an example of a qualitative study of women's understanding of an abnormal cervical-smear-test result, drawing on long interviews with Australian women. Previous research demonstrated a statistical link between an abnormal cervical smear result and psychological and sexual difficulties of various kinds. Kavanagh and Broom described the experiences of the women during their interaction with the health-care services that may have contributed to these difficulties. In particular they showed how the interaction during the medical encounter often created fear and did not allow for the development of trust or for the women to gain an understanding of what was happening to them. While the women wanted to participate in decisions about their treatment, they found this difficult because doctors provided little information during the consultation and did not encourage them to ask questions. Kavanagh and Broom concluded that 'the inherent power structure of medical practice combined with time pressures often make it difficult for doctors to give the detailed information and reassurance patients need when a diagnosis is distressing or when investigation and treatment are strange and upsetting' (p. 1388). Their qualitative methodology allowed them to examine the experiences and interpretations the women gave to the medical encounter. This methodology, in turn, can be used to make sense of the statistically observed relationships. However, only a qualitative methodology can identify these interpretative processes and, as a consequence, suggest changes to the medical interaction that might alleviate them.

Analysis and Reporting of Qualitative Research

Similarly, for qualitative research the structure of analysis and the nature of research reports are quite different to statistical studies. The analysis process does not aim to follow correct procedures to produce objective results, although good procedure is important. Rather, qualitative analysis methodologies, such as thematic analysis (Kellehear, 1993), **grounded theory** (Strauss & Corbin, 1990), narrative analysis (Riessman, 1993), and cultural studies (Alasuutari, 1995), all aim to analyze data by interpreting them. The process of interpretation can be described, but it cannot be systematized. This difference is clearest in the computer packages developed to assist qualitative data analysis. These computer packages do not analyze the qualitative data for the researcher; rather, they assist the analysis through sophisticated search, coding, and filing mechanisms (Rice & Ezzy, 1999). It is impossible to automate the process of qualitative data analysis, as can be done with statistics, because the process of interpretation and understanding is central to the analytic process. Similarly, qualitative research reports are difficult to produce as short summaries similar to those that appear in many medical journals. The heart of

grounded theory

Usually associated with qualitative methods, it refers to any social theory that is derived from (or grounded in) empirical research of social phenomena.

qualitative research is in the detail. Such research aims to provide understanding of the meanings and details that shape why people do what they do. To do this kind of research well requires long quotations and careful explanation of cultural and social context.

Orona (1990) provides one of the clearest accounts of the process of analyzing qualitative data using a grounded theory methodology. She emphasizes the role of uncertainty and the exploratory nature of the analytic process. She describes how she read and re-read her interviews so that she became immersed in the world of her participants. This process of imaginative participation is at the heart of good qualitative research. In this way it is possible to genuinely listen to and be transformed by the voice of participants and, as a consequence, discover new understandings. Orona emphasizes the need to embrace uncertainty, to explore, and to use her intuition and creativity as part of the analysis process. As she immersed herself in her data, she began to see patterns and relationships, and began to build a theory of the experience of identity loss during Alzheimer's disease, which was the focus of her research.

Qualitative researchers read and re-read their interviews and focus group discussions with participants. Their goal is to understand the participants' perspectives in terms of their lived reality. The voice of the participants is privileged, rather than that of the researcher. In this way it is possible to discover new meanings and see relationships between social phenomena. (For one example, see Hornosty and Doherty, 2003, 2004.) This explicit engagement with personal subjectivity and the interpretative process may sound far from scientific. However, the alternative is to pretend that you can avoid the interpretative process. Qualitative researchers are increasingly arguing that it is impossible to avoid the role of subjectivity in the research process and that researchers must make their values explicit. The aim is not to avoid subjectivity but to allow researchers to engage in a dialogue with the participants in their research (Lincoln, 1995). Rigorous qualitative research aims to genuinely hear the voice of the participants. To do so requires engaging in a dialogue in which researchers are honest about the influence of their own subjectivity on the research process.

Future Directions: Qualitative Innovators

While qualitative research is increasingly becoming an accepted methodology, it is typically understood as a poor cousin to the so-called stronger statistical methods, such as surveys and RCTs. However, some qualitative researchers are pushing their methodology even further away from the theory and practice of the positivist tradition, using research such as **participatory action research**, which argues for a greater degree of engagement by participants in the research process (Reinharz, 1992). An example of participatory action research is that by Hornosty and Doherty, referred to on page 52. Prior to beginning their research they had open-ended discussions with abused rural women who had left their abusive relationships. These women assisted the researchers by helping them understand what types of questions to ask and what to be sensitive to. They also helped develop a framework of issues to be explored in future interviews and made suggestions for specific questions to ask. During the subsequent interviews, Hornosty and Doherty asked women for examples of specific strategies they felt would be useful to address family violence issues in farm and rural communities. In a similar vein, Aboriginal communities

participatory action research

A more activist approach to research whereby researchers work with local communities, social groups, or individuals to empower the group or its representatives. Often involves participants in formulating the research questions.

in Canada advocate principles of participatory action research for research that looks at issues in their communities.

Qualitative innovations, of course, are deeply disturbing to those who espouse the more traditional methodologies. Some researchers still try to portray qualitative research as a scientific method, and apply all the rhetoric and terms of the statistical methods to qualitative research (Green, 1998). These researchers believe that they should be objective, distancing themselves from their research; that the research should be validated and reliable; and that the report should not contain any account of the researcher's subjective experience but be politically neutral and written in standard scientific format. The problem is that this attempt to make qualitative methods seem more scientific devalues the central process that qualitative methods aim to examine—the process of interpretation. While qualitative methods can be moulded to fit this scientific world view, researchers are increasingly arguing that such an approach is deceptive and does not produce research that is as useful, insightful, respectful, or as politically appropriate as it could be (Denzin, 1997; Ezzy, 2001).

Estroff (1995) draws on her study of chronic illness to demonstrate that qualitative interviews are not events in which objective information is gathered from subjects. People do not have objective, unchanging stories of events that they carry around in their heads and that a qualitative researcher can simply gather like statistical measurements. Rather, people shape and change their stories, often unconsciously, to fit the particular interactive context. Interviews, then, are moments of the co-creation of narratives (Estroff, 1995). To pretend otherwise is to deceive ourselves as researchers. This does not mean, however, that interviews are useless, just that they are more complex to negotiate and require a more sophisticated theory (Holstein & Gubrium, 1995).

Further, Estroff argues that interviews need to be seen as relationships that involve mutual obligations and responsibilities as the interviewer and interviewee attempt to make sense of the experience together. This approach leads to a number of complex ethical and political questions about the extent to which participants can or should be involved in the research process. Qualitative researchers committed to participatory action research include participants as co-researchers at different stages of the research process. Others take a more guarded approach.

Some qualitative innovators have experimented with other aspects of the research process, exploring new writing styles and making the researcher the subject of the research. For example, Ellis (1995, 1998) provides a detailed study of loss and illness through her autoethnographic account of her 10-year relationship with her dying partner. An **autoethnography** is, as the name implies, an **ethnographic** study that focuses on the experience of the researcher: 'Autoethnography blurs distinctions between social science and literature, the personal and the social, the individual and culture, self and other, and researcher and subject' (1998, p. 49). Ellis's autoethnography *Final Negotiations* is a story-like account that at times feels like a popular autobiography but that also demonstrates the influence of a careful social-science approach to observation, analysis, and recording of experience. Ellis says that the aim of writing about her intimate experiences grew out of her frustration with traditional methodologies and reports that failed to engage with the detail of daily experiences of those living with chronic illness. See Box 3.1 for an excerpt from Ferrari and Drew, 2005, another autoethnography.

autoethnography

An ethnography that focuses on the experience of the researcher.

ethnography

A research method that is based on direct observation of a particular social group's social life and culture—of what people actually do.

BOX 3.1 Excerpts from *Different Minds* (2005)

By Dr Leo Ferrari and Lorna Drew, Fredericton, NB

By sharing experiences of our uninvited encounter with Dr. Alzheimer's disease we can break through the barriers of silence and loneliness. Let us speak out proudly and loudly about it—even laugh and realize that we too have our contributions to make to the rich tapestry of human life!

The metaphor that I like is that my life is like a fog. I've lived by the sea, and I always loved the mistiness of it. You can sit on a boat and see the shore—and sometimes you can't. If I don't write down what I did yesterday, it'll be gone. But I can still see the distant shores. I can remember my childhood vividly, but I can't remember the last few days.

— Leo Ferrari

Stories heal, and making narrative sense of a life lived with Alzheimer's disease gives me both the perspective to stand outside events (and sometimes laugh) and the feeling that I have some sort of mastery over an illness whose symptoms more often than not play havoc with what used to be an ordinary life.

— Lorna Drew

Autoethnography, the inclusion of participants as researchers, and various other innovations developed among qualitative researchers are hotly debated. Some argue that autoethnography is literature, not social research. Others point out that there is considerable value in experimenting with a variety of methodologies, analytic procedures, and writing styles in order to better understand social life and to respond to the epistemological and methodological issues raised by the postmodernists (Richardson, 1994).

Conclusion

The methodology one chooses is shaped by the amount of existing knowledge about a topic, the nature of one's research question, the purpose of one's study, and the intended audience. Today, an increasing number of researchers are using a combination of quantitative and qualitative methodologies, often referred to as mixed methods research, to address a particular research problem. Despite some authors' claims and assumptions to the contrary, no research methodology is objective or inherently superior to another. Each type of research method reflects particular philosophical, political, and theoretical interests that can influence the collection of data and their interpretation. This means that the privileging of biomedical research methods tends to benefit the political interests of those involved in biomedical professions and industries. The privileging of qualitative research gives voice to those who are frequently marginalized from mainstream culture. This chapter advocates a balanced approach and highlights the contributions of epidemiology and traditional and innovative qualitative methodologies to health research.

Summary of Main Points

- Health research includes a number of different methodologies. Each methodology has its place and provides important and useful information about different aspects of contemporary experiences of health and illness.
- RCTs are used to test the efficacy of medications and different types of treatments.
- Some methodologies, such as RCTs, are often considered more important than others and, as a consequence, our contemporary understandings of health tend to emphasize biomedical and individualistic responses.
- In contrast, epidemiological and qualitative methodologies informed by sociological theory recommend health policy responses that are more focused on social, cultural, and public health factors.
- No research methodology is objective. Each reflects particular political and theoretical interests.
- It is important to recognize the valuable contributions of survey data, such as epidemiology, and traditional and innovative qualitative methodologies alongside the contributions of positivist and biomedical research.

 Sociological Reflection:
The Methods Made Me Do It

Identify three advantages and disadvantages of quantitative and qualitative research methods when studying health issues. Think of a health issue that is important to you. What methodology would be most appropriate to use to do research on that issue? Explain why you chose the particular method you did.

 Discussion Questions

1. What are the implications for public health of the privileging of randomized control trials (RCTs)?
2. What is evidence-based medicine (EBM)? What are some of the advantages of EBM? What are some of the limitations of EBM?
3. Identify one health issue that can be addressed by epidemiological research, and one that cannot.
4. What distinctive contributions do qualitative methods make to health research?
5. What distinctive contributions do quantitative methods make to health research?
6. Why is it important to have alternative ways of studying, interpreting, and reporting research findings?
7. Why are positivist approaches so frequently used in health research?

Further Investigation

1. Find a recent journal article that reports a randomized control trial for the treatment of HIV/AIDS, cancer, or tuberculosis. Find another journal article that discusses the same health issue but from a critical perspective, that focuses on the role of social and economic factors that shape the distribution of the disease. Compare and contrast these two articles. What different conclusions can you make from these two articles about the particular health issue you chose?

2. Why is it important to study meanings and culture in order to understand health in contemporary society? Draw on at least three published qualitative studies of a health issue to illustrate your argument.

Further Reading

Bryman, A., & Teevan, J. (2005). *Social research methods: Canadian edition*. Toronto, ON: Oxford University Press.

Denzin, N. (1997). *Interpretive ethnography*. London, UK: Sage.

Reinharz, S. (1992). *Feminist methods in social research*. New York: Oxford University Press.

Rice, P., & Ezzy, D. (1999). *Qualitative research methods: A health focus*. Melbourne: Oxford University Press.

Web Resources

International Institute for Qualitative Methodology
www.uofaweb.ualberta.ca/iiqm/

International Consortium for the Advancement of Academic Publication (ICAAP): Free Resources for Program Evaluation and Social Research Methods
http://gsociology.icaap.org/methods

Sage Publications: Research Methods
www.sagepub.com/research-methods.sp

SocioSite: Research Methodology and Statistics
www.sociosite.net/topics/research.php

PART 1

The Social Production and Distribution of Health and Illness

'All animals are equal but some animals are more equal than others.'

— *George Orwell, Animal Farm*

- Why do manual workers have a lower life expectancy than other people?
- Why do women outlive men but report greater illness during their lives?
- Why is the life expectancy of First Nations people 20 years below the Canadian average?
- Why is ethnicity an important determinant of health?

The chapters in Part 1 concern the first dimension of the social model of health, which we introduced in Chapter 1: the social production and distribution of health. Most people generally assume that health and illness are simply undisputed facts, that medicine is best equipped to deal with health problems, and that illness is a matter of bad luck, fate, or individual responsibility. Health sociology debunks the myth that illnesses are solely the fault or responsibility of the individual. While health problems are experienced by individuals, they also have wider social determinants.

The chapters in this part address the questions above, by examining the evidence and explanations of health inequalities in Canada, and focus on five social determinants of health: class, gender, 'race'/ethnicity, Aboriginal status, and environment. The fact that there are significant social patterns in the distribution of health and illness, in which some groups of people suffer much higher rates of illness and premature death than others, implies not only that health inequalities have social origins but also that the removal of such inequalities requires social action and social reform.

Part 1 is divided into five chapters:

- Chapter 4 examines the links between class and other related social determinants of health and health inequality.
- Chapter 5 explains how gender is an important determinant of health and illness.
- Chapter 6 explores the links between ethnicity, racialized groups, and health status.
- Chapter 7 examines the reasons for the poor health status of Aboriginal Canadians: First Nations, Inuit, and Métis peoples.
- Chapter 8 considers the role of our environment in the production of health and illness.

CHAPTER 4

Class, Health Inequality, and Social Justice

Jennie Hornosty & John Germov

Overview

- What is class and how does it help to explain health inequalities in Canada?
- What are the major social determinants of health?
- How do these social determinants impact health?
- What can be done to address class-based health inequalities?

There is a significant amount of research that shows the connection between class and health. People with less income and wealth have higher rates of death and illness than wealthier people do. This chapter discusses the concept of class, provides up-to-date evidence of class-based health inequality in Canada, and examines different explanations of health inequality. Classes arise from the social structure; therefore, class-based health inequality needs to be addressed primarily through structural changes to the economy, to the workplace, and to the community, guided by public policies based on social justice.

Key Terms

class (or social class)
economic rationalism
empirical
epidemiology/social
   epidemiology
gross domestic product (GDP)
life chances
Medicare

neo-liberalism
public health/public health
   infrastructure
risk factors
risk society
ruling class
social capital
social cohesion

social Darwinism
social determinants of
   health approach
social justice
social structure
trickle-down theory
victim blaming

We all have some basic notion of **class** and class difference. We see such differences every day—between low-priced and expensive cars, fast-food and fine-dining restaurants, public and private schools, and downtown ghetto areas and exclusive suburbs. Debates over the importance of class focus on the extent to which class determines your **life chances**—that is, your chances of social mobility, of gaining an education, and of getting a certain type of job. While most people acknowledge the existence of class, few recognize that social class is one of the strongest inequality-based determinants of health in Canada (Veenstra, 2009, p. 362). Despite access to free public health services through **Medicare**, the most disadvantaged people in Canada still die younger and have the highest rates of illness and disability. As the evidence presented in this chapter will show, class is a significant basis of health inequality in Canada. Yet what, exactly, is class?

Defining *Class*

Popular notions of class tend to focus on lifestyle differences, particularly fashion, as social markers of status. While consumption patterns may indicate class membership in a general sense, they shed little light on how class differences are generated in the first place. Sociological analyses of class tend to focus on the underlying factors that actually produce and reproduce class differences. The different theoretical perspectives that sociologists use (as discussed in Chapter 2) have resulted in continuing debate over appropriate definitions and theories of class, most of which today focus on Erik Olin Wright's neo-Marxist and John Goldthorpe's neo-Weberian class models. However, these debates are not addressed here (see Goldthorpe, 1996; Grabb, 2007; Wright, 1997).

Most discussions of social class are rooted in Marxian and Weberian approaches. For Marx, classes are a product of social relations and are defined by one's relationship to the means of production. Marx spoke of two major classes—the bourgeoisie (those who owned the means of production) and the proletariat (those who sold their labour power). However, he also described another class, the petite bourgeoisie (such as independent and small business owners), whom he expected would disappear with more advanced forms of capitalism. Weber shared Marx's belief that economic inequalities, that is, class, were central in explaining an individual's life chances; however, he refined Marx's notion of class relations to include hierarchies of prestige and political inequalities. Weber referred to these structures of inequality as class, status, and party. There is ongoing debate about the precise meaning of *class* today and how best to measure it. In fact, there are many models of class.

Canadian sociologist Edward Grabb (2009, pp. 3–7) points out that one ongoing debate is whether *class* refers simply to those who share similar economic circumstances or whether *class* should be used only when referring to a group of people who share both an economic category and a sense of common membership or purpose—what Marx referred to as 'class consciousness'. Grabb suggests that the different perspectives on class cannot be incorporated into a single definition. According to him, classes exist primarily as categories of people who do not necessarily share a sense of group membership. However, classes are not merely equivalent to strata or ranked statistical aggregates determined by variables such as income, education, or occupation. Class divisions involve more fundamental and uniform cleavages and are generally defined as economically based entities;

class (or social class)

A position in a system of structured inequality based on the unequal distribution of power, wealth, income, and status. People who share a class position typically share similar life chances.

life chances

Derived from Max Weber, the term refers to people's opportunity to realize their lifestyle choices, which are often assumed to differ according to their social class.

Medicare

Canada's universal health-care program funded and administered by federal, provincial, and territorial governments.

they 'exist as structural entities because certain enforceable rights or opportunities—such as the right to own and to exclude others from owning productive property—define them and distinguish them from each other' (p. 3). Both relations of domination and exploitation and the distribution of material benefits (e.g., income) are ways of delineating classes. However, there is no agreement about how many classes actually exist in modern societies. Nevertheless, Grabb goes on to argue that although Canada is complex and internally diverse, this country does have a class structure that consists of three basic elements. The first is the dominant class of large-scale owners of productive property (what Marx referred to as the capitalist class); the second is the subordinate class of workers who live by selling their labour power to the owning class (the proletariat); the third middle group or class is more heterogeneous, consisting of educated professional, technical, or administrative personnel, small-scale business owners, and various salaried employees or wage earners with credentials, training, or skills.

According to those working within a Marxist tradition, a relational understanding of social class is necessary, where the primary organizing principle is material oppression. McMullin writes that material oppression occurs when the material welfare of one group depends on the material deprivations of another, which entails being excluded from access to productive forces (2010, p. 37). Like Grabb, McMullin suggests that in Canada there are three broad classes that can be distinguished on the basis of ownership of the means of production and occupation. Members of the upper class own the means of production and/or controls the labour process; included in this group are company presidents and CEOs. The middle class includes workers who have more control over the work process than those in the working class; this group includes those in middle-management positions, professionals, and the self-employed. Those in the working class, the third class, have little control over the work process; they are excluded from access to productive forces and are in an oppressive relationship with their employers (McMullin, 2010, pp. 37–8).

To add to the confusion as to the precise meaning of *class*, some scholars use the term interchangeably with that of 'socioeconomic status' (SES). SES is somewhat equivalent to what Grabb refers to as 'strata'. SES is determined by ranking people, usually according to income, education, and occupation levels, and grouping them into corresponding high, medium, and low SES groups. Categorizing people into SES groups is a relatively straightforward process, and this is why most of the **empirical** evidence of class inequality tends to be based on SES. However, SES is a descriptive classification system and offers little insight into how and why such inequality exists, effectively ignoring such questions by transforming 'the lived reality of class . . . to an abstraction for the purpose of statistical treatment' (Connell, 1977, p. 33). Nevertheless, class inequality in society is often described in terms of comparisons between strata, usually using income or wealth as a basis of stratification. As we shall see, many studies on inequality in health use these as proxies for social class.

empirical

Describes observations or research that is based on evidence drawn from experience. Empirical observations or research are therefore distinguished from something based only on theoretical knowledge or on some other kind of abstract thinking process.

Class Inequality in Canada

Canadians tend to underestimate the amount of class inequality in our society. Although Canadians like to think of themselves as being a middle-class nation, the reality is that the gap between the rich and the poor in Canada continues to increase. While the poor become poorer, the rich become richer (Osberg, 2006). In 2004, for example, the average earnings of the richest 10 per cent of families in Canada was 82 times more than that earned by the poorest 10 per cent (Yalnizyan, 2007). A further indication of growing inequality is seen by comparing the percentage of earnings by Canadian families in the top half with those in the bottom half over a 30-year period (1976–2004). See Figure 4.1 (taken from Yalnizyan, 2007: 11).

While Canada has experienced relative affluence since the Depression years, this has not uniformly been the experience for all Canadians. Between the 1950s and the 1970s, Canadians enjoyed rising incomes and general economic prosperity. However, by the early 1980s family earnings began to stagnate despite the increasing number of women who entered the labour force (Urmetzer & Guppy, 2009, p. 83). Then, in the 1990s incomes for those at the very top began to increase dramatically. For example, from 1992 to 2004, the average incomes of the top 0.01 per cent increased by 142 per cent (Osberg, 2008, p. 11).

Inequality in Income Distribution

One frequently used indicator of class inequality is income distribution. A common way to measure inequality in income distribution is to divide the population into fifths or quintiles (each representing 20 per cent of the population) and then compare the share of total income that each group received. Data show that in 2005, the highest quintile got 46.7 per cent of all income earned in Canada. By comparison the lowest quintile received only 4.1 per cent of all income (Urmetzer & Guppy, 2009, p. 85). A comparison of income distribution at different points in time shows that the highest quintile received the biggest increase since 1951 (from 42.8 per cent to 46.7 per cent) while the portion going to the lowest quintile has decreased (from 4.4 per cent to 4.1 per cent). Urmetzer and Guppy

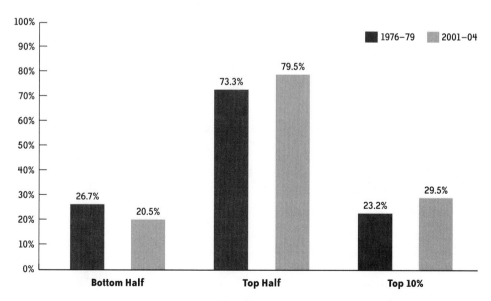

FIGURE 4.1 Change in the Distribution of Earnings between Families in the Top and Bottom Half

Source: Adapted from Yalnizyan, A. (2007). *The rich and the rest of us.* Canadian Centre for Policy Alternatives (CCPA). Available from www.policyalternatives.ca/publications/reports/rich-and-rest-us

(2009, p. 85) further point out that the majority of losses have occurred at the second and middle quintile, as shown in Table 4.1.

One way for governments to redistribute income so as to increase equality is through taxation and transfer payments, such as unemployment insurance, social assistance, and pensions. An examination of income distribution after taxation and transfers shows that changes in the proportion each quintile received was altered somewhat. In 2005 the lowest quintile received 4.7 per cent of income after taxes while the highest quintile received 44.0 per cent. This suggests that transfer payments have some equalizing effect as they raise the income of those at the bottom, if only minimally (Curry-Stevens, 2009). However, the ongoing assault on social programs and the progressive dismantling of the welfare state by the current federal government could significantly alter this distribution in the future (Curry-Stevens, 2009; Osberg, 2008; Townson, 2004). The New Brunswick government, for example, was planning to bring in a flat tax structure, which would significantly reduce corporate taxes and income taxes for those in the highest income bracket. While those in the lower brackets would also pay less tax, this would not benefit them to the degree that it would those who are wealthier. More importantly, a lower tax base would inevitably mean cuts to social programs, most of which provide benefits to those in the lowest income bracket. Such measures would further exacerbate the gap between the top and lowest quintiles.

Inequality in Wealth

Another important measure of economic inequality is that of wealth, which refers to an individual's value of all assets minus any debts at a given point in time. Assets include bank deposits, investment certificates, pension plans, stocks, and shares, bonds, mutual funds, owner-occupied dwellings, real estate, and equipment. Included in debts are mortgages, credit-card balances, and various types of loans. In Canada, as in other countries, wealth is generally more unequally distributed than income. Because wealth represents one's total worth, it is argued that wealth distribution is a more accurate picture of inequality in a society.

TABLE 4.1 Percentage of Total Before-Tax Income going to Family and Unattached Individuals by Quintile, 1951–2005

	1951	1961	1971	1981	1991	2001	2005
Lowest quintile	4.4	4.2	3.6	4.6	4.5	4.1	4.1
Second quintile	11.9	10.6	10.9	10.1	9.7	9.6	9.6
Middle quintile	18.3	18.3	17.6	17.6	16.5	15.6	15.7
Fourth quintile	23.3	14.3	24.9	25.1	24.7	23.8	23.9
Highest quintile	42.8	41.4	43.3	41.7	44.2	46.8	46.7

Source: Adapted from Statistics Canada. (1951, 1961, 1971, 1981, 1991, 2001, 2005). *Income in Canada.* Available from www.statcan.gc.ca/bsolc/olc-cel/olc-cel?catno=75-202-X&lang=eng.
Table reproduced from Urmetzer, P. & Guppy, N. (2009). Changing income inequality in Canada. In E. Grabb, & N. Guppy (Eds.). *Social Inequality in Canada* (5th ed.). Toronto, ON: Pearson Prentice Hall, (pp. 82–91).

While difficult to measure accurately, the available data show that wealth inequality in Canada is high, regardless of which survey we look at. In 2005, one calculation shows that the highest quintile had a total share of 75.0 per cent of the wealth. The share of the top 10 per cent, or top decile, was 58.2 per cent (Davies, 2009, p. 95). By comparison, the share of the bottom quintile was -0.6 per cent. Table 4.2 shows the increase in wealth inequality over two decades.

While the poorest 40 per cent of Canadian families lost ground in terms of wealth between 1999 and 2005, the richest 10 per cent of families saw their wealth increase by 123 per cent (Curry-Stevens, 2009, p. 50). As shown in Table 4.2, wealth inequality in Canada has increased steadily over the past two decades (Davies, 2009; Osberg, 2008). According to Davies, some of this increased inequality in wealth is related to the rise in house prices and increased savings in financial assets, such as registered retirement savings plans and other tax-sheltered savings accounts .

Inequality in Economic Power

Research on power and class in Canada shows that economic power is still highly concentrated among a small group of powerful and interconnected corporations. In the past, many of these companies were owned or controlled by a few established families who formed the economic elite—including the Irvings, the McCains, the Westons, and more recently the Stronachs and the Aspers (Grabb & Hwang, 2009). According to Bill Carroll (2009, p. 30), companies in Canada with assets greater than $25 million or annual revenue greater than $100 million claim 79.4 per cent of all business assets.

There is limited information on the top 5 per cent of Canadians in the 2005 Survey of Financial Security. However, in *Forbes* magazine's 2007 list of the world's 946 billionaires, there were 23 Canadians. The wealthiest Canadians were as follows:

- David Thomson, who at $22 billion ranked tenth in the world; in 2007, the Thomson family's net worth (*Canadian Business Online*, 2007) was $25.35 billion
- Galen Weston, who at $7.9 billion ranked ninety-third (cited in Davies, 2009, p. 97)

TABLE 4.2 Distribution of Wealth among Families and Unattached Individuals, Canada, 1984, 1999, and 2005

	By percentage		
	1984	**1999**	**2005**
Bottom quintile	0.5	-0.6	-0.6
Second quintile	2.2	1.7	1.3
Middle quintile	9.1	7.5	6.9
Fourth quintile	20.0	18.4	17.4
Top quintile	68.5	73.1	75.0

Source: Modified table found in Davies, J. (2009, p. 95). The distribution of wealth and economic inequality. In E. Grabb, & N. Guppy (Eds.). *Social inequality in Canada* (5th ed.). Toronto, ON: Pearson Prentice Hall (pp. 92–105).

- Ted Rogers, Jr, the president and CEO of Rogers Communications Inc, whose net worth was $7.6 billion
- The Irving family of New Brunswick, whose net worth was listed at $5.3 billion (*Canadian Business Online*, 2007)

Using a list compiled by Diane Francis in 1986 that indicated that there were 32 families worth more than $100 million in Canada, Davies 'guesstimated' that the share of the wealthiest 1 per cent in the 1970s and 1980s was around 25 per cent (Davies, 2009, p. 97). According to *Canadian Business Online* (30 November 2007), among the 100 most affluent Canadians there are now more billionaires than millionaires.

How are those in the economic elite affected by financial crises? In 2008, Canadians, as others, were hit by a worldwide economic recession; however, this did not impact negatively on Canada's 100 highest paid CEOs. In 2008, the average pay of the highest paid 100 CEOs was 174 times more than the pay of the average worker. Put another way, these CEOs earned a year's worth of minimum wage work by 2:23 p.m. on New Year's Day. Their average compensation was $7 300 884 compared to total average Canadian income of $42 305 (Mackenzie, 2010). Not all of this income comes just from salary, however; a significant amount comes from stock options and from pension entitlements, which further increases CEOs' accumulation of wealth.

Debates about the upper class concern not only its wealth but also its influence—on whether it acts as a **ruling class**. While few theorists would argue that the upper class rules in a direct way, there is also little disputing that through their companies, members of the upper class can affect investment, employment, and the stock market. In this way, their economic power provides them with significant political influence. The upper class may not pull the strings directly but its members share similar interests. For example, they may pressure governments to adopt policies of low taxation and deregulation to aid the pursuit of profit maximization; such policies tend to benefit the already well-off. However, such a situation is not beyond change; no natural law of profit and wealth operates here. Class inequality is an outcome of the **social structure** and as recent history teaches us, the structure of a society can be subject to social change—social policies and taxation rates can work to either consolidate or redistribute wealth (see Carroll, 2009, 1984; Clement, 1975; Grabb, 2009, 1990).

On the other side of the economic coin, poverty rates in Canada have fluctuated over the years; however, 2007 data from the National Council on Welfare indicate that the incidence of poverty is declining. Nevertheless, in 2007 2.9 million Canadians lived in poverty, that is, 9.2 per cent of the population (National Council on Welfare, 2009). Given that poverty rates are tied to economic conditions, the National Council on Welfare predicts that given the experience of past recessions, poverty rates in 2008 and beyond will increase. Racialized Canadians—including Aboriginal peoples—as well as females and youth are those most likely to be among the poor. One indication of the extent of poverty is the growing use of food banks. In March 2008, 704 414 Canadians used a food bank at least once, and food banks have reported difficulty meeting the demands for their services (Duffy & Mandell, 2010). Another indication of poverty is the number of homeless people. It is estimated that in Canada each year 200 000 to 300 000 people are homeless (Duffy & Mandel, 2010). Social assistance, the Canada Child Tax benefit, free drug coverage, and

ruling class
This is a hotly debated term used to highlight the point that the upper class in society has political power as a result of its economic wealth. The term is often used interchangeably with 'upper class'.

social structure
The recurring patterns of social interaction through which people are related to each other, such as social institutions and social groups.

the availability of food banks ameliorate some of the worst excesses of poverty, but these do nothing to change the growing gap between the rich and the poor.

A decade of policies influenced by **neo-liberalism** and **economic rationalism**—during which financial and labour markets were deregulated, government spending was cut, and taxation was lowered—has revealed the **trickle-down theory** to be without substance. Proponents of trickle-down theory oppose state intervention in economic matters and argue that the best way to stimulate the economy is to provide tax breaks to corporations in the belief that this will result in more jobs being created with higher wages for the average worker. The assumption is that economic growth flows from the top to the bottom. This is the opposite of Keynesian economic theory, which urges active government intervention in the marketplace and public policies that promote full employment and price stability as the best way to stimulate economic growth. Keynesian economics is often associated with the establishment of the welfare state, in which the government assumes primary responsibility for the welfare of its citizens in such matters as education, health care, employment, and social security. Neo-liberals contend that the welfare state interferes with economic growth and the virtues of a market economy. The result is a reduction in social expenditures in areas like health, social assistance, and social insurance programs, including unemployment insurance—that is, those measures that are important in reducing inequalities. In recent years, Canadians have seen a substantial erosion of a number of these social safety nets (Osberg, 2006).

Inequality in Health

Canada is considered one of the wealthiest countries in the world, and generally speaking Canadians are a privileged and healthy people. But health inequality, like social inequality, is a reality in Canada. Health Canada, according to its official website, is committed to improving the health of all of Canadians, and a goal of Canadian health policy is to reduce or eliminate socio-economic inequalities in health (Wilkins et al., 2008b). However, if we accept that we should aim to live in a society that has equality of health outcomes— that is, there are no health inequalities based on group membership, such as class—then by current standards there is considerable room for improvement. Studies of morbidity (illness) and mortality (death) have consistently shown that the poor have the highest rates of illness and the shortest life expectancy. As Chapter 1 discussed, health inequality was a key focus of early **public health** efforts in the 1800s, particularly through the work of Friedrich Engels, Edwin Chadwick, and Rudolph Virchow (Engels, 1958/1845; Porter, 1997; Rosen, 1993). Despite these early efforts, it was not until 1980 and the publication of *Inequalities in Health* (DHSS, 1980) in the United Kingdom, commonly referred to as the Black Report after its chairman Sir Douglas Black, that interest in health inequality was renewed (see Marmot, 2004; Marmot & Wilkinson, 1999; Townsend, et al., 1992; Whitehead, 1987, 1998; Wilkinson, 1996.). In Canada the 1974 Lalonde report, *A New Perspective on the Health of Canadians*, and the 1986 Epp report, *Achieving Health for All: A Framework for Health Promotion,* both signalled the government's recognition that social and economic conditions had a part to play in health outcomes. Subsequently, Canadian researchers identified income and its distribution as one of the key social determinants of health (see Health Canada, 2002c; Raphael, 2009a).

neo-liberalism

Economic policies and ideology that advocate a free market for the production and distribution of resources, an enhanced role for the private sector and a reduction of government involvement in the economy.

economic rationalism

Term used to describe a political philosophy based on small-government and market-oriented policies, such as deregulation, privatization, reduced government spending, and lower taxation.

trickle-down theory

The theory that everyone benefits by allowing the upper class to prosper relatively unfettered. If wealthy capitalists are allowed and encouraged to maximize their profits, it is believed that this increased wealth will eventually 'trickle down' to the workers.

public health/public health infrastructure

Public policies and infrastructure to prevent the onset and transmission of disease among the population, with a particular focus on sanitation and hygiene, such as clean air, water, and food, and immunization. *Public health infrastructure* refers specifically to the buildings, installations, and equipment necessary to ensure healthy living conditions for the population.

Are widening inequalities making Canadians less healthy? The unequivocal answer is 'yes'. Research in Canada and other countries has consistently found that social inequalities in society, no matter what measure is used, lead to social inequalities in health (Health Canada, 1999c; Raphael, 2009a). Although the overall standard of health in Canada has improved, this high standard of health has not been shared equally by all sectors. Socioeconomic status, living conditions, working conditions, Aboriginal status, the environment, and gender all have a bearing on the health status of individuals. Health status also varies across and within Canadian cities, provinces, and territories. For example, in 2003 life expectancies ranged from a high of 80.8 years in British Columbia to a low of 68.5 years in Nunavut (Senzilet, 2007). Socio-economic factors are key influences in the health of populations; a wealth of international evidence has shown that there is a clear relationship between socio-economic status and health (Navarro, 2004; Navarro & Muntaner, 2004; Marmot et al., 1997; Marmot & Wilkinson, 2006). Poor health, however, is not simply concentrated among those in the lowest quintile; rather, there is a social gradient that runs right across the population. Health status declines as one's socio-economic status declines (Health Canada, 1999c; Marmot et al., 1991). The evidence shows that higher economic status and income are associated with better health.

Income is also a good predictor of mortality from a range of diseases (Auger & Alix, 2009; Marmot et al., 1997; Raphael, 2009b; Statistics Canada, 1999; Wilkins et al., 2002). Canadians who live in the poorest neighbourhoods are more likely to die from cardiovascular disease, cancer, diabetes, and respiratory diseases than other Canadians. A review of Canada's census metropolitan areas (CMAs) found that life expectancy is highest in CMAs with the highest average household income, the highest proportion of postsecondary graduates, and the largest share of the population comprising immigrants (Senzilet, 2007). As Raphael (2009b) has argued, income is a determinant of health in itself but it also is marker of other social determinants, such as education, working conditions, employment, food security, and quality of housing. A higher income also means greater choices and more control over one's life. According to the Second Report on the Health of Canadians (Health Canada, 1999c), low-income Canadians are more likely to die earlier and suffer more illnesses than those with higher incomes, regardless of age, sex, race, and place of residence. Susan Crompton (2000) found that despite the introduction of universal health care in Canada just over 40 years ago, low-incomes earners have lower life expectancies and higher rates of morbidity. This disparity exists even though low-income Canadians use health-care services more frequently.

The Whitehall studies in England in the 1960s (see Marmot et al., 1991, 1999) first found a 'social gradient' in the mortality rate of British civil servants, whereby life expectancy increased for each employment level up to the top of the public-service hierarchy. The social gradient of health was evident along the whole occupational hierarchy, suggesting that health inequality affected not only those at the bottom but also the relatively well-paid white-collar workers. The researchers also found that **risk factors**, such as being overweight, smoking, drinking alcohol, and not exercising, accounted for only a small percentage of the social gradient and could not explain the health inequality between the occupational grades of the civil servants in the studies (see Marmot et al., 1997, 1999; Marmot, 2000).

Subsequent research has shown that a gradient in health status from low to middle to highest income quintile can be observed on nearly all measures of mortality and

risk factors

Conditions that are thought to increase an individual's susceptibility to illness or disease, such as abuse of alcohol, poor diet, or smoking.

morbidity. For example, a study by Wilkins et al. (2002) found that in Canada the aver-age life expectancy in the highest income quintile was 78.5 years, compared to 74.8 years for those in the lowest quintile; the difference was greater for men than for women. The same was the case for infant mortality rates (Raphael, 2001). Wilkins et al. also esti-mated that 22 per cent of total potential years of life lost (PYLL) prior to age 75 among Canadians can be attributed to income differences (Raphael, 2001, p. 230). The findings are consistent with those presented in the Health Canada report. These findings con-tinue to remain true. A comparison of health-adjusted life expectancy (HALE) across income groups show that at birth women in the highest income groups have a HALE that is 3.2 years higher than women in the lowest group. Similarly, men in the high-est income group have a HALE 4.7 years higher than men in the lowest group (Health Canada, 2006a, p. 31). A decade earlier, Roberge et al. (1995) used a Health Status Index to measure the health of Canadians. They found, as did others, that a low level of edu-cational attainment, unemployment, and low income were all related to having lower health levels across all age groups. Differences in health status were particularly strong among adults aged 45 to 64. They also found that the type of job one has affects health status: unskilled workers had lower health levels than skilled workers or professionals. In a nationally representative population-based cohort study in Canada, Wilkins et al. (2008b) found that regardless of whether status was measured by education, occupation, or income, people of higher socio-economic status had lower mortality rates than those of lower socio-economic status. They found a clear gradient with the greatest difference between those in the bottom two quintiles.

What explains the strong relationship between income inequalities and health? Possible theoretical pathways include the following:

1. Material/structural pathways. That is, income inequities lead to other material inequi-ties, such as inadequate nutrition or poor housing, which may lead to health disparities.
2. Behavioural/cultural pathways. That is, health disparities may be the result of differ-ent behaviours or lifestyles among different socio-economic groups, such as smoking or drinking.
3. Psychosocial pathways. Stress associated with living at the bottom of the social hier-archy may lead to disease or related health outcomes (Gupta & Ross, 2007, pp. 27-28).

> The lowest mortality rates were among the university-educated, the employed, those in professional and managerial occupations, and those in top-income brackets. The highest mortality rates were among people with less than secondary graduation, those who were unemployed or not in the labour force, those in unskilled jobs, and those in the lowest income brackets. (Wilkins et al., 2008b, p. 38)

As we saw earlier, the gap between the rich and poor in Canada continues to increase. Given the current fiscal policy, this trend will continue as the social safety net continues to be eroded by neo-liberal policies. Since research indicates clearly that there is a rela-tionship between health and income, one should expect that unless there are policy chan-ges the health status of Canadians overall will see a decline in the years ahead. Given the strong relationship between socio-economic status, income inequality, and health outcomes, addressing income inequality and poverty are crucial to improving the health status of all Canadians. According to a senior policy analyst for the Canadian Council on Social Development, 'no amount of money or reform with the health care system will effectively reduce inequalities in health status until geographically-based income and social disparities are addressed' (Health Canada, 2002c, p. 2).

While individual income is obviously a factor in health status, the distribution of income in society is an equally if not more important determinant of health. In *Unhealthy Societies*, Richard Wilkinson (1996) presents empirical evidence to support a thesis that societies with lower levels of income inequality have the highest life expectancy. His argument is that once a country reaches a certain amount of wealth, determined by **gross domestic product** (GDP) per capita (per head of population), and undergoes the 'epidemiologic transition' from infectious disease to chronic disease as the major cause of mortality, increases in national wealth have little impact on population health. Raphael (2001) notes that studies show that as economic inequality increased in Great Britain, the most affluent in Britain had higher death rates among adult men and infants than the least well off in Sweden, even though the British had higher absolute incomes. Similarly, an American study found that even after controlling such variables as income, sex, race, educational level, body mass, and smoking, residents in the most unequal states were more likely to report poor or fair health than those living in states with less inequality. A 1998 study reported in *The Lancet* found that American cities with large inequalities in the distribution of income tend to have much higher death rates than cities that are more homogeneous in terms of income (see also Kaplan et al., 1996; Lynch et al., 1998). Wilkinson's argument is that it is not the total wealth of a society that is important but, rather, the distribution of that wealth—the more egalitarian a society is, the better the life expectancy and hence the less likelihood of health inequality. While there is no definitive explanation for the link between societal inequality and health, Raphael suggests these findings can be explained in part because the degree of income inequality in a society leads to decreased social cohesion, which in turn influences people's health. Wilkinson's work has spawned a significant literature debating the merits of his study and its conclusions. While some studies have supported his findings (see Raphael, 2001) others have cast doubt on the accuracy and strength of his claims. For example, in a significant study by Ken Judge and colleagues (1998), statistical associations between income inequality and population health were found to be small, posing 'a serious challenge to those who believe that the relationship is a very powerful one' (Judge et al., 1998, p. 578).

The Social Determinants of Health

Class inequalities affect everyone; however, not everyone has the same chance of being wealthy or living in poverty. Racialized persons, those with less education, and Aboriginal peoples are at greater risk of having poor health. Research suggests that these differences can not be explained by a biomedical approach to health and illness. The **social determinants of health approach** grew out of researchers' attempts to find social mechanisms to explain why different groups of people experienced different degrees of illness. It is a relatively new term, although the concept can be linked back to early work of Rudolf Virchow and Friedrich Engels. Dennis Raphael, the Canadian researcher most associated with the concept, defines the social determinants of health as the economic and social conditions that

gross domestic product (GDP)

The market value of all goods and services that have been sold during a year.

social determinants of health

Refers to the social and economic environments in which people live and that determine their health. Examples of social determinants include housing, job security, working conditions, education, income, social class, gender, Aboriginal status, and the social safety net. The quality of these determinants is a reflection of how society is organized and how it distributes its economic and social resources.

shape the health of individuals and communities. They are, Raphael (2009b) argues, the primary determinants of whether individuals stay healthy or become ill. Such an approach focuses on how society is organized and how it distributes its economic and social resources as predictors of health and illness (Raphael, 2009b). While the term 'social determinants of health' was first used in 1996 by British researchers, two earlier reports from Great Britain, the Black Report (1980) and the Health Divide Report (1992), had sparked considerable interest in examining the health outcomes among different employment groups.

Theory Link
See Chapter 1 for a discussion of the work of Virchow and Engels.

As mentioned earlier, Marc Lalonde's 1974 report signalled the first government recognition that good health was influenced by a number of factors, including a person's social and economic environment. In 1986, then minister of health Jake Epp tabled a government framework for health promotion that highlighted the need for government to reduce income-related health inequalities. The Ottawa Charter for Health Promotion, which developed from the First International Conference on Health Promotion in Ottawa in 1986, more explicitly identified the prerequisites of health as peace, shelter, education, food, income, a stable ecosystem, sustainable resources, social justice, and equity (Ottawa Charter for Health Promotion, 1986). These prerequisites, Raphael points out, are all concerned with structural aspects of society rather than with individual behaviours, as is the focus in medical and behavioural approaches. Concerned about what he considered shortcomings in the social determinants of health field, Raphael expanded the concept of social determinants to reflect more accurately the Canadian reality. The 12 determinants that emerged from the Social Determinants of Health across the Life-Span Conference at York University, 2002, were as follows:

1. Aboriginal status
2. Early life
3. Education
4. Employment and working conditions
5. Food security
6. Gender
7. Health-care services
8. Housing
9. Income and its distribution
10. Social safety net
11. Social exclusion
12. Unemployment and employment security (Raphael, 2009b, p. 7)

These have become the basis for critical materialist approaches to health inequality among Canadian researchers.

Social determinants are not discrete variables; rather they are an interrelated set of factors. The scenario in Box 4.1 illustrates the mechanism and pathways by which socio-economic factors influence health. From a materialist perspective, the story in Box 4.1 also shows how individual behaviour, such as play, is structured by the material conditions of a person's life. Gender, ethnicity, race, Aboriginal status, and age are other important pathways by which social determinants of health affect health status. These are discussed in later chapters.

Income, education, and employment are inextricably linked; a good education is necessary to obtain a secure, well-paying job. These factors in turn determine the neighbourhood in which a person lives, the quality of housing, access to higher education, the ability to purchase nutritious food, leisure activities, and the quality of early childhood health—all of which influence physical, emotional, and psychological well-being. In his first report on the state of public health in Canada, Dr David Butler-Jones, Canada's chief public health officer, examined many of the ways socio-economic factors affect the lives of Canadians. Unemployment and low income can lead to financial and life stress, which can have health consequences such as high blood pressure and heart disease. A lack of resources and skills affect the degree to which people can exercise control over their lives, which can contribute to poorer health behaviours, such as smoking and over-consumption of alcohol and fewer health coping skills. The quality of early childhood, moreover, helps set a trajectory for a healthier life. Providing children with stimulating and supportive environments, particularly during the first six years of life can mitigate poor health outcomes in later life (2008, pp. 35–59).

BOX 4.1 But Why?

Why is Jason in the hospital?
Because he has a bad infection in his leg.

But why does he have an infection?
Because he has a cut on his leg and it got infected.

But why does he have a cut on his leg?
Because he was playing in the junk yard next to his apartment building and there was some sharp, jagged steel there that he fell on.

But why was he playing in a junk yard?
Because his neighbourhood is kind of run down. A lot of kids play there and there is no one to supervise them.

But why does he live in that neighbourhood?
Because his parents can't afford a nicer place to live.

But why can't his parents afford a nicer place to live?
Because his Dad is unemployed and his Mom is sick.

But why is his Dad unemployed?
Because he doesn't have much education and he can't find a job.

But why . . . ?

Source: " Toward a Healthy Future, Second Report on the Health of Canadians, Paragraph titled: "What Makes Canadians Healthy or Unhealthy?", p. vii, Health Canada, 1999c. Reproduced with the permission of the Minister of Public Works and Government Services Canada, 2011.

Explaining Health Inequality

Explanations of health inequality can be roughly divided into two main categories: individualistic explanations and materialist/structural explanations. More recently, some researchers have looked at psychosocial factors, such as social cohesion. Individualistic perspectives focus on individual biomedical and behavioural risk factors as the primary contributors to poor health. Conversely, materialist/structural explanations are concerned with the role of social, economic, and political factors in determining the social distribution of health and illness.

Individual-Level Explanations

Three of the categories introduced in the Black Report (DHSS, 1980) can be categorized as individual-level explanations:

1. The artifact explanation suggests that links between class and health are artificial and are the result of statistical anomalies or the inability to accurately measure social phenomena. This viewpoint is easily disputed by the vast amount of evidence that has demonstrated that health inequality exists (see Raphael, 2009a; Wilkins et al., 2008b).
2. **Social Darwinist** explanations suggest that social and health inequalities are due to biological inferiority. This viewpoint acknowledges the relationship between class and health but explains it by assuming that inequality is 'natural' and thus inevitable, meaning nothing can or should be done about it. Such a viewpoint has been effectively dismissed by social-science research, but Macintyre (1997) suggests there is a 'soft' version (her term) of this explanation that is still commonly ascribed to and has some explanatory power. The soft version suggests that social selection can play a part, whereby poor health early in life results in poor educational performance and occupational achievement. The central idea here is that people's health disadvantage (for example, disability) causes social disadvantage, such as poverty. However, ignored in this approach is the fact that these health disadvantages are often the result of socio-structural factors.
3. Cultural/behavioural explanations focus on the individual to explain health inequality in the form of risk-taking or illness-related behaviour, such as smoking, drug taking, excess alcohol consumption, and poor dietary intake, as the primary causes of ill health. Such accounts have rightly been criticized for their **victim blaming** and overly simplistic account of inequality.

A focus on changing the behaviour of individuals assumes they exist in a social vacuum and ignores the social context, social relations, and social processes that affect their lives. Individuals are blamed for their 'failure to seize the opportunity or to work sufficiently hard within the current social structure'; any inadequacies and inequities within the current social structure are ignored (Travers, 1996, p. 551, cited in Raphael, 2009c, p. 21). As noted in Chapter 1, there are illness-inducing factors that lie outside an individual's control, such as stressful work environments or the marketing efforts of corporations. The concept of the **risk society** (Beck, 1992) epitomizes the social basis of risk-imposing environments that impact people's health and influence health-related behaviours.

social Darwinism

The incorrect application of Charles Darwin's theory of animal evolution to explain social inequality by transferring his idea of 'survival of the fittest' among animals to 'explain' human inequality.

victim blaming

The process whereby social inequality is explained in terms of individuals being solely responsible for what happens to them in relation to the choices they make and their assumed psychological, cultural, and/or biological inferiority.

risk society

A term coined by Ulrich Beck (1992) to describe the centrality of risk calculations in people's lives in Western society, whereby the key social problems today are unanticipated hazards, such as the risks of pollution, food poisoning, and environmental degradation.

Therefore, a focus on the individual as the cause and cure of illness, particularly through behaviour modification (which has often been the prescription of much medical, **epidemiological**, and psychological research), will have limited success and also assumes that individuals have the time, resources, and motivation to change their lifestyle.

**epidemiology/
social epidemiology**

The statistical study of patterns of disease in the population. Originally focused on epidemics, or infectious diseases, it now covers non-infectious conditions such as stroke and cancer. Social epidemiology is a sub-field aligned with sociology that focuses on the social determinants of illness.

Theory Link
See Chapter 8 for a discussion of environmental links to health.

Materialist/Structural Explanations

Materialist/structural explanations concern the role of social, economic, and political factors in determining the social distribution of health and illness. The focus is on the distribution of economic and social resources. Materialist/structural explanations have been particularly addressed by Marxist and Weberian perspectives, which direct attention away from individualistic and victim-blaming accounts and toward the basic class structure of society. The value of class analysis is evident when examining the role of income inequality in understanding and addressing health inequality.

Theory Link
See Chapter 2 for a discussion of Marxism and Weberianism.

Using social determinants of health, such as income, employment, Aboriginal status, or gender, to examine the reasons for health inequalities illustrates a materialist or structural approach. The focus is on how society is organized. Material circumstances are related to health directly and indirectly via the social and work environments, which have an impact on psychological factors and health-related behaviour. To illustrate how societal decisions shape health and health status, Brunner and Marmot (2006, cited by Raphael, 2009c, pp. 22–3) provided a model that shows the influences of social structure on health via three pathways: material, psychosocial, and behavioural. Material factors are the concrete living conditions that individuals find themselves in, for example, nature of employment and income. These factors determine an individual's degree of political influence and social standing. Those in low-skilled jobs are near the bottom of the social hierarchy and in turn have little political influence, which can create psychological stress and feelings of hopelessness and despair. These feelings can lead to health-threatening behaviour, which leads to illness and poor health. In turn, these behavioural responses can lead to organ damage, negative early life experiences for children, feelings of exclusion, etc. These different pathways, according to Raphael, do not occur in a linear fashion but, rather, operate in a feedback loop (2009c, pp. 22–23).

Building on the model of Brunner and Marmot, Raphael (2009c, pp. 23–36) specifies four additional specific pathways that mediate the social determinants of health and health status: materialist, neo-materialist, life-course, and social comparison models. He explains that from a materialist view, the three key mechanisms are experience of material living; experience of psychological stress; and adoption of health-supporting or health-threatening behaviours. The first component, the quality of material life conditions, influences individual development, family life, and community environments. Poverty and wealth, for example, are associated with the likelihood of developing physical problems, such as chronic disease; developmental problems, such as impaired cognitive abilities; educational problems, including learning disabilities; and social problems, such as dysfunctional family life. The second component of this model focuses on the relationship between living conditions and life-threatening stress as explained by Brunner & Marmot (2006). The third component focuses on the relationship between stress, a consequence of poor material conditions, and various health-threatening behaviours. As Raphael notes, a number of Canadian studies have found that the unemployed, people with low income, and those with inadequate housing are less likely to be physically active and are more likely to consume excessive alcohol or to smoke. Chapter 7 addresses these pathways from the experiences of Aboriginal peoples in Canada.

Neo-materialist explanations share the basic premises with materialism as to the importance of material conditions in explaining health outcomes, but extend their analysis to looking at how these living conditions come about. That is, neo-materialist explanations look at how various societies allocate economic and social resources among their citizens. One explanation as to why Canadians generally enjoy better health than Americans as measured by infant mortality rates and life expectancy is that Canada has a more equitable distribution of income and wealth, as a result of its redistributive income policies. (A closer look at the health of Canadians is found in Chapter 13.) Materialist and neo-materialist approaches are favoured by researchers working within a political economy perspective.

Theory Link
See Chapter 2 for a discussion of political economy.

Life-course approaches pay attention to how the various social determinants of health influence health across the lifespan and emphasize the accumulated effects of adverse social and economic conditions. Hertzman (2000a, cited by Raphael, 2009c) outlines three types of health effects that are relevant: latent effects, pathway effects, and cumulative effects. Latent effects are biological or developmental early life experiences, such as low birth weight, which can be good predictors of heart disease and adult-onset diabetes in later life. Similarly, early exposure to environmental toxins can lead to respiratory problems in adults. Pathway effects refer to experiences that set individuals onto trajectories that influence health and well-being over the lifespan. For example, as we have seen earlier, living conditions influence children's reading ability, which can lead to lower educational achievements, which can result in poor employment opportunities, which results in lower income and a greater likelihood of illness and poor health. Cumulative effects refer to the accumulation of these various advantage or disadvantages over time.

Theory Link
See Chapter 8 for a discussion of environmental links to health.

Finally, explanations of health inequality based on the social comparison approach downplay the material and social conditions of life and focus on social distance and individuals' position in a social hierarchy as an explanation of health differences. The argument is that in unequal societies individuals compare their status and material conditions to that of others. Feelings of shame, worthlessness, and envy can lead individuals to participate in conspicuous consumption, to take on additional employment, or to adopt poor coping behaviours, such as smoking, alcohol consumption, or overeating—all of which lead to negative health outcomes. Inequalities create hierarchies that at the community level can weaken social cohesion, making individuals more distrusting of one other, and result in a deterioration of communal structures and social programs. This approach shares a commonality with the psychosocial explanations discussed below.

Psychosocial Explanations

The focus of structural and materialist approaches has been on the unequal distribution of economic and social resources, including policy recommendations to eliminate social inequalities. This is combined with a **social justice** framework that advocates health as a fundamental human right for all, including those most disadvantaged in society. The emphasis is on changing the inequitable material conditions in which people find themselves. More recently, however, a number of researchers have pointed to psychosocial factors and the lack of **social cohesion** or **social capital** as the basis for the persistence of health inequality in developed countries.

The psychosocial thesis is a neo-functionalist perspective that proposes that societies with greater income inequality have less social cohesion or social capital. The idea of social cohesion or social capital is a reworking of Émile Durkheim's (1984/1893; 1951/1897) concept of social solidarity. More recently, the concept of social capital has been advanced in the work of Pierre Bourdieu (1986), Jonathon Coleman (1988), and Robert Putnam (1993). Social capital refers to social relations and networks that exist among social groups and communities and that provide access to resources and opportunities for mutual benefit. Social capital depends on a high level of community participation, altruism, trust, and an expectation of reciprocity. It has been suggested that a lack of social capital or social cohesion explains why certain social groups adopt health-damaging behaviour, such as using alcohol or drugs. The assumption is that access to social capital will lead to improved health outcomes by lowering stress, and by providing outlets for social interaction and opportunities for enhancing control over one's life through democratic participation in community life (Winter, 2000a, b).

social justice

A belief system that gives high priority to the interests of the least advantaged.

social cohesion

A term used to refer to the social ties that are the basis for group behaviour and integration. See *social capital*.

social capital

A term used to refer to social relations, networks, norms, trust, and reciprocity between individuals that facilitate cooperation for mutual benefit.

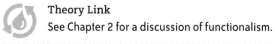

Theory Link
See Chapter 2 for a discussion of functionalism.

Critics of this approach point out that not all groups in society have the same access to social capital. Differential access to social capital based on identities such as race, class, and gender is a reality in Canadian society. Proponents of social capital also downplay the possibility that it can have negative implications, whereby communities and membership of certain clubs and associations can be used for the social exclusion of others, such as ethnic minorities.

The preferred policy prescription of psychosocial approaches is to facilitate social cohesion (trust, reciprocity, cooperation, community participation) rather than advocate political and economic change. Class relations that create income inequality in the first place are downplayed (Coburn, 2000; Lynch, 2000; Muntaner & Lynch, 1999; Raphael, 2001). As David Coburn (2000) argues, there is an implicit assumption that wider reform, such as income redistribution to decrease inequality, is beyond reach. Instead, attention is focused on psychosocial factors at the level of the individual and the community in which an individual lives rather than on the wider structural factors, such as the social and economic policies that governments pursue to foster economic inequality. By marginalizing the role of public policy in both undermining and creating social capital, there is the potential to fall into the trap of a 'community-level version of "blaming the victim"' (Muntaner & Lynch, 1999, p. 59).

Conclusion: Class Matters

The concept of social class is difficult to operationalize definitively in modern complex societies. Different theorists have different notions of how to define *class*. Nevertheless, the concept remains a useful one since it makes clear that the unequal distribution of wealth and power is embedded in the social structure. The benefits of a class analysis can be clearly seen when examining socio-economic variables, such as income or poverty and illness. Materialist and neo-materialist explanations, in particular, focus on the role of social, economic, and political factors in determining the social distribution of health and illness. The concept of the social determinants of health provides a framework to explain some of the different pathways through which economic and social conditions affect health status. The social patterning of behaviour clearly indicates that health inequality is not simply an outcome of individual choice—there are social processes at work. Individual behaviour occurs in a social context of living and working conditions that create exposure to health-enhancing or damaging environments. It has been suggested that no single theory offers an adequate explanation of health inequality; rather, a way forward is offered by a multifactorial approach that addresses structural, cultural, and psychosocial factors (Macintyre, 1997; Vågerö & Illsley, 1995). Only such theoretical pluralism can effectively deal with the range of social and psychological determinants of health inequality. Raphael (2009b) and McMullin (2010) remind us that the specific pathways by which various social determinants affect health are shaped by factors such as gender, race, ethnicity, Aboriginal status, age, and disability. Hankivsky and Christoffersen (2008) also argue for an intersectionality approach to understand the complex ways in which the determinants of health relate, intersect, and mutually reinforce one another. Researchers like David Coburn and Vicente Navarro focus on political and economic pathways, and illustrate how neo-liberalism and economic globalization help explain the growing economic inequalities among citizens in countries like Canada.

Summary of Main Points

- Different theorists have different definitions and understandings of class.
- Class inequality exists in Canada, with the gap between the rich and poor increasing.
- Growing social inequalities have a negative impact on health status.
- The social determinants of health are economic and social conditions that affect the health of individuals and social groups.
- Socio-economic status, living conditions, working conditions, Aboriginal status, the environment, and gender all have a bearing on the health status of individuals.
- Income and wealth are good predictors of most measures of mortality and morbidity.
- An intersectionality approach to understanding the social determinants of health is necessary.
- There is evidence in Canada and elsewhere of a stair-stepped social gradient of health: for people further down the socio-economic ladder, life expectancy is shorter and most diseases are more common.
- More research is needed that focuses on how economic inequalities are created in the first place.
- There are various explanations for health inequality:
    - Individual-level explanations look at differences in behaviour as an explanation of health inequality.
    - Materialist/structuralist explanations focus on the role of social, economic, and political factors in determining the social distribution of health and illness.
    - Psychosocial explanations look at social capital and social cohesion in communities to explain health differences.
- Health inequality can be reduced through social justice strategies that address class inequality through structural change in the economy, the workplace, and the community.

 # Sociological Reflection: Examining Social Determinants

Raphael (2009b,c, 2006) and others suggest that social determinants of health are important predictors of health outcomes. Which of the determinants mentioned do you consider most important, and why? Take one social determinant and, using an empirical example, explain the pathways through which it affects health.

 # Discussion Questions

1. What might be done to increase public awareness about the significance of the social determinants of health?
2. In what ways can class analysis shed light on why health inequality exists?

3. Will current federal government policy to cut social spending have an impact on people's health? If so, will certain groups of people be more affected than others?

4. How can we explain the persistence of health inequalities in Canada despite our system of universal health care?

5. Why is an intersectionality approach to health essential for an understanding of the existence of health inequalities?

6. Given that there are social patterns of health-related behaviour, to what extent are individuals responsible for their health?

7. Which of the three types of explanations of health inequality discussed in the chapter do you think is most useful? Explain the reasons for your choice.

 ## Further Investigation

1. For a two-week period, analyze how your local newspaper covers health-related stories. Is there a particular bias in terms of how health issues are covered? If you were basing your understanding of the causes of health and illness on these media accounts, what conclusions about health would you come to?

2. Equal access to health care does not lead to equal health outcomes. Discuss.

3. In what ways does public policy in Canada attempt to improve various social determinants of health, such as poverty, homelessness, and unemployment?

4. Health education as a policy response to addressing health inequality individualizes the social origins of illness in a risk society. Discuss.

 ## Further Reading

Armstrong, P., Armstrong, H., & Coburn, D. (Eds.). (2001). *Unhealthy times: Political economy perspectives on health and care.* Toronto, ON: Oxford University Press.

Bartly, M. (2003). *Health inequality: An introduction to concepts, theories and methods.* Cambridge, UK: Polity Press.

Blaxter, M. (1997). Whose fault is it? People's own conceptions of the reasons for health inequalities. *Social Science & Medicine, 44*(6), 747–756.

Butler-Jones, D. (2008). *Report on the State of Public Health in Canada: Addressing Health Inequalities.* Ottawa, ON: Public Health Agency of Canada.

Coburn, D. (2000). Income inequality, social cohesion and the health status of populations: The role of neo-liberalism. *Social Science & Medicine, 51*(1), 135–146.

Coburn, D. (2004). Beyond the income inequality hypothesis: Class, neo-liberalism, and health inequalities. *Social Science and Medicine, 58*(1), pp. 41–56.

Hankivsky, O., & Christoffersen, A. (2008, September). Intersectionality and the determinants of health: A Canadian perspective. *Critical Public Health, 18*(3), 271–283.

Health Canada. (1999). *Intersectoral action . . . towards population health: Report of the Federal, Provincial and Territorial Advisory Committee on Population Health.* Ottawa: Health Canada.

Health Canada. (1999b). *Toward a healthy future: Second report on the health of Canadians.* Ottawa, ON: Health Canada.

Hofrichter, R. (Ed.) (2003). *Health and social justice: Politics, ideology, and inequity in the distribution of disease.* San Francisco, CA: Jossey-Bass.

Kawachi, I., & Kennedy, B. (2002). *The health of nations: Why inequality is harmful to your health.* New York, NY: New Press.

Macintyre, S. (1997). The Black Report and beyond: What are the issues? *Social Science & Medicine, 44*(6), 723–745.

Marmot, M., & Wilkinson, R. G. (Eds.). (2006). *Social determinants of health* (5th ed.). Oxford, UK: Oxford University Press.

Muntaner, C., & Lynch, J. (1999). Income inequality, social cohesion, and class relations: A critique of Wilkinson's neo-Durkheimian research program. *International Journal of Health Services, 29*(1), 59–81.

Muntaner, C., Lynch, J., & Davey Smith, G. (2001). Social capital, disorganized communities and the third way: Understanding the retreat from structural inequalities in epidemiology and public health. *International Journal of Health Services, 31*(2), 213–237.

Navarro, V. (Ed.). (2001). *Political economy of social inequalities: Consequences for health and quality of life.* Amityville, NY: Baywood Publishing.

Navarro, V. (2004). Inequalities are unhealthy. *Monthly Review, 56*(2), pp. 26–30.

Navarro, V. (Ed.). (2007). *Neoliberalism, globalization and inequalities: Consequences for health and quality of life.* Amityville, NY: Baywood Publishing.

Raphael, D. (1999). Health effects of economic inequality. *Canadian Review of Social Policy, 44,* 25–40.

Raphael, D. (Ed.). (2009). *The social determinants of health* (2nd ed.). Toronto, ON: Canadian Scholars Press.

Waitzkin, H. (2000). *The second sickness: Contradictions of capitalist health care* (2nd ed.). Lanham, MD: Rowman & Littlefield.

Whitehall II Study Team. (2004). *Work, stress and health: The Whitehall II study.* London, UK: PCSU.

Wilkinson, R. (1996). *Unhealthy societies: The afflictions of inequality.* London, UK: Routledge.

Wilkinson, R., & Marmot, M. (Eds.). (2003). *Social determinants of health: The solid facts* (2nd ed.). Copenhagen: World Health Organization. Available from www.epha.org/a/856

Web Resources

Canadian Centre for Policy Alternatives (CCPA)
www.policyalternatives.ca

Canadian Council on Social Development (CCSD)
www.ccsd.ca/

Centre for Social Justice (CJS)
www.socialjustice.org

health-evidence.ca
www.health-evidence.ca

International Society for Equity in Health (ISEQH)
www.iseqh.org

Merrill Lynch: World Wealth Report 2004
www.ml.com/media/18252.pdf

National Council of Welfare (NCW)
www.ncw.gc.ca/h.4m.2@-eng.jsp

Public Health Agency of Canada: Population Health Approach
www.phac-aspc.gc.ca/ph-sp/index-eng.php

Statistics Canada: Research Projects from the National Longitudinal Survey of Children and Youth (NLSCY)
www.statcan.ca/english/rdc/rdcprojectsnlscy.htm

*Stoney Brook University: Centre for the Study of
Working Class Life*
www.stonybrook.edu/workingclass/

Working Group on Extreme Inequality
www.inequality.org

World Bank: Social Capital
web.worldbank.org/WBSITE/EXTERNAL/
TOPICS/EXTSOCIALDEVELOPMENT/
EXTTSOCIALCAPITAL/0,,contentMDK:2
0642703~menuPK:401023~pagePK:148956
~piPK:216618~theSitePK:401015,00.html

*World Health Organization (WHO): Ottawa
Charter for Health Promotion*
www.euro.who.int/__data/assets/pdf_
file/0004/129532/ Ottawa_Charter.pdf

*World Health Organization (WHO): Social
Determinants of Health*
www.who.int/social_determinants/en/

CHAPTER 5

Women's Health in Context: Gender Issues

Pat Armstrong

Overview

- Why focus on women's health?
- Why explore differences among women?
- Why does context matter in health?

Women's bodies must be understood within a context characterized by inequities not only among women and men but also among women. That context, which includes the social and physical environments, employment, and income, structures inequities in ways that can be harmful to health and that are unequally harmful to women and men. Similarly, the way health services are organized and practised has unequal consequences for women as patients and as care providers, and can promote inequities among women. Personal health practices and educational achievement matter, as do coping skills and social networks—so, too, does genetic endowment. But until we address these structural and health inequities through public policy and until we educate both policy-makers and health practitioners about how gender matters, we cannot expect women or men to live lives that are as healthy as possible.

Key Terms

bodies	education	relations of ruling
context	gender	sex
determinants of health	inequities	women's health movement
dichotomies	public care	
disabilities	public health-care system	

Introduction

This chapter is about women's health, broadly defined. Too often, women's health is reduced to a discussion of their reproductive organs. Indeed, women's health issues are understood as universal and are, therefore, universally interpreted, treated, and experienced. This chapter challenges those assumptions, locating women's health within global, national, regional, and local contexts and in what Dorothy Smith calls **relations of ruling**. Bodies are not irrelevant, but they can only be understood within specific locations, times, spaces, and relations. Those relations are highly gendered and characterized by inequalities. The focus is on Canada and Canadian research, policies, and practices, with Canada understood within the larger context of global patterns and exchange. Although one country serves as a focus and a way of illustrating the importance of specific locations, many of the patterns can be found throughout the high-income countries.

Feminist political economy provides the theoretical frame, although this approach is informed by a range of perspectives. Starting from this framework means emphasizing **context** and the inequities shaped by political and economic forces, including those related to **gender**. At the same time, most modernist and post-structuralist perspectives teach us to challenge the **dichotomies** that have often been part of political economy and to attend to discourses (Moss & Teghtsoonian, 2007) while other feminist approaches stress the intersection of gender and class with other social, sexual, and geographic locations (Hankivsky et al., 2007).

Because **bodies** have been the starting point for much of the literature on women's health, the chapter begins with an examination of the role women's bodies play in shaping their health. Because context matters in the very structure of bodies as well as in their treatment, the chapter then moves on to explore the contexts that shape women's health.

Nature and Nurture

There have long been debates in the social sciences about what is biologically determined and what is socially constructed, arguments often characterized as nature versus nurture. In briefly reviewing the issues in the debates, this section seeks to make three basic points. First, there are no simple dichotomies between the physical and the social or even between women and men. This first point leads to the second one: namely, that all health issues are women's issues while recognizing that there are significant differences among women and no clear boundaries among genders. Third, bodies still matter and there are broad similarities among women related to their bodies that must be taken into account even while acknowledging that there are a host of other factors that shape bodies in variable ways. Equally important, women frequently are treated as a group in ways that shape their opportunities.

Traditionally in the social sciences, *sex* is used to refer to bodies. Based on their review of the term's usage, Johnson et al. (2009) conclude that, **sex** 'is a multidimensional biological construct that encompasses anatomy, physiology, genes, and hormones, which together affect how we are labelled and treated in the world' (p. 5). *Gender*, on the other hand, is 'a multidimensional social construct that is culturally based and historically specific, and thus constantly changing' (p. 6).

relations of ruling
Dorothy Smith used this term to emphasize how social processes are structured by the powerful in ways that shape our consciousness and our practices.

context
Refers to the social, political, physical, and economic environment.

gender
Most frequently understood as 'a multidimensional social construct that is culturally based and historically specific, and thus constantly changing' (Johnson et al., 2009, p. 6), but this chapter challenges the possibility of separating gender from sex.

dichotomies
Refers to distinctions made between two parts that are understood to be distinct and quite different.

bodies
Material constructs, usually talked about as physically separate from the environment but are here understood as shaped by the environment.

sex
Most frequently understood as 'a multidimensional biological construct that encompasses anatomy, physiology, genes, and hormones, which together affect how we are labelled and treated in the world' (Johnson et al., 2009, p. 5). (However, this chapter challenges the possibility of separating gender from sex.)

This notion of sex has helped us explore differences between women and men that go well beyond those linked to reproduction. So, for example, research by Abramson (2009, p. 54) has shown that women's 'cardiovascular risk factors and symptoms differ from those of men', with 'women more likely to experience vague pain or discomfort in the chest, neck, back or arms' (p. 53). Such evidence helps alert physicians and women to the possibility that symptoms in women may not follow what are thought to be the key indicators of a heart attack and thus avoid an untimely death. This evidence also emphasizes the importance of exploring the possibility that differences shape all aspects of bodies and not just those related to breasts, wombs, and hormones. However, it is important to note that Abramson talks about women being more likely to have these experiences and symptoms of heart attacks. She is not setting out a dichotomy, a clear line between women and men, but, rather, identifying patterns that are more common in women than in men. Part of the reason it is difficult to draw clear lines between women and men is that nurture shapes nature, creating biological differences among women as well as between women and men. As Fausto-Sterling (2005) concludes in the first of two articles that use research on bones to explore the impact of anatomies and physiology, the 'sex-gender or nature-nurture accounts of difference fail to appreciate the degree to which culture is a partner in producing body systems commonly referred to as biology—something apart from the social' (p. 1516). Her later investigation of the relationship between race and bones leads her to argue that 'race turns out to not be a useful variable per se' (2008, p. 682), either. She concludes that 'nurture, culture, environment, geography, experience, and history—however we describe it—shape nature; nature influences how such shaping proceeds'.

In short, there is no simple dichotomy between sex and gender, between bodies and their social and physical environments. They are mutually constituted, with the result that there are significant physiological differences among women as well as differences in the way female bodies are interpreted and experienced. Moreover, bodies are constantly changing in relation to environments. To quote Fausto-Sterling again (2008), bodies 'emerge over the lifecycle as a response to specific lived lives' (p. 658). In addition, there is not even a simple genetic dichotomy that separates everyone into two sexes as controversy over who can play on female Olympic teams has shown (Simpson et al., 2000). 'Therefore our common binary understanding of sex (male/female) is limiting and unrepresentative of the breadth and variety that exists with respect to human sexual characteristics' (Johnson et al., 2009, p. 5).

Simple dichotomies also limit our notions of sexuality and the binary division implied by heterosexuality. With the rise of queer studies have come challenges to fixed sexual categories. Similar to arguments about the nature/nurture dichotomy, debates about sexuality emphasize the importance of historical and social context along with the power relations that shape bodies and practices (Spade & Valentine, 2008).

Nevertheless gender, like sex, remains a useful concept. Just as sex draws our attention to the physiological and alerts us to differences embedded in bodies, gender reminds us that context matters and that some differences are primarily environmental. Indeed, we do not have language that allows us to easily capture this lack of dichotomy and must rely on the terms *male/female* to talk about physiological aspects of differences, and *masculine* and *feminine* to reference those differences associated more with the environment. Equally important, there are often strategic or analytical reasons for doing such dichotomizing, as the case of symptoms for heart attacks shows. We need to keep reminding ourselves, though, that these are neither fixed categories nor simply dichotomous ones.

What this means is that we cannot understand bodies outside their environments. But bodies still matter: only women menstruate, lactate, and gestate; only men can produce semen. Not all women do all of these things and not all men produce semen, but most women and most men have the potential to do so, respectively. Moreover, hormonal balances differ in most women and men, as do chromosomes. Indeed, researchers have claimed that every organ has the capacity to respond differently in women and men (Gesensway, 2001). However, these physiological differences are not only altered by environments; they are also interpreted by them. For example, the meaning of having babies or breasts varies significantly with place and time, is experienced differently, and has different consequences depending on our social, physical, and historical locations and depending on other social relations, such as sexual ones.

Contexts and the Factors that Shape Health

This leads us to examine the environments or contexts that shape women's bodies and their health. Health Canada recognizes 12 **determinants of health**:

1. Income and social status
2. Employment
3. Education
4. Social environments
5. Physical environments
6. Healthy child development
7. Personal health practices and coping skills
8. Health services
9. Social support networks
10. Biology and genetic endowment
11. Gender
12. Culture

determinants of health
Refers to the social, economic, and physical factors that influence an individual's or a group's health. The term has become widely used in academic and policy circles to indicate that health is structured by more than health services, although the specific determinants on the list vary.

There is a broad consensus that all these factors influence health, although not all governments include gender in their list and lists vary somewhat among governments. There are three interrelated problems, though, with the way these factors are often understood. First, these determinants are frequently seen as independent variables rather than as interconnected ones. Employment and income, for example, are inextricably intertwined. A second and related problem has to do with the profound **inequities** in power, not only among individuals but also among groups, that set the context for these factors—inequities that are not usually part of the discussion in the government's determinants of health literature. Finally, all of these factors are profoundly gendered.

Nevertheless, this list of determinants provides a useful frame for exploring women's health. At the same time, it is important to recognize the fundamental inequities that shape all aspects of health. In recognition of the interpenetration of these factors, what follows lumps several of them together and treats all of them as gendered.

inequities
A term used instead of *inequality* because it implies injustice and because it does not imply the objective of treating everyone the same, as is implied by *equality*. Equitable treatment or conditions require recognizing differences and addressing them in ways that are socially just.

Healthy Child Development

The shaping of our bodies and our health begins at least at conception, and so, too, do sex/gender divisions. According to the website for the Public Health Agency of Canada (PHAC) (2001), 'new evidence on the effects of early experiences on brain development, school readiness and health in later life has sparked a growing consensus about early child development as a powerful determinant of health in its own right' (p. 1). PHAC goes on to explain that the most important period of development is from conception to age six, which leads directly to questions about both conception and maternal health.

Until 1969, it was illegal to provide information on or to sell methods for birth control. Abortions were also illegal in Canada. All this changed in 1969, in large measure as a result of the **women's health movement** (Boscoe et al., 2004). Women today have much more choice in whether and when they get pregnant. By the time of the Public Health Agency's maternity experiences survey report in 2009b (12), more than 90 per cent of women said they were happy or somewhat happy to find out they were pregnant. As McKay (2006) explains in his study of the significant decline in teen pregnancies since the laws were changed and services expanded, this trend 'can be viewed as a fairly direct indicator of young women's increasing opportunities and capacity to control their sexual and reproductive health' (p. 157). This decline, he goes on to point out, cannot be primarily explained in terms of women seeking abortions, given that abortion rates have been declining since 1990. New services and better **education** are more important factors. There are, however, provincial and territorial variations in teen pregnancy rates that can be attributed at least in part to limited access to sexual and reproductive health services in rural and northern communities (Maticka-Tyndale et al., 2001, p. 29). Similarly, there are variations among adult women, with more limited access for those who are poor, homeless, or from Aboriginal communities.

Supports for pregnant mothers have also improved. Perhaps most importantly, women have won the right to paid maternity leave. Not all women benefit, however. According to the Public Health Agency study (2009, p. 17), just over two-thirds of women received some maternity or parental benefits. Moreover, in the federal support scheme the maximum benefits are set at 55 per cent of income, with a firm upper limit that leaves the overwhelming majority of women without enough money to support themselves. Women with **disabilities** frequently fail to qualify for paid maternity leave because of their interrupted work patterns. Yet women with disabilities are particularly in need of support when they have young children (Pinto, 2009).

At the same time that more women are successfully using contraception, more women are seeking services that will help them get pregnant. Such fertility problems are not simply about bodies but, rather, also reflect social factors, such as delaying pregnancy until women are established in paid jobs and long-term use of birth control pills. Women have only limited access to publicly funded fertility services in Canada, making money a factor in access. Women who do use fertility clinics for such assistance are more likely to have multiple births, which may mean health problems for both mother and child (Bissonnette et al., 2007; Tulandi et al., 2006).

Once pregnant, maternal health is obviously a critical concern for future child health as well as for the woman: 'By international standards, Canada ranks among the best in the world in maternal and child health' (Sutherns, 2009, p. 19). One reason we do so well

---

women's health movement

In Canada, included both formal and informal organizations of women that addressed issues ranging from birth control to poverty. The movement did not have a single voice or leader but, rather, encompassed a variety of groups and activities, collectively known as the women's health movement.

education

Refers to formal schooling.

disabilities

The social model of disabilities understands physical and mental limitations as primarily the result of social conditions while the medical model understands these limitations as primarily the result of bodies.

is our public health system, which provides services without charge and of high quality, making them broadly accessible. But as this author goes on to explain, however, Canada has been moving down in the rankings, and both poor women and Aboriginal women have disturbing rates of maternal and infant mortality. Women in rural areas have more limited access and many poor women cannot take time off work to seek pre- or postnatal care. The closure of many rural hospitals in recent years has made care more difficult to find, and cutbacks in the number of hospital beds in urban areas has exacerbated the problem (Kornelsen, 2006), especially for immigrant women and for women who have difficulty communicating in English or French (Bierman et al., 2010). At the same time, family doctors are leaving obstetrics in part because of burnout and limited support, and they are in particularly short supply in rural and remote communities (CIHI, 2004).

Nevertheless, almost all women get **public care** even if it may be distant from the relatives and friends who can provide support. Nearly 60 per cent of women receive their care from an obstetrician, and another third see a family physician (Public Health Agency of Canada, 2009, p. 12), with two-thirds of mothers attended by an obstetricians/gynecologist at the birth. Although physicians have undoubtedly contributed to Canada's good record, the women's health movement has been critical of the high involvement of specialists and the treatment of most births as an illness involving multiple medical interventions. Their protests have helped change how doctors handle birth in hospitals, have influenced the decreased use of such practices as enemas and shaves, and have encouraged the attendance of partners at births. The women's health movement also worked successfully to make midwifery not only legal but also publicly funded in a number of provinces. Women fought for midwifery because midwives approach pregnancy as a health rather than an illness issue and because they provide continuous support from early on in the pregnancy to well after birth. However, the number of midwives is limited and only 7 per cent of mothers report having a midwife or nurse-practitioner as their care providers (Public Health Agency of Canada, 2009, p. 12).

Although maternity-care services are important, they are not the only factor in maternal and child health. Exposures to environmental contaminants in our food, water, air, households, and paid workplaces can have negative consequences for a mother and the fetus she carries: 'These harmful effects may emerge early as miscarriages, and may result in life-time deficits for the expected child such as lower IQs or learning disabilities' (Wordsworth & Armstrong, 2009, p. 26). Drugs, including prescribed medications, may have a negative impact on maternal health as well (Mintzes & Jureidini, 2009). Nutrition and appropriate housing are also critical for pregnant women, but many women can neither afford the kinds of food or shelter that good health requires nor have other resources, such as time, to ensure a healthy diet. Both are beyond the reach of the growing number of homeless women who give birth. Personal health practices also play a role. Smoking and drinking in particular have been implicated in poor health outcomes for the fetus, but here education campaigns may have had an effect. Only one in ten women reported drinking alcohol during pregnancy, with the lowest rates among those with the lowest incomes. In contrast, women with lower levels of formal education and lower income were more likely than other women to smoke during pregnancy, although most do not and it is important to consider the particular stresses on their lives that can contribute to such practices (Public Health Agency of Canada, 2009b, p. 13). In addition, women may enter pregnancy in a state of health that complicates their pregnancy: 'Specific biological

public care
Refers to health care provided by health-care professionals in a public setting, such as a doctor's office or hospital. Public care is part of Canada's publicly funded, universal health-care insurance policy.

conditions, such as obesity, hypertension, and pre-existing chronic conditions are linked to an increased maternal mortality rate' (The Source, 2009).

Men also contribute to the health of the mother and the fetus, although much less attention is paid to the male contribution. The health of the sperm matters, but we have only limited research on the factors that may make male sperm harmful. The male influence on pregnancy often goes beyond their sperm contribution, however. Spousal physical and sexual assault during and following pregnancy are far too common, as they are at other times. The Public Agency of Canada (2009, p. 13) survey found that one in ten women report being abused before pregnancy. While nearly half of them said the abuse decreased during pregnancy, one in twenty reported an increase in abuse during this time and 16 per cent said it increased after birth.

All these factors, both personal and structural, contribute to the health of the woman and the fetus she carries and thus to differences among women and their children. Most women report that they and their children are healthy after birth. However, women under age 20, women with low incomes, and women with low levels of formal education are less likely than other women to report that their babies are in excellent health (Public Health Agency of Canada, 2009, p. 17). We do not have much information on differences related to most other social locations, although there is evidence that Aboriginal women are less likely than the general population to give birth to babies in excellent health, reflecting a host of factors from low income to discrimination.

The kinds of support women receive after they have children have a profound impact on both mother and child, in part because women still bear the primary responsibility for child care. In Canada, women who are recognized as landed immigrants or citizens are eligible to receive $100 a month per child under six years of age. While this amount does help, it is not enough to pay for child care or indeed for most of a baby's daily needs: 'Currently, only 12% of preschool aged children in Canada can access regulated childcare spaces' (Angus, 2009, p. 1). Indeed, Canada lags far behind most high-income countries in terms of both the support for and availability of daycare services, ranking last among 25 industrialized countries (Angus, 2009, p. 1). The only province that comes close to having a universal child-care program is Quebec. In 1997, the province introduced a $5-a-day child-care program and full-day kindergarten. Evidence suggests that this program, along with generous parental leave and affordable housing, has been the main factor in reducing poverty in that province by 40 per cent (Goar, 2009, p. A20).

As Cleveland & Krashinsky (1998) show, 'stimulating day care can have strong and lasting effects on child development' (p. 4). At the same time, they (Cleveland & Krashinsky, 2003) challenge the notion that the best care is always care by the mother and that all mothers can provide adequate care. Child care can also mean the family has a decent income while the children grow up, allowing mothers to return to paid work after childbirth. Based on her review of the literature, Waldfogel (2002) concludes that early supports not only 'improve mother–child interaction' but also 'raise maternal employment and education' and that this is especially the case for mothers with the least education (p. 531).

Children, fathers, and mothers may also benefit from father care (Kramer & Thompson, 2005). The Father Involvement Research Alliance (FIRA) (2010, p. 1) recognizes that women still do the bulk of child care even though men are doing more (2010, p. 6). And few men take paternity leave, in part because in most cases the household cannot afford to lose the higher male income and in part because it is still difficult to gain acceptance for males to take time off from their paid jobs. However, FIRA cites a host of research to argue that the 'provision of accessible, affordable, high-quality child care can facilitate the support, education and connection of both mothers and fathers' (p. 6).

There are two main points to this section on healthy child development. The first is to show that this factor overlaps with others, is highly gendered, and is influenced by relations of power. The second is to reveal some of the patterns for women as a group and for different groups of women. In sum, women's access to means for planning birth as well as to appropriate maternity care and child care are central to early child development. All these processes are shaped by women's location, relations, and resources. The following sections are similarly constructed, with similar purposes in mind for other factors.

Education and Social Status, Income and Employment

It is useful to consider education and social status, income and employment together because they are so closely intertwined. Education can mean we develop knowledge and skills necessary for survival; it can be an indicator of social status. But perhaps most important, education can have a profound impact on what kind of job we get and what kind of income we earn. As is the case with early childhood development, these factors deserve at least a chapter on their own. What follows, then, is a brief outline of how they are intertwined in ways that shape women's health.

If level of education is an independent factor determining health, then women should be healthier than men. The number of women graduating from university has been rising much more rapidly than the number of men. By the 1990s, the majority of undergraduate diplomas and certificates were granted to women. Although women formed the overwhelming majority in traditional female areas such as health professions, education, social sciences, humanities, and the arts, they now also account for almost half of those graduating with diplomas in agriculture, nearly a third of those in mathematics and physical sciences, and a quarter of those in engineering and applied sciences. Similarly, women accounted for the majority of full- and part-time community college students by the 1990s. At the other end of the education scale, men are more likely than women to have less than a grade 9 education. Employed men are also less likely than employed women to have a postsecondary degree or diploma (Statistics Canada, 2006d, Chapter 4). According to 2006 census data, 42 per cent of the men in the labour force did not have a degree or diploma while this was the case for 39 per cent of the women. Only in the case of postgraduate degrees do men form a significant majority of graduates and women are rapidly catching up. Moreover, the absolute number of men with postgraduate degrees remains very small. Yet, at the same time that women were passing men in terms of education levels, men's life expectancy was increasing faster than women's (Statistics Canada, 2006d, p. 65). Clearly, something more than education is involved in health.

While women as a group have been gaining on men in terms of education, there are significant differences among women's level of education. According to Statistics Canada (2006d), Aboriginal women are the least likely to have advanced education and they have a lower life expectancy than other women, and '[w]omen with disabilities generally have a lower level of education than women with no disabilities' (p. 293). The women most likely to have university degrees are those who are foreign born and those who identified themselves as visible minority (Statistics Canada, 2006d, pp. 223 and 246). But these higher levels of education do not guarantee the health of immigrant or racialized women. Although immigrants initially tend to be healthier than those already in Canada, their health gradually converges with that of long-term residents (McDonald & Kennedy, 2004). And the health of racialized women tends to be lower than that of other women in Canada (Agnew, 2009). Although education is important to health, the impact clearly varies and operates in unison with other factors, some of which themselves help explain the low levels of education.

One of those factors is income, along with parental level of education. More women than men live below the poverty line: 'In Canada, the most vulnerable to poverty are Canadians from racialized communities, recent immigrants (many of whom are also from racialized communities), Aboriginal people, and persons with disabilities. . . . But in all the vulnerable groups, poverty rates for women are higher than those for men' (Townson, 2009, p. 5). Even when transfer payments and tax credits are taken into account, a quarter of the women in lone-parent families have incomes that keep them in poverty (Townson, 2009, p. 6). The causes are many. Welfare is worth less and less, and has become more and more difficult to get. Many men fail to make support payments after relationships dissolve, leaving many women who parent alone with little income. In addition, women are less likely than men to have employment-related pensions and as a result often must depend on Old Age Security in their senior years, a dependency that puts them in a low-income category. Women are also less likely than men to be eligible for unemployment insurance and frequently receive less money when they are deemed eligible. And poverty is hazardous to women's health. For example, poverty 'is one of the primary forces that create conditions of HIV risk' and helps account for the fact that women now account for a growing number of those with HIV (Buhler, 2008, p. 2).

Not only women without jobs or without higher education are poor, however. Minimum wage in Canada does not lift people above the poverty line if they do not have full-time, full-year employment and access to affordable housing. Given that women account for the majority of those employed at minimum wage and those employed part-time or part-year, many women with paid work still live in poverty. The link between poverty and women's mental health has long been established (Belle, 1990), and poverty usually means poor housing and nutrition as well.

As a result of their successful struggles to gain access to both higher education and jobs, women have been able to enter the labour force in large numbers and even make it into jobs with better pay and conditions that take them above poverty levels. In spite of these gains, however, employed women still tend to make less than employed men. Furthermore, although education does make a difference to the wage gap, there is a wage gap even if men and women are matched for age and education. For example, in 1995 women 35 to 44 years of age who graduated from high school were paid 71 per cent of the male wage; those with postsecondary degrees or diplomas were paid 74 per cent of the male wage; and those with a university degree, 77 per cent. By the 2006 census, when this group was in the 45- to 54-year-old age group, women with high school faced a wage gap of 73 per cent compared to their male counterparts, and for college graduates the gap was 72 per cent. University graduates did somewhat better, with those in this age group paid 82 per cent of the male wage. In 1995, women 35 to 44 years of age with a postsecondary certificate or diploma employed full-time all year earned less than men of similar age, with the exception of the men with an education level of grade 8 or less. And their earnings were only $1139 a year more than the men with the least education. In 2006, women in this age group with college education had median annual incomes that were more than $6000 less than men with only high school and about the same as men without high school—$38 005 versus $37 570 (Statistics Canada, 1996, Table 10; 2008, Table 6).

Moreover, lack of education hurts women more than it hurts men, while more education often does not translate into benefits for racialized and/or immigrant women: 'Women with very little education have very low income levels, but poorly-educated men are much better off in comparison to their better educated counterparts' (Chung, 2006, p. 1). Between 2000 and 2005, young men without high school education saw their incomes rise by 7–8 per cent while young women saw no gains. A man with an education of eight years or less in 1995 averaged earnings higher than a woman with a postsecondary certificate or diploma, even if both were employed full-time (Statistics Canada, 1995). These wage differences reflect in part the segregation of the labour force into male and female jobs, with female jobs given lower value.

Lower wages for women mean less social status as well as more limited access to the kinds of goods and services that can help women maintain their health. Indeed, lower wages frequently reflect discrimination, which itself can be harmful to women's health. Furthermore, when women take on paid jobs most still bear primary responsibility for household and care work. As a result of the double shift at paid and unpaid work, women often experience time poverty (Turner & Grieco, 2000). This, too, can be harmful to women's health, adding to their levels of stress. Moreover, the prospect of taking on the double load can contribute to women delaying childbirth, which in turn may have other health consequences. For example, the higher rates of breast cancer among teachers have been 'explained as a result of delayed childbirth among this occupational group' (Messing, 1998, p. 4). Women with paid jobs are, however, often more healthy than those without paid work, in part because paid employment not only provides access to income and to social networks, it can also mean rewards from using their education and skills in a socially recognized way.

However, women's paid jobs are not without hazards of their own (Briar, 2009). As Messing (1998) explains in *One-Eyed Science*, research on workplace hazards has focused mainly on male work and has applied male standards even when women's work is examined. Women's jobs, especially those involving working in an office, teaching children, or caring for others, are too often assumed to be safe, without risks. Yet Messing convincingly demonstrates that women face a host of visible and invisible hazards at work that are only now being revealed, and many have yet to be recognized by workers' compensation boards that still reflect male standards. Health-care workers, for example, suffer from mental stress caused by 'work overload, pressure at work, lack of participation in decision-making, poor social support, unsupportive leadership, lack of communication/feedback, staff shortages or unpredictable staffing, scheduling or long work hours and conflict between work and family demands' (Yassi & Hancock, 2005, p. 35).

For women, lack of full-time employment or casual and temporary work can also increase stress, and so, too, can lack of control over their work, a problem that more women than men face in the labour force. The resulting stress can have both mental and physiological consequences, including increased blood pressure and stress hormone response (Fox et al., 1993; Theorell et al., 1993). Women's jobs also frequently involve physical risks, although such risks are often cumulative, appearing over a long period rather than resulting from a sudden, obvious injury. Messing's (1998) research on teachers, for instance, shows that women who work for years with young children commonly suffer from severe back problems resulting from their work. In addition, violence, sexual harassment, and bullying are far too common, especially for women employed in jobs traditionally dominated by men. The hazards women face in their other job at home, caring for children, the elderly, and houses, tend to be particularly invisible, hidden in the household away from public scrutiny (Rosenberg, 1990). And women who are dependent on males for support may be especially vulnerable to violence at home that they may find more difficult to resist when they have no income of their own.

In sum, more women have higher education and more have paid employment as well as higher incomes than in the past. For some, this has meant better health. But persistent inequality, not only in comparison to men but also among women, is harmful to the health of many women. Higher education does not necessarily mean higher incomes nor does a white-collar job or staying at home necessarily mean safe work.

Health Services

Health services obviously have an impact on women's health, although they are not the only or even the main factor. It is not surprising, then, that 'the women's health movement has focused on three main issues: the healthcare delivery system, the development and analysis of the social determinants of health, and a commitment to increase the participation of women in all aspects of health care' (Boscoe et al., 2004, p. 8). These issues overlap and interpenetrate, with the social determinants as important within heath services as they are outside them.

Women fought hard in the nineteenth century to gain access to medical schools, and to maintain their place as midwives. While they did manage to enter medical schools before the turn of the century, quotas on female students were not lifted until the 1970s. Once women were able to compete for entry on the same basis as men, they began to flood into medical schools and now outnumber men. They were less successful in midwifery, and it is only now that the majority of Canadian jurisdictions have made midwifery legal and supported. The late nineteenth century was also the period when women fought to make nursing a respectable profession but it was not until nurses organized in unions that they gained decent wages and working conditions (Armstrong & Silas, 2009). Nevertheless, nursing remains a female-dominated profession, with more than nine out of ten nurses women. Debates continue about women's natural caring capacities and about whether this makes them more suitable than men to nursing (Nelson & Gordon, 2006). And issues still remain regarding access to employment in care, especially in relation to the recognition of foreign credentials. But health and social services now provide employment for nearly one in five women in the labour force (Armstrong et al., 2008).

Theory Link
See Chapter 15 for a discussion of nursing in the twenty-first century.

Today, four out of five people employed in health services are women, and women take the major responsibility for unpaid personal care (Grant et al., 2004). This does not necessarily mean that women run the show or that the system is responsive to women's needs, however. The women's movement has long been critical of the medical approach to care and of the way more and more aspects of women's lives have been defined as medical problems (Lorber, 2000; Moss & Dyck, 2003). Childbirth is one example of medicalization, as birth became increasingly treated as an illness to be medically managed rather than as a process often mainly requiring support. Mental health is another example, with women frequently defined as neurotic and treated with drugs when their main problem was the discrimination they faced in their daily lives or the attitudes of physicians (Smith & David, 1975). Women fought to put women's health in women's hands and to educate both male and female providers, who had been trained in the old ways, about women's health from women's perspective. They have enjoyed some success in reducing medical interventions, but there are still high rates of Caesarean births, and drugs are still too often used in ways that are harmful to women's health (Rochon Ford & Saibil, 2010).

The women's health movement was not only concerned with the medical establishment's emphasis on surgery and drugs, and its attitudes toward women. The movement was also concerned with the dichotomy assumed between minds and bodies and between being sick and being well. The mind/body distinction contributed to the dismissal of many problems as simply being in women's heads. At the same time, the distinction between sickness and health left many of those with chronic health issues and those with disabilities not only without the kinds of support they required but also excluded (Smith & Hutchinson, 2004). Assumptions about heterosexuality were also pervasive, leaving lesbian and other women who do not fit into this box fighting for appropriate care (Travers, 2009). And approaches that focus only on bodies or minds, outside their environments, are inadequate in restoring or promoting health and ignore the interconnections among the determinants of health. A woman without housing, for example, cannot easily follow doctor's orders on wound care.

Although practices within care remain open to criticism, it is clear that women as a group have benefited significantly from access to quality health services. As noted earlier, the introduction of a **public health-care system** without fees has been particularly important to women. It also meant more and better jobs for women. Women use health services more than men and are more likely than men to take their children to care, but women are less likely than men to have private health insurance or the money to pay for care in the absence of public care (Women and Health Care Reform, 2008). Moreover, medical advances have contributed to women's longevity and to women's quality of life. For example, women are more likely than men to suffer from the arthritis that ruins their hips and knees, so the methods for replacing hips and knees have been particularly important for them (Jackson et al., 2006).

However, women have not benefited equally from the health-care system. Immigrants and racialized women may find it difficult to access services because of language and cultural barriers that are too often combined with discriminatory practices (Bierman et al., 2010; Zazzera, 2007). Women with disabilities face not only physical and attitudinal barriers but financial and transportation ones as well (Ethno-Racial People with Disabilities

public health-care system
Refers to Canada's universal, publicly funded health-care system.

Coalition of Ontario and the Ontario Women's Health Network, 2008). They also feel they are 'perceived as a great drain because as women with disabilities, they take too much time from an already strained system' (p. 4). Similarly, elderly women, who make up the majority of those living in residential care, often experience less than adequate care.

Moreover, reforms over the last couple of decades have also been detrimental to women's health in a number of ways (Armstrong et al., 2002). The move throughout the high-income countries to shorter patient stays in hospitals, to outpatient services, and to the closure of many long-term care facilities has meant a significant increase in women's unpaid care work (Morris, 2004). People are sent home quicker and sicker or not admitted at all, leaving the care primarily to women, even if they have paid jobs as well. It is the women with the least income who are the most likely to provide the paid care because they cannot afford to pay for supports (Guberman, 1999). Equally important, the patients who are sent home alone and without the necessary care are most likely to be women. The costs of care are also shifted in the process, given that the Canada Health Act—the federal legislation that sets out the principles on which public health-care services are based—only requires that hospital and doctor care be provided without fees. Women are disproportionately affected because they are less likely than men to have private health insurance or high incomes to cover payments. The resulting stress and physical demands can be harmful to women's health.

Within paid services, work has been transformed in ways that undermine the health of those employed in health care (Armstronget al., 2008). The adoption of managerial practices taken from the for-profit sector has meant work speedup and loss of control for many of the women who provide paid care. According to Statistics Canada, those in health services are the most likely to be absent from work for illness or injury (Perspectives on Labour and Income, 2009, Table 4), and these rates have been rising along with reforms. Infection rates among patients have also been rising, with part of the problem being the cutbacks in cleaning within care facilities, which is primarily done by women. The determinants of health approach tells us the work organization and clean environments are critical to health, but not enough attention is paid to these determinants within health services.

In sum, health services are largely care for women by women. Access to care improved dramatically with public health care, especially for poorer women, and so did women's health. However, the quality of care women receive remains an issue, and differences among women are if anything increasing as more care requires payment and as more work is sent home. As Bierman (2007) puts it, 'women and men differ not only in patterns of illness and disease risk factors, but also in their social contexts. Consequently, they have different experiences with health care, including differences in access, quality and health outcomes'.

Personal Health Practices and Coping Skills; Social Support Networks; Social and Physical Environments

Undoubtedly, personal health practices along with coping skills and support networks are important to women's health. But these personal practices, coping skills and support networks are shaped by context and culture—in other words, by the social and physical environments identified as other determinants of health. It is women who take primary responsibility for health promotion in the home and women who are primarily held responsible for health promotion in the home: 'Regardless of location, however, women tend to be the primary seekers of health information for their children and other family members, as well as for themselves' (Wathen & Harris, 2006, p. 1). And increasingly women are held responsible for their own care and health, as self-care is promoted at the same time as there are cutbacks in health services (Meadows et al., 2001). Women have long been centrally involved in keeping their families healthy and engaged, but their capacity to do so may be limited or expanded by their environments as well as by their access to education and resources.

In short, the barriers to health promotion and self-care among women extend far beyond individual will. Take diabetes as an example. Diabetes has reached epidemic proportions and is particularly common among First Nations women, with rates four times higher than among non–First Nations women and two-and-a-half times higher than in First Nations men (Dyck et al., 2010, p. 1). Diabetes prevention and management is now largely the responsibility of the patient, with the expectation that prescribed diet, exercise, monitoring, and injections will be carried out by the individual (Collins et al., 2009). Yet the development of diabetes is frequently beyond the control of these women: 'What is clear is that the rapid appearance of type 2 diabetes particularly among First Nations people and other indigenous and developing populations has been precipitated by environmental rather than genetic factors.' Once diagnosed, access to the kinds of food prescribed is beyond the reach of many First Nations women and so is the equipment required for easy monitoring.

Exercise provides another example. Fitness is increasingly stressed as important to health and self-care. However, research from 2009 shows that fitness levels among children and youth have declined since 1981, with more girls than boys needing improvement (Tremblay et al., 2010). Part of this decline can be attributed to more time with sedentary electronic equipment, but part can be attributed to the cutbacks in school physical fitness programs and after-school access to facilities or programs. The lack of exercise for fitness among adult women can be linked to their time-poverty and to their limited access to the kind of early learning that develops strategies for staying fit throughout life.

Social support can help promote self-care strategies and can help women cope with maintaining the health of their families. This support may be emotional or material; it may involve providing information or positive feedback. Women tend to provide material support more in terms of services such as caregiving than in terms of money. They are more frequently the ones who provide emotional support for their families and health information to their friends and relatives. Women also tend to have more extensive social networks than men, and such networks can contribute to everything from better mental health to lower rates of breast cancer (Fuhrer et al., 1999). Women are also active in their cultural communities, often providing the glue that keeps traditions and practices alive. However, providing support for others, without this being reciprocal, can undermine health. Equally important, social networks and cultural communities may exert pressures to conform or even express condemnation that may be harmful to health. A culture of violence within a community, for example, can be harmful to women. Moreover, many women lack significant social networks or the kinds of social supports that help them stay well and sustain them when they are not. But we need more research on these supports, their impact, and their differences. For instance, on the basis of their research on women with HIV/AIDS, Maggi & Daly (2006) conclude this:

> With the changing face of the HIV epidemic in Canada, we need to know more about what unique social and emotional supports women with HIV/AIDS need, given their gendered life experiences, their multiple roles (e.g., mother, partner, caregiver, worker, community participant), and what resources they are able to access, given their life circumstances. (p. 1)

Developing and maintaining social networks are one means women use to cope. These are far from the only ones, however. Women usually learn multiple skills from each other to cover a range of situations, from bleeding noses to thinning soup as a means of feeding large families on little money. Their strategies address not only their own illnesses and those of their families but also their environments. Research suggests that women are more likely than men to cope with pain by problem solving and by using affirmative statements (Unruh et al., 1999). Cohen (1991) has documented how women who come to Canada as live-in domestics cope with racism and exploitation by developing contacts outside these private households, by redefining the situation, and by using resources they find within the homes where they work. The women who take up this domestic work and leave their families behind are displaying a coping strategy in the very act of leaving their countries to find means of supporting their families back home. Acharya and Northcott (2007) talked to East Indian women immigrants to Canada who dealt with the pain of cultural shock and alienation by keeping busy. Homeless young women develop a variety of means coping, from camouflaging their bodies to exchanging sex for shelter as a way of coping with their lack of homes, while living on the street may itself be a way of coping with sexual assault at home (Oliver, 2010).

Not all women have had the opportunity to learn the kinds of coping strategies that are effective in particular situations, either because they have lacked teachers or because their skills were learned in another environment and do not work in their current one. And not all women have access to the kinds of resources that would help them cope. Some environments just make it too hard to cope. Workplaces that create the conditions of harassment and racism, for example, and that deny women the means to resist and support in altering these conditions can leave women without coping methods. Similarly, working conditions that speed up the work, make employment precarious, and allow workers little control, along with physical spaces or demands that strain the body can slowly undermine health in spite of women's strategies. When another job at home is added to the load, women's health can collapse. Not all women have the capacity to cope in some areas, due to illness, injury, or disability, often combined with a lack of resources and barriers that are difficult to overcome.

In short, it is hard to address issues of health-promoting activities for women and for those they care for without also addressing issues of environments. Women tend to build strong social networks and social supports, but these can be disrupted or prevented by social and physical environments. As Paltiel (1997) summed it up more than a decade ago, 'healthy public policy calls for action for reducing inequities, building supportive environments, and enhancing measures that favour coping and control'.

Conclusions

This chapter argues that bodies must be understood within a context characterized by inequities not only among women and men but also among women. That context—often termed the social and physical environments, employment, and income—structures inequities in ways that can be harmful to health and that are unequally harmful to women and men. Personal health practices and educational achievement matter, as do coping skills, social networks and genetic endowment. But until we address those inequities through public policy, we cannot expect women or men to live lives that are as healthy as possible.

Summary of Main Points

- There is no simple dichotomy between sex and gender, or between bodies and their social and physical environments. They are mutually constituted, with the result that there are significant physiological differences among women as well as differences in the way female bodies are interpreted and experienced. Moreover, bodies are constantly changing in relation to environments.
- The determinants of health overlap, are highly gendered, are influenced by relations of power, and are shaped by context.
- There are some patterns that can be identified for women as a group and for different groups of women. All these processes are shaped by the women's location, relations, and resources.
- All health issues are women's issues, and collective action on health issues can make a difference.

 Sociological Reflections on Women's Health

- Why is women's health a sociological issue?
- Can we understand women's health without sociology?
- What are the key components in a sociology of women's health?
- Does a feminist political economy approach help us understand women's health?

 Discussion Questions

1. What difference can education make to women's health?
2. Is poverty a women's health issue?
3. Can we talk about women's health without talking about men?
4. Can we analyze the health of women as a group or should we focus exclusively on particular groups of women?
5. Can a women's health movement stay focused on health services issues?
6. What happens to our understanding of women's health if we treat the determinants as independent variables?

Further Investigation

1. Are health-care reforms benefiting women as a group? Are they benefiting particular groups of women?
2. What are the conflicts, if any, between women as care providers and women as patients?

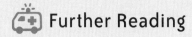

Further Reading

Abramson, B. (2009). Women and health: Taking the matter to heart. In P. Armstrong and J. Deadman (Eds.). *Women's health intersections of policy, research, and practice* (p. 53–60). Toronto, ON: Women's Press.

Armstrong, P., Armstrong, H., & Scott-Dixon, K. (2009). *Critical to care: The invisible women in health services.* Toronto, ON: University of Toronto Press.

Armstrong, P., Amaratunga, C., Bernier, J., Grant, K., Pederson, A., & Willson, K. (Eds.). (2002). *Exposing privatization: Women and health care reform.* Aurora, ON: Garamond.

Johnson, J. L., Greaves, L., & Repta, R. (2009, 6 May). Better science with sex and gender: Facilitating the use of a sex and gender-based analysis in health research. *International Journal of Health Equity.* doi: 10.1186/1475-9276-8-14

Messing, K. (1998). *One-eyed science. Occupational health and women workers.* Philadelphia, PA: Temple University Press.

Moss, P., & Dyck, I. (2003). *Women, body and illness.* Oxford, UK: Roman and Littlefield.

Moss, P., & Teghtsoonian, K. (Eds.). (2007). *Contesting illness processes and practices.* Toronto, ON: University of Toronto Press.

Rochon Ford, A., & Saibil, D. (Eds.). (2010). *Push to prescribe. Women and Canadian drug policy.* Toronto, ON: Women's Press.

Rosenberg, H. (1990). The home is the workplace: Hazards, stress and pollutants in the household. In M. Luxton & H. Rosenberg (Eds.). *Through the kitchen window.* Toronto, ON: Garamond.

Web Resources

Atlantic Centre of Excellence for Women's Health
www.acewh.dal.ca/

British Columbia Centre of Excellence for Women's Health
www.bccewh.bc.ca

Canadian Institutes of Health Research
www.cihr-irsc.gc.ca

Canadian Women's Health Network
www.cwhn.ca/en

National Network on Environments and Women's Health
www.nnewh.org

Prairie Women's Health Centre of Excellence
www.pwhce.ca

The Source: Women's Health Data Directory
www.womenshealthdata.ca/default_en.aspx

CHAPTER 6

Ethnicity and Health: Social and Cultural Factors

Jennie Hornosty

> 'I have to worry about feeding, clothing, and housing my children. I don't have time to think about AIDS.'
>
> — *African-Canadian woman in Toronto study (cited in Galabuzi, 2009)*

Overview

- What does the research evidence tell us about the health of Canada's ethnically diverse population?
- How important is ethnicity (or culture) in determining health outcomes for Canada's ethnically diverse and racialized population?
- Are social and economic inequalities in access to resources and gender more powerful determinants of health than ethnicity, or is it the migration and settlement experience that distinguishes the health profiles of immigrants?

This chapter examines the pattern of immigration in Canada, the current composition of ethnic groups today, and how these factors are related to health status and use of health services. The salience of culture or ethnicity as the sole factor in differential health outcomes is questioned, and the relevance of social determinants, such as poverty, unemployment, and social exclusion, are highlighted. Thus, ethnicity is examined in terms of its implications for social location rather than as a purely cultural phenomenon. Research evidence is used to support the argument that structural factors are more significant than (cultural) ethnicity per se. It is argued that the provision of health care in a culturally diverse society requires structural changes, especially changes in the structure of health-care services.

Key Terms

acculturation	healthy immigrant	refugees
biomedicine/	effect	social construction/
biomedical model	immigrants	constructionism
culturally competent	Medicare	social exclusion
health care	racialized groups	visible minority
ethnic group	racism/racist	

Introduction

The latest Canadian Census on Immigration and Citizenship reported that there are now over 200 ethnic origins in Canada (Statistics Canada, 2008c). (Statistics Canada notes that this list included Canada's Aboriginal peoples.) This is a dramatic contrast from the turn of the twentieth century, when the census recorded about 25 different **ethnic groups** in this country. It has been estimated that since 1990 Canada has received on average 200 000 **immigrants** per year, proportionately more than any other country. It is not surprising, therefore, that there has been a growing interest in issues relating to the health and illness of Canada's ethnic groups and immigrant population. Understanding the health patterns and behaviour of the immigrant community is important since immigrants constitute a large proportion of the population (Pérez, 2002). Immigrants, especially those who are first generation, are sometimes viewed as people with problems because they do not fit neatly into the culture and structure of the Canadian health-care system. The challenge for health-care service providers is to address the needs of this ethnically diverse group of peoples, whose understandings of health and illness may be different from those of the once dominant Anglo majority.

The Social and Cultural Construction of Health and Illness

Health and *illness* are terms that we typically take for granted. We know what it means to be healthy, and we know when someone is ill. We tend to assume that these are objective facts: states of the body and the mind that can be measured against what is viewed as normal. Sociologists and anthropologists, however, have shown us that health and illness are **social constructions**; they are not objectively defined. Definitions of *health* and *illness*, and understandings of appropriate health care vary over time and across cultures. For example, in Australia during the 1950s and 1960s, many childhood diseases, such as measles, were defined as normal. Thus, children were encouraged to interact with others who had the virus so that they would be exposed to and get the measles. However, since the development of new medical knowledge—in this case, a vaccine—measles is viewed as a serious illness and children are encouraged to avoid exposure to the virus (Manderson & Reid, 1994).

Furthermore, in any society, some members have more power than others to define health and illness. Some people are the custodians of so-called legitimate medical knowledge, while other members of society, who do not have specialist knowledge, are encouraged to define health and illness in the same ways as those who are considered experts. In Canadian society, the dominant cultural model of health and illness is that of **biomedicine**, and the experts are health professionals, such as doctors. The structure of the health-care system (for example, hospitals and physicians' private practice) reflects the dominance of this model; it locates these medical 'experts' in positions of power. In other societies, however, there may be different models, as is the case for Aboriginal Canadians, who take a more holistic approach to health and illness.

>
> **Theory Link**
> See Chapter 7 for a discussion of Aboriginal Peoples and health.

ethnic group

A group of people who not only share an ethnic background but also interact with each other on the basis of their shared ethnicity.

immigrants

First-generation immigrants are those who were born outside of Canada. Second generation refers to those who are Canadian-born and have at least one parent who was born outside Canada. Third generation or more are the offspring of Canadian-born parents (Statistics Canada, 2003).

social construction/ constructionism

Refers to the socially created characteristics of human life based on the idea that people actively construct reality, meaning it is neither natural nor inevitable. Therefore, notions of normality/ abnormality, right/wrong, and health/illness are subjective human creations that should not be taken for granted.

biomedicine/ biomedical model

The conventional approach to medicine in Western societies, based on the diagnosis and explanation of illness as a malfunction of the body's biological mechanisms. This approach underpins most health professions and health services, which focus on treating individuals, and generally ignores the social origins of illness and its prevention.

Different cultures have different understandings of health and illness, and people within societies are differentially located with respect to access to expert knowledge in this area. Their understanding and experience could affect both their willingness to seek medical attention as well as their ability to access medical services. Cultural understandings and the structure of health care both play important parts in determining how health and illness are approached by different groups of people.

Ethnic Diversity in Canada

Canada today is a multicultural society with a diversity of ethnic groups. Historically, it has been and continues to be shaped by different waves of immigrants to this land. Canada accepts proportionately more immigrants and refugees than any other country (Pérez, 2002). In 2006, for example, nearly one in five (19.8 per cent) of those living in Canada were foreign-born, the highest proportion in 75 years. A large number of these people are recent immigrants, having come to Canada between January 1, 2001 and May 16, 2006. These newcomers made up 17.9 per cent of the total foreign-born population (The Daily, 2007d).

The composition of immigrants has changed significantly over the years. At the beginning of the twentieth century, the majority of immigrants came from the United Kingdom or the United States. However, by the 1910s and 1920s there were increased numbers from European countries, such as Russia, Ukraine, Hungary, and Italy. Immigration from Asia was low, and there is evidence that Canada's immigration policy had **racist** undertones. For example, although Chinese immigrant workers had played an import role in the building of the TransCanada Railway, a so-called head tax was first imposed in 1885 as a way of regulating future Chinese immigration. This tax required every Chinese person entering Canada to pay a large sum of money, a policy that made it virtually impossible for Chinese men to bring brides or wives to Canada (Boyd & Vickers, 2009). In 1923, the federal Parliament passed the Chinese Immigration Act, also known as the Chinese Exclusion Act, which restricted virtually all immigration from China to Canada: only diplomats, children born in Canada, merchants, and students would be permitted. This act effectively stopped immigration to Canada between 1923 and 1947 (the year it was repealed).

In the 1920s, 1930s, and 1940s, there was increased immigration from European and Eastern European countries. However, when WWII was declared, Canada prohibited immigration from countries with which Canada was at war. These barriers also meant that many Jewish refugees attempting to leave the chaos and persecution in Europe were turned away. Another example of racist policy in Canada was the war-related measures that forced Japanese Canadians who were living within a 100-mile area of British Columbia's coastline to relocate to detention-style camps, even though most were native-born or naturalized Canadians (Boyd & Vickers, 2009). Although the post-war era saw an immigration boom, immigration policies at the time basically precluded certain groups of people from coming to Canada. The Immigration Act of 1952 indicated national origin as a possible ground for exclusion. Admissible persons were those who were born or had citizenship in the United Kingdom, Australia, New Zealand, the Union of South Africa, the United States, and selected European countries (Boyd & Vickers, 2009).

racism/racist

Racism refers to a set of false beliefs that one racial group is naturally superior to another group based on biological differences. It perpetuates notions of cultural superiority and inferiority and is one basis for social exclusion and discriminatory practices.

A change came in 1967 when immigration regulations replaced national origin as a criterion with an assigned points system based on an applicant's age, education, language skills, and economic characteristics. The change also allowed immigrants to sponsor relatives to immigrate to Canada. In 1978 a new Immigration Act incorporated humanitarian grounds as a basis for admission. The most recent legislation introduced in June 2002, the Immigration and Refugee Protection Act, retains the following three criteria for admission: labour market considerations, family reunification, or humanitarian grounds (Boyd & Vickers, 2009, p. 247).

Changes in immigration policies over the past century have shaped the ethno-cultural composition of Canada. The most dramatic difference in the face of Canada between the first two-thirds of the twentieth century and the Canada of today is the large proportion of immigrants from non-European countries. In 2006, the largest number of recent immigrants (those who came since 2001) were born in Asia (including the Middle East); they comprised 58.3 per cent of newcomers. By contrast, only 12.7 per cent of the recent immigrants in the 1971 period were born in Asia. The situation was reversed in the case of European immigrants: of those who came to Canada during the 2001–2006 period, only 16.1 per cent were born in Europe, whereas in 1971, Europeans accounted for 61.6 per cent of newcomers (The Daily, 2007d). Between 2001 and 2006, Canada's **visible minority** population increased by 27.2 per cent, a situation largely due to the high proportion of recent immigrants who belonged to visible minorities: 75.0 per cent of those who arrived since 2001 were from racialized groups. See Figure 6.1, which illustrates the major visible

visible minorities

A term used by Statistics Canada and other government bodies 'to refer to persons, other than Aboriginal peoples, who are non-Caucasian in race or non-white in colour', as defined by the Employment Equity Act.

in thousands

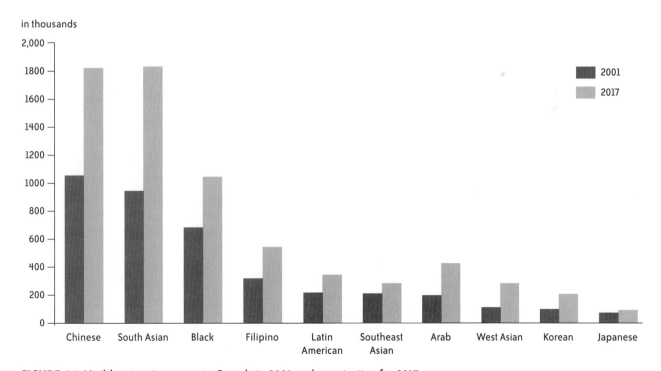

FIGURE 6.1 Visible minority groups in Canada in 2001 and a projection for 2017

Source: Statistics Canada. (Website). Canadian Demographics at a Glance. Available from www.statcan.gc.ca/pub/91-003-x/91-003-x2007001-eng. pdf, 2008, p. 33.

minority groups in Canada in 2001 and projects these numbers to 2017 if current patterns of immigration continue.

In 2006, first-generation Canadians accounted for 23.9 per cent of the population 15 years and older. Of these, nearly one-quarter reported East and Southeast Asian origins: the most common were Chinese, East Indian, Filipino, and Vietnamese, all of whom are **racialized groups**. People of European origin made up just over one-third of the first generation: the leading groups were Italian, German, Polish, and Portuguese (Statistics Canada, 2008c). Immigrants are unevenly distributed throughout the country but tend to concentrate in areas with major urban centres. In 2001, for example, 62 per cent of all Canadians of South Asian origin made Ontario their home, while another 22 per cent lived in British Columbia. At the same time, 8 per cent lived in Alberta and 6 per cent lived in Quebec (The Daily, 2007d). The 2006 census also indicated that 20 per cent of the population of Canada were allophones, that is, people whose mother tongue is neither English nor French. It is understandable that such ethno-cultural diversity of Canada's population poses a variety of challenges in providing equitable health services to all Canadians.

> **racialized groups**
> The term preferred by those who work with immigrants and refugees when talking about visible minorities. The term captures the fact that certain groups are treated as inferior by the dominant group.

How Are Ethnicity and Health Related?

In comparison to information available from Australia and the United States, there is relatively little analysis on the relationship between ethnicity and health in Canada. This may be due in part to the greater racial and ethnic homogeneity throughout much of Canada's history. However, as we see from the preceding discussion, this homogeneity is rapidly changing. In response to the rapid influx of new immigrants, a number of Canadian researchers have looked at whether the health of immigrants is different from those who were born in Canada. The Canadian government is also interested in knowing more about immigrants' health as evidenced in two major reports recently commissioned by Health Canada (see Health Canada, 1999a; Hyman, 2001). The major focus of both reports was to identify the main findings of immigration health research, to identify gaps in the research, and to consider the implications of the research for policy-makers. Both studies indicate that there are still many gaps in our understanding of whether the health of immigrants differs from that of the Canadian-born population and, if so, why this may be the case.

The 'Healthy Immigrant Effect'

There is a belief among some Canadians that immigrants are not healthy and that they overutilize health-care services. Research, however, suggests that this is not the case (Health Canada, 1999a; Hyman, 2001). In fact, it has been well documented that when immigrants first arrive in Canada they are in better health than native-born Canadians, and they also have lower mortality rates (Beiser, 2005; Hyman, 2004; Newbold, 2005; Newbold & Danforth, 2003; Ng et al., 2005a,b). They are, moreover, less likely to have chronic conditions or disabilities and are more likely to rate their health as good, very good, or excellent. However, once they have lived in the country for a number of years, their health status declines and shows patterns that are similar to those of native-born Canadians or immigrants who have been in Canada for a period longer than 10 years.

This health advantage that newly arrived immigrants appear to have is referred to as the **healthy immigrant effect**. Similar findings have been observed in other countries, such as the United States and Australia (Hyman, 2001, p. 10).

A couple of possible reasons have been given for the healthy immigrant effect. One explanation might be that the immigration process is such that it selects what are perceived as the best immigrants on the basis of education, language ability, job skills, and health and screens out those people who have serious health problems (Ali et al., 2004; Hyman, 2001). Canada's Immigration and Refugee Protection Act states that an applicant should be rejected if he or she 'is likely to be a danger to public health' or if it is expected that she or he would 'cause excessive demand on health and social services' (cited in Beiser, 2005, p. s31). Another possible reason might be self-selection. That is, people who choose to emigrate are in better health and as a result are able and motivated to move, excluding those who are sick.

With the exception of tuberculosis and some groups' tendency toward diabetes, recent immigrants appear to be less like likely to suffer from chronic illnesses and disability. They have a longer life expectancy and more years of life free from disability. However, studies have also shown that there is a gradient of worsening health, that is, that the health advantage new immigrants enjoy appears to deteriorate the longer they reside in the host country, sometimes as soon as five to ten years after arrival (Ali et al., 2004; Newbold, 2009). Using the information from the 2000/01 Canadian Community Health Survey, Pérez (2002) also found that the rate of chronic conditions among immigrants were significantly lower than that observed for the Canadian-born population (Ali et al., 2004). The pattern was similar for both men and women although women had a higher prevalence of chronic conditions than men. However, Pérez did not find a correlation between length of time in Canada and increased risk for specific chronic conditions, such as diabetes, high blood pressure, and heart disease in women and cancer in men when factors such as age, education, and household income were taken into account. For example, immigrant men who had lived in Canada for 20–29 years had lower odds of being diagnosed with cancer; with respect to heart disease, women showed no advantage regardless of when they immigrated. Similarly, Karen Kobayashi et al. (2008) found that health advantages of certain ethno-cultural groups, such as the Chinese and South Asians, regardless of immigrant status, can best be attributed to differences in social, structural, and lifestyle environments. They conclude that 'health differences between ethnic foreign-born and [Canadian-born persons who share the same ethnocultural origin] generally converge after controlling for sociodemographic, socioeconomic status (SES), and lifestyle factors' (p. 129).

In a 2005 study of recent immigrants to Ontario that was published in the *Canadian Medical Association Journal*, Creatore et al. (2010) found that after controlling for factors such as age, level of education, time since arrival, immigration category, and level of income, the risk of diabetes among immigrants from South Asia was triple that of immigrants from Western Europe and North American origin. It appears from their study that beyond factors such as age and obesity, risk for diabetes is not evenly distributed across ethnic groups. However, similar to other studies that have shown that the health of immigrants deteriorates after their arrival, Creatore et al. found that the risk for diabetes increased the longer immigrants lived in Canada. Using longitudinal data collected over the period 1994/95 to 2002/03, Ng et al. (2005a) found that based on self-reports of health

healthy immigrant effect

Refers to the finding that newly arrived immigrants appear to have a health advantage but after a period of time their health status tends to converge toward that of the host population.

status, immigrants' health did deteriorate but that this deterioration applied only to immigrants from non-European origins, especially those who had arrived since the mid-1980s. Recent non-European immigrants were twice as likely as the Canadian-born population to report a deterioration in their health. Ng et al. suggest that a possible explanation for this is that immigrants of European origin are more likely to share a similar culture to people born in Canada and therefore may encounter fewer social, economic, and lifestyle barriers in comparison to immigrants from non-European countries (see Figure 6.2).

Decline in Immigrant Health Post-Immigration

So how might we explain the different findings that suggest immigrant health deteriorates after arrival? A possible explanation is that the longer immigrants live in their new country the more likely they are to take on the health behaviours and values of the host country. The process by which this is believed to occur is called **acculturation**. Acculturation is a multidimensional process by which the ideas, values, and behaviours of immigrants' place of origin are replaced by those in the new culture (Hyman, 2001). One suggestion then as to why healthy immigrants lose their health advantage over time is because their lifestyle behaviours begin to more closely resemble the behaviours of Canadians in general. To determine whether changes in lifestyle did explain differences in immigrant health, Pérez

acculturation

A process by which newcomers to a country take on the values and behaviours of their host country.

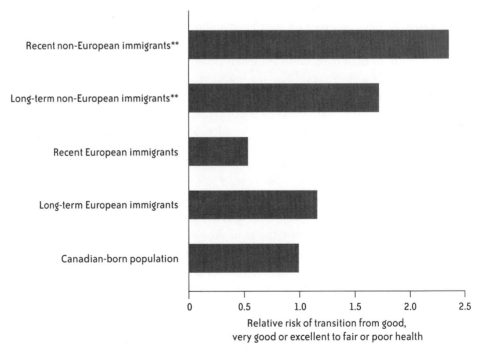

FIGURE 6.2 Comparison of self-reported health status for European immigrants and non-European immigrants

Source: Ng, et al. (2005). Dynamics of immigrants' health in Canada: Evidence from the National Population Health Survey. In Statistics Canada, *Healthy today, healthy tomorrow? Findings from the National Population Health Survey.* Available from www.statcan.gc.ca/pub/82-618-m/2005002/pdf/4193621-eng.pdf

**Significantly different from estimate for Canadian-born (p < 0.01)

looked at behaviour patterns, such as smoking, excess drinking, and eating fatty foods. While immigrants' patterns of behaviour varied with the length of time in Canada, they did not necessarily become more like Canadians in this respect. He concluded that health behaviours did not explain differences in health between immigrant groups and those born in Canada. Age is another possible variable that might explain differences. Recent immigrants tend to be younger than the Canadian population as a whole. As a result they would experience fewer health problems, such as diabetes, obesity, cardiovascular and coronary disease, and respiratory problems, which tend to be disproportionately found among aging populations. However, as Creatore et al. (2010) found in their research, the risk for diabetes was higher among some ethnic groups even after controlling for age. The changing face of immigration may be another explanation (Beiser, 2005). It is also conceivable that the healthiest immigrants migrate again to another country and those who remain were less healthy when they first arrived. Unlike the study conducted by Ng et al. (2005a), a limitation of the previously mentioned studies is that the data was not longitudinal (that is, researchers did not follow the same cohort over time).

The different material conditions of immigrant groups have major implications for health. Immigrants, for example, are more likely to experience stressors such as unemployment, poverty, and lack of access to services, all of which adversely affect health as immigrants begin the resettlement process. For example, they are much more likely than native-born Canadians to live in poverty, especially during their first 10 years, which increases their likelihood of exposure to risk factors for various diseases and compromises their access to treatment (Beiser, 2005). Using data from the 2000/2001 Canadian Community Health Survey, Karen Kobayashi et al. (2008) concluded that the seeming health advantage of immigrants when they first arrive can be best explained by social structural and lifestyle environments. After periods of unemployment, limited income, inadequate housing, and limited social support, immigrants' health begins to decline: '[p]oor social and economic conditions and inequalities in access to resources and services affect an individual or group's health and well-being' (Galabuzi, 2009, p. 252).

Immigrants are not a homogeneous group. Their reasons for coming to Canada, their country of origin, the skills they bring are all factors that will shape their experience shortly after arrival, affecting the sorts of jobs they get, how much they earn, where they live, what social supports they may have, etc. Certain subgroups are more likely to experience socio-economic disadvantages and the health problems associated with these disadvantages (Hyman, 2001). For example, **refugees**, women, and members of racialized groups are more likely to have no job security, to be poor, and to experience discrimination and social exclusion.

Refugees and Health

The number of refugees entering Canada in a given year varies. In 2001 close to 45 000 refugees entered the country, whereas in 2005 fewer than 20 000 made Canada their home (Canadian Council for Refugees, 2007). Refugees generally have greater health needs than other immigrants, particularly related to emotional and mental health (Newbold, 2009). They are more likely to have very high rates of unemployment and welfare dependency compared with those born in Canada and with other immigrants. This is largely a result of the fact that they arrive in Canada with few, if any, economic resources or may lack the documentation and/or English language skills that are needed to find skilled

refugees

Individuals who flee their country of origin because of a fear of persecution for reasons of race, religion, political opinion, nationality, or membership in a particular social group.

employment. They may come from countries where health services are inadequate and living conditions are poorer. Thus, refugees are 'at increased risk from infectious diseases . . . viral hepatitis, parasitic diseases . . . dental disease, vitamin D and other nutritional deficiencies, and chronic diseases' (Biggs & Skull, 2003, p. 65).

The refugee experience and the resettlement process is often traumatic; a loss of personal and cultural identity, depression, post-traumatic stress disorder, developmental problems in children, and family violence are commonly identified as health issues (Fowler, 1998). Refugees often are without a network of friends or family, which can increase feelings of isolation and loneliness as well as make it more difficult to find the necessary health services and appropriate health care. A welcoming host community could play an important role in offsetting the negative emotional impact of adapting to a new country (Fowler, 1998).

Racialized Groups and Health

There are substantial differences within ethno-racial groups. Many people from visible minority groups have managerial and professional jobs and high incomes, and live in expensive homes. However, national data show that racialized people are two or three times more likely to be poor than other Canadians (Galabuzi, 2009, p. 257). They are also more likely to experience disproportionate levels of poverty, homelessness, inadequate housing and discrimination (Access Alliance, 2005). In Ontario, for example, visible minority children make up 43 per cent of children living in poverty, even though visible minority children comprise only 23 per cent of children in Ontario (Access Alliance, 2005). These structural inequalities have serious health implications (Raphael, 2009c), and we know that there is a significant link between poverty and a range of health behaviours (Auger & Alix, 2009; Galabuzi, 2009; Raphael, 2002). It has been shown that Canadians who live in the poorest 20 per cent of urban neighbourhoods are much more likely to die from cardiovascular disease, cancer, diabetes, and respiratory diseases (cited in Access Alliance, 2005). Those living in poverty also lack basic needs, such as decent housing and healthy foods, and are more likely to be exposed to health-threatening environmental conditions (Raphael, 2002). Furthermore, children who live in poverty are more likely to have higher rater of depression, anxiety, and antisocial behaviours (Samaan, 2000, cited in Access Alliance, 2007).

Theory Link
See Chapter 4 for a further discussion of the relationship between socio-economic factors as determinants of health.

social exclusion

A process whereby some groups in society are denied access to material and social resources, thereby excluding their full participation in society. It produces inequality in outcomes.

Approximately two-thirds of the racialized community is made up of immigrants (Galabuzi, 2009). Members of these groups are more likely to be unemployed, to work in lower skill jobs at low pay, and may have disproportional numbers of one-parent families (Ornstein, 2006). These inequalities in material conditions are the result of **social exclusion** and affect the health and well-being of individuals and groups: 'Groups experiencing some form of social exclusion tend to sustain higher health risks and lower health status' (Galabuzi, 2009, p. 252). Poor jobs and working conditions can result in more workplace injuries, harassment, and exposure to environmental hazards such as toxic substances. These groups are also subject to discrimination and racism, which are often at the root of social exclusion. Racism, which perpetuates notions of cultural superiority and inferiority, has been identified as a major contributor to health problems as well as a barrier to accessing and benefiting from health services (Access Alliance, 2005; 2007). And experiences of racism can lead to depression, psychological distress, hypertension, and high blood pressure. Racism, like poverty, income inequality, and unemployment, is therefore a significant social determinant of health.

Immigrant and Refugee Women and Health

The health status of immigrant women in Canada has not been well studied, although they comprise another sub-group that is most likely to experience socio-economic disadvantages and associated health problems. The Canadian Task Force (1988), for example, found more mental health problems among immigrant and refugee women. Another study found a high rate of depression among women in four ethnic groups, and research on child bearing and mental health found high rates of postpartum depression among immigrant women. The psychiatric symptoms that refugee women experience have been attributed to multiple traumas, such as rape, and is an important health issue (Hyman, 2001). Psychiatric illness among immigrant women may also be attributed to high levels of isolation from the receiving society (Cox, 1989), which can lead to loneliness, mental stress, and depression. Newly arrived immigrant women may also be separated from their traditional support networks, making it more difficult to get information about health services.

Immigrant and refugee women are overrepresented in contingent employment and low-wage jobs, often have little or no job security, and experience unsafe work conditions (Ontario Council of Agencies Serving Immigrants, 2005). Although family violence cuts across all social classes and ethnic groups, Brownridge and Halli (2002) found that immigrant women to Canada from developing countries experienced the highest prevalence of violence. Moreover, immigrant women are more likely to face special problems and have fewer alternatives to leave abusive relationships. A study of South Asian immigrant women in Toronto found that the main reasons women gave for delayed help-seeking from professionals were 'social stigma, rigid gender roles, marriage obligations, expected silence, loss of social support after migration and limited knowledge about available resources and myths about partner abuse' (Ahmad et al., 2009, p. 613). Social stigma was related to concerns that their disclosure would lead to disrespect for the family and parents. They also spoke of the cultural assumptions that so-called real South Asian women would remain silent about their situation, would maintain their marital obligations, and would remain subordinate to their husbands. Many immigrant women are also isolated because of limited language skills, lack of support networks, and economic dependence on their spouses, and may be fearful that speaking out will lead to deportation. They turn for help only after experiencing pronounced mental and physical health problems (Ahmed et al., 2009).

Culture and Health

Culture is an important variable to consider when looking at health issues (Lai, 2004). Cultural beliefs and values play an important role in an individual's understanding of health and illness. These beliefs influence how symptoms are recognized and what they are attributed to (Anderson et al., 2003). Therefore, in part illness must be viewed in a context shaped by culturally defined parameters of illness recognition and behaviour (Murray & Chen, 1992). The Vietnamese, for example, believe that physical and emotional illness is caused by an imbalance in the forces of *am* and *duong* (similar to the Chinese yin and yang). One cause of mental illness is believed to be possession by ancestral spirits who have been offended and have become angry (Lien, 1992). Among Latin Americans, the word *susto* refers to illnesses associated with unexpected experiences of fright that produce symptoms such as loss of appetite, nervousness, and depression. According to folklore, *susto* is caused by 'the separation of the spiritual element from the physiological element of the person' (Allotey, 1998, p. 70; Holloway, 1994). In a classic study in the United States on the effects of culture on pain, Zborowski found that pain and the significance attributed to pain symptoms varied by culture and ethnicity (cited in Anderson et al., 2003, p. 69). Different ethnic groups may also have different expectations of what constitutes appropriate treatment, which will, in part, reflect different cultural understandings of the causes of health and illness. For example, in the postpartum (following birth) period, a Vietnamese mother must not leave the house for 30–40 days, must not speak loudly, must not clean her teeth with a toothbrush, must not read or strain her eyes, and must not wash her hair or have a bath for at least a week, and in some cases a month (Tran, 1994).

The above studies indicate that cultural beliefs and experiences influence how symptoms are identified, what their causes and prevention are, and what are considered appropriate treatments. Such beliefs and experiences may influence attitudes toward health care and health-care-seeking behaviours, when health services are sought, and a willingness to report certain health problems. In a qualitative study of perceptions of health by a diverse group of immigrant women in Prince Edward Island, MacKinnon and Howard (2010) found that the women generally did not see a physician as part of their personal health practices, except in cases of serious illness. Rather, for routine illnesses they relied on traditional or herbal remedies. One woman described how in her country of origin one dealt with headaches in the following way: 'When I have a headache, my mom go out in garden and just pick some leaves and put on my head' (MacKinnon & Howard, 2010, p. 202).

Using a random sample of immigrant ethnocultural groups, Kirmayer et al. (2007) found that in comparison to anglophone- and francophone-Canadian born, Vietnamese, Caribbean, and Filipino immigrants were significantly less likely to use primary-care mental-health services or to seek out specialty mental health care. The immigrant groups were more likely to seek sources of help in their community, including from religious leaders or traditional healers, or to rely on traditional or alternative medicine at home. But according to Kirmayer et al., the lower rates of mental health service use among the immigrant groups could not be attributed simply to differences in levels of distress or to their use of alternative sources of help. This difference may be explained in part by cultural differences. In some cultures, for example, there is a great deal of stigma attached to mental health problems; such problems are understood as personal ones that are best dealt with alone or through religious or community institutions. The significance of different cultural understandings of mental health is well illustrated by some of the women that MacKinnon and Howard interviewed (2010). One woman stated that

'It [mental health issue] is my problem, I would solve it. Best to fight that by yourself or with the help of family, friends or with herbal medicines.' (MacKinnon & Howard, p. 202)

Another woman explained it this way:

'. . . if we have problem, in our culture they say you only supposed to talk to family, like you shouldn't talk outside the family because you always want the family looks good. So, most . . . people is pretty shy to talk about their personal life, even [if] have problem.' (MacKinnon & Howard, p. 202)

In another qualitative study, Whitley et al. (2006) identified three significant factors that helped to explain the reluctance of immigrants to use mental health services. The overwhelming majority perceived doctors as being too eager to write prescriptions for everything; immigrants did not have faith in pharmaceutical medications as a method for dealing with many health issues. Immigrants were also turned off by what they perceived as the lack of time and the dismissive attitude on the part of doctors. The third factor that the authors identified was immigrants' belief in the curative power of nonmedical interventions, including God and traditional folk medicine and healers.

In a cross-cultural, comparative study of seven cultural groups in Canada, Kopec et al. (2001) found that there were substantial differences between the groups in their reporting of pain, emotional function, and cognitive function, which could not be explained by differences in socio-economic status and self-reported chronic conditions. They concluded that cultural factors such as different conceptions of health and cultural differences in the meaning and reporting of illness may play a significant role in explaining some of the observed differences. In another study that explored the intersections of ethnicity, gender, age, and immigrant status as determinants of the health status of Canadians, Karen Kobayashi (2003) found that there are significant differences in health status and health-care utilization among immigrant groups. She concluded that cultural characteristics along with socio-structural factors are salient predictors of population health. According to Kobayashi, the key emergent issue with regard to adults' health status is 'the clash between the ethno-cultural values and beliefs of foreign-born . . . and the health care system' (p. 10).

We have seen from the above studies that an adequate understanding of the ethnic patterning of health and illness must take into account the cultural factors influencing the ways in which different ethnic groups understand, experience, and manage illness. However, ethnic groups are not homogeneous, unified wholes that speak with one narrative voice; moreover, culture is not static but changes over time (Este, 2007). New immigrants to Canada will likely retain some parts of their culture of origin, but over time they will begin to embrace certain aspects of Canadian culture, thus forging a new culture that will evolve, develop, and change over time (Kobayashi, 2003, p. 95). To meet the health needs of immigrant groups, this shifting and fluid dimension of culture must be kept in mind. As well, one must be careful not to equate culture with minority ethnicity. The dominant anglo-Canadian view that scientifically based Western medicine is superior has also been influenced by culture.

Culture is only one of many factors that have an impact on the health of individuals and social groups. Ethnic groups differ not only in terms of culture but also, and perhaps more importantly, in terms of their social location—that is, in terms of their location in the structure of social inequality. Structural factors such as class, education, racialization, occupation, and access to goods and services also have a significant impact on health outcomes. To more fully understand the relationship between ethnicity and health, it is necessary to examine the interaction of all these social determinants.

How To Provide Culturally Competent Health Care

As we discussed earlier, Canada is one of the most ethnically diverse countries in the world. Each wave of immigration has both changed and increased the country's ethno-cultural diversity. The challenge of multiculturalism for health-care providers is to ensure that health resources and services are equitable for all Canadians, regardless of cultural characteristics, including ethnic origin, immigrant status, or charter language ability (Kobayashi, 2003). It has been suggested that racial and ethnic health disparities can be reduced in part by the provision of **culturally competent health care** (Anderson et al., 2003). *Cultural competency* has been defined as 'the ability to conduct professional work in a way that is consistent with the expectations which members of distinctive cultures regard as appropriate among themselves' (cited in Este, 2007, p. 95).

culturally competent health care

Delivery of health-care services in a way that recognizes the cultural beliefs and needs of those they serve.

One component of culture competency is the ability to deliver health services in the language of those needing the care. Linguistic and communication barriers hinder equitable access to health care, especially for people who do not speak one of Canada's official languages fluently (Alliance Access, 2005). In their study of first-generation immigrant groups in Montreal, Leduc and Proulx (2004) found that language and ethnic origin were two of the main criteria used in choosing health-care providers. These families felt that the ability to speak the same language allowed them to better explain their illnesses and concerns. Not being able to communicate their health needs or not fully understanding the instructions given to them added additional tension to new immigrant families who were already under considerable stress. Similarly, nearly all of the immigrant women in MacKinnon and Howard's study (2009) identified language as a major barrier affecting their health. The following comments made by the women illustrate this clearly:

> Language stresses out. Not being able to communicate.
>
> [Language] big problem, because you can't say anything you want to say.
>
> When you know the language is easy to do anything fast.
>
> You want to talk to somebody, just to talk. Without language you can't, you feel frustrated. (MacKinnon & Howard, p. 204)

Linguistic barriers also occur when trained professional interpreters are unavailable or if health information is not translated in multiple languages (Access Alliance, 2005). Clear communication between patient and health-care worker is crucial in the delivery of quality health care (Bischoff et al., 2003). Interpreters are necessary in order to make appropriate diagnoses and to comply with treatment regimes. For this to occur, however, it is necessary to employ professionally trained interpreters who 'have a good grasp of medical technology' (National Health Strategy, 1993b, p. 82). When immigrants lack the necessary language skills they find it difficult to schedule appointments, to describe their problems, or to understand verbal and written instructions, all of which compromise the quality of care. An inability to communicate also undermines the faith a patient has in the care received and decreases the likelihood of returning for further help (Anderson et al., 2003; Leduc & Proulx, 2004).

Another aspect of cultural competency is the need to provide services that are seen as culturally appropriate. Arabic women, for example, tend to have a strong cultural preference for antenatal care provided by women, but this is often unavailable (Bennett & Shearman, 1989). The gender of health professionals is also important for Sri Lankan, Filipina, and Vietnamese women, especially for gynecological services (Leduc & Proulx, 2004). Half of the immigrant women in MacKinnon and Howard's study similarly expressed preference for a female doctor, especially in situations where they had to remove their clothing. One woman stated it bluntly: 'If there is no female doctor, I would not get a gynecological exam' (MacKinnon & Howard, 2009, p. 205). Research has highlighted the need for hospitals to take account of different cultural practices in relation to childbirth and postpartum confinement (Allotey et al., 2001; Manderson & Mathews, 1981; Rice, 1994; Rice et al., 1994).

A Euro-centric orientation in services, cultural insensitivity, discrimination, and a lack of health-care providers from the same cultural background have been identified as significant barriers for ethnic groups (Access Alliance, 2005; Anderson et al., 2003; Hyman, 2001):

> They were coming from a completely different culture . . . They didn't understand my culture and it didn't seem like they made an effort to either. It was more just like, 'Well, it shouldn't be that way' and it's almost like my own culture was being put down. (Women's Health in Women's Hands Community Health Centre, 2003, p. 28)

For many ethnic minorities, especially racialized groups, perceptions that health professionals may not understand their culture or may be prejudiced against it had an impact on their use and selection of health-care services (Access Alliance, 2005; Egan & Gardner, 1999; Hyman, 2001; Women's Health in Women's Hands Community Health Centre, 2003). In a participatory action study with young 'women of colour' in the Toronto area, the researchers found that one in five women reported that they had experienced racism when they had used the health-care system (Women's Health in Women's Hands Community Health Centre, 2003). One young woman described her experience this way:

> I guess it was racism. Just because, when someone tries to make themselves, you know, superior to you because of their culture and their ways, it is racism. So I mean, it didn't affect me greatly but the fact that it was there scared me. Because I mean, who knows what levels that could have been taken to. That's in their practice and who knows what they're preaching subconsciously to people. (p. 27)

Many of the young women in the Toronto study (Women's Health in Women's Hands Community Health Centre, 2003) reported having positive experiences with the health-care system and good relationships with their doctors. However, nearly one-third (29.6 per cent) reported having negative experiences; reasons for this included lack of trust and different views of appropriate care, poor communication between doctor and patient, language difficulties, cultural insensitivity, lack of knowledge of patients' culture, and discrimination (p. 25). Cultural and communication barriers have also been identified as a reason that Pap smear screening tests are underutilized by many immigrant and ethnic minority women in Canada (McDonald & Kennedy, 2007).

Medicare

Canada's universal health-care program funded and administered by federal, provincial- and territorial governments.

Canada's system of **Medicare** has reduced some of the economic barriers to obtaining health care. However, although there is universal coverage for most health-care services, prescription drugs, dentistry, and eye examinations are generally not covered.

Equitable health services for all Canadians means more than just removing financial barriers. To meet the health needs of people of various ethnic origins, it is necessary to have a multifaceted approach to health, recognizing both diversity and difference within Canada. Health equity and social justice require culturally appropriate care that is readily available in all areas and for all health services (Anderson et al., 2003; Fenta et al., 2007; Simich et al., 2005). Moreover, culturally sensitive health care needs to include a mix of the following: a culturally diverse staff that reflects the communities served, professionally trained interpreters and translators, training for health-care providers about the culture of the people they serve, linguistically and culturally appropriate educational materials, and culturally specific health-care settings (Anderson et al., 2003). These services need to be examined from a gender lens as well as for their sensitivity to difference based on factors such as age, sexual orientation, and disability.

Some Canadian research suggests that, with some exceptions, patterns of health-care utilization are similar for immigrants and non-immigrants, (Kirmayer et al., 2007; studies reviewed in Hyman, 2001); however, it has also been shown that ethnic minorities, especially racialized persons, encounter various barriers when trying to access health care. The current health-care system is structured to meet the ethnic needs of its Anglo- and Franco-Canadian populations but creates barriers for those whose appearance, speech, behaviours, or values reflect cultural difference. Efforts to encourage cultural tolerance, while beneficial in their own right, will do little to achieve a socially just health system (Hage, 1998). Studies show that reducing income inequality decreases mortality rates and increases the overall health status of the population. If we are to have a truly equitable system, broader structural changes in society that address other social determinants of health, such as income inequalities and poverty, unemployment, housing, and racism, are also required.

Conclusion

Although Canada is a multicultural society, social exclusion, racism, and socio-economic disparity between ethnic and immigrant groups remains a reality, especially for racialized groups (Galabuzi, 2009; Hou et al., 2009; Ornstein, 2006). The review of research on the relationship between ethnicity and health demonstrates that both cultural and structural factors can play a significant role in health outcomes and health-care experiences.

Culturalist explanations of health recognize the importance of cultural differences in the meaning of health and illness among people of different ethnic backgrounds, as well as the effects of these in diagnosis and treatment. Such explanations focus on the processes of interaction between patient and health-care provider and the problems that arise through cultural misunderstandings and poor communication. Structuralist (or materialist) explanations stress the significance of social location as a major factor in health outcomes. These explanations look at social inequality and social determinants of health as important predictors of health status. The challenge for the future in health-care delivery is to integrate these two approaches. Increasingly, more researchers are doing this by focusing on the complex interrelationships between these factors and ethnicity and culture (Galabuzi, 2009, 2001; Kobayashi et al., 2008; Access Alliance, 2005).

Summary of Main Points

- Canada is an ethnically and culturally diverse society.
- Health and illness are social constructions. Definitions of health and illness and understandings of appropriate health care vary over time and between cultures.
- The greatest difference between the ethnic composition of Canada for most of the twentieth century and Canada today is today's increased numbers of immigrants from non-European countries.
- Ethnic groups are differentially located in the structure of social inequality in Canada.
- In general, levels of mortality and morbidity for recent immigrants tend to be lower than those for the Canadian-born population, which is referred to as the healthy immigrant effect. With length of residence, however, these tend to converge to the Canadian-born rates.
- Immigrants are not a homogeneous group.
- Certain groups, such as refugees, racialized peoples, and immigrant women, are more likely to experience socio-economic disadvantages and the health problems associated with these.
- Members from racialized communities are more likely to experience social exclusion and racism.
- Research has identified a number of areas of concern with respect to the health of Canada's immigrants and refugees. These include the need to understand racism as a social determinant of health and the need for culturally appropriate health care services.
- Culture has an influence on peoples' understandings of health and on health-care-seeking behaviours.
- There are two broad types of explanation for the ethnic patterning of health: culturalist and structuralist (materialist). Culturalist explanations emphasize the problems that arise from cultural differences, misunderstandings, and poor communication; structuralist explanations stress the significance of social location and view health as a product of the intersection of a range of factors, such as class, ethnicity, gender, age, and immigrant status.
- Culturally competent health services are needed to ensure that health resources and services are equitable for all people living in Canada.
- The equitable provision of health care in a culturally diverse society requires structural changes that address the social determinants of health, such as inequities in income, poverty, unemployment, housing, and racism.

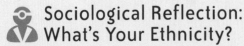 ## Sociological Reflection: What's Your Ethnicity?

We often think of ethnicity as something that immigrants possess, noting how 'they' are different from 'us'. Yet we all have an ethnic identity that reflects the culture in which we have been socialized. Being conscious of your own ethnicity can help you to understand cultural differences and avoid ethnocentrism (judging the beliefs and practices of different cultures from the perspective of one's own culture).

- How would you describe your ethnic background?
- What are some distinctive features of your ethnicity?
- Why might some people be labelled as ethnic in Canada and others not?
- In what ways might ethnocentrism affect the quality, accessibility, and appropriateness of health-care delivery?

Discussion Questions

1. Choose one of the following groups: immigrant women, racialized immigrant groups, or refugees. In what ways would their health concerns be similar to and/or different from those of the Canadian-born population?
2. What kinds of social and economic barriers do members of racialized groups experience in obtaining health care?
3. Are the challenges that confront immigrant women in finding health services different from those confronting immigrant men?
4. In what ways does social exclusion lead to poor health?
5. What do you think is the best explanation for the healthy immigrant effect? Give reasons for your answer.
6. What do you think should be done to improve access and remove barriers to health-care services for immigrants generally?

Further Investigation

1. Critically assess the relative significance of pre-migration and post-migration factors on the health of immigrants in Canada. What patterns (if any) are apparent?
2. *The Spirit Catches You and You Fall Down* (Fadiman, 1997) is a fascinating account of the difficulties that arise when the members of an ethnic minority with a non-Western view of health and illness (in this case the Hmong in the United States) interact with the Western health-care system and its experts. Read this book and (a) identify the key factors contributing to the problems that arose, and (b) suggest possible changes to the Canadian health-care system that would increase the likelihood of positive health outcomes. (Note: You will need to consider who is defining the 'problem' and who is defining 'positive health outcomes'.)
3. Find out the ethnic composition of the population in your area (if possible, you might also get an age and gender breakdown). What changes would you make to current services in your area in order to meet the needs of the whole community?

🚑 Further Reading

Access Alliance. (2005). *Racialized groups and health status: A literature review exploring poverty, housing, race-based discrimination and access to health care as determinants of health for racialized groups.* Available at http://accessalliance.ca/sites/accessalliance/files/documents/Literature%20 Review_Racialized%20Groups%20and%20Health%20Status.pdf

Beiser, M. (2005, March/April). The health of immigrants and refugees in Canada. *Canadian Journal of Public Health, 96,* supplement 2, 30–44.

Galabuzi, G.E. (2005). *Canada's economic apartheid: The social exclusion of racialized groups in the new century.* Toronto, ON: Canadian Scholars Press, Inc.

Kalbach, M., & Kalbach, W. (2000). *Perspectives on ethnicity in Canada.* Toronto, ON: Harcourt Canada.

Lindsay, C. (2007). *Profiles of ethnic communities in Canada.* Ottawa, ON: Statistics Canada.

Ng, E., Wilkins, R., Gendron, F., & Berthelot, J-M. (2005). *Healthy today, healthy tomorrow? Findings from the National Population Health Survey.* Ottawa, ON: Statistics Canada.

Razack, S. (Ed.). (2002). *Race, space and the law: Unmapping a white settler society.* Toronto, ON: Between the Lines.

Simich, L., Beiser, M., Stewart, M., & Mwakarimba, E. (2005). Providing social support for immigrants and refugees in Canada: Challenges and directions. *Journal of Immigrant Health, 7*(4), 259–268.

🩹 Web Resources

Access Alliance, Multicultural Community Health Centre
www.accessalliance.ca

Canadian Council for Refugees
www.ccrweb.ca

Inclusive Cities Canada
www.racialequitytools.org/resourcefiles/
inclusivecitiescanada.pdf

Canadian Race Relations Foundation
www.crr.ca

Canadian Research Institute for the Advancement of Women

www.criaw-icref.ca/
ImmigrantandRefugeeWomen

Immigrant Women Canada
www.immigrantwomencanada.info/

LEGIT: Canadian Immigration for Same-sex Partners
www.legit.ca

CHAPTER 7

Canada's Aboriginal Peoples and Health: The Perpetuation of Inequalities

Jennie Hornosty, Dennis Gray, & Sherry Saggers

Overview

- Who are Aboriginal Canadians and what is their reality?
- How is the health inequality experienced by Aboriginal Canadians being addressed?
- Why do such health inequalities persist today?

Canada has a publicly funded health-care system that many Canadians understandably are proud of. However, not all peoples have benefited equally. The health status of Canada's Aboriginal peoples on virtually all indicators of health is below that of non-Aboriginal Canadians. They have higher mortality and morbidity rates and higher incidences of tuberculosis, alcoholism, and suicide than the rest of the population. They also are more likely to be unemployed, to live in poverty and substandard housing, and to have lower education attainment levels. This chapter explores possible explanations for these inequities and situates the existing inequality in a broader social and historical context of Aboriginal people's experiences of colonization, dispossession, and marginalization from the dominant economy. As well, the chapter explores the health implications of these processes. Although efforts have been made to improve the health status of Aboriginal peoples, many structural inequalities remain.

Key Terms

Aboriginal peoples
assimilate/assimilation
biomedicine/biomedical
   model
colonization/colonialism
First Nations

Indian Act
Indigenous peoples
infant mortality
Inuit
Métis
risk factors

Royal Commission on
   Aboriginal Peoples (RCAP)
social determinants of health
   approach
unemployment rate

Introduction: Who Are the Aboriginal Canadians?

Aboriginal peoples
Refers to all the original peoples in North America and their descendants.

First Nations
Refers to all those people called 'Indian'.

Métis
Refers to people of Aboriginal and mixed European ancestry.

Inuit
Replaces the term *Eskimo* and refers to Aboriginal people who live primarily in Arctic Canada.

Indigenous peoples
Used interchangeably with the term *Aboriginal peoples*.

In order to talk about the health status of Aboriginal peoples we need to define the people we are talking about. **Aboriginal peoples** is a collective name for all the original peoples of North America and their descendants (Aboriginal and Northern Affairs Canada, 2011). The Canadian Constitution Act of 1982 recognizes three distinct groups of Aboriginal people: Indians (today commonly referred to as **First Nations**), **Métis**, and **Inuit**. Some use the terms *Indigenous* or **Indigenous peoples** interchangeably with *Aboriginal peoples* to collectively describe these three distinct groups. Each group has its own unique history, languages, spiritual beliefs, and cultural practices. The most recent census taken in 2006 indicates that there were just under 1.2 million Canadians who identified as belonging to one of the three groups of Aboriginal peoples, and they accounted for almost 4 per cent of the total Canadian population (Statistics Canada, 2008a).

Métis are persons of mixed Aboriginal and European ancestry who identify themselves as Métis. They account for 33 per cent of the overall Aboriginal population and speak a variety of First Nations languages. The Métis population is concentrated in the West (87 per cent); nearly one-quarter (22 per cent) reside in Alberta (Gionet, 2009b). Inuit are the smallest group of Aboriginal peoples, comprising just 4 per cent. They speak several different dialects, and while they share a common culture and traditions there is also linguistic and geographic diversity among the different regions. The Inuit live primarily in Arctic Canada, that is, in Nunavut, the Northwest Territories, Northern Quebec, and Labrador nearly half (49 per cent) reside in Nunavut (Gionet, 2008). See Figure 7.1 for a breakdown of the Aboriginal population in Canada.

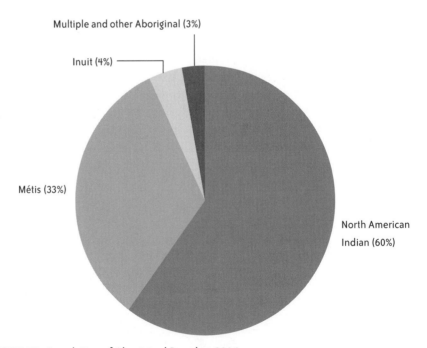

FIGURE 7.1 Population of Aboriginal Peoples, 2006

Source: Statistics Canada. (2008). *Aboriginal peoples in Canada in 2006: Inuit, Metis and First Nations, 2006 Census.* Ottawa: Statistics Canada (Cat. No. 97-558-XIE).

The diversity of Aboriginal peoples is further evident when we look more closely at First Nations people, who make up over 60 per cent of Aboriginal Canadians. Within the First Nations group there are 633 First Nations bands, which represent 52 nations or cultural groups and more than 60 languages. Each nation has its own history, spirituality, and traditional political structure. Many First Nations people still prefer to be referred to by the specific nation to which they belong (for example, Cree, Blackfoot, Dene, Maliseet, Mi'kmaq, etc.) (Assembly of First Nations, 2002). A further distinction is that some First Nations live on-reserve while others live off-reserve. According to the 2006 census, 75 per cent of First Nations people lived in urban areas, with the largest number living in Winnipeg, followed closely by Vancouver (Statistics Canada, 2008a). As well, there is an important distinction between 'status' and 'non-status' Indians. Status Indians are those who are recognized as Indians under the **Indian Act** and are entitled to certain rights and benefits under the law. They account for 81 per cent of the First Nations people (Statistics Canada, 2008a). Non-status Indians are those who consider themselves Indians or members of a First Nation but are not entitled to be registered under the Indian Act, perhaps because their ancestors were never registered or because they lost their status under former provisions of the Indian Act. Non-status Indians are not entitled to the same rights and benefits that are available to Status Indians (Assembly of First Nations Fact Sheet, 2002). In 2006, 40 per cent of First Nations people lived on-reserve, nearly all of whom were Status Indians (98 per cent). Sixty per cent of First Nations people lived off-reserve, just over 75 per cent of whom resided in urban areas (Statistics Canada, 2008a).

Aboriginal peoples live in all regions of Canada, although the majority (54 per cent) live in urban areas. Figure 7.2 indicates the concentration of Aboriginal peoples in each province and territory, whereas Figure 7.3 shows the distribution of Aboriginal peoples in each.

Indian Act

Sets out certain federal government obligations and regulates the management of Indian reserve lands, Indian moneys, and other resources. The act defines an Indian as 'a person who, pursuant to this Act, is registered as an Indian or is entitled to be registered as an Indian'.

Evidence of Health Inequality

Canadians are among the healthiest people in the world. However, study after study has shown that the qualify of life and health outcomes for Aboriginal peoples in Canada, while improving, is among the worst (Adelson, 2005; Hackett, 2005; MacMillan et al., 1996; Newbold, 1998; Mills, 1959; Royal Commission on Aboriginal Peoples, 1996a,b). In this chapter, we attempt to reveal the 'public issues' behind some of these intensely 'personal troubles' (Mills, 1959, p. 14). According to C. Wright Mills, we experience poverty or ill health as our personal problems and do not realize that a lot of other people may be in the same situation. If something affects only a few individuals, the problem is best addressed in an individualistic manner, by helping the individual concerned. However, if a large number of people find themselves with the same problems, we need to look for the societal roots or social causes; social or structural changes will be necessary to remedy the problem. To understand why health inequalities persist for Aboriginal peoples, then, we need to look at some of the social determinants of health. See Box 7.1 for the story of Barb and Naomi, who are not simply statistics or isolated cases. Their story represents the experiences of many of Canada's Aboriginal peoples. Such experiences help to explain why so many Aboriginal peoples today have health problems and die early.

It is difficult to get an accurate and complete assessment of the health status of Aboriginal peoples since such information is not systematically collected for all three Aboriginal

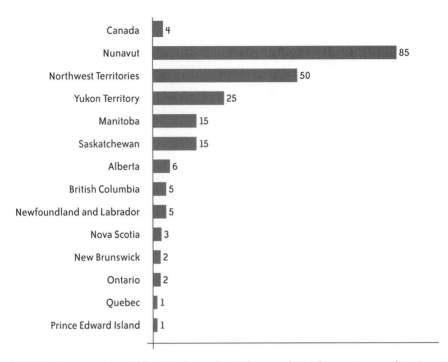

FIGURE 7.2 Percentage of Aboriginal peoples in the population by province and territory, 2006

Source: Statistics Canada. (2006). *Census of Population, 2006.* Ottawa: Statistics Canada (Cat. No. 97-558).

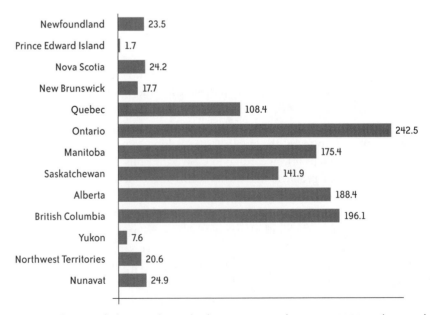

FIGURE 7.3 Distribution of Aboriginal peoples by province and territory, 2006, in thousands

Source: Statistics Canada. (2006). *Aboriginal peoples in Canada in 2006: Inuit, Metis and First Nations, 2006 Census.* Ottawa: Statistics Canada (Cat. No. 97-558-XIE).

BOX 7.1 Barbara's Story[1]

Barbara (or Barb, as she prefers to be called) is a 60-year-old First Nations Status Indian who lives on-reserve in the Maritimes. A survivor of drug and alcohol addiction, sexual abuse, and poverty, Barb grew up with four sisters and her mother in a single-bedroom house. All of them shared the same bed. Often times her cousins and aunt stayed with them as well because her uncle was an alcoholic. She and her family moved around regularly because their homes often lacked running water and rarely had any kind of insulation, although she recalls that one house was insulated with old newspapers.

Barb's father drank heavily. After her parents split up, Barb became the 'father and brother' of the household and as a result was required to do certain chores, such as chopping firewood. As a child, she was sexually abused by a female relative and barely escaped the same kind of abuse from a nun at the Catholic school she attended.

Barb went to live with her father when she was 12, but despite her father's newfound sobriety she began to drink. Trouble at school led Barb to leave home yet again, this time for British Columbia. She met someone she was attracted to when she was 19 years old and at 21 gave birth to her first daughter. Barb soon became addicted to drugs as well as alcohol. Things didn't work out with her partner so she eventually left him and moved around to different places in Canada and the United States for years afterward. When Barb eventually returned home to the Maritimes, she lived in an old, condemned house. She was not warmly received by members in her community; one band counsellor, for example, condemned her for bringing 'a bastard child' into the community. She turned to the welfare department for assistance but was turned away because she violated the rules by living in a condemned house. Her daughter, Naomi, left home at a young age because of Barb's substance abuse problems and the verbal abuse she suffered.

When Naomi had her own children they were taken from her by social services because of her own substance abuse. Barb took her grandchildren in but verbally abused them as well. Social services neglected to help Barb raise her grandchildren, claiming that Barb and Naomi were conspiring together to get money from the government. Naomi eventually recovered from her drug and alcohol abuse and returned to her children. However, one of her sons got into trouble with the law and was sent to jail. In order to protect her youngest daughter, Naomi has not made contact with her imprisoned son due to his abusive nature.

Today Barb suffers from chronic stress and hypertension. 'The thought of suicide was always there with me,' Barb recalled. 'It was always an option.' Fortunately for Barb and Naomi, they have recovered from many of their struggles. Unfortunately, not all do.

---

1. The story is based on an interviewed conducted by Kyle Lewis, a graduate student in the sociology department at the University of New Brunswick.

groups. This is due in part to 'the multi-jurisdictional complexity of health services to First Nations and Inuit' (Health Council of Canada, 2005, p. 16). Neither Health Canada nor Indian and Northern Affairs, for example, collects specific health information on the Métis population. In addition, the indicators for Aboriginal people may be either incomplete or lacking in comparison to those available for the population as a whole (Health Council of Canada, 2005).[2] However, the data collected show that on virtually every known indicator of health status, the health of Aboriginal peoples is poorer in comparison to the rest of the Canadian population: Aboriginal peoples' life expectancy is significantly lower, their mortality and morbidity rates are higher, their infant mortality is higher, their rate of diabetes is triple, AIDS/HIV deaths are double, and drug-induced deaths are four to seven times higher. Moreover suicide, especially among young people, continues to be high (Vancouver Coastal Health, n.d.; Health Council of Canada, 2005).

Life expectancy is one valuable indicator of a population's health status. The measure represents 'the average number of years a person of a given age and sex can expect to live, if current age-sex-specific death rates continue to apply throughout his or her lifetime' (Trewin & Madden, 2003, p. 182). Overall, the life expectancy of Aboriginal peoples is estimated to be anywhere between five to fourteen years less than that of non-Aboriginal Canadians. However, life expectancy differs not only by sex but also by Aboriginal group.[3] For a comparison, see Table 7.1. As we can see, life expectancy for Métis people was highest among the three Aboriginal peoples but still significantly below that for non-Aboriginal peoples. Until recently, there were no national life expectancy data for Inuit because Inuit identity was not collected for deaths that took place in the provinces (Wilkins et al., 2008). The estimates used in Table 7.1 come from a recent geographic-based approach that looked at Inuit-inhabited areas to determine the average life expectancy for Inuit (Wilkins et al., 2008).

infant mortality

Refers to the number of infants who die in the first year after birth per 1000 births.

Although declining steadily, the **infant mortality** rates among Aboriginal peoples are estimated to be higher than the rate for the general population. Infant mortality rates are an important measure of the well-being of infants, children, and pregnant women because they are associated with a variety of factors, such as maternal health, quality, and access to medical care, and socio-economic conditions. For on-reserve First Nations people, the rate of infant mortality is estimated at 7 deaths per 1000 live births, compared to 5 deaths per 1000 for the general population. However, because of limitations in how data are gathered, this figure may be an underestimation of the actual rate of infant deaths. In Nunavut, where approximately 85 per cent of the population is Inuit, the estimated infant mortality rate is 16 deaths per 1000 (Butler-Jones, 2008). Rates of infant mortality for the Métis are unknown (Health Council of Canada, 2005).

Adult Aboriginal peoples are more likely than other Canadian populations to die from cardiovascular diseases; from external causes, such as accidents, poisoning, and violence; from respiratory disorders; and from various forms of cancer. For example, acute myocardial infarction (heart attack) rates among First Nations are around 20 per cent higher

---

2. The health statistics collected and the reporting of these varies for the different groups. This is the case even for First Nations peoples; there is separate reporting for those living on-reserve and those living off-reserve. In some instances, the reported data are not for the same years, thus making it difficult to compare.

3. Different dates are compared based on the availability of data.

TABLE 7.1   Life Expectancy for Aboriginal Peoples and Non-Aboriginal Canadians

Year	Status First Nations		Non-Aboriginal Canadians	
	Male	**Female**	**Male**	**Female**
2002	68.9	76.6	77.0	82.1
	Métis			
	Male	**Female**		
2004	70.4	76.9		
	Inuit (variable by region)			
	Male	**Female**		
2001	63.2 – 65.6	68.7 – 70.9		

Sources: Health Canada. (2005). First Nations Comparable Health Indicators; Canada Aboriginal Peoples Roundtable. (2004). Métis National Council Health Policy Session Paper; Wilkins, R. et al. (January 2008). Statistics Canada. (March 2008). Life Expectancy in the Inuit-inhabited Areas of Canada, 1989 to 2003. *Health Reports, (19)*1.

and stroke rates are almost 50 per cent higher than among non-Aboriginal Canadians (Health Canada, 2005a). The prevalence of diabetes among First Nations adults is 19.7 per cent, almost four times that of the general population. Tuberculosis also continues to be a major health problem for all Aboriginal peoples; in fact, tuberculosis infection rates are 8 to 10 times higher than the national average (Pan American Health Organization, 2007, p. 174). See Figure 7.4 for a comparison of the prevalence of selected health conditions among First Nations on-reserve peoples with the general Canadian population.

Aboriginal peoples are overrepresented in the HIV epidemic and infected at a younger age (Larkin et al., 2007). First Nations persons comprise 7.2 per cent of the national HIV/AIDS cases even though they only make up about 2 per cent of Canada's population (Pan American Health Organization, 2007, p. 169). And between 1998 and 2005, women accounted for 47 per cent of all new HIV diagnoses among Aboriginal peoples (Canada Year Book, 2007). Genital chlamydia among First Nations persons, moreover, is six times higher than the Canadian rate (Health Canada, 2005a, p. 6).

The death rate from injuries and poisoning is four times higher for First Nations and Inuit than for the general population. And suicide among Aboriginal peoples between the ages of 10 and 19 years is 4.3 times higher than among the rest of the country; among all ages of the Inuit, suicide is 11 times higher (Pan American Health Organization, 2007, p. 169). Suicide rates for the Métis are unknown (Health Council of Canada, 2005, p. 31).

Although there is comparatively little research available on the health and well-being of the Métis population, the data available indicate that their health status is generally poorer than the general population. According to the Aboriginal Peoples Survey, 2006, they had higher rates of such chronic health conditions as arthritis and/or rheumatism (21 per cent), high blood pressure (16 per cent), asthma (14 per cent), and diabetes (7 per cent). In the case of asthma and diabetes, their rates were almost double (Janz et al., 2006).

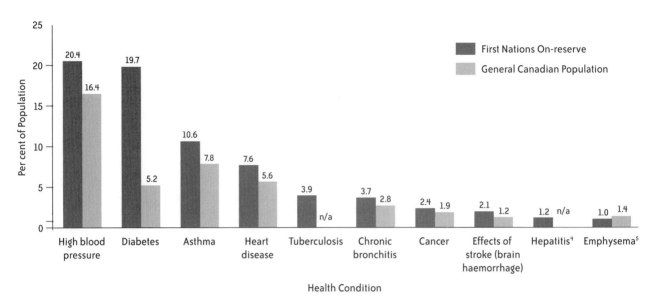

FIGURE 7.4 Age-Standardized prevalence of selected health conditions, First Nations on-reserve compared with general Canadian population

Sources: First Nations Information Governance Committee (FNIGC). (2002–2003). First Nations Regional Longitudinal Health Survey (RHS).

Assembly of First Nations (AFN). (2005, November). Results for Adults, Youth and Children Living in First Nations Communities.

Statistics Canada. (2003). Canadian Community Health Survey (CCHS). In Health Canada. (2002–2005). Statistical Profile on the Health of First Nations in Canada, Self-Rated Health and Selected Conditions. Available at www.hc-sc.gc.ca/fniah-spnia/alt_formats/pdf/pubs/aborig-autoch/ 2009-stats-profil-vol3/2009-stats-profil-vol3-eng.pdf

Social Production of Aboriginal Ill Health

risk factors

Conditions that are thought to increase an individual's susceptibility to illness or disease, such as abuse of alcohol, poor diet, or smoking.

Certain behaviours are associated with people's poorer health status. Smoking, for example, is a **risk factor** for certain types of cancers, heart disease, and stroke (Tjepkema, 2002). It is estimated that 16.6 per cent of all Canadian deaths can be attributed to smoking (Butler-Jones, 2008, p. 54). In 2002, 56.9 per cent of First Nations adults—20 years and older—smoked, a rate that is double the Canadian rate. The highest smoking rate of 72 per cent was among the Inuit (Health Council of Canada, 2005). In 2006, 31 per cent of Métis adults smoked (Janz et al., 2006). Alcohol consumption can also be a factor in people's poor health. While both on-reserve and off-reserve First Nations people reported lower rates of weekly drinking than the rest of the Canadian population, a significantly higher proportion of those living off-reserve reported being heavy drinkers: 22.6 per cent compared to 16.1 per cent for the non-Aboriginal population (Tjepkema, 2002, p. 8). Twenty-seven per cent of First Nations youth living on-reserve reported heavy drinking (Butler-Jones, 2008, p. 58).

In addition, a lack of physical activity can lead to obesity and is a risk factor for a range of chronic diseases, including cardiovascular disease, diabetes, and depression (Butler-Jones, 2008, p. 55). In 2001, 11 per cent of First Nations people living on-reserve had been diagnosed with diabetes, compared with 8 per cent of First Nations adults living off-reserve, 6 per cent of Métis, 2 per cent of Inuit, and 3 per cent of the general population

(Canada Year Book, 2007). Dr Jay Wortman, who is researching the health effects of diet in First Nations communities, hypothesizes that the high prevalence of diabetes is the result of a shift from traditional Aboriginal diets based on wild regional foods, such as fish, seafood, moose, elk, deer, and seasonal plants and berries, to the carbohydrate-laden diets of today. He argues that the traditional diet provided plenty of protein and fat with little in the way of carbohydrates; previously, diabetes and metabolic syndrome (a cluster of risk factors for both heart disease and diabetes) were unheard of (Schanfarber, 2007).

Depression, suicide, injury, and poisoning are a major concern for Aboriginal peoples. Intentional injury and poisoning account for 38 per cent of deaths among First Nations youth and 23 per cent of adult deaths (Probert & Poirier, 2003). Among First Nations the rate of completed suicide is significantly higher than for the population as a whole (Health Canada, 2005a, p. 5). Furthermore, suicide rates among sectors of First Nations and Inuit youth are five to six times higher than for non-Aboriginal peoples (Smylie, 2009, p. 293).

Understanding the Health Inequities

For a long time, Aboriginal peoples have experienced poorer health in comparison to the rest of Canadians. However, this wasn't always the situation. Various historical documents have confirmed that Aboriginal peoples in Canada were in good health upon the arrival of the Europeans (Health Council of Canada, 2005, p. 3). Rather, the European explorers were the ones more likely to be sick. Aboriginal healers provided those who were interested with herbal remedies and suggested unfamiliar cures. However, hundreds of thousands of Aboriginal peoples got seriously sick or died after their encounters with Europeans: 'Famine and warfare contributed, but infectious diseases were the great killer. Influenza, measles, polio, diphtheria, smallpox and other diseases were transported from the slums of Europe to the unprotected villages of the Americas' (Royal Commission on Aboriginal peoples, 1996b, Volume 3, Chapter 3, 1.1, p. 2). These diseases significantly reduced the Aboriginal population and the subsequent decline has been described as 'genocide or a holocaust' (p. 2).

As mentioned in Chapters 1 and 4, sociological approaches to health are different from **biomedicine** or **biomedical approaches**. Whereas the latter approach illness as a malfunction of the body, sociological explanations look for social patterns and social determinants of health. Sociological explanations attempt to throw light on why people are not randomly afflicted by disease and illness. Indeed, many studies have revealed the relationship between health status and social indicators, such as class, poverty, ethnicity, and gender. Canadian researchers have demonstrated that there are inequalities in health status based on socio-economic factors, such as employment, income, poverty, and social exclusion (see the various contributions in Raphael, 2009a). People in lower socio-economic status groups, such as Aboriginal peoples, have poorer health throughout their lifespan than other Canadians (Health Canada, 2009a; Royal Commission on Aboriginal Peoples, 1996b; Smylie, 2009).

Using the Social Determinants of Health

As one of the richest countries in the world, Canada is well placed to right past wrongs and ensure that all Canadians, including Canada's First Peoples, are able to enjoy

biomedicine/ biomedical approach

The conventional approach to medicine in Western societies, based on the diagnosis and explanation of illness as a malfunction of the body's biological mechanisms. This approach underpins most health professions and health services, which focus on treating individuals and generally ignore the social origins of illness and its prevention.

living conditions that promote health and well-being. The biggest barrier at this time appears to be the political will of those who are experiencing privileged access to societal resources . . .

— *Smylie, 2009, p. 298*

In Canada, the idea that an individualistic and biomedical approach was insufficient for understanding good health was first put forth in 1974 by then minister of health Marc Lalonde with the publication of *New Perspectives on the Health of Canadians*. The report outlined the importance of looking at determinants of health outside the health-care system and highlighted the importance of social inequalities in understanding health inequalities of a population. This position was reiterated by then minister of health Jake Epp in 1986, with the tabling of *Achieving Health for All: A Framework for Health Promotion*, which further outlined the importance of reducing income inequities as part of a strategy for improving the overall health of all Canadians. Today, a **social determinants of health approach** guides both the implementation of public health policy and much of the research on how it is that social determinants influence health. It is especially important for understanding the inequities in health experienced by Aboriginal peoples.

Dr David Butler-Jones identified a number of socio-economic determinants of health in his 2008 *Report on the State of Public Health in Canada*. The following socio-economic determinants of health were identified (2008, p. 35):

- Income
- Employment, and working conditions
- Food security
- Environment and housing
- Early childhood development
- Education and literacy
- Social support and connectedness
- Health behaviours
- Access to health care

Employment and job security, for example, provide people with income and economic opportunities, including better housing and food security. Inadequate housing with poor indoor air quality aggravates asthma and other respiratory problems. Overcrowding and poorly ventilated houses can lead to mental stress and increase the risk of acquiring tuberculosis. Healthy eating requires having sufficient resources to purchase nutritious foods. Growing up in poverty has a long-term impact on childhood development; it also reduces the chances of acquiring postsecondary education or even completing high school. Poor people are often marginalized from participation in their community and may lack a sense of social connectedness, so critical for mental health. And while Canada has a publicly funded universal health-care system, certain groups in society may experience racism and discrimination, which affects their experiences of health care.

On every above-mentioned social determinant, Aboriginal peoples are at a disadvantage. In the words of the **Royal Commission on Aboriginal Peoples (RCAP)**, 'Aboriginal people endure ill health, run-down and overcrowded housing, polluted water, inadequate schools, poverty and family breakdown at rates found more often in developing countries

social determinants of health approach

Refers to the social and economic environments in which people live and that determine their health. Examples of social determinants include housing, job security, working conditions, education, income, social class, gender, Aboriginal status, and the social safety net. This approach shows how society is organized and how it distributes its economic and social resources.

Royal Commission on Aboriginal Peoples (RCAP)

Created by the Canadian government in 1991 to address economic, social, and political issues related to First Nations, Métis, and Inuit peoples in Canada. The commissioners held 178 days of public hearings, visited 96 communities, consulted dozens of experts, and commissioned research studies. They came up with hundreds of recommendations to address the inequities faced by Aboriginal peoples.

than in Canada' (Royal Commission on Aboriginal Peoples, 1996a, p. 31). Research consistently indicates that income is an important predictor of health status and that those in the lowest quintile consistently have a lower life expectancy, higher levels of infant mortality, and a higher rate of morbidity (Auger & Alix, 2009). By comparing the situation of Aboriginal peoples, in terms of social determinants of health, with non-Aboriginal Canadians we can see the many levels of disadvantage. The socio-economic status and education level of Aboriginal people is low. The median annual income in 2005 of First Nations people 15 years and older was $11 000 lower than, or 56 per cent of, the non-Aboriginal population, whose median income was $25 955. Men had a higher median income than women. Those living on-reserve had a lower median income by just over $6000 than those living off-reserve (Gionet, 2009a, p. 57). In the same year, the median income of Inuit was $9000 less than that reported by the non-Aboriginal population, a significant gap given the higher cost of living in the North, where the majority of Inuit reside (Gionet, 2008, p. 62). The Métis were comparatively better off: their median income for 2005 was only $5000 less, but still only at 82 per cent of that of the non-Aboriginal population (Gionet, 2009b, p. 22).

Education correlates with income, which in turn is correlated with housing, food security, and employment conditions. While it is significant that levels of postsecondary education for Aboriginal peoples have improved over the past 30 years (Smylie, 2009, p. 291), they are still below the Canadian average. In 2006, only 42 per cent of First Nations people (25–64 years of age) had completed a postsecondary education compared to 61 per cent of the non-Aboriginal population. Furthermore, only 7 per cent had a university degree compared with 23 per cent of non-Aboriginal people. First Nations people living off-reserve were more likely to have completed a postsecondary education than those living on-reserve, and First Nations women were more likely to do so than men (Gionet, 2009a, p. 55). The education level of the Inuit was the lowest of the three Aboriginal groups. Half of the Inuit population had less than a high school diploma in 2006; 36 per cent had a postsecondary diploma or degree, and of those, only four per cent had attained a university degree. Unlike First Nations people, Inuit women and men had similar rates of postsecondary completion (Gionet, 2008, p. 61). The completion rates of postsecondary education for Métis adults aged 25 to 64 was the highest of the three Aboriginal groups: in 2006, 50 per cent had attained a postsecondary education and 9 per cent had a university degree (Gionet, 2009b, p. 22).

Employment and unemployment rates are also associated with health inequalities. Unemployment, underemployment, job security as well as stressful work environments all impact negatively. In 2006, 60.5 per cent of First Nations people between the ages of 25 and 54 were employed compared to 81.6 per cent of the non-Aboriginal population. The employment rate of those living on-reserve was 14.4 per cent less than that of those living off-reserve (Gionet, 2009a, p. 55-56). The **unemployment rate** for First Nations people was two to three times higher than for non-Aboriginal peoples (Gionet, 2009a, p. 56; Smylie, 2009, p. 281). Similar differences exist for the Inuit and Métis. In 2006, the employment rate for Métis was 74.6 per cent and the unemployment rate was 8.4 per cent as compared to 5.2 per cent for the non-Aboriginal population (Gionet, 2009b, p. 22). The Inuit fared worse on both variables; although there was some variation between the regions of Canada, the employment rate for Inuit was 61.2 per cent, and the unemployment rate was 19.0 per cent (Gionet, 2008, p. 61).

unemployment rate
Estimates the proportion of people who are not employed but who are actively looking for work.

In October 2005, the plight of people living on the Kashechewan reserve in Northern Ontario hit the media. Dr Trussler, chief of staff at Weeneebayko General Hospital, which serves as a base hospital for the people on the James Bay Coast, described the conditions on the reserve as 'atrocious' (*The Globe and Mail*, October 24, 2005, p. A5). Raw sewage was being pushed into the water-treatment plant by the tides in James Bay, and since the plant was not working properly *E. coli* bacteria flourished. The local school had to be closed as a result. The high levels of chlorine put into the water to try to kill the bacteria further aggravated skin diseases, which were endemic in Kashechewan. Dr Trussler felt that the only solution to this problem was to relocate the people, which the government eventually did. While this may be an extreme example, Kashechewan's problem with its drinking water was not an isolated incident. According to Dr Trussler, '[t]here's 100 native communities in Canada currently under a boil-water advisory' (p. A5). Such water problems lead to a probability of cases of hepatitis A (*The Globe and Mail*, 2005). Nearly 25 per cent of First Nations on-reserve households have water that is deficient in quantity or quality; of those, 2 per cent have no water service (Health Canada, 2009a, pp. 34–35).

Housing and living conditions can directly or indirectly impact on health (Butler-Jones, 2008, p. 45). Although housing conditions for Aboriginal peoples have improved in the past decade, according to the 2006 census Aboriginal peoples are four times more likely than non-Aboriginal people to live in overcrowded conditions, and three times as likely to live in a dwelling in need of major repairs (Statistics Canada, 2008a). These conditions varied greatly among Aboriginal groups, as well as by where they lived. First Nations people are five times more likely to live in crowded homes—15 per cent as compared to 3 per cent for non-Aboriginal Canadians; the situation is especially dire for those living on-reserve, where 26 per cent are living in crowded homes. Forty-four per cent of those living on-reserve are in homes in need of major repairs compared to 7 per cent of those in the general population (Gionet, 2009a, pp. 57–58). In terms of crowding, the housing conditions of Métis are no different than that of the non-Aboriginal population, although there are regional variations; however, Métis are twice as likely to live in dwellings in need of major repairs (Gionet, 2009b, pp. 21–22). Inuit, however, are 10 times more likely to live in crowded conditions and 4 times more likely to live in homes in need of major repairs (Gionet, 2008, p. 60). Inadequate housing can lead to health problems, such as respiratory disease, allergies, and mental-health problems, and to the spread of potentially deadly viruses, such as H1N1 today. Dramatic levels of overcrowding may account for the fact that Inuit children have among the highest rates of severe lower respiratory tract infection in the world (Smylie, 2009).

Healthy eating requires that individuals have economic and physical access to sufficient and nutritious food. Inadequate income, employment status, and geographic isolation are significant barriers to food security for Aboriginal peoples. High rates of poverty, environmental pollution—which has affected traditional food systems—and climate change as well as high rates of diet-related disease are further indications that '[f]ood insecurity is an urgent public health issue for Aboriginal people in Canada' (Power, 2008, p. 95). Food insecurity rates are much higher for Aboriginal peoples; indeed, in 2002 33 per cent of off-reserve households reported food insecurity. For on-reserve populations, rates for food insecurity varied from 21 per cent to 83 per cent (Smylie, 2009, p. 291).

In remote or isolated areas, foods such as fresh fruit and vegetables are both scarce and costly. When Aboriginal peoples lost their connection to their land, they were forced to give up their traditional diet for one similar to the dominant culture. Not only is this new diet now costly for them to maintain, according to Dr Wortmann it also leads to serious health issues such as diabetes (Schanfarber, 2007). In the words of one First Nations woman, 'Almost everyone eats canned food here . . . Buying fresh food is so expensive. Ten pounds of potatoes will cost you $20.00' (Linda Wynne, quoted in *The Globe and Mail*, October 31, 2005, n.p.). Similarly, a study conducted in 2001 found that a healthy food basket for a family of four in a northern Inuit community cost $327.00 compared to $135.00–$155.00 in southern cities (Smylie, 2009, p. 292).

The Legacy of Colonialism

In 2007, at the International Symposium on the Social Determinants of Indigenous Health, it was agreed that the on-going effects of **colonialism/colonization** is a critical social determinant of health (Smylie, 2009, pp. 281–282). Many if not all of the factors that underlie the health inequities endured by Aboriginal peoples in Canada—the forced relocation of communities, the loss of lands and resources, the creation of the reserve system, the forced removal of children and subsequent placement into residential schools, policies of cultural suppression and forced assimilation, and ongoing racist attitudes— are all a terrible part of the legacy of colonialism in this country (Adelson, 2005; Royal Commission on Aboriginal Peoples, 1996a; Smylie, 2009). Though the outcome of colonialism has not proven positive, the initial contact between the first European newcomers and the first peoples (Aboriginal peoples) of this land, which is now Canada, was that of 'cautious co-operation' (Royal Commission on Aboriginal Peoples, 1996a, p. 7) and acceptance of each other's right to co-exist as distinct and independent. While prejudices and stereotypes existed in this early period between the two culturally divergent societies, there is also evidence of relationships of mutual respect among individuals and groups who worked, traded, and sometimes lived together for long periods of time, and even intermarried. The offspring of these unions were later recognized as having a distinct identity—the Métis people (Royal Commission on Aboriginal Peoples, 1996b, Volume 1, Part One, Stage 2, p. 6).

This early cooperation between Aboriginal and non-Aboriginal peoples was formalized in treaties and in the Royal Proclamation of 1763. The proclamation offered protection and recognized Aboriginal nations as autonomous political entities with a right to have their own land and govern their own affairs. Along with the influx of more immigrants came a shift in power in favour of non-Aboriginal peoples, both in terms of population and economic and military strength. Aboriginal peoples were no longer viewed as valued partners but were seen as 'impediments to progress' (Royal Commission on Aboriginal Peoples, 1996a, p. 9). In the 1800s, protection soon came to mean cultural assimilation and domination: '[It] took the form of compulsory education, economic adjustment programs, social and political control by federal agents. These policies, combined with missionary efforts to civilize and convert Indigenous people, tore wide holes in Aboriginal cultures, autonomy and feelings of self-worth' (Royal Commission on Aboriginal Peoples, 1996a, pp. 8–9).

To accommodate colonial expansion, Aboriginal peoples were forced off their land onto reserves to make room for a new economy based on timber, minerals, and agriculture. This forced relocation of Aboriginal peoples from their traditional lands onto reserves

colonialism/ colonization

A process by which one nation imposes itself economically, politically, and socially upon another.

destroyed their culture and their economic livelihood, which was tied to these lands (Royal Commission on Aboriginal Peoples 1996b, Volume 3, Chapter 3). Food and clothing materials, which were acquired by hunting, trapping, and fishing, quickly diminished. These changes further disrupted the traditional style of life as well as their diet, which further affected the health of Aboriginal peoples (Health Council of Canada, 2005). Research of the Royal Commission shows that the effects of relocation continue to be felt today and continue to manifest in ways such as the negative health status of Aboriginal peoples (Royal Commission on Aboriginal Peoples, 1996b, Volume 1, Part 2, Chapter 8, p. 5).

Canadian Confederation was negotiated without reference to Aboriginal nations. The country's first prime minister, Sir John A. Macdonald, made clear that it was his government's policy to '**assimilate** the Indian people in all respects with the inhabitants of the Dominion' (Royal Commission on Aboriginal Peoples, 1996a, p. 11). Aboriginal peoples were completely excluded as active participants. The British North America Act made 'Indians, and the Lands reserved for the Indians' subject to government regulation (Royal Commission on Aboriginal Peoples, 1996a, p. 11). That is, the act legalized the removal of Aboriginal communities from their homelands to government controlled reserve lands. Parliament passed laws, codified in the Indian Acts of 1876, 1880, 1884, and later, which eliminated traditional Aboriginal governments, confiscated valuable resources located on reserves, outlawed important cultural ceremonies, such as the potlatch and the sun dance, and imposed European standards of marriage and parenting. Traditional healing methods were decried as witchcraft and idolatry.

The residential school systems, which came into being in 1849, are considered by many one of the worst legacies of colonialism. These schools were government-funded, church-run institutions as part of the government's assimilation plan, first codified in the 1857 Civilization of Indian Tribes Act. The intent of residential schools was to educate, to civilize, that is, to assimilate and integrate Aboriginal peoples into the dominant European society. When the Indian Act was amended in 1884, attendance at residential schools became mandatory for status Indians under age 16. Children were taken from their families at a young age to a place where their language, customs, and culture were suppressed (Royal Commission on Aboriginal Peoples, 1996a, p. 11). In place of their traditional belief systems, they were required to adopt Christianity. They were forcefully taught either English or French and were severely beaten if they were caught speaking an Aboriginal language. As a result, the bonds between Aboriginal children and their families and nations were broken. The human costs of this psychological violence are still seen today in the survivors of the residential school system and their families.

The Indian Act of 1876 spelled out who was considered an Indian and who was not. According to the act, the term *Indian* applies to 'Any male person of Indian blood reputed to belong to a particular band, any child of such person, and any woman who is or was lawfully married to such person' (Indian Act, 1876, excerpted in Smylie, 2009, p. 287). Under this act, any woman who married an Indian gained Indian status and any of the benefits that accrued, while an Aboriginal woman who married a non-Indian lost her Indian status and rights. (This was changed with the 1985 amendment to the Indian Act, which reinstated Indian status to such women.) The Indian Act also excluded the Métis who had received scrip—transferable land or cash allowances. Following the act, Aboriginal peoples who lived on reserves were required to carry an identity card every time they stepped off reserve land. The Indian Act legitimated the authority of the federal

assimilate/assimilation
Refers to the expectation that Aboriginal peoples and immigrants will give up their culture and become indistinguishable from the dominant Canadian majority.

government to intervene in the affairs of Aboriginal peoples. It was a powerful vehicle for breaking up Aboriginal societies in its attempt to assimilate Aboriginal peoples into the mainstream culture (Royal Commission on Aboriginal Peoples, 1996b, Volume 1, Chapter 4, Stage 3, p. 4).

The impact of colonialism on Aboriginal peoples, then, was profound. The physical displacement destroyed their traditional sources of livelihood; the social and cultural displacement undermined their ability to pass on their culture and traditional values; and political displacement attempted to destroy their governing structures in favour of colonial-style institutions (Royal Commission on Aboriginal Peoples, 1996b, Volume 1, Stage 1, p. 3). Colonialism led to the loss of dignity and self-esteem of Aboriginal peoples, and this continues to have a lasting and negative impact on the population. Today, '[m]any Aboriginal people are suffering not simply from specific disease and social problems, but also from a depression of spirit resulting from 200 or more years of damage to their cultures, languages, identities and self-respect (Royal Commission on Aboriginal Peoples, 1996b, Volume 3, Chapter 3, p. 3). This loss of spirit has led to negative behaviours, such as alcohol and substance abuse, suicide, injuries, and family violence. The health problems Aboriginal peoples face today are not just problems of the individual but, rather, must be understood in the wider social and historical contexts (Adelson, 2005).

How to Improve the Health Status of Aboriginal Peoples

To address the myriad health problems of Aboriginal peoples today will require not only addressing the socio-economic determinants of health but also finding a means to help people heal from the cultural and psychological damage caused by the legacy of colonialism. The Report of the Royal Commission on Aboriginal Peoples (1996b) contains hundreds of recommendations on how to begin to address this situation. It calls on the government of Canada to commit to renewing the relationship between Aboriginal and non-Aboriginal people according to basic principles of respect, recognition, sharing, and responsibility. One place to begin is to understand how Aboriginal peoples define *health* and *well-being*. Unlike the biomedical approach, which separates the body from other aspects of the person, Aboriginal concepts of health and healing are holistic. Aboriginal peoples take the view that all living things are interdependent and that well-being flows from the balance of the physical, spiritual, mental, and emotional elements of personal and collective life. These components are intertwined. The medicine wheel (circle) represents the inseparability of the individual, the family community, and the world: 'The circle embodies the notion of health as harmony or balance in all aspects of one's life . . . Human beings must be in balance with their physical and social environments . . . in order to live and grow' (Royal Commission on Aboriginal Peoples, 1996b, Volume 3, Chapter 3, Conclusion, p. 4). From a holistic perspective, achieving health requires more than just attending to an individual's physical body. This is similar to the World Health Organization's definition of *health* as a 'state of complete physical, mental and social well-being and not merely the absence of disease or infirmity' (see https://apps.who.int/aboutwho/en/definition.html). Such an approach is often neglected in the formalized biomedical environment (Adelson, 2005).

Speakers who appeared before the Royal Commission put forth a vision of health care that approaches each person in relation to family and community: 'Restoring health and well-being to Aboriginal people requires services and programs founded on an integrated, or holistic, view of human health' (Royal Commission on Aboriginal Peoples, 1996b, Volume 3, Chapter 3, section 2.4, p. 3). They emphasized that health and social problems cannot be cured in isolation from one another, and they stressed that Aboriginal peoples needed greater control of health care to redesign health and social programs that more fully reflect their values and diverse cultures (Royal Commission on Aboriginal Peoples, pp. 5–8). As others have noted, conventional biomedical approaches are inadequate: '[I]f we are to understand "healing as the rebuilding of nations" and a process of de-colonization, then we must find ways by which health can be effectively articulated at the levels of the individual, family, community and nation' (Adelson, 2005, p. s47). In the view of those who testified before the Royal Commission on Aboriginal Peoples, in order for healing to occur it is imperative that traditional medicine, values, and healing practices be integrated into current health and social services for Aboriginal peoples.

Improve Health Service and Health Policy

The federal government started to provide intermittent health care to Aboriginal peoples at the beginning of the twentieth century. Aboriginal health and social conditions were so bad at the time that in 1904 the government appointed a medical superintendent in the department of Indian Affairs to be specifically responsible for improving the health of Aboriginal peoples. In the following years, some basic health services were provided, initially by an assortment of RCMP agents, missionaries, and officers and then later by a growing number of nurses and doctors employed by the federal government. In 1945, Indian health services were transferred from Indian Affairs to Health Canada (Health Canada, 2011). By the 1950s, Health Canada had established nursing stations, health centres, and small regional hospitals (Royal Commission on Aboriginal Peoples, 1996b, Volume 3, Chapter 3, section 1.1, p. 3), and in 1962, Health Canada began providing direct health services to status First Nations people and to Inuit in the North. However, the health services operated on a biomedical model and did not address the underlying reasons for Aboriginal peoples' poor health status. Nearly all the providers were non-Aboriginal with little or no understanding of the cultural practices, traditions, and values of Aboriginal Peoples (Royal Commission on Aboriginal Peoples, 1996b, Volume 3, Chapter 3, section 1.1, p. 4).

Partly in response to Aboriginal peoples' protests over proposed cuts to non-insured health benefits, the federal government in 1979 introduced a new Indian Health Policy, which acknowledges some of the social roots of Aboriginal peoples' poor health (Health Canada, 2007b). This policy outlined the federal government's recognition of its legal and traditional responsibilities to Aboriginal peoples, including its special responsibility for the health and well-being of First Nations people and Inuit. The policy states, in part, that improving the health status of Aboriginal communities must be built on three pillars:

1. Community development, including socio-economic, cultural, and spiritual development
2. Opening up communications and encouraging a greater involvement of Aboriginal peoples in the planning, budgeting, and delivery of health programs

3. Using the resources of the Canadian health system to assist Aboriginal communities in taking a more active role in public health activities and decisions affecting their health.

Justice Thomas Berger's 1980 *Report of the Advisory Commission on Indian and Inuit Health Consultation* further added its support to the concept of community control by Aboriginal people in the provision of their health care.

In 1988, the federal government provided a framework for transferring greater control of health services to First Nations and Inuit people when it introduced the Indian Health Transfer Policy. This made it possible for Aboriginal peoples to design programs and allocate funds according to community priorities. Then, in 1995 the federal government announced the *Inherent Right to Self-Government Policy,* which further recognized that First Nations and Inuit have the constitutional right to shape their own forms of government in accordance with their historical, political, economic, and cultural needs. The policy also provided greater flexibility to bands to establish program priorities to improve health services in their communities (Health Canada, 2005b). Although initially there was some hesitancy about the transfer policy, by March 1996, 141 First Nations communities had undertaken administrative responsibility for health-care services, either individually or collectively, through multi-community agencies or tribal associations; another 237 were involved in the pre-transfer process (Royal Commission on Aboriginal Peoples, 1996b, Volume 3, Chapter 3, section 1.1). There were important benefits of transfer, including flexibility in the use of funds and increased freedom to adapt services to local needs; however, the program has been criticized for failing to recognize health as an Aboriginal treaty right, for reproducing pre-existing dependent relationships, for not formally recognizing the role of traditional healers, for the cap on funds regardless of need, and for not funding the training of First Nations health-care professionals (Adelson, 2005, p. s58).

Acknowledge Aboriginal Peoples' Authority in Health Care

When the Report of the Royal Commission on Aboriginal Peoples (RCAP) was finally released in 1996, it affirmed what many Aboriginal peoples had been saying for some time. It forcefully stated that 'self-determination for Aboriginal peoples is an immediate necessity' (Volume 3, Chapter 3, section 2.4, p. 4), of which reclaiming control over health and social services is one aspect. While the health status of Aboriginal peoples had improved over the previous few decades, 'the persistence of ill health and social dysfunction in Aboriginal communities demonstrates that existing services fail to connect with real causes' (Volume 3, Chapter 3, section 2.4, pp 4–5). Moreover, the report called on the government to develop a new strategy for Aboriginal health and health care. Specifically, with respect to health and health care, the Royal Commission on Aboriginal Peoples made the following recommendation:

> Aboriginal, federal, provincial and territorial governments, in developing policy to support health, acknowledge the common understanding of the determinants of health found in Aboriginal traditions and health sciences and endorse the fundamental importance of:
> • holism, that is, attention to whole persons in their total environment;

- equity, that is, equitable access to the means of achieving health and equality of outcomes in health status;
- control by Aboriginal peoples of the lifestyle choices, institutional services and environmental conditions that support health; and
- diversity, that is, accommodation of the cultures and histories of First Nations, Inuit and Métis people that make them distinctive within Canadian society and that distinguish them from one another. (1996b, Volume 3, Chapter 3, section, 2.4, pp 6–7)

By 'equity' the commissioners meant that the health status of Aboriginal peoples should be equivalent in all ways to that of other Canadians. *Equity* also implied that all Aboriginal peoples, regardless of their status as First Nations (on-reserve or off-reserve), Métis, or Inuit, should be provided with equitable health care and social-service provisions. A holistic approach would address the interconnectedness of the physical, spiritual, emotional, and social dimensions of well-being and the social determinants of health that have contributed to ill heath. In the view of the commissioners, Aboriginal authority over health care would ensure that programs and services reflected the priorities of the community as well as increase their effectiveness. As there is a relationship between ill health and feelings of powerlessness, giving people control over their life circumstances would also improve their health outcomes. Since there are differences between Aboriginal and non-Aboriginal peoples' approach to health and healing as well as differences within Aboriginal cultures and communities, health care and social services need to reflect this diversity to ensure culturally appropriate programs.

The federal government's 1998 document *Gathering Strength—Canada's Aboriginal Action Plan* provided a framework for establishing new partnerships with First Nations, Inuit, Métis, and non-status Indians as a response to the Royal Commission on Aboriginal Peoples' recommendation. This document acknowledged the government's role in suppressing Aboriginal peoples' culture and values, and the impact these racist behaviours and attitudes had on the well-being of Aboriginal peoples. In a Statement of Reconciliation, the government also acknowledged its role in the creation of residential schools, the sexual and physical abuse perpetrated there, and the resulting damage to individuals and communities. In the Statement of Reconciliation the government offered the following apology: '*To those of you who suffered this tragedy at residential schools, we are deeply sorry.*' The document makes reference to the tragic death of Louis Riel and states that as part of the reconciliation process the government would look for ways to affirm the contributions of the Métis people (Gathering Strength, 1998). In terms of health policy, an important aspect of the plan was the establishment of the Aboriginal Healing Foundation, a not-for-profit corporation governed by a board of directors made up of representatives (male and female) from the three Aboriginal groups: First Nations (status and non-status), Métis, and Inuit. The foundation's mandate is to design, manage, and implement a healing strategy for Aboriginal peoples. According to the mission statement, the role of the foundation is to

> provide resources which will promote reconciliation and encourage and support Aboriginal people and their communities in building and reinforcing sustainable healing processes that address the legacy of physical,

sexual, mental, cultural, and spiritual abuses in the residential school system,
including intergenerational impacts. (Aboriginal Healing Foundation, n.d.)

In 2000, the Medical Services Branch of Health Canada, responsible for the delivery of
health services to First Nations and Inuit, was renamed the First Nations and Inuit Health
Branch (FNIHB) 'in recognition of the unique status and needs of First Nations and Inuit
in Canada' (Health Canada, 2008c). Its mandate is to ensure the availability and accessibility of health services to First Nations and Inuit communities, to assist these communities in addressing health barriers, and to establish a renewed working relationship with
First Nations and Inuit, including the transfer of direct health services, to find the best
way to achieve effective and appropriate health care (Health Canada, 2005c). Today, the
FNIHB works with First Nations governments in the delivery of health services. It provides
for, or supports, the delivery of community-based health programs, including primary
care services in remote and isolated areas, to First Nations people who live on-reserve
and in Inuit communities, as well as drug, dental, and ancillary health services to all First
Nations and Inuit people regardless of residence. However, the Métis are not eligible for
FNIHB programs and services; instead, they obtain health-care services from provincial
or territorial sources (Health Council of Canada, 2005, p. 16). As of April 2007, the FNIHB
employed 675 nurses and 22 physicians. It has established 223 health centres, 41 alcohol
and drug treatment centres, and 74 nursing stations, and has provided home and community care in 600 communities and primary health care in about 200 remote communities (Health Canada, 2008c, FNIHB).

Conclusion

The health status of Aboriginal peoples has improved considerably over the past couple of
decades; however, on virtually every measure of health, they continue to fare more poorly
than non-Aboriginal Canadians. As we have seen, they have higher rates of respiratory diseases, circulatory diseases, and chronic illnesses, as well as lower life expectancy and higher
infant mortality rates. Rates for suicide, alcohol, and drug dependency, self-inflicted injuries, and homicide are significantly higher than for the non-Aboriginal population. As well,
family and interpersonal violence continues to escalate in Aboriginal populations (Adelson,
2005). Although there are no national studies on the rates of family violence in Aboriginal
communities, an Ontario study found that 8 out of 10 Aboriginal women had personally
experienced family violence (Health Canada, 1996). In a study conducted in 2002, Aboriginal
females identified family violence as one of their chief health concerns. Substance abuse,
mental health issues, and diabetes were the other key issues they identified (Health Council
of Canada, 2005). On every social determinant of health, Aboriginal peoples also fare much
worse. Surveys continue to show that in terms of poverty, educational levels, unemployment
levels, income, food security, and living conditions, the gap between Aboriginal and non-
Aboriginal Canadians is high (Gionet, 2008, 2009a,b; Health Canada, 2009a).

These disparities in health and social conditions are the result of colonialism and
the accompanying racist polices of oppression and domination. Aboriginal peoples were
displaced from their lands; the basis of their livelihood, destroyed; their culture, undermined; their governments, suppressed; their children, placed in residential schools; and
their families, broken apart. As a result, poverty, poor health, and social disorganization

only got worse. Over the past century, the Canadian government's assimilation policies effectively stripped Aboriginal peoples of their identity. The loss, humiliation, and frustration they experienced resulted in violence and self-destruction. As the executive director of a treatment centre in the Northwest Territories explained,

> The oppressed begin to develop what they call 'cultural self-shame' and 'cultural self-hate' which results in a lot of frustration and anger. At the same time . . . we begin to adopt our oppressors' values, and in a way, we become oppressors ourselves . . . We begin hurting our own people. (cited in Royal Commission on Aboriginal Peoples, 1996a, p. 35)

Those who testified before the Royal Commission commented that systemic and individual racism in some workplaces continues to make it difficult for young Aboriginal youth to find employment. And Aboriginal women continue to face marginalization in health care and encounter racism and discrimination from mainstream health-care providers (Browne & Fiske, 2001).

If we want to improve the health of Aboriginal peoples, it is essential to acknowledge that traditional biomedical approaches, which focus on individual behaviour, are inadequate. Research and testimony have shown that the inequalities in Aboriginal peoples' health status today are a consequence of, and reflect, more fundamental structural inequalities related to the dispossession of Aboriginal peoples and their continued economic and political marginalization. Therefore, public-health policies and infrastructure must address these structural inequalities underlying the causes of ill health. These underlying causes are what we mean by the determinants of health, one of which is culture. Culture is important in shaping how people interact with the health-care system, including their participation in health-promotion programs and prevention (Spack, 2003). Health determinants such as income, social environments, personal health practices and behaviours, and physical environments do not exist in isolation from each other. Social and economic factors, the physical environment, and individual behaviour all interconnect to determine one's health status (Raphael, 2009c). For Aboriginal peoples, these determinants have been shaped by their historical and cultural experiences of colonialism. The impacts of colonization have also been identified internationally as fundamental determinants to which all other social inequalities are linked (Smylie, 2009, p. 298).

The Royal Commission on Aboriginal Peoples set out a clear policy framework for developing a new strategy to improve the health status of Aboriginal peoples. A fundamental requirement was that strategies for health and health care originate from within Aboriginal cultures. The essential characteristics include a holistic approach to dealing with problems, including addressing the social and economic inequities, and Aboriginal authority over health systems. Over the past decade, the First Nations and Inuit Health Branch of Health Canada has taken steps to transfer control and design of health services to Aboriginal communities. This is in keeping with its mission, which is to forge a 'renewed relationship with First Nations that is based on the transfer of direct health services and a refocused federal role and that seeks to improve the health status of First Nations and Inuit' (Health Canada, 2008c). While it is too early to tell whether these initiatives and rectifying socio-economic inequalities will improve the health status of Aboriginal peoples so as to be comparable to the rest of Canadians, there is reason to be hopeful.

Summary of Main Points

- While the causes of illness and death among Aboriginal and non-Aboriginal Canadians are similar, Aboriginal peoples are between two and five times more likely to be hospitalized and to die from these causes.
- People are not randomly afflicted by disease. The patterns of health and illness in any population reflect social inequalities, such as Aboriginal status, social class, and gender.
- Attempts to explain the poor health in Aboriginal peoples in terms of lifestyle and risk factors focus on individual attributes rather than on broader structural factors that inhibit people's abilities to lead healthy lives.
- The contemporary ill health of Aboriginal peoples must be located in the historical context of colonialism and existing inequalities.
- Social determinants of health, such as income, education, employment, food security and environment, have the greatest impact on health status.
- Aboriginal peoples have a holistic view of health, which means a balance of physical, spiritual, mental, and emotional elements of personal and collective life.
- Aboriginal community-controlled health services are an important part of a total health service that should be accessible, appropriate, affordable, and acceptable to all Aboriginal peoples.
- For over a century, there has been insufficient attention and resources directed to the fundamental inequalities experienced by Aboriginal peoples.

 ## Sociological Reflection: Racism in Medicine

Apply the four parts of the sociological imagination template (discussed in Chapter 1) to identify the influence of racism in medicine in terms of the following:

- Historical factors: What are some early examples of racism in medicine?
- Cultural factors: In what ways has racism influenced popular understanding of illness suffered by Aboriginal Canadians?
- Structural factors: How has racism affected modes of health-service delivery for Aboriginal Canadians in terms of quality, accessibility, and appropriateness?
- Critical factors: In what ways have racial stereotypes been addressed in the health-care system? How effective do you think they have been?

Discussion Questions

1. How is health inequality measured, and what evidence is there of inequalities between Aboriginal and non-Aboriginal Canadians?
2. What are Aboriginal peoples' perspectives on health and how to improve it?
3. Describe the past and present impact of the reserve and residential schools on the health of Aboriginal peoples.
4. How is the Canadian health-care system organized and how well equipped is it to deal with the health problems of Aboriginal peoples?
5. Is racism still a factor in the delivery of health care to Aboriginal peoples?
6. What key policies have been implemented over the past 30 years designed to improve Aboriginal people's health?
7. What are some of the major differences between mainstream health services and those that are community controlled?

 Further Investigation

1. Critically analyze the assertion that racism and the legacy of colonialism continue to perpetuate structures of inequality that lead to poor health outcomes for Aboriginal peoples.
2. How might one reconcile holistic approaches to health and health care that are integral to Aboriginal peoples' understanding of health with the dominant biomedical approach to illness practised by most health-care providers in Canadian society? Given the differences, what strategies would be most effective in providing appropriate health care to Aboriginal peoples?

 Further Reading

Adelson, N. (2005, March/April). The embodiment of inequity: Health disparities in Aboriginal Canada. *Canadian Journal of Public Health, 96*, s45–s60.

Health Canada. (2003, March). Closing the gaps in Aboriginal health. *Health Policy Research Bulletin*, Issue 5.

King, M., Smith, A., & Gracey, M. (2009). Indigenous health part 2: The underlying causes of the health gap. *The Lancet, 374*, 76–85.

Newbold, K. B. (1998). Problems in search of solutions: Health and Canadian Aboriginals. *Journal of Community Health, 23*(1), 59–73.

Royal Commission on Aboriginal Peoples. (1996b). *Report of the Royal Commission on Aboriginal Peoples*. Ottawa, ON: Indian and Northern Affairs.

Smylie, J. (2009). The health of Aboriginal Peoples. In Raphael (Ed.), (2009), *Social determinants of health* (2nd ed.) (pp. 281–299). Toronto, ON: Canadian Scholars' Press, Inc.

United Nations General Assembly. (2007). *United Nations Declaration on the Rights of Indigenous Peoples*. Geneva: United Nations. Available from http://www.iwgia.org/sw248.asp

Web Resources

Aboriginal Healing Foundation
  www.ahf.ca

Assembly of First Nations
  www.afn.ca

Congress of Aboriginal Peoples
  www.abo-peoples.org

Government of Canada: Aboriginal Canada portal
  www.aboriginalcanada.gc.ca/acp/site.nsf/en/index.html

Indian and Northern Affairs Canada
  www.ainc-inac.gc.ca

Inuit Tapiriit Kanatami
  www.itk.ca

Métis National Council
  www.metisnation.ca

National Aboriginal Health Organization (NAHO)
  www.naho.ca

Native Women's Association of Canada
  www.nwac-hq.org

CHAPTER 8

Environmental Links to Health

Zelda Abramson

Overview

- What role do the petrochemical and nuclear industries play in determining health and illness?
- What are the barriers to linking ill health to environmental factors?
- Why does the Canadian government prefer a policy of risk assessment over the precautionary principle?
- Why are poorer communities at greater risk for environmental health effects?

On any day we do not give much thought to the air we breathe and the water we drink or use for cleaning and bathing. Our relationship to the food we eat is more complex, a factor of what we can afford to buy. Nevertheless, we are told that we need to eat a well-balanced diet, a mix of fruits, vegetables, grains, and dairy products. We assume that everything we buy is safe because it is neatly packaged on the shelves of our grocery store. In this chapter, we take a closer look at whether our air, water, and land are safe for consumption and at what effect our environment has on our health. We also provide various frameworks in which to understand (1) why it is so difficult to link health effects to the environment and (2) the complex relationships between industry, the state, and environmental health policies.

Key Terms

agribusiness	growth imperative	mortality
endocrine disruptors	manufacturers of illness	precautionary principle
environmental racism	McDonaldization	prove harm
epidemiology	morbidity	risk assessment

Introduction

I am fortunate to live in the Annapolis Valley, in a small community that overlooks the Minas Basin of the Bay of Fundy. I refer to this area as an oasis, not only for the milder climate compared to other places in the Maritimes but also for its exquisite beauty. The Annapolis Valley is the breadbasket of Nova Scotia: the land is rich and fertile and the crops are plentiful. The valley, as it is commonly referred to by locals, is bedded between North and South Mountains. North Mountain is the barrier between the farmland and the Bay of Fundy, home of the world's highest tides.

Early every morning I walk my dog at a local reservoir, popular for swimming and walking. The reservoir is located at the base of South Mountain and overlooks Cape Blomidon, the red sandstone bluffs that guard the entrance to the Minas Basin. According to Mi'kmaq mythologies, Blomidon was the home of the first man, Glooscap, who was bestowed with wondrous power.

One warm summer morning, I am startled to hear the sound of a tractor. There is a foglike cloud surrounding the noise. Just below the reservoir is an apple orchard that gets sprayed three times during the growing season, a fellow dog-walker soon thereafter informs me. On these days, we should not be walking the dogs and I am told to leave immediately. As I leave the reservoir, I look for signs announcing that pesticides are in use or signs telling dog owners to keep their dogs on lead for the next few days in order to keep them away from the orchard. There are no such signs. Months later, in the fall, the dogs are drawn to the apples that have fallen on the ground. They eat as many as they can before their owners pull them away. I begin to worry as I recall that day of spraying. How safe is this beautiful place? How safe are the children who swim in the reservoir? How safe is my dog and all his dog friends? I ask a fellow dog walker if there have been any studies in this area that looked at cancer rates and animals in agricultural areas. ' I do not know of any', he answers but then adds, 'my last two dogs died of cancer'.

In this chapter, we examine the complex relationship between our environment and our health. There are three ways the environment can affect our health and that is through air, land, and water: we breathe the air, eat from the land, and drink the water. Should the air, water, and land become contaminated with pollutants, intuitively we would think that our health might be compromised. However, proving that this is the case has been enormously challenging.

Rachel Carson in her groundbreaking book *Silent Spring* alerted the world to this possibility 50 years ago. Carson made the public aware that certain chemicals known as organic compounds (used for pesticides and herbicides) are highly persistent in the environment. Such chemicals are stored in animal tissues—in mother's milk, for example—and they cause water contamination and, in turn, kill fish, and have led to the decline of some bird populations. Carson's book was a bestseller both in North America and Europe and at the same time was highly criticized by the agricultural chemical industry, who launched an attack on Carson's professional integrity and credibility. Carson was accused of being sinister, hysterical, and bland. Despite the industry's efforts, a presidential advisory committee was formed and it supported Carson's findings. In 1972, one of the chemicals, DDT (discussed below), was banned. Rachel Carson, however, died in 1964 of breast cancer.

She is seen today as the leader of the contemporary environmental movement, and her research and viewpoints have inspired this chapter.

Rachel Carson in *Silent Spring* repeatedly refers to World War II as a pivotal time of change that led to the development of (1) the petrochemical industry, which includes the manufacturing of a wide range of synthetic products, from pesticides to plastics; and (2) the nuclear industry, which not only includes atomic bombs but also refers to the subsequent development of nuclear energy and nuclear medicine.

The Petrochemical Industry: Links to Health

The petrochemical industry manufactures synthetic products largely using raw materials, such as crude oil (petroleum) and gas. The resulting products include plastics, paints, detergents, and synthetic fabrics, such as polyester, rubber, and fertilizers. Carson argued that carcinogens are produced from these industries in such great amounts that their effects are felt throughout our environment.

The Industry's Effect on the Air We Breathe

On very hot and humid summer days when temperatures break 30 degrees Celsius, should you live in Toronto, it is increasingly common to hear that all elderly people, people with asthma, and young children should avoid going outdoors. Should you fly over Toronto during such blistering hot and humid days, you will notice a purple haze that clouds the city. This purple haze is more commonly referred to as smog. The source of smog is from ground-level ozone, which is formed through a chemical reaction of pollutants from industrial plants and vehicle emissions combined with sunlight and stagnant air. That is why smog is mostly a summer problem.

There are four known health effects from smog: respiratory diseases, such as asthma; cardiovascular disease; allergies; and neurological effects, such as lower IQ. Illnesses related to air pollution 'cause increased medication use, increased doctor or emergency room visits, more hospital admissions and even premature death' (Environment Canada, 2009, n.p.), and approximately 5900 deaths a year, according to Health Canada. Emissions from industrial plants 'include about seventy different known or suspected human carcinogens' (Steingraber, 1998, p. 179).

Not all ozone is bad, however. High in the atmosphere, there is an ozone layer that protects the earth from harmful ultraviolet radiation from the sun. However, the earth's ozone layer is also a victim of industrial pollution. In the late 1970s, the depletion of the earth's ozone layer was linked to a chemical called chlorofluorocarbon (CFC). Developed in the 1930s, CFCs were believed to be safe and were widely used, such as in aerosol spray propellant, refrigeration, and air conditioning.

A depleted ozone layer has the potential of causing serious health problems around the world, including increased risk of serious sunburn, which in turn leads to an increased risk of skin cancer and cataracts (eye damage), and immunosuppressive diseases and premature aging of the skin (Environment Canada, 2009). Certain forms of skin cancers are known to be caused by ultraviolet radiation, and scientists claim that 'a sustained 10% depletion of the ozone layer would lead to a 26% per cent increase in non-melanoma skin cancer. This could mean an additional 300 000 cases per year world wide' (Environment Canada, 2009, n.p.).

Since the late 1980s, there has been a concerted effort to eliminate the causes of ozone depletion. Consequently, there has been a dramatic drop in the use of ozone-depleting substances. However, scientists continue to be concerned for three primary reasons: (1) there is uncertainty whether the ozone layer can return to its original thickness; (2) in recent years, the production and use of CFCs has recently increased; and (3) there is a decreasing sense of urgency to this problem as there is a popular misperception that ozone depletion has resolved itself (Auditor General of Canada, 1999).

The Industry's Effect on the Land that Feeds Us

The effect of the petrochemical industry is specifically noteworthy with regard to the manufacturing of pesticides for use in modern agriculture. The history of pesticides dates back to the 1880s when sulphur was applied to grape plants to combat a fungal disease known as powdery mildew. Shortly thereafter, Paris green (an arsenic-containing compound) was sprayed on potato plants to ward off the Colorado potato beetle, an insect that causes serious damage to potato plants, often eradicating whole crops. By the late 1890s, there were 42 insecticides that were available on the market. The petrochemical industry revolutionized agriculture and today there are approximately 40 000 pesticide products available for use. In 1939, a Swiss chemist by the name of Paul Müller developed a compound called dichlorodiphenyltrichloroethane more commonly known as DDT. DDT was used in World War II to control insect- and parasite-causing diseases in humans, such as typhus, malaria, and yellow fever (Wargo, 2006). During the 1940s pesticides 'conveyed an image of responsible and scientific land stewardship' (p. ix).

Many advantages to pesticide use were offered, including the following: pesticides greatly increase crop productions without rotating crops; they are highly cost effective and one farmer is able to work a large piece of land efficiently; there is decreased soil loss; and produce is picture-perfect, which consumers have grown to demand. Although not scientifically based, the common belief at that time was that these pesticides were safe as they disintegrated into the environment (Wargo, 2006). However, the wonders of DDT were not as innocuous or as easily controlled as originally believed; insects very quickly become resistant to pesticides, and pesticides persist in the environment and collect in plant and animal tissues and 'penetrate the germ cells to shatter or alter the very material of hereditary upon which the shape of the future depends' (Carson, 1962, p. 8).

DDT belongs to a group of chemicals in the environmental movement commonly referred to as persistent organic pollutants, better known as POPs. Initially there were a dozen of these chemicals, known as 'the dirty dozen'; in 2009, nine more chemicals were added to this list. According to Schapiro (2007), 'if The Hague had a list of chemical war criminals . . . POPs chemicals would be on it' (pp. 67–68). They 'act like light switches of toxicity upon the human body' (p. 68). When released into the environment, POPs are long-lasting and are spread through soil, water, and air. When they enter the body (of humans, fish, birds, and animals), they accumulate in fatty tissues, and concentration levels increase at high levels of the food chain. POPs have been linked to cancer, to nervous system and reproductive disorders, and to birth defects. As well, they are known to be **endocrine disruptors**.

endocrine disruptors
They mimic natural hormones circulating in the body, either enhancing or blocking the production of these hormones.

When wildlife moves from place to place, so too do the POPs. And POPs have been found throughout the world, often thousands of miles from the source of its use. Thus, dioxin emitted from a smokestack in Indiana, according to Johansen (2002), can be found in the breast milk of women living in Nunavut. The Arctic, which in our minds is pristinely clean, is in fact 'one of the most contaminated places on Earth—a place where Inuit mothers think twice before breast-feeding their babies because high levels of dioxins and other industrial chemicals are being detected in their breast milk and where a traditional diet of "country food" has become dangerous to the Inuit's health' (p. 479). Johansen explains that the Arctic acts as a 'cold trap', storing industrial pollutants (p. 480). Consequently, POP levels found in the blood and fatty tissues of the Inuit living in the Arctic are 'five to ten times greater than the national average in Canada or the United States' (p. 480).

DDT was banned in the United States in 1972 and in Canada in 1974, more than 10 years after Rachel Carson's damning evidence (Steingraber, 1998). Although DDT has been banned, Steingraber (1998, p. 9) informs us that the chemical continues to be present around us. First, since DDT is long-lasting, it continues to be present in the soil. What this means is that DDT residues can still be found in food crops. Second, DDT residues are found on certain birds and freshwater fish. Third, it is commonly found in hazardous waste sites. Fourth, traces of DDT are detected in carpet dust. Fifth, DDT is not banned in all countries and can be carried through global air currents. Finally, DDT has been found to surface in the deep waters of the Great Lakes.

The Industry's Effect on Farming

Pesticide use since World War II has changed the face of farming. Farming has become more intensive, with each acre of land producing higher yields. The smaller farms with a range of crops are less common; typically, larger farms produce fewer crops planted over greater acreage. Even though the number of farms has steadily declined since 1961, crop production has increased where 'the real value of production has tripled' (Agriculture and Agri-food Canada, 2008, n.p.). According to Sparling & Laughland (2008), 'large farms carry the economic clout in both revenue and profits' (p. 4).

The ability to rid any plant of disease or fungus enhances crop productivity and increases profits for farmers but at what cost to the environment? What effect has pesticide use had on the environment? Box 8.1 illustrates how pesticides affect our soil.

BOX 8.1 Soil Erosion

Soil erosion occurs when the topsoil is rapidly removed by wind or water. Each year in Canada, tonnes of soil are lost in this way. Soil erosion is problematic for many reasons. The topsoil is the most fertile part of the soil, and, should it be removed, the soil's stability is weakened. During a surface runoff the soil is deposited into rivers, lakes, and reservoirs, clogging these water systems. Clogged water systems increase the likelihood of flooding, thereby destroying the habitats of fish as well as other aquatic life (Trautmann et al., n.d.). The topsoil also carries manure, fertilizers, and pesticides, and these chemicals are potentially threatening water safety for fish, animals, and humans.

PEI Potato Farming: A Case Study

Prince Edward Island (PEI), aside from *Anne of Green Gables*, is well known for its ruby-red soil and potatoes; as a result, the province is particularly vulnerable to late blight fungus, one of the most serious potato diseases worldwide. Although PEI's soil conditions are ideal for growing potatoes, the high humidity also provides an ideal growing environment for the dreaded fungus. Because PEI is so small, fields are very close to one another. Should one field become infected, there is a strong likelihood that all fields will follow. In order to prevent crop infections, all potato growers take preventative measures (Blight Alert, 2007). Thus, PEI potatoes receive up to 20 dousings of chemical sprays in each growing season, which can cost the farmer up to $100 000 a year (The Perfect Potato, 2002). In 1999, torrential rainfalls hit PEI and tonnes of the red topsoil were swept away. For days after, the colour of the rivers was red. Then, dead fish appeared on the banks of the rivers and stream (Spills Lead to Fisheries Act Convictions, 2000, n.p.).

The PEI government introduced new laws in 2002 to limit the amount of runoff from the potato fields (Agricultural Crop Rotation Act, 2002). However, according to CTV's *W5* (2002), 'In one month alone, enforcement officers spotted nearly 100 violations. But only a couple of farmers have been charged, with minimal fines of about $200.00' (p. 4). Farmers say they spray because they need to, not because they want to (2002). Consumers demand perfect fruits and vegetable; and to please their consumers, farmers need to use lots of chemicals to avoid insect infestation. Farmers would prefer not to spray. Aside from the cost, farmers are also concerned that spraying may have adverse effects on their health. This concern has been denied by physicians and the PEI Department of Public Health:

> I asked the doctor one time, was it connected? And he told me, flatly, no. That there was no possible connection that he could make. And that's what I wanted to know. That was five years ago. So if I had even an inkling that I was doing something that caused my wife to be sick or somebody else's wife to be sick, I wouldn't do what I do. (*W5*, 2002, p. 2)

Linda Van Til, an epidemiologist for the PEI Department of Health, believes that cancer trends in PEI are no different than those in the rest of Canada (Delaney, 2006). However, Dr Matsusaki, who was relatively new to PEI in 2006 and worked in numerous emergency rooms across Canada and the United States, disagrees that cancer is not a problem in PEI: 'Nowhere, nowhere did I see cancer that in any way resembles the cancers that I saw when I came to PEI' (Mittlestaedt, 2006, n.p.). Matsusaki believes the source of cancer is the pesticides used on potatoes.

According to Steingraber (1998), farmers experience such cancers as prostate, melanoma, and multiple myeloma at much higher rates than the rest of the population. Brain cancer and non-Hodgkin's lymphoma also occur at higher rates but 'these excesses are more modest' (p. 65). Multiple myeloma and leukemia are higher in rural areas than in industrial ones.

The estimated cancer rates for men in PEI reveal that, compared with men in the rest of Canada, men in PEI have higher incidence rates of, to name a few, bladder cancer, melanoma, and leukemia. The incidence rate of prostate cancer in PEI is the highest in Canada (156/100,000 compared to 122/100,000 in Canada).

It is curious, then, that the PEI Ministry of Health claims that cancer rates in PEI are similar to other places in Canada. What would it mean for the government to admit there is a health problem and that pesticides are to blame? What policies are in place to protect citizens from pesticide residues? According to Albritton (2009, p. 112), the answer to the latter question is not straightforward as we do not know who determines what is an acceptable limit of pesticide residue. How do we establish safe limits given the diversity of people's body size, age, and health status, and is there a synergistic effect with pesticides and other chemicals? Although pesticide use has dramatically increased over the past couple of decades, the lack or absence of research on pesticide residues and policies identifying safety standards is disconcerting (Albritton, 2009).

Carson, in the early 1960s, identified three forms of silence that ultimately serve industry, not people. Two forms of silence continue to be relevant today: (1) environmental debates occur and stay behind closed doors of government offices; and (2) 'the hushed complicity of many individual scientists who were aware of—if not directly involved in documenting—the hazards created by chemical assaults on the natural world' (Steingraber 1998, p. 17). With silence comes protection. Who is the government protecting, if not its citizens?

How Agribusiness Controls Food, the Environment, and Our Health

Farming today is part of an integrated larger system that not only includes produce growers but also suppliers, distributors, and food manufacturers. This network is referred to as **agribusiness** and it is intricately linked to local and global markets. This section uses McDonald's food and the coffee industry as two examples that illustrate how corporations control the manufacturing of food, the environment, and our health.

agribusiness
Farming today is part of an integrated larger system that not only includes produce growers but also suppliers, distributors, and food manufacturers.

manufacturers of illness
Corporations who not only manufacture material goods and services—their products can also produce illness and death.

John McKinlay (2005), an epidemiologist, coined the term **manufacturers of illness**. McKinlay argues that 'in addition to producing material goods and services, [corporations] also produce, as an inevitable byproduct, widespread morbidity and mortality' (pp. 551–552). McKinlay illustrates that the food industry is a good example of how corporate profits contribute to ill health; yet ultimately, individuals are held accountable for their health. Since the 1960s, there has been a widespread decline in dietary standards in the United States and this is illustrated by increasing rates of overweight and obesity. More than half of all Americans are overweight and this is also true for Canadians. Tjepkema's (2007) study on obesity in Canada found that 59.2 per cent of Canadians are either overweight or obese (see Table 8.1). In fact, McKinlay believes that being overweight 'has reached epidemic proportions' (p. 555).

McKinlay (2005) provides evidence of how the food industry developed a campaign to shift our 'image of food' away from healthy basic staples, such as dairy products, fruits, and vegetables, to food that is synthetic and highly processed. Highly processed foods are cheaper to produce and this way 'makes good economic sense' (p. 555). But the consumer cost for corporate profit is poor nutritional value. Processed foods contribute to what is referred to as diseases of civilization or lifestyle diseases that afflict people living in Western countries. The diseases often include cardiovascular diseases and certain cancers, which are caused by alcohol and fat consumption, possibly in combination with environmental pollution.

Students may say we have choice in what we eat and how we eat. In this way, should a health problem arise, the individual is held responsible. However, the reality is that this is

TABLE 8.1 Adult BMI by Sex and Province

	Underweight, BMI under 18.50	Normal weight, BMI 18.50 to 24.99	Overweight, BMI 25.00 to 29.99	Obese, BMI 30.00 or higher	Total overweight and obese
	%	%	%	%	
Canada	**2.0**	**38.9**	**36.1**	**23.1**	**59.2**
Males	1.4 ᴱ	33.6	42.0	22.9	64.9
Females	2.5	44.1	30.2	23.2	53.4
Newfoundland and Labrador	**F**	**28.1**	**37.1**	**33.9**	**71.0**
Males	F	18.7	47.6	33.3	80.9
Females	F	37.3	26.8	34.5	61.3
Prince Edward Island	**F**	**32.5**	**40.2**	**26.3**	**66.5**
Males	F	27.5	49.8	22.1	71.9
Females	F	37.2	31.0	30.3	61.3
Nova Scotia	**F**	**37.7**	**35.0**	**24.7**	**59.7**
Males	F	39.8	40.1	18.8 ᴱ	40.1
Females	F	35.6	30.2	30.3	60.5
New Brunswick	**F**	**34.7**	**35.3**	**29.2**	**64.5**
Males	F	29.1	39.5	30.8	70.3
Females	F	40.1	31.1	27.6	58.7
Quebec	**2.2 ᴱ**	**41.5**	**34.5**	**21.8**	**56.3**
Males	F	36.3	41.2	20.9	62.1
Females	2.7 ᴱ	46.6	28.0	22.7	50.7
Ontario	**2.3 ᴱ**	**39.1**	**35.9**	**22.7**	**58.6**
Males	F	34.6	40.9	23	63.9
Females	3.1 ᴱ	43.5	31.0	22.4	53.4
Manitoba	**1.3 ᴱ**	**36.2**	**34.3**	**28.2**	**62.5**
Males	F	28.5	39.8	30.4	70.2
Females	F	43.6	28.9	26.0	54.9
Saskatchewan	**F**	**29.6**	**37.3**	**30.8**	**68.1**
Males	F	25.3	44.5	28.8	73.3
Females	F	33.9	30.2	32.9	63.1
Alberta	**F**	**37.3**	**35.7**	**25.2**	**60.9**
Males	F	29.5	41.1	27.7	68.8
Females	F	45.3	30.3	22.6	52.9
British Columbia	**F**	**40.0**	**39.8**	**19.2**	**59.0**
Males	F	33.5	47.3	18.2	65.5
Females	1.0 ᴱ	46.3	32.5	20.1	52.6

Note: Data with a coefficient of variation (CV) from 16.6% to 33.3% are identified by an (E) and should be interpreted with caution.

Source: Adapted from: Statistics Canada. (2004). Dynamics Nutrition: Findings from the Canadian Community Health Survey, Measured Obesity, 82-620-MIE2005001, no.1, July 2005. Available from www.statcan.gc.ca/pub/82-620-m/2005001/t/4053595-eng.htm

not the case; indeed, choice is socially and culturally constructed. Two examples are (1) poverty and (2) mass media and advertising.

Individuals who live in poverty have limited choices in what foods they can eat (Green et al., 2008). Their choice depends on the money they have, which often does not allow them to purchase fresh fruits and vegetables, or the foods they get from food banks. In both instances, the food is likely processed. Eating highly processed food is linked to an array of chronic diseases, cardiovascular disease (heart disease, stroke, and atherosclerosis) being the most prevalent (Green et al., 2008).

George Ritzer in 1993, drawing on Weber's theory of rationalization, coined the term **McDonaldization** to capture 'the process by which the principles of the fast-food restaurant are coming to dominate more and more sectors of American society as well as the rest of the world' (Ritzer, 2008, p. 1). The emphasis of McDonaldization is on profits at the expense of food quality. Thus, the food is highly processed and is high in fat, salt, and sugar. The food industry is well aware that there is an addictive quality to fat, sugar, and salt, especially in children. Foods that are high in nutrients, in contrast, taste bland. The preference for fast food, which develops in childhood according to Birch (1999), continues into adulthood and 'can promote patterns of food preference and intake that foster the development of overweight and obese individuals' (p. 57). In this way, an aggressive advertising campaign that is geared to children not only lays the groundwork for lifelong customers but also for chronic health conditions.

The growth of the international food industry has not only contributed to widespread **morbidity** and **mortality**, but it also has resulted in deforestation to accommodate intensive farming. The coffee industry is one such example. Since the 1970s, a coffee craze emerged in North America and the demand for coffee skyrocketed; this resulted in a change in the way coffee is grown. Coffee has now become second to oil in dollar value and is traded globally.

The old way of growing coffee was underneath a canopy of trees (called an overstorey) because the coffee plant was intolerant of sunlight. The overstorey also protected the coffee plant from any harsh weather and provided natural mulch to preserve the soil quality and reduce the number of weeds (Perfecto et al., 1996). This way of growing coffee could not meet the growing demand and, between the early 1970s and the early 1990s, the United States Agency for International Development (USAID) invested approximately $80 000 000 to 'technify' the coffee industry in the Caribbean and Central America by replacing the shade coffee plant with new varieties that tolerate sun (Rice & Ward, 1996). These plants produced more plants per acre (a four- to sixfold increase) and more coffee crop per tree (Perfecto et al., 1996).

However, in order to maintain the high-yield crops, lots of spraying was needed (remember there was no overstorey that provided protection to the plant). Coffee has become the third most heavily sprayed crop after cotton and tobacco (Pendergast, 1999). Pesticides that have been banned in Canada, the US, and many European countries continue to be used on coffee. This is problematic both for consumers of coffee and for coffee plantation workers. Coffee that is sprayed with chemicals that are illegal in Canada continues to be imported, and consumers are unknowingly being exposed to pesticide residues. Thus, according to Steingraber, 'we have one foot each in lifestyle and environment' (1998, p. 61).

McDonaldization

A term coined by George Ritzer to expand Weber's notion of rationalization; defined as the standardization of social life by rules and regulations, such as increased monitoring and evaluation of individual performance, akin to the uniformity and control measures used by fast-food chains. These principles are now applied to other sectors, both locally and globally.

morbidity
Rates of illness.

mortality
Rates of death.

Coffee workers may be unaware of the dangers of the pesticides they are using. Research from Tanzania showed that workers did not wear protective gear when spraying and were not informed about proper procedures (no mixing instructions) for applying pesticides (Ngowi et al., 2001). In instances where safety precautions are in place, according to a 1997 study done by the US Labor Education in the Americas Project (USLEAP), the safe waiting period for re-entering a sprayed area was at times ignored, and spraying occurred in areas that were forbidden, such as near drinking water or near houses (A day in the life of a coffee worker, 2010). Linda Diebel, an investigative journalist for the *Toronto Star,* describes the harsh conditions of coffee workers in plantations in Guatemala as 'a brutal place of working children, starvation wages, bonded labor, threats and intimidation, plastic sheeting for shelter, lack of sanitation and flooding, high infant mortality, bone-breaking work and far too many deaths from easily preventable, and treatable, diseases' (1997, n.p.). USLEAP reports that a more recent survey and anecdotal evidence indicate that little has changed since 1997.

The story of coffee illustrates how agribusiness and governments turn a blind eye and allow crops that have been sprayed with pesticides that are legally banned in their own countries to be sold here. It also shows how the most impoverished people living in cash-strapped economies are exposed to harsh and dangerous working conditions. Their choice is either not to work and be unable to support their family or to work and be exposed to serious health risks.

How Farming is Linked to Our Drinking Water: Walkerton, a Case Study

This section examines the relationship between farming, government regulation, and our drinking water. Although water and food are regulated in similar fashions, acceptable levels are more rigorous for water than for food. That being said, water can still be contaminated by pesticides yet fall below the regulated criteria. In theory, water is regulated on an ongoing basis. However, this was not the case in Walkerton, Ontario. Walkerton, according to Prudham (2004, p. 344), 'is an example of broad regulatory failure and the systematic production of environmental risks by neoliberal governance reforms'.

In May 2000, Walkerton, a small town in southwestern Ontario surrounded by rich agricultural land, appeared on the front pages of all newspapers in Canada when the town's drinking water became contaminated with *Escherichia coli,* better known as *E. coli.* Typically *E. coli,* a bacterium that lives in the intestines of mammals, is transmitted through eating meat that is undercooked or drinking milk that is not pasteurized. Walkerton is the first known case in North America of water-borne *E. coli.* The bacterium can wreak havoc on the intestines causing fever and diarrhea, which may lead to dehydration, to an increase in blood pressure, to lower red blood cell and platelet counts, and, in the worst case, to death. In Walkerton, 2300 of the town's approximate population of 5000 fell ill, and there were seven deaths (Schabas, 2002).

The source of the *E. coli* was in one of the town's wells, Well 5, which was dug in 1978 and was located next to a farm of cattle, on low-lying land (Perkel, 2002). It was not a deep well and from the onset the water showed signs of contamination. The Ministry of the Environment approved Well 5 with the understanding that the water be disinfected and routinely tested. The ministry also recommended that the land surrounding Well 5 be declared a protection zone to reduce the risk of contamination by agriculture and that Well 5 be viewed as an interim source of water supply for Walkerton. These recommendations were never signed upon, nor did the ministry oversee whether its recommendations were implemented.

In May 2000, Walkerton experienced many days of heavy rain, and on Friday May 12, according to Perkel (2002, p. 59), '[the] storm had pushed a lethal bacterial predator down beneath the emerging crops and fertile soil in the aquifer that fed the well that was being pumped to the taps of the town' (p. 60). The water from Well 5 had been contaminated from the adjacent land where 95 cattle roamed (Prudham, 2004). The strain of *E. coli* found in Well 5 lives in the guts of cattle and is spread through the cattle's feces. If water that is contaminated by the feces is ingested by humans, the results are catastrophic. On May 15, the local Public Utilities Commission (PUC), in routine fashion, sampled the local water supply. Of note, a water sample of Well 5 earlier in May had found bacteria (not *E. coli*) in both the raw and treated water; no one in the PUC, however, seemed concerned. The results for the May 15 test were faxed to the PUC on May 17 and the results showed that the water sample was contaminated with *E. coli*.

The first patients with symptoms (bloody diarrhea, vomiting, cramps, and fever) of *E. coli* were treated on May 15, and four days later the Medical Health Office (MHO) was informed that there were several patients experiencing these symptoms. The MHO contacted the PUC, who offered assurances that the water was safe, even though tests showed bacteria and *E. coli* present in the wells. Each day thereafter, more cases of illness were reported and the PUC held firm that the water was safe. The MHO warned the community not to drink the water and began doing independent water tests. On May 23, the MHO's test results revealed the water was contaminated with *E. coli*. The PUC in response admitted knowing this and also informed the MHO that water from another well, for some time, was not being chlorinated due to equipment failure. The suppressing of information of tainted water, or the 'silence' as Carson would say, did not only occur locally, but Ontario's Ministry of the Environment was also implicated. The ministry had in fact received information in April, one month before the crisis erupted, that the water supply in Walkerton was bad, but municipal water systems was 'as the highest-level ministry managers had decided, a non-priority' (Perkel, 2002, p. 120).

The premier of Ontario at this time was Mike Harris, a Conservative whose policies were shaped by a neo-liberal ideology known as the 'Common Sense Revolution'. Harris's government was committed to reducing the deficit and lowering taxes through deep cuts to or elimination of certain government programs. Thus, the Common Sense Revolution, which rolled back environmental regulations, created the conditions that allowed the Walkerton tragedy to occur (Prudham, 2004). The government in this instance was the 'manufacturer of illness'. The Walkerton story 'serve[s] as a reminder that social regulation of nature under late capitalism is meant to protect us from the self-regulating market, and not the other way around' (p. 357). The Ontario government's neo-liberal policies of 'fiscal austerity, administrative de-regulation and re-regulation; and privatization' (p. 344) contributed to the tragedy by 'undermin[ing] agricultural and water quality regulation' (p. 344).

The health effects of the contaminated water in Walkerton are long lasting. An ongoing Walkerton health study as a result of the tainted water shows some children have lasting kidney problems; those residents who experienced severe gastroenteritis are at increased risk for high blood pressure and kidney damage (Canadian Press, 2008).

The Petrochemical Industry and Plastics: Links to Health

Look under your sink; what do you see? Look in the refrigerator; what do you see? Look in your bathroom cabinet; what do you see? Chances are you will see plastic. Dishwashing detergent, stainless steel cleaner, yogurt, milk, Tupperware, and medicine are mostly all stored in plastic containers. So, why are plastics a problem?

In 2008, CBC produced a documentary called *The Disappearing Male,* which asks the question, 'Are males an endangered species'? The film is based on a study (Mackenzie et al., 2005) that showed decreasing numbers of male children being born in Aamjiwnaang, a First Nations community. Particularly noteworthy is that Aamjiwnaang is located near Sarnia, Ontario, and borders on what is known as Chemical Valley, named for the large numbers of petrochemical plants. Examining birth records from 1984 to 2003 (see Figure 8.1), Mackenzie et al. (2005) showed there has been a substantial decrease in births of baby boys in the 10-year period between 1993 and 2003. The ratio of boys to girls born in this time period is 46 to 132, compared to 105 to 100 overall in Canada. Although definitive conclusions are difficult to make because 'several potential factors may be contributing to the observed decrease in sex ratio' (p. 1297), the researchers nevertheless believe 'the close proximity of this community to the large aggregation of petrochemical industry and potential exposures to compounds' explains the difference (p. 1297).

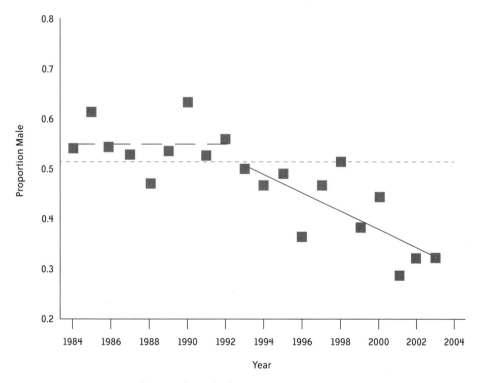

FIGURE 8.1 Proportion of Live Male Births for Aamjiwnaang First Nation, 1984–2003

Source: Mackenzie, C.A., Lockridge, A., & Keith, M. (2005). Declining sex ratio in a First Nation community. *Environmental Health Perspectives, 113*(10), doi:10.1289/ehp.8479.

A decade earlier, Colborn et al. (1996), in their book *Our Stolen Future*, documented the catastrophic effect certain chemicals have on the reproductive systems of some animal species, such as a dramatic decrease in sperm count over two decades (1970s to 1990s); numerous cases of alligators with shrivelled penises and testicles; feminized male behaviours; and female infertility. Colborn argued that there were 51 man-made chemicals, although thousands were yet to be tested, that disrupt or scramble hormonal communications. The chemicals to which Colborn is referring are PCBs and DDT, as Rachel Carson had pointed out more than a decade earlier.

These chemicals are known as endocrine disruptors, which either mimic natural hormones such as estrogen circulating in the body, thus enhancing estrogens' effect or they 'block or interfere' with the production of these hormones. They are also known as 'environmental estrogens' (Larkin, 1995, p. 25). In women, estrogen is necessary for normal sexual development and a healthy reproductive system. Should the body produce too little estrogen in women of child-bearing age, infertility may result; too much estrogen increases a woman's risk for cancer of the uterus and breast, and for gallbladder disease. Men's bodies produce much lower levels of estrogen than women's. Too much estrogen in a man's body, however, can reduce sperm production and testes growth (Larkin, 1995). Environmental estrogens come from 'industrial products and byproducts, such as chemicals used to make plastic packaging or those contained in pesticides . . . and may also be used as ingredients in cosmetics' (p. 25). Environmental estrogens also include synthetic estrogen products, such as the birth control pill, hormone replacement therapy, and diethylstilbestrol, better known as DES (see Box 8.2).

Plastics: An Estrogen Mimicker

In the late 1980s two cell biologists, Ana Soto and Carlos Sonnenschein, were studying the relationship between estrogen and breast cancer and made an 'accidental discovery'. In one of their plastic test tubes, they found that breast cancer cells with no estrogens began to divide in similar fashion to those containing estrogen. Soto, in an interview, said, 'We spent four months trying to figure out where the unknown estrogen came from until we verified that it was something shedding from the test tubes that we used to store the serum components' (Taube, 2009, n.p.). The researchers were able to isolate those test tubes that leaked estrogen. Ana Soto describes their findings:

> It turned out to be nonylphenol, an antioxidant that's also used in the synthesis of detergents. Carlos and I published our findings and then went looking for other places where nonylphenol was used. It turned out that it's also in the spermicides used in condoms and in creams applied with diaphragms . . . right there we knew it could be a big problem. (n.p.)

Soto and Sonnenschein found that nonylphenol is estrogenic, and the nonylphenol test tubes made breast cancer cells grow faster. Since this finding, many more chemicals have been recognized as estrogen mimickers.

Surfactants and plasticizers are two widely used groups of synthetic compounds. Surfactants are added to detergents, herbicides, paint, shampoo, hair conditioners, shaving cream, spermicides, and adhesives, to name a few, to allow for either adherence or

BOX 8.2 Synthetic Estrogen

DES was commonly prescribed to pregnant women to prevent miscarriage between the mid-1940s and 1971. DES was discovered in 1938; it was seen as a pharmaceutical breakthrough as it was the first time a drug with estrogenic effects was marketed in pill form. DES was approved in the United States by the Food and Drug Administration in 1941, even though preliminary research on laboratory animals found that DES 'caused cancer and problems with sexual development in laboratory animals' (Langston, 2008, n.p.). An estimated 5 million women took DES when pregnant. The first studies that challenged the safety of DES appeared in 1952; they revealed that DES had no beneficial effect in high-risk pregnancies and there was some evidence that DES increased the risk of miscarriage. But these studies were largely ignored until the late 1960s.

The case of DES is particularly instructive as it 'provide[s] one of the first confirmed examples of how these chemicals can affect not only those who are directly exposed but also future generations' (Chatterjee, 1996, p. 18). Beginning in 1968, an American gynecologist identified a link between eight young women who were diagnosed with a rare form of vaginal cancer and their respective mothers, who used DES during their pregnancies. Although eight cases is not a large number by any means, it raised suspicion because there were only three other similar cases previously reported in the medical literature. Cancer was not the most common side effect; other more common side effects included miscarriages, ectopic pregnancies, and premature births in daughters of DES users; and epididymal cysts (testicular masses), undescended testes, higher risk for prostate cancer, and low sperm count and motility in their sons. Women who took DES were also at a higher risk for breast cancer.

lubrication: for example, paint, which is smoothly applied to a wall; and shaving cream, which allows the razor to glide easily on the skin. A team of English researchers found that surfactants could stimulate breast cancer cell growth and possibly feminize male fish (Steingraber, 1998, p. 111). Although there have been numerous reported incidents of fish 'with hormonal abnormalities consistent with exposure to estrogenic substances in river-borne sewage' (p. 112), it is not clear whether the feminization of fish in these sewage waters is totally due to sewage polluted with surfactants or to an 'exposure to natural and synthetic estrogens found in women's urine' (p. 112). (Think about the birth control pill.)

Phthalates, perhaps the most well-known plasticizer, has been widely used to make plastics soft and flexible; however, phthalates are also estrogen mimickers. When first marketed, phthalates were ubiquitous; they were widely used, for example, in baby's products, such as soothers, toys (the rubber ducky), and jars for baby food; as well as in plastic wraps for food and plastic containers that store food; in shower curtains, shampoo bottles, and even perfume. When either ingested or inhaled (remember babies put everything in their mouths), phthalates become absorbed by the cells of the pituitary gland, which regulates several different hormonal systems, including sex hormones. Phthalates have been found to reduce testosterone levels, which can then lead to sexual malformations (Schapiro, 2007). Swan and her colleagues (2005) tested the urine of 134 pregnant women from the United States Midwest and California for phthalate levels. They found that the anogenital distance (AGD) (the distance between the anus and the scrotum) in their newborns was 'shortened and testicular descent impaired in boys whose mothers had elevated prenatal phthalate exposure' (p. 1061). In an interview with Schapiro (2007), Swan expressed concern that phthalates may account for 'the feminization of infant boys' (p. 47).

In 1999, the European Union, drawing on European and American research, placed a temporary ban on six phthalates, and in 2004 the ban became permanent. In the United States, a ban on the manufacturing and selling of children's products using certain types of phthalates with concentrations greater than 0.1 per cent was enacted in August 2008 and the law came into effect in February 2009. And in Canada on June 19, 2009, a decade later than in Europe, the government announced a ban on six phthalates (DEHP, DINP, DBP, BBP, DNOP, and DIDP) used in children's toys and products. Although phthalates have been banned in children's products, they continue to be used in prescription and over-the-counter drugs, with timed-release coating (Cone, 2008, n.p.).

The Nuclear Industry: Links to Health

At the same time the petrochemical industry was hitting its stride around the Second World War, the nuclear industry added to the melee with the introduction of its own toxic materials. The difference between chemicals and radiation, according to Bertell, is 'whereas chemicals must touch us or be consumed by us with water or in food in order to poison us, radiation is able to harm us even at a distance' (1999, p. 43). Radiation is typically classified into electromagnetic and particulate radiation. Electromagnetic radiation is either ionizing, which comes from radioactive material, or non-ionizing. Examples of ionizing radiation are X-rays, microwaves, and radio waves. Sunlight hitting the earth's surface is an example of non-ionizing radiation. Particulate radiation is responsible for the atomic bomb, which the Americans dropped on Hiroshima and Nagasaki in August 1944. More than 100 000 people died immediately and many more thousands experienced acute radiation syndrome, which included fever, nausea, vomiting, bloody diarrhea, hair loss, bruising, mouth sores, and ulcers (Radiation Health Effects, 2007). Individuals exposed to radiation were diagnosed with cancers such as multiple myeloma, a cancer with previously low incidence in Japan. Radiation is also used to support nuclear reactors for nuclear energy. The **growth imperative**, since the end of World War II, led to energy demands beyond the scope of hydroelectric plants. As such, nuclear electricity was developed and today comprises over 16 per cent of the world's electricity (World Nuclear Association, 2009). In order to generate nuclear energy, nuclear reactors are needed ' to make steam to generate electricity'. It goes without saying that nuclear energy has been the source of much world-wide controversy. Hossay, for example, says, 'Necessary safety measures meant that it was more expensive than initially promised; and the problem of disposing of waste with a dangerous life in thousands of years proved politically difficult' (2006, p. 75).

In order to support both nuclear reactors and nuclear weapons, extensive uranium mining is necessary, which has led to health problems of its own. Uranium is usually found in land that has been of little use. Bertell points out that 'it is no coincidence it has

growth imperative
Economic growth that is long term and sustained, supported by government policies that promote free markets.

been found primarily on the lands of Indigenous Peoples' (1999, p. 47), as is the case in Canada. Canada is the world's largest producer of uranium, producing 20.5 per cent of the world's output. The only active mine today is in northern Saskatchewan, which exports 80 per cent of its production to nuclear electric utility customers worldwide. Although lung cancer has been linked to uranium mining, other health effects are difficult to establish (Elias et al., 1997). In one study of Navaho children living in New Mexico, researchers reported a statistically significant increase in birth defects, stillbirths, and deaths in children born near uranium mine dumps. Yet the researchers were unable to link the health effects to 'reported duration of exposure, and other possibilities may explain the increase, including paternal employment in the mines, which was marginally significantly associated with the elevated risk for adverse outcome' (p. 47).

Dr David Maxwell (2008), a Nova Scotia emergency medicine physician and retired professor of family medicine and emergency medicine at Dalhousie University, unequivocally believes that 'radioactivity damages cells' (n.p.). In an interview with the Environmental Health Association of Nova Scotia, Dr Maxwell said that radiation causes 'chromosome breaks, which cause genetic defects, pregnancy losses, lowered fertility and all the things that happen when you disrupt people's genetic makeup' (n.p.). As well, uranium is an endocrine disruptor that when ingested can 'cause neurologic damage or endocrine damage'. Ingestion can occur when drinking water or eating food that is contaminated with uranium, or through hand-to-mouth activities when touching contaminated soil. Should a fire occur in a uranium storage facility, uranium deposits are re-suspended into the air and can be carried by wind.

The accident at the Chernobyl nuclear plant in the Ukraine on April 26, 1986, is an example of the profound effects of a nuclear accident on a community, if not a continent. Two explosions occurred within the plant that led to numerous fires and a 10-day intense graphite fire responsible for the dispersion of radionuclides and fission fragments high into the atmosphere (Chernobyl, 2002, n.p.). The Chernobyl power plant was located in a populated area. There were over 100 000 people living within a 30-km radius of the plant and all were evacuated. However, most European countries experienced the effects of deposited radionuclides: Austria, Eastern and Southern Switzerland, parts of Southern Germany, and Scandinavia experienced the greatest amounts. The effects on the environment and on health from the nuclear accident were both immediate and long term. Contamination of forests, waters, and agricultural land occurred in Belarus, Ukraine, and Russia. Agricultural land that is highly contaminated will produce food with excessive levels of radionuclides. There continues to be concerns over levels of radioactivity of food products, such as berries, mushroom, and game meat, from forested areas in the Ukraine, and although drinking water for the time being appears to be safe, contamination of fish may be a long-term problem. There were 31 deaths, and 134 people needed treatment for acute radiation syndrome shortly after the accident. Long term, there has been a statistically significant increase in rates in cancer of the thyroid in children (see Table 8.2) and to a lesser degree in adults.

The challenges of storing nuclear wastes in combination with the risks of another nuclear disaster for many environmentalists mean that nuclear energy is not a viable solution to the increasing demand of energy. Instead, the solution lies in 'solar, wind, hydro, geothermal, and biomass energy—coupled with rapid improvement in the efficiency with which power is used' (Flavin, 2006a; n.p.).

TABLE 8.2 Number of Cases of Thyroid Cancers in Children under 15 Years Old at Diagnosis and Cancer Incidence Rates (Number of Cases per 100 000 Children)

	1986	1987	1988	1989	1990	1991	1992	1993	1994	1995	1996	1997	1998
Belarus	3	4	6	5	31	62	62	87	77	82	67	73	48
	0.2	0.3	0.4	0.3	1.9	3.9	3.9	5.5	5.1	5.6	4.8	5.6	3.9
Russian Federation	–	1	–	–	1	1	3	1	6	7	2	5	–
		0.3			0.3	0.3	0.9	0.3	2.8	2.5	0.6	2.2	
Ukraine	8	7	8	11	26	22	49	44	44	47	56	36	44
	0.2	0.1	0.1	0.1	0.2	0.2	0.5	0.4	0.4	0.5	0.6	0.4	0.5
Total	11	12	14	16	58	85	114	132	127	136	125	114	92

Source: Reproduced from *British Medical Journal*, V.A. Stsjazhko, A.F. Tsyb, N.D. Tronko, G. Souchkevitch, K.F. Baverstock, 310, © 1995 with permission from BMJ Publishing Group Ltd.

The Nuclear Industry's Links to Environmental Racism

In the 1980s, civil rights activists brought people's attention to the fact that many African Americans in the United States were disproportionately living in communities that neighboured with industries that emitted wastes that were either carcinogenic or that led to other serious health outcomes, such as breathing problems and miscarriages (Westra & Lawson, 2001). **Environmental racism** is now used to describe how disadvantaged communities are disproportionately exposed to environmental health factors and disasters brought about by government or industrial policies. In theses instances people have little choice in terms of where they live and where they work. The most compelling example of environmental racism in Canada is that of First Nations people living on reserves (see Box 8.3).

This environmental racism is evident in the number of communities in Canada whose members live their daily lives with unsafe water even though Health Canada's water program mandates the 'protection of public health from microbiological pathogens, chemical and physical, and radiological contaminants found in drinking water and recreational water supplies' (Assembly of First Nations, 2009, n.p.). According to the Assembly of First Nations, '20 per cent of communities live with contaminated water', and 'there are currently 93 boil water advisories in First Nations communities across the country, some of which are long-standing' (Halpin, 2009, p. 18). Although in principle First Nations people should have access to the same water quality as all Canadians, at this time there are no legislative and regulatory frameworks to ensure this occurs. Neskantaga chief Roy Moonias responded to this injustice by saying 'Nowhere else in Canada would anyone accept this . . . It's a violation of our fundamental human rights . . . We're being treated as second-class citizens' (quoted in Petersen, 2008, n.p.).

environmental racism

A term used to describe how disadvantaged communities are disproportionately exposed to environmental health factors and disasters brought about by government and/or industrial policies.

Theory Link
See Chapter 7 for a discussion of Aboriginal peoples' health.

First Nations people depend on water for 'fishing, hunting and spiritual practices' (McCurdy, 2001, p. 20). The struggle for many First Nation groups throughout North America is that both their land and water have been contaminated by mining, by

BOX 8.3 Environmental Racism and First Nations

Africville was a black settlement in the north end of Halifax, Nova Scotia, where 'blacks became a poorly educated, economically marginalized and socially excluded subculture in Nova Scotian society that governments felt no obligation to respect' (McCurdy, 2001, p. 99). Africville, from its beginning (in the mid-1850s), was environmentally attacked. For example, by the late 1800s, the residents of Africville were neighbours to 'an oil plant/storage complex, a fertilizer plant, a rolling mill, two slaughter houses, a coal handling facility, a tar factory, a tannery, a shoe factory, several stone-crushing facilities, a foundry, and a fertilizer-producing plant' (McCurdy, 2001, pp. 101–102). Africville was home to waste-disposal pits and in the 1950s, the city council of Halifax 'moved the open city dump to Africville because it was too much of a "health menace" to locate anywhere' (p. 102). Africville is an example of the relationship between race, class, and exposure to environmental hazards. Being poor and black limits the choices of where to live. At the same time, the government feels entitled to pollute land where poor people live. McCurdy (2001) points out that 'Africville was a victim of the NIMBY [not in my backyard] principle which was practiced in many predominant white urban and suburban communities in North America' (p. 107).

petrochemical plants, and by hydroelectric dams. As well, according to Laduke (1999), reservations 'have been targeted' for nuclear waste dumps (p. 2). The Great Lakes, which drain into the St. Lawrence River, for example, are home to one-quarter of all North American industry, and 'puts the Akwesasne [Mohawk] reservation downstream from some of the most lethal and extensive pollution on the continent' (p. 15). All these industries used PCBs (one of the POPs) until they were banned in 1978. In the meantime, PCBs contaminated the air, water, and soil, and then moved through the food chain. PCBs have been linked to 'liver, brain, nerve and skin disorders in humans, shrinking testicles in alligators and cancer and reproductive disorders in laboratory animals' (p. 15). Breast cancer is the number one cancer among First Nations women, and in Ontario, these rates are increasing.

First Nations people have higher rates of infectious diseases; higher rates of certain chronic diseases, such as diabetes and heart disease; and higher rates of birth defects, such as cleft palate, club foot, and Down syndrome. Moreover, both men's and women's life expectancy is shorter than their non-First Nations counterparts. (See Chapter 7 on the health of First Nations peoples.) Some of these differences can be attributed to social determinants of health, such as income and education; however, another important determinant is environment. The contamination of their air, land, and water by industry has direct and indirect effects on health. For example, there are noted birth defects as those listed above; higher incidences of leukemia, lung, and renal cancers (López-Abente et al., 1999; 2001); and chromosome aberrations (Au et al., 1995) for people either working in or living close to uranium mines. Many First Nations reserves are located in close proximity to either active or closed uranium mines. The effect of contamination through industry or mining has changed First Nations' people's traditional way of living (Laduke, 1999). Unable to either fish or farm, in combination with limited income, has meant a diet high in carbohydrates and low in protein. In this instance, poor eating is an outcome of environmental devastation.

Challenges in Linking Health to the Environment

There are numerous cases of communities or groups of people coming together to try and make sense of what they perceive to be clusters of serious illnesses emerging in their respective communities (see Box 8.4 for one such example). Should a cluster of illness arise, more often than not the community is confronted with resistance from public health officials because 'common people' are unable to 'grasp the statistical concept of randomness' (Steingraber, 1998). It is very difficult to meet the criteria of scientific rigour statistically. First, reaching statistical significance with a small sample is challenging. Second, as Steingraber (1998) points outs,

epidemiology

The statistical study of patterns of disease in the population. Originally focused on epidemics, or infectious diseases, it now covers non-infectious conditions, such as stroke and cancer.

> In cluster studies, **epidemiologists** look for an increase over and above some background level, but if the people in the background are also becoming increasingly contaminated, the researchers are paddling a boat in a moving stream [and] differences are harder to see. Finally, a researcher cannot ask a group of citizens to not move from an area, which is potentially contaminated, so they can have a decent case-control study. (p. 76)

Another challenge of linking cancer to the environment has to do with lag time. Cancer generally occurs many years after exposure to a contaminant, complicating exposure assessment. As a result, researchers rely on records and on people's memory (Steingraber, 1998). Old records may be incomplete or nonexistent and people's memories, fragile and thus often unreliable. As well, there are a multiple of factors that may lead to cancer, such as environmental exposure to pesticides, to fires (think about the smoke billowing high above the Hudson River after the September 11 bombing of the World Trade Center in New York City), and to cigarette smoking. Or there may be trace amounts of residues in any one item, let's say food, which is deemed to be safe, but perhaps there is a cumulative effect. As Carson (1962) explains, 'any single supposedly "safe dose" may be enough to tip the scales that are already loaded with other "safe doses"' (p. 237). Isolating a single cause, therefore, is often difficult.

Finally, people move not only within their community but also to different geographical regions or even countries. A physician who is untrained in environmental health may not think about asking 'Where did you live on September 11, 2001?'

Risk Assessment, Prove Harm, and the Precautionary Principle

This chapter discussed how chemicals such as pesticides were approved for use even though their full effects on human health were unknown, how drugs were marketed even though research on animals showed there were adverse effects, and how governments deny responsibility when a toxic hazard occurs. **Risk assessment** is the process governments use to assess a chemical's potential for injury on humans and the environment. Risk assessment determines government policies on, for example, acceptable levels of drug residues in beef or pesticide residues in food; the amount of bacteria or other pollutants that are allowed in drinking water; acceptable levels of toxic chemicals being

risk assessment

The process governments use to assess a chemical's potential for injury on humans and on the environment.

BOX 8.4 Shannon, Quebec

Communities that have been situated next to old dumpsites may be at higher risk for cancer although this is difficult to prove. Shannon, Quebec, is one such community. Shannon is a community of 2000 residents just outside Quebec City. It also neighbours a military complex, Base Valcartier. In the 1970s the military buried vast quantities of trichloroethylene (TCE) residues.

TCE is an industrial solvent used to degrease metal parts; it is also used in paint removers, spot removers, and rug cleaners. In 2007, the Canadian Environmental Protections Act mandated a 65 per cent reduction in TCE use as it is recognized as a possible human carcinogen. Animal studies have also shown there is a possible link in rats between TCE exposure and kidney and testicular tumours; and in mice, to pulmonary and liver tumours.

In 1997 the military found that its drinking water was contaminated with TCEs and as a result changed its drinking water supply. However, the military did not notify the town of Shannon until 2000, and residents continued to drink water contaminated with TCE 200 times the safe level. The residents of Shannon were convinced that cancer was rampant and rates were much higher compared to those generally in Canada. After much denial from the province, in 2009 a team of Montreal researchers supported what the community knew:

> . . . through DNA testing a common pattern in the cancerous tissue of patients exposed to TCE, a pattern not seen in other cancerous tissues. . . 'Here in Shannon we have a population of maybe 4,000 . . . and actually I have 12 cancers of the brain. It's at least 12 times more than it should be.' (Researchers Find Link, 2009, n.p.)

Even though the government now recognizes there is a link between TCE and cancer, it refuses to acknowledge that this is the case in Shannon; the Shannon residents 'were not exposed to high enough concentrations over a long enough period to become ill' (DND denies blame, 2010). Their struggle continues.

emitted from petrochemical plants; radiation limits for technicians working in hospitals; and workplace safety (Montague, 2004).

There are three components to risk assessment: (1) estimating how hazardous the chemical is; (2) estimating the number of people exposed to the chemical and at what levels exposures occur; and (3) estimating the potential for harm among those exposed to the chemical (Montague, 2004). To assess risk, a mathematical probability is presented that calculates the risk of ingesting or being exposed to a certain chemical. The role of government policy-makers, then, is to decide whether one in a million deaths is an acceptable level or to increase or decrease the risk to what *is* deemed acceptable.

Thus, risk assessment is a highly political process, requiring value judgment (Hossay, 2006); assumptions, not science, shape decision-making around risk assessment (McBane, 2005). Montague (2004) argues that the process of risk assessment is fundamentally biased to large corporations who can manipulate the outcomes of research to their benefit. This is done by hiring scientists who 'can select and manipulate the data and choose particular assumptions (often silently), thus allowing them to reach almost any conclusion they set out to reach. Then they package it as "science" even though the conclusions are based on judgment and is not in any way reproducible' (p. 30). Or, more insidiously, corporations are partnered with governments, with each working for their own agenda.

For example, at the same time that this chapter was written, there was an article on asbestos that appeared in *The Globe and Mail* (Simpson, 2010). Asbestos, widely used as a fire retardant, is a known carcinogen and is no longer used anywhere in Canada. However, mining of asbestos continues to be active in Quebec, and the asbestos is exported to countries in the global South, in particular to India. Simpson reports that 'asbestos represents 11 per cent of Québec's exports to India, a tidy sum of $427-million' (p. A5). The manufacturers of asbestos focus on profit and not on health; the workers need jobs to support their families. But why are the federal and provincial governments complicit in selling carcinogenic material to countries in the global South instead of putting a stop to this practice? According to Simpson, the 'fear of offending Québec has put a sock in the mouth of federal governments, and fear of losing a few votes has forced Québec governments into acrobatic flight of hypocrisy to defend the indefensible' (p. A5).

prove harm
Scientific proof that a product is harmful.

Partnered with risk assessment is the notion of **prove harm**: unless there is scientific certainty that harm exists, 'anything goes' (Montague, 2004, p. 25). For example, the World Trade Organization's rules state that there can be no restrictions placed on products for unknown health effects or if there is no definitive evidence that the product is unsafe, even though safety concerns have been raised (Hossay, 2006). In this way, business is protected at the expense of an individual's health, and the burden of proof is placed on the consumers to prove the product unsafe before protective action will occur. Steingraber (1998) argues that the prove harm approach is 'tantamount to running an uncontrolled experiment using human subjects' (p. 270). Instead, she calls for an upstream approach, one that prevents harm before it occurs.

precautionary principle
The principle of taking into account not just known risks, but also potential risks, even if the evidence for those potential risks is weak. In these circumstances, (e.g. a drug) the precautionary principle would say that the product should either not be marketed or should be marketed under significant restrictions.

The **precautionary principle** is one such approach. The basic tenet of the precautionary principle is to safeguard human life so that 'when an activity raises threats of harm to human health or the environment, precautionary measures should be taken even if some cause and effect relationships are not fully established scientifically' (Steingraber, 1998, p. 284). In this way, the burden of proof is not on the public to demonstrate that harm has occurred but, rather, the burden is on industry to prove the product is unequivocally safe.

Conclusion

In Canada, we have ignored Rachel Carson's warnings from 50 years ago. There is some evidence that the precautionary principle is taking hold in Europe (Raffensperger & Tickner, 1999), but in Canada there is less room for optimism. According to a press release put forth by the Canadian Environmental Law Association, the federal government's proposals that manage toxic chemicals 'are neither preventive nor protective for Canadians, [and] . . . we are giving industry a free pass to continue with business as usual' (Environmental Organizations Issue Criticism, 2008, n.p.). It appears that Canada's government commitment lies in a risk-assessment approach and that the government has demonstrated no interest in adopting standards based on the precautionary principle.

Summary of Main Points

- Drawing on Rachel Carson's research, this chapter examines the complexities between our environment and our health and the difficulties and strategies involved in proving these linkages.
- The widespread use of pesticides and herbicides and their effect on health and the environment is studied through the PEI potato industry and pesticide use. Cancer rates, particularly those linked to pesticide use, in PEI for both men and women have steadily been increasing at a faster rate than in all of Canada.
- The networks of agribusiness are described using examples of McDonaldization and the coffee industry. Both produce widespread environmental devastation as well as health hazards to workers in large part through heavy pesticide use. Pesticides, banned in Canada, continue to be used on coffee, and consumers are unknowingly being exposed to pesticide residues.
- The manufacturing of synthetic compounds such as plastics in everyday consumption are examined. Plastics are known to be estrogen disruptors, which either mimic or block estrogen production. Estrogen disruptors can increase a woman's risk for cancer and in men, can reduce sperm production and testes growth.
- The nuclear industry is examined in relation to the health effects of mining uranium, radiation, and nuclear power plants. Lung cancer is an occupational health hazard among mine workers, and birth defects and stillbirths have been observed in communities situated close to mines. In Chernobyl, thyroid cancer is particularly high among children exposed to radiation due to fire at the nuclear plant.
- Environmental racism and popular epidemiology are described using the examples of Africville, Nova Scotia; First Nations communities; and Shannon, Quebec. Disadvantaged communities, where people have little choice in terms of where they live and work, are disproportionately exposed to environmental health factors and disasters brought about either actively by government and or industrial policies or passively through silence—turning a blind eye or denying that a problem exists.
- The frameworks of risk assessment, burden of proof, and the precautionary principle are examined. Canada adopts a prove harm approach where the burden of proof is on the public to demonstrate harm.

 Sociological Reflection:
Frederick Street and Burden of Proof

Maude Barlow and Elizabeth May published the book *Life and Death on Canada's Love Canal* based on the lives of residents living on Frederick Street in Whitney Pier, a neighbourhood in Sydney, Nova Scotia. Whitney Pier was not just any neighbourhood; it was home to a steel plant and North America's worst toxic waste site. The emissions from the steel plant were a toxic soup of chemicals. The book reports the conditions that residents of Whitney Pier endured: high cancer rates, heart and lung diseases, headaches, nosebleeds, respiratory infections, dying pets, and even one report of a dog glowing in the dark. After many deaths and illnesses and arsenic appearing in basements and frustrated by the government's lack of concern and inaction, the residents organized an association and successfully challenged the government to evacuate the residents of Frederick Street and to demolish the homes. The homes on neighbouring streets, however, continue to stand and be inhabited as the government does not see that it is its responsibility to provide further aid.

- Reflect on some of the reason why you think the government initially resisted helping the residents of Frederick Street.
- How is Frederick Street an example of environmental racism?
- Some health scholars believe that the starting point of health regulation is the precautionary principle. Others counter by arguing that such a policy would work against the economy. What do you think?

Discussion Questions

1. On heavy smog days in large urban areas, do you think that private vehicles should be banned?
2. Farmers say they use lots of pesticides because they have no choice. This is what the market demands. Should the government subsidize organic farming? Is this a problem or a solution?
3. What role, if any, should the government play in preventing another Walkerton from occurring?
4. Why are those members of our society who are most economically disadvantaged at greater risk for health problems related to our environment?
5. Why is the Canadian government so resistant to shifting from a risk-assessment model to one based on the precautionary principle?

Further Investigation

1. The relationships between consumers, farmers, and the manufacturers of food are complex and not straightforward. Describe how each of these groups affects food policies surrounding food costs and availability.
2. What role does the state play and what role should the state play in ensuring that food products are safe for consumer use? Your answer should include a discussion of risk assessment and precaution.

Further Reading

Brown, P., & Mikkelsen, E. J. (1997). *No safe place: Toxic waste, leukemia, and community action.* Berkeley, CA: University of California Press.

Carson, R. *Silent spring.* (1962). Cambridge, MA: The Riverside Press Cambridge.

Colborn, T., Dumanoski, D., & Peterson, M. J. (1996). *Our stolen future: Are we threatening our fertility, intelligence, and survival? A scientific detective story.* New York, NY: Dutton Penguin.

Gibbs, L. M. (1998). *Love Canal: The story continues...* Gabriola Island, BC: New Society Publishers.

Laduke, W. (1999). *All our relations: Native struggles for land life.* Cambridge: South End Press.

May, E., & Barlow, M. (2000). *Frederick Street: Life and death on Canada's Love Canal.* Toronto, ON: HarperCollins Publishers Ltd.

Perkel, C.N. (2002). *Well of lies: The Walkerton water tragedy.* Toronto, ON: McClelland & Stewart Ltd.

Schlosser, E. (2002). *Fast food nation: The dark side of the all-American meal.* New York, NY: Perennial.

Steingraber, S. (1998). *Living downstream: A scientist's personal investigation of cancer and the environment.* New York, NY: Vintage Books.

Web Resources

Agriculture and Agri-food Canada, 2008
www4.agr.gc.ca/AAFC-AAC/display-afficher.do?id=1201189157429&lang=eng#alternate

Canadian Centre for Occupational Health and Safety
www.ccohs.ca/

Canadian Environmental Law Association
www.cela.ca

DES Action
www.desaction.org/

Earth Trends, Environmental Information
http://earthtrends.wri.org/

Environmental Defence Fund (EDF)
www.edf.org/

Environmental Research Foundation: Rachel's Environment & Health News
www.rachel.org/?q=en/newsletters/rachels_news/956

Environment Canada
www.ec.gc.ca/default.asp?lang=en

Greenpeace International
www.greenpeace.org/

PlanetFriendly
www.planetfriendly.net/health.html

Science Watch: Tracking Trends & Performance in Basic Research
http://sciencewatch.com/ana/st/bis/09sepBisSoto/

Scorecard: The Pollution Information Site
www.scorecard.org/

Sierra Club
www.sierraclub.org/

Statistics Canada: Case Study: Ozone Layer Depletion and the Montréal Protocol
www.statcan.gc.ca/edu/power-pouvoir/ch5/casestudy-edudedecas/5214797-eng.htm

World Nuclear Association: Representing the People and Organisations of the Global Nuclear Profession
www.world-nuclear.org/info/inf32.html

PART 2

The Social Construction of Health and Illness

'I enjoy convalescence. It is the part that makes illness worth while.'

— *George Bernard Shaw, Back to Methuselah*

The second dimension of the social model of health is the social construction of health and illness. *Social construction* refers to the socially created characteristics of human life—the way people actively make the societies and communities in which they live, work, and play. Differences in values, religions, and ways of life generally are manifestations of the social construction of reality. In other words, human life and the way we interact with one another is not natural or inevitable and varies between cultures and over time. Social construction, when applied to how we view health and illness, reveals that assumptions about normal/abnormal, right/wrong, and healthy/unhealthy reflect the culture of a particular society at a given point in time. Our understandings of health and illness are shaped also by social identities, such as gender, ethnicity, age, and sexual orientation.

Social construction is rooted in the symbolic-interaction perspective and focuses on individuals and the way they create meaning. However, we must also keep in mind the social and economic contexts in which meanings are constructed. Not all groups of people have equal status in society; some have more power to shape the way meanings are constructed by others. In other words, knowing how people view their health and their experiences with the health-care system provides an important lens, but we should not lose sight of the fact that social determinants have an effect on the health status of different groups and their use of health services, which in turn may influence their interpretations of their experience.

Part 2 consists of three chapters that examine how culture, power, social identities, and economics play a part in socially constructing notions of health and illness.

- Chapter 9 looks at medicalization and how parts of life come under medical scrutiny. It also considers who has power to define behaviours as illnesses and the social consequences of such.
- Chapter 10 examines how disability and chronic illness are socially located and looks at the experience of chronic illness or disability for individuals, and how societal arrangements construct disability.
- Chapter 11 explores the social construction of aging, death, and dying, which are biological realities yet distinctly social processes.

CHAPTER 9

The Medicalization of Society[1]

Sharyn L. Roach Anleu & Jennie Hornosty

Overview

- How is it that certain areas of human life come to be defined, or not, as medical issues?
- Who defines social expectations?
- What social forces promote medicalization?
- What are the individual and social consequences of medicalization?

What is defined as sickness and how it gets treated are related to the larger social and political milieu. Is shyness a sickness? When is being short considered abnormal? When is behaviour, such as very active children or gambling, indicative of an illness in need of medical treatment? How did homosexuality, once considered pathology, become acknowledged as normalized behaviour? The concept of sickness, as Freidson (1970) has argued, is not a neutral scientific concept but is fundamentally a moral one that designates certain behaviour as desirable and normal and other behaviour as deviant. Throughout its history, psychiatry has played a critical role in designating various forms of behaviour as evidence of mental illness that requires therapeutic intervention. Psychiatry has developed notions of normal (and deviant) behaviour in such areas as sexual behaviour and identity, mental health, gambling, alcohol and drug use, criminal behaviour, eating, reproduction, and child development. Today we have what Conrad (2007, p. 133) refers to as 'shifting engines of medicalization' and new market-based forms of medicalization.

Key Terms

andropause	discourse	sick role
biomedicalization	empirical	social constructionism
commodification of health	gender	social control
demedicalization	medicalization	social iatrogenesis
deviance	Prozac	
Diagnostic and Statistical Manual of Mental Disorders (DSM-IV)	risk/risk discourse	

---

1. This is the title of Peter Conrad's 2007 book, which provides a comprehensive overview of medicalization and its effects.

Introduction

Why is it that deviation from certain behaviours and expectations becomes defined and treated as illness or as a medical phenomenon requiring intervention and treatment by medical personnel? The **medicalization** of behaviour considered deviant is a historical and social process, and is the outcome of professional and social-movement activity. The dominance of the medical model in explaining certain types of behaviour or conditions means that the emphasis is on the individual, who must be treated in some way in order to restore conformity or health, rather than on the social environment. When society accepts these definitions, the medical profession becomes an agent of social control that has been given the power to certify individuals as being sick. Medicine continues to play a key role in medicalization; however, other forces, such as the pharmaceutical industry, consumer groups, biotechnological discoveries, and health insurance, are important 'engines of medicalization' (Conrad, 2007, p. 145). This chapter outlines the concept of medicalization, and examines the relationship between medicalization and social control. It looks at the role of psychiatry in identifying and regulating **deviance** and the role of pharmaceutical companies in manufacturing illness. It also considers some of the social consequences of medicalization.

Several kinds of questions can be asked regarding the concept of deviance: What causes or motivates someone to deviate from social expectations? Who defines what those expectations are? What kinds of sanctions are invoked and under what conditions? What is the relationship between various forms of **social control** (for example, between legal regulation and medical intervention)? To what extent does the type of deviance or societal reaction depend on gender, age, socio-economic status, ethnicity, sexual identity, or other social attributes and structural inequalities? Medicine is one kind of social audience; it is concerned with identifying various conditions as deviations from a model of health and well-being that makes assumptions and values about normality.

medicalization

The process by which nonmedical problems become defined and treated as medical issues, usually in terms of illnesses, disorders, or syndromes.

deviance

Behaviour or activities that violate social expectations about what is normal.

social control

Mechanisms that aim to induce conformity or at least to manage or minimize deviant behaviour.

Medicalization and Social Control

> In every society, medicine, like law and religion, defines what is normal, proper, or desirable. Medicine has the authority to label one man's complaint a legitimate illness, to declare a second man sick though he himself does not complain, and to refuse a third social recognition of his pain, his disability, and even his death. It is medicine which stamps some pain as 'merely subjective', some impairment as malingering, and some deaths—though not others—as suicide.
>
> *Illich, 1976, p. 65*

Increasingly, human experiences are coming under medical scrutiny with numerous aspects of daily life being defined as medical issues, resulting in what Illich (1976) has called 'the medicalization of life'. Is this medicalization due to an actual increase in medical problems or to better reporting? Or is it that some aspects of life and behaviour that once were considered normal are now subject to medical diagnosis and treatment? *Medicalization* describes the process whereby nonmedical problems or phenomena become defined and treated as medical issues, usually in terms of illnesses, disorders, or syndromes (Conrad, 2007, p. 4). Successful medicalization means that the dominant

sick role

A concept used by Talcott Parsons to describe the social expectations of how sick people should act and of how they are meant to be treated.

form of social control is therapeutic and that individuals diagnosed as deviating from a model of health confront a new set of normative expectations stemming from the **sick role**. Talcott Parsons (1951a, b) first specified the connections between deviance and illness in his conception of the sick role. In addition to the constraints of physiological conditions, the sick role exempts people from fulfilling their normal social duties; it does not hold individuals responsible for their conditions (at least to some extent) and obliges them to seek medical assistance. By entering into a relationship with medical personnel, the sick person becomes a patient with attendant expectations and requirements.

Theory Link
See Chapter 2 for an overview of the sick role and functionalism.

While the sick role legitimates some kinds of social behaviours and imposes a new set of social norms (and social control), access to this status is not automatic. The manifestation of certain physiological conditions is not the only or indeed a necessary prerequisite for contact with institutionalized medicine. For example, individuals identified as potential deviants from medical (and social) norms may be viewed as being at risk for some types of illness or deviance and may be subject to medical surveillance in the name of preventing or reducing the so-called **risk** behaviour. Public health programs may target certain groups of people, such as Aboriginal peoples, female-headed households, gay men, or young people, for early intervention or education in order to prevent illnesses or conditions such as AIDS and to prevent drug addiction, child abuse, and suicide.

risk/risk discourse

Risk refers to 'danger'; *risk discourse* is often used in health-promotion messages warning people that certain actions involve significant risks to their health.

Conrad (2007) explains that early studies of medicalization focused on the medicalization of deviance; however, today the concept is applied to broad areas of human life that now are subject to medical interpretation and intervention. The medicalization of deviance includes categories such as alcoholism, mental disorder, substance addictions, eating disorders, sexual dysfunction, and learning disabilities. The process of medicalization also has created new categories, such as attention deficit hyperactivity disorder (ADHD), premenstrual syndrome (PMS), and post-traumatic stress disorder (PTSD). Other aspects of life have also been medicalized, including anxiety and mood, infertility, menopause, aging and death. Some behaviours that were once deemed immoral, sinful, or criminal have been given medical meaning, moving them from badness to sickness (Conrad, 2007). The key to medicalization is definition; illness is not ipso facto a medical problem but, rather, becomes defined as such.

social construction/ constructionism

Refers to the socially created characteristics of human life based on the idea that people actively construct reality, meaning it is neither natural nor inevitable. Therefore, notions of normality/abnormality, right/ wrong, and health/illness are subjective human creations that should not be taken for granted.

The medicalization thesis posits that physical conditions do not, by their nature, constitute illness; rather, they require identification and classification, which entail subjective and value-laden considerations—that is, they are socially constructed. **Social constructionism** counters medicine's claims to be scientific, objective, and disinterested. Like Illich (1976), Eliot Freidson (1988) argues that medicine actively and exclusively constructs illness and therefore determines how people must act in order to be treated. Rather than disinterestedly detecting symptoms and physiological causes and administering scientifically validated therapeutic techniques, medical practice involves interpreting and judging what is normal and abnormal—determining which circumstances are suitable for medical intervention and which are not. The symptoms do not speak for themselves; they are neither self-evident nor naturally occurring. Indeed, their interpretation and categorization are informed by social values and assumptions about what constitutes health (normal) and illness (deviant). The success of the medical profession in monopolizing definitions of health and illness provides it with considerable authority and scope for social control.

Within this context, **empirical** research identifies the social conditions under which certain illnesses emerge, and it analyzes the effect of medical practitioners' claims on the development of conceptions of illness. The medicalization of infertility is a recent example. Traditionally, involuntary childlessness was considered a personal and private issue, but now it is viewed as a condition warranting medical attention and intervention. The experience of infertility also causes many people, especially women, to feel as though they are deviating from gender norms that specify motherhood as essential to womanhood, even when it is the male partners, not the women themselves, who are infertile. In Canada, this view is slowly changing as a growing number of women and couples are making a choice not to have children. However, this group is a minority. Women who choose in vitro fertilization (IVF) are subject to complicated medical procedures and expectations. Nonetheless, conceptive technologies, especially IVF, do not cure infertility but, rather, circumvent it by attempting to achieve a pregnancy and live birth (Roach Anleu, 1993).

Discussions of medicalization often refer to psychiatry as the primary example or prototype of medical social control. Such discussions tend to emphasize the negative and coercive aspects of social control, in contrast to medical **discourses** that focus on medical intervention as positive and necessary for health and well-being. On this point, Conrad (2007) notes that medicalization describes a process and that it is important to distinguish between a disorder that most people would agree is truly medical, such as epilepsy, and the medicalization of life's normal processes, such as menopause or aging (2007).

Ivan Illich (1976), a critic of the medical establishment, popularized the term **social iatrogenesis** to talk about the extent to which medicine has gained control over every stage of the life cycle, beginning with prenatal checkups to monitor a fetus's development to the decision to not resuscitate at the end of life. In his view, modern medicine creates illness and disease in its attempt to deal with pain and sickness. Critics point out that theorists such as Illich, Zola (1972), and Navarro (1976) tend to view medicalization as wholly negative and coercive—as something that should be averted. They also suggest that arguments about medical imperialism—and about medicine's displacement of religion and law as a source of social control—are exaggerated, rhetorical, and not borne out in practice (Strong, 1979). They argue that medicalization can also confer certain benefits, including legitimation of the conditions as real rather than imaginary; access to the sick role; and access to insurance. Szasz (2007), for example, while highly critical of medicalization and the role of psychiatry, recognizes this when he argues that there is a distinction between medicalization from above, by coercion, and medicalization from below, by choice.

The medicalization thesis today focuses on both dimensions; that is, on how medical categories are increasingly applied to all parts of life, and, how, at the same time, people have internalized medical perspectives and actively seek or demand medical remedies (Conrad, 2007). Catherine Kohler Riessman in her seminal article 'Women and Medicalization: A New Perspective' (1983) acknowledges the feminist critique of

empirical

Describes observations or research that is based on evidence drawn from experience. It is, therefore, distinguished from something based only on theoretical knowledge or on some other kind of abstract thinking process.

discourse

A domain of language use that is characterized by common ways of talking and thinking about an issue (for example, the discourses of medicine, madness, or sexuality).

social iatrogenesis

Iatrogenesis is a concept popularized by Ivan Illich that refers to adverse effects caused by, or resulting from, medical treatment. *Social iatrogenesis* refers to the process by which biomedicine extends its domain over every stage of life. Illich talked about three dimensions of iatrogenesis: clinical, social, and cultural.

medicalization and the sexual politics embedded in conceptions of sickness; however, she argues that medicalization involves a symbiotic relationship in which 'both physicians and women have contributed to the redefining of women's experience into medical categories' (p. 3). Physicians medicalize experience because of their specific beliefs and economic interests, but at the same time '[w]omen collaborate in the medicalization process because of their own needs and motives, which in turn grow out of the class-specific nature of their subordination' (pp. 3–4). Consumer health movements today play an important role in promoting and/or endorsing medical treatments for a range of human problems. Cosmetic surgery, such as breasts implants and liposuction, for example, while being promoted by plastic surgeons, is driven largely by the consumer market. Often times, individuals diagnosed with a particular illness, such as PTSD or fibromyalgia, will mobilize to promote and shape their diagnosis as a means to legitimate their illness and their access to the sick role (Conrad, 2007). That is, consumers frequently are active collaborators in the medicalization of their problems.

Types of Medicalization

Historical analyses and case studies identify the ways that various phenomena come to be defined in medical terms and to be viewed as warranting medical intervention. Medicalization occurs on several levels:

- *Conceptual level,* at which a medical vocabulary is used to describe or define an issue or problem, but medical professionals and treatments may not be involved. For example, alcohol abuse, interpersonal problems, depression, seasonal affective disorder (SAD), and some criminal activities may be defined as pathological or as evidence of sickness or mental impairment, but their management—although it may be viewed as therapeutic—does not necessarily entail intervention by medical personnel.
- *Institutional level,* at which organizations may adopt a medical approach to particular problems and medical personnel may be gatekeepers for the organization, but the everyday routine work is performed by nonmedical personnel. Access to some workers' compensation schemes requires a referral from a medical practitioner, even when human services personnel, such as psychologists, counsellors, or social workers, implement the rehabilitation program.
- *Interactional level,* at which medicalization occurs as part of doctor–patient interaction, with the former medically defining and/or treating the latter's problem. The doctor provides a medical diagnosis and prescribes a medical treatment (Conrad, 1992).

The practices and processes that result in greater medicalization at these different levels are diverse. Individual medical practitioners might claim that a problem or set of issues should be in the domain of medicine; however, successful medicalization usually involves collective action and coalitions between different groups (Brown, 1995; Halpern, 1992). Less tolerance of mild symptoms stemming from such things as menstruation, menopause, or erectile dysfunction has spurred a 'progressive medicalization of physical distress in which uncomfortable body states and isolated symptoms are reclassified as diseases' (Barsky & Boros, 1995, cited in Conrad, 2007, p. 6). Patients and support groups may lobby with medical practitioners to have a condition recognized as a medical problem so as to have access to the benefits that medicalization might entail. Conrad & Potter (2000) show how in the 1990s the largest attention deficit [hyperactivity] disorder (AD[H]D) support group in the US combined its efforts with a giant pharmaceutical firm (the manufacturer of Ritalin, a major treatment for hyperactivity), with medical professionals, as well as with the media to successfully extend the diagnosis of AD[H]D to adults. ADHD among adults is generally the result of self-diagnosis; after reading about the disorder and believing it applies to them, they seek professional confirmation of their new identity. As a result, they interpret all their difficulties through the lens of ADHD. Without this self-labelling, adult ADHD would not have become the foremost self-diagnosed condition to explain everyday events such as poor motivation, job failure, and lack of success (Conrad, 2007). Similarly, post-traumatic stress disorder (PTSD), originally applied to Vietnam War veterans to diagnose anxiety, sleep problems, and flashbacks emanating from their combat experience, has been extended to survivors or witnesses of horrendous accidents and crimes, such as earthquakes, sexual abuse and murder.

Medicalization is not only about defining nonmedical problems as sickness or disease but also includes broadening pre-existing medical categories to include more potential sufferers and situations. The process is dynamic—not 'simply doctors colonizing new problems or labeling feckless patients' (Conrad and Potter, 2000, p. 560). Such attempts to medicalize a problem or expand a medical category vary in their level of success. The support and agreement of individual medical practitioners or professional medical associations often bolster claims for biomedical explanations and intervention. Pharmaceutical companies have played a significant role in the expansion of medicalization. For example, the popularity of **Prozac** (fluoxetine), marketed as a drug to help people feel better, created a social context in which it became acceptable to use medications to deal with a variety of life's problems. Clarke et al. (2005) argue that medicalization today is being reconstituted through the development of technoscientific biomedicine. Such processes are situated within political-economic contexts: 'In the biomedicalization era, what is perhaps most radical is the **biomedicalization** of health itself. In commodity cultures, health becomes another commodity, and the biomedically (re)engineered body becomes a prized possession' (p. 447). Within a context of cutbacks to health-care funding, individuals are told that their health is an ongoing individual moral responsibility. Risk and surveillance practices are institutionalized and shape both the technologies and discourses of biomedicalization. Rather than illness, the 'normal' is problematized (Clarke et al., 2005, p. 447).

The History and Role of Psychiatry in Medicalization

Psychiatry is frequently associated with medicalization. The emergence and dominance of a medical approach to madness (later to be redefined as mental illness) began in the late eighteenth century. The asylum emerged during the nineteenth century as the state's solution to the increasing numbers of people identified as insane, and the history of psychiatry and its authority is inextricably intertwined with this development. Back in the seventeenth century, enormous houses of confinement had been opened to accommodate diverse populations of what were referred to as deviants, including so-called mad people,

Prozac

A new type of medication (selective serotonin reuptake inhibitor [SSRI]) introduced in 1987 to treat depression.

biomedicalization

Describes increasingly complex, multi-sited, and multi-directional processes of medicalization.

criminals, libertines, beggars, vagabonds, prostitutes, the unemployed, and the poor—that is, people deemed to be economically (and politically) marginal. These institutions of confinement had arisen in order to accommodate increasing poverty—with growing numbers of people unable to engage in productive work—and as a way of managing or segregating all forms of behaviour defined as immoral (Ingleby, 1985, p. 147). Later, separate institutions developed to deal with more homogeneous subgroups: the almshouse, the workhouse, the insane asylum, and the prison. These institutions remained the dominant way of managing these people until the 1950s. Despite the lack of cures or explanatory theories of madness, physicians assumed a small but central role as gatekeepers of the asylums: from 1774, a physician's certificate was required for commitment to a British asylum. As Michel Foucault (1988) observes,

> The physician . . . played no part in the life of confinement. Now he becomes the essential figure of the asylum. He is in charge of entry . . . the doctor's intervention is not made by virtue of a medical skill or power that he possesses in himself and that would be justified by a body of objective knowledge. It is not as a scientist that *homo medicus* has authority in the asylum, but as wise man. (p. 270)

There was considerable optimism and hope that new scientific advances in medicine would be able to solve problems associated with mental illness (Conrad & Schneider, 1992). By the end of the eighteenth century, reformers sought to eliminate the physically punitive aspects of life in the insane asylum and to reinforce the benefits of moral treatment. Physicians argued that as both moral and medical responses were appropriate they should have a monopoly on dispensing both. Their successful bid to provide moral assistance was especially important since they were unable to show the physiological causes of mental illness and had not demonstrated any cures. The decline of the Church, the scientific discoveries of the Enlightenment, and the humanitarianism of the Renaissance all aided physicians' 'professional dominance' in this area and fostered a unitary conception of mental illness—that is, a single illness category to encompass diverse conditions and symptoms. At the close of the eighteenth century, the notion of mental illness as a disease and as a topic of medical and scientific intervention was becoming the dominant conception of madness, and the influence of religious or supernatural explanations was waning (Conrad & Schneider, 1992, pp. 47–48).

Medicalization today encompasses more than just psychiatry, but in the words of Thomas Szasz, '[p]sychiatry is medicalization, through and through' (2007, p. xx). Psychiatry has always been involved in the identification and regulation of deviance. As an emergent occupation and as a segment of the medical profession, psychiatry has developed notions of normal behaviour in areas such as sexual behaviour and identity, mental health, gambling, alcohol and drug use, eating, reproduction, and child development. Psychiatry seeks to locate a pathological basis within the individual for such deviance and views certain types of behaviour as evidence of addiction, syndromes, conditions, personality disorders, or other mental illnesses. It attempts to attribute causes to—or, perhaps more accurately, to identify sites of intervention on the basis of—individual rather than social or definitional factors. Conditions that psychiatrists view as warranting their intervention include deviations from what were once considered moral or religious norms (for example, gambling or alcohol use, which may be diagnosed as evidence of addictive behaviour, personality disorder, or depression), or deviations from legal norms (for example, child abuse, juvenile delinquency, rape, or homicide). Psychiatry in this context is an example of what Szasz refers to as medicalization from above, that is, the ability of the other to punish and control.

The separation of deviants was an essential precondition for the development of a medical specialty (the forerunner of psychiatry) that claimed to possess specific expertise in dealing with madness. This, in turn, further legitimized the concept of mental illness as a distinct phenomenon (reflecting and caused by an underlying pathology), rather than the amorphous cultural view of insanity that had previously prevailed and that had emphasized demonological and nonhuman influences (Scull, 1975; 1977). During the nineteenth century, psychiatrists identified ill health, religious anxiety, disappointed love, pecuniary embarrassment, acid inhalation, suppressed menstruation, and general poor health as causes of mental illness. Their interventions included physical restraints, cold baths, tooth extractions, and surgery of the brain and reproductive systems. By the close of the nineteenth century, a whole range of new personal problems paralleled enormous social changes, especially in the US. Everyday problems became defined as nervous diseases, providing a focus for new professional groups.

The growth of asylums consolidated the professional development of psychiatrists; however, psychiatry was not approved as a medical specialty until 1934 (Neff et al., 1987). Psychiatrists successfully monopolized the treatment of insanity by officially defining it as a medical condition with identifiable causes, but moral judgments and lay concerns still influenced diagnosis. Insanity was an elastic concept—a category of residual deviance— that could be applied to a variety of individuals whose deviance stemmed from poverty, homelessness, or physical disability. Unlike confinement in other custodial institutions, commitment to an insane asylum entailed neither a trial, a fixed term of internment, nor the legal protection associated with criminal proceedings (Sutton, 1991).

Case studies of psychiatric hospitals illustrate the power of psychiatric diagnosis, the pervasiveness of psychiatric discourse, and the high status of psychiatrists (Goffman, 1961). A stark example is provided in D. L. Rosenhan's article 'Being Sane in Insane Places' (1973). He describes an experiment in which eight sane people gained secret admission to psychiatric institutions. The pseudo-patients claimed that they had been hearing voices, but upon admission to the hospital ward ceased simulating any symptoms of abnormality. The only people who detected that they were not suffering from a psychiatric condition were the other patients, not the medical staff. Indeed, the label 'schizophrenic'—that is, the diagnosis—determined psychiatrists' and nurses' perceptions and interpretations of the pseudo-patients' behaviour, even when it was completely 'normal' (p. 253).

Close links exist between mental hospitalization and social control. Erving Goffman's classic study of a state mental hospital shows that very few of the everyday activities of the institution are devoted to therapy or treatment; most activities are oriented to maintaining the organization, performing routine tasks, and achieving social control among the patients. The psychiatrist's presence is brief and the input, non-specific (Goffman, 1961). Mental institutions also play a role in wider social policy and in the regulation of sub-populations that are identified as problematic. The increasing numbers of people confined to mental hospitals in the US between 1880 and the 1920s did not indicate an epidemic of mental illness. Rather, the pattern stemmed from the government's incapacity to systematically address and solve poverty, especially among the aged; from the closure of the almshouses, combined with flexibility in the medical concept of insanity; and from the relatively simple commitment procedures (Sutton, 1991).

Other significant developments in the history of psychiatry include the rise of psycho-analysis and the introduction of psychotropic drugs. Psychoanalysis enabled psychiatrists to help people who were anxious and depressed and who experienced problems with everyday life, as well as to treat the insane. Sigmund Freud, a physician and a neurologist, provided a new approach to understanding personal problems. He replaced a biological model with a psychogenic explanation and intervention that was based on free discussion (by the patient) in the context of a relationship with the therapist (Conrad & Schneider, 1992). In the 1950s new psychotropic (mood-altering) drugs became available, which were used in mental hospitals as well as to enable more people to be discharged and treated outside the hospital. However, the use of prescription drugs raised questions of compli-ance and self-medication. While drug treatment reinforced the medical model of mental illness, the curative effect is contested, and critics argue that the drugs merely sedate, and thereby regulate, the behaviour of people identified as mentally ill.

In the 1960s, criticisms of psychiatry, the unitary conception of mental illness, the social control functions of mental hospitals, and the so-called therapeutic relationship became more evident. Proponents of the labelling perspective doubted that diverse symp-toms, behaviours, and conditions constituted a single classification of mental illness. Thomas Scheff, for example, argues that mental illness became almost a label of conven-ience for a range of norm-breaking behaviour that could not be accommodated within other types of deviance. He termed this behaviour 'residual deviance' to include crime, alcoholism, and illness (Scheff, 1966, pp. 31–54). Commentators identified enforced drug therapy—which violated patients' rights by denying them informed consent and due pro-cess—as an unacceptable outcome of the influence of psychiatry in the mental health and criminal justice systems (Kittrie, 1971).

Thomas Szasz (1961, 1973), one of the strongest proponents of the anti-psychiatry movement, maintains that medicine's replacement of the Church as the institution of social control merely redefines and re-labels deviance with medical terminology. He argues that the term *mental illness* is widely used to describe something that is very dif-ferent from a disease of the brain, and suggests that problems in living derive from the stresses and strains inherent in social interactions among complex human personalities in modern societies (1960, p. 113). The concept of mental illness serves the same social con-trol function in the contemporary world as witchcraft did in the late Middle Ages. Both are imprecise and all-encompassing concepts. A contemporary example of a controversial psychiatric classification, and associated diagnosis and treatment, is that of personality disorder. The past 20 years has seen a rapid elaboration of this category in the **Diagnostic and Statistical Manual of Mental Disorders** (DSM-IV). Nonetheless, personality disorders do not include obvious organic or psychological impairment but are identified through their interpersonal effects, including chaotic and distressing relationships, instability of identity, or incurred criminal records (Manning, 2000). The DSM distinguishes personal-ity disorders according to such descriptive terms as 'odd and eccentric' and 'anxious and fearful' (Nuckolls, 1997, p. 52), thus attesting to the classification's broad scope.

Another, more ambiguous psychiatric or psychological classification is depression. Szasz's claim, more than four decades ago, that most of the conditions and complaints

Diagnostic and Statistical Manual of Mental Disorders (DSM-IV)

A manual published by the American Psychiatric Association that lists all mental health disorders for both children and adults. It also indicates causes, types of treatment, and prognosis.

subsumed under the label *mental illness* are not biomedical in origin but are caused by 'problems in living' that stem from the complexities of modern life is no less true today. Some suggest that the recent and continued popularity of Prozac—the antidepressant drug—can be explained to some extent by the increasing tendency of individuals to redefine life's problems, stresses, anxieties, and disappointments as evidence of depression. Prozac is not only prescribed to people suffering serious disturbances. Its application is more ordinary: 'a formulation that could improve the lives of people with minor disturbances and distresses' (Conrad & Potter, 2000, p. 571). Psychiatrist David Healy, in his controversial book *Let Them Eat Prozac* (2003), shows the role of the drug industry in promoting mood-altering drugs such as Prozac while minimizing the potential serious side-effects, such as increased risk for suicide. More recently shyness has emerged as a new 'crippling affliction' that doctors argue can be appropriately treated with various psychotropic medications (Scott, 2006).

Psychiatry has played a central role in the medicalization of behaviour; however, its influence has been resisted and challenged. Psychiatrists' ability to identify, diagnose, and treat mental illness is contested by other disciplines that are concerned with human relations or personal problems, such as psychology, social work, and counselling, as well as by other medical specialties and kinds of knowledge. Its claims to provide precise and exact explanations are questioned, and its ability to demonstrate etiology is difficult, making psychiatry particularly vulnerable to the criticism that its knowledge base is socially constructed and historical. Indeed, psychiatry continues to be one of the most contested areas of medicine. Discussion about the causes of mental illness—genetic, physiological, psychological, and social—is far from conclusive, and psychiatrists' ability to predict the potential for mental illness in patients is highly questionable (Cocozza & Steadman, 1978). Arguably, then, psychiatry's jurisdiction over certain conditions and patients stems from its own self-interested quest to achieve and maintain professional status. Current research—as part of the human genome project to map the genes that (allegedly) determine mental illness, alcoholism, Alzheimer's disease, and even depression—has the potential to renew psychiatrists' claims that they offer scientific explanations, diagnoses, and treatments that are not socially constructed.

Other Interests in Medicalization

While the medical profession, especially psychiatry, has been a key player in constructing certain behaviours as deviant and in need of medical intervention, others have participated or been complicit in this process. Some social movements, consumers, and occupational groups, such as teachers, are also involved in normative work—that is, identifying problematic behaviour and proposing medical, including psychiatric, intervention to achieve normality. For example, Alcoholics Anonymous (AA) is a hybrid organization that combines elements of the disease model of alcoholism with a spiritual program emphasizing individual change and recovery and the achievement of inner peace (Valverde & White-Mair, 1999). Another example, the National Alliance for the Mentally Ill (NAMI), one of the most influential mental health organizations in the US, grew from concern that the families of the mentally ill had insufficient input in the management of their afflicted relatives. NAMI adopts the medical model, viewing schizophrenia and manic depression as diseases caused by chemical imbalances in the brain. This organization focuses on the mental patient's inability to hold and exercise rights, and criticizes the legal extension of rights to individuals involuntarily committed to mental institutions. It maintains that psychotherapeutic approaches—which may view family dynamics rather than a chemical imbalance as responsible for the disease—stigmatize caregivers, and that the patient's legal right to refuse medication establishes an inappropriate adversarial relationship between patients and their families (Milner, 1989).

Other research shows that teachers and family members have been particularly influential in the construction of hyperactivity in children as evidence of a psychiatric disorder, namely attention deficit [hyperactivity] disorder (AD[H]D) (Lloyd & Norris, 1999, pp. 505–508). In Britain, as elsewhere, active parents' organizations articulated their rights and the right of their children to be classified as having a medically defined disorder requiring prescribed medication, thus rejecting a more social model of the deviantization of certain childhood behaviours. In a recent Canadian study, Malacrida (2004) found that teachers (in Canada) were primarily responsible for labelling a child as having ADD/ADHD. The mothers she interviewed told her that although they may have seen their child as different in early childhood, 'it was really only once the child went to school that these differences came to be identified as problematic enough that the child was identified for formal intervention' (p. 67). Mothers also stated that their decisions to medicate their children were the result of indirect school pressure, such as constant phone calls and questions as to whether the child was still on medication. On the other hand, British educators had a 'strong antipathy' toward medicalizing childhood behaviour problems (p. 70). One possible explanation for this difference, according to Malacrida, is that educators in Canada have fewer alternatives in maintaining classroom discipline than their British counterparts. It also may reflect the different degrees of medicalization of ADD/ADHD in each culture.

Women and Medicalization

A number of researchers have suggested that women's life experiences are more likely to be medicalized than men's (Bell, 1987; Berenson, et al., 2009; Davis, 1996; Lorber, 2000; Riessman, 1983). As Riessman notes 'a plethora of female conditions has come to be either reconceptualized as illnesses or understood in ways that connote deviation from some ideal biological standard' (1983, p. 7). In other words, women may be more vulnerable to medicalization because their bodies and physiological processes deviate from the so-called ideal male norm. Women's bodies also come under increased medical scrutiny because of the beauty ideal in Western society. While much of this could be considered the result of patriarchy, medicalization is effective only if, at least to some degree, there is acquiescence on the part of those involved. Riessman (1983) traces the medicalization of pregnancy and childbirth to the ability of obstetricians (at the beginning of the twentieth century) to convince medical colleagues and the general public that birth was a pathological process. Women participated in the medicalization of childbirth for a complex set of reasons. There was no contraception so pregnancy every other year was the norm. Hence, women wanted relief from the pain, exhaustion, and frequent debilitation associated with pregnancy and painful parturition. As well, upper- and middle-class women wanted to be attended by obstetricians (rather than midwives) because doctors possessed instruments and surgical techniques that could be beneficial should there be any complications: 'Women wanted to reduce the control that biology had over their lives' (p. 7).

The menstrual cycle is another aspect of the reproductive body that has been increasingly medicalized. Berenson et al. (2009) note that the discovery of this new period of disease evolved from accounts of individual women, who reported menstrual-related difficulties to their doctors. From this small sample, premenstrual syndrome (PMS) was expanded to include *all* menstruating women as sufferers. Some women have been active participants in the construction of PMS as a disorder and seek its inclusion in the DSM. It is significant that the original term was *premenstrual tension*; the use of the term *syndrome* indicates increased medicalization. DSM-IV, the most recent edition and published in 1994, proposes premenstrual dysphoric disorder (PMDD) as an official category for possible inclusion in later editions following further research. The discussion of PMDD in the appendix of DSM-IV identifies symptoms such as markedly depressed mood, feelings of hopelessness or self-deprecating thoughts, marked anxiety, affective lability interspersed with frequent tearfulness, and decreased interest in usual activities as the essential features of the disorder (American Psychiatric Association, 1994). Some have argued that PMDD is a real biological condition for which effective treatment is available; others, however, suggest that PMS and PMDD are 'culture-bound' with no evidence that they actually exist (Daw, 2002, p. 58). According to Paula Caplan, by including PMDD in the DSM-IV, emotional displays such as anger and irritability that are considered normal in men are seen as a mental disorder in women (cited in Daw, 2002).

Both medical and popular literatures tend to emphasize the negative, debilitating symptoms of PMS. An analysis of popular magazines and self-help books shows that PMS is portrayed in a generally negative tone, which effectively defines how a normal woman should feel or behave in contrast to an abnormal woman, who experiences PMS. Women themselves use the PMS label to dismiss or explain what is described as their deviant behaviour: 'Don't mind me, I'm PMSing' (Berenson et al., 2009, p. 243). Popular discourse identifies the causes as physiological and focuses on women's hormones as the source of the problems. Intervention and alleviation of the symptoms identified—ranging from dizziness, backache, and lack of concentration to decreased school or work performance, mood swings, and irritability—include drug therapy and management of individual lifestyles through diet, exercise, and rest, rather than considering the relevance of social, structural, or cultural factors (Markens, 1996; Martin, 1987). In the twenty-first century, the medicalizing process of PMS is taking a new twist. New technological advances in the form of different types of birth control pills allow females to hormonally curtail or eliminate menstruation altogether (Berenson et al., 2009).

The medicalization of PMS presents a dilemma for women: on the one hand, it legitimizes the experiences of premenstrual symptoms as real and worthy of medical and public attention, but on the other, it reasserts the pathology of women's bodies, especially their reproductive systems, and views women's actions and thoughts as being determined by biology (in this case, by their hormones). Opponents worry that medicalization could lead to stigmatization and result in sex discrimination. This is an example of a situation in which some medicalization, but not necessarily psychiatrization, may be helpful in order to have complaints taken seriously by medical practitioners, and for strategies to be adopted for alleviating or managing symptoms. In another example, research on chronic fatigue syndrome and fibromyalgia finds that diagnosis—that is, medicalizing a condition during consultation—can enable patients to explain their symptoms and to feel more in control of their situations; they are not dismissed as having imagined their symptoms or as malingerers. On the other hand, medicalization that reflects preconceived notions about gender-specific behaviour—for example, that women are naturally emotional, hysterical, or prone to depression or hypochondria—is unhelpful (Broom & Woodward, 1996).

Current debates about the utility of psychiatric categories to explain women's behaviour—especially that which deviates from **gender** norms—have historical parallels. In the nineteenth century, dominant medical theories linked a woman's uterus and ovaries to irrationality, emotional disorder, and mental disease. Indeed, the term *hysteria* derives from the Greek word for *uterus* and refers to what was regarded as a quintessential female condition, indicated by weeping, fainting, screaming, tantrums, and moodiness (Turner, 1987, p. 89). A scientific explanation of the so-called disease was that it was localized in the nervous system, but its diagnosis reflected expectations and attitudes regarding appropriate female behaviour and demeanour. Attributes thought to be natural and normal for women—affection, emotion, nurturance, preference for the domestic sphere, and moral sensibility—were also viewed as precursors of mental instability. Hysteria was linked to cultural definitions of femininity via its range of physical and emotional symptoms, including sobbing, fainting, fits, laughter, and general malaise (Seale & Pattison, 1994). The diagnosis of hysteria became a general label for abnormal or nonconforming behaviour on the part of women, and medical intervention became a form of social control.

Currently, the diagnosis of hysteria is very rare (it is not included in the DSM), and it refers to an entirely psychological condition with no specific physical correlates. In addition to reflecting changes in medical knowledge, the decline of hysteria as a flexible diagnostic category indicates changes in gender norms and the activism of women in resisting medicalization (Seale & Pattison, 1994). Nevertheless, the stereotype of the hysterical woman remains pervasive, and behaviour that in the past may have resulted in a diagnosis of hysteria may today be diagnosed as either schizophrenia, a personality disorder, or PMS.

> **gender**
>
> Refers to the socially constructed categories of feminine and masculine (the cultural values that dictate how men and women should behave), as opposed to the categories of biological sex (female or male).

Men and Medicalization

Medicalization can also expand in new directions. One such area of expansion is the increased medical scrutiny of men's aging bodies (Conrad, 2007). In much the same way that medicalization of women's bodies is related to conceptions of femininity, the medicalization of men's bodies is connected to notions of masculinity. Conrad explains that the medicalization of male aging, baldness, and sexual performance is rooted in a masculine identity that embodies physical strength and energy, hirsutism, and sexual vitality. This can be seen in the growing market for testosterone, hair-loss treatments, and the popularity of medications like Viagra, Cialis, and Levitra. He goes on to note that although such medicalization is driven by medical and pharmaceutical enterprises, it is also embraced by 'men's own concerns with their masculine identities, capacities, embodiments, and presentations' (p. 23). In her study of the history of male menopause, Elizabeth Watkins (2007) argues that male menopause became medicalized by a model perpetuated by lay people and medical popularizers rather than by clinicians and researchers. She points out that the US in the late twentieth century was a culture obsessed with youth as the standard of both health and beauty; in this context, both women and men sought ways to look and feel good.

Growing old was once viewed as normal, inevitable, and unalterable; however, today men's and women's aging bodies are often constructed in pathological terms. As a consequence, both seek medical solutions to slow down and mask the aging process. Although

andropause is not an easily identifiable condition, testosterone 'is marketed as a miraculous substance to help healthy men restore or enhance their masculinity' (Conrad, 2007, p. 33). Conrad suggests that testosterone replacement therapy will become increasingly important in the medicalization of men's aging bodies. Treatments for hair loss or baldness are not new, but the medicalization of baldness is gaining momentum due to new medical treatments being developed for hair loss, which some men spend thousands of dollars on (Conrad, 2007). Men seek treatments for baldness because of its negative connotations in much the same way that women resort to liposuction or to Botox injections for wrinkles. For some men baldness has negative psychological impacts.

A third example of medicalization that Conrad discusses is that of erectile dysfunction. Viagra was approved by the US Food and Drug Administration (FDA) in 1998 as a treatment for erectile dysfunction intended primarily for older men and for erectile dysfunction associated with medical problems such as prostate cancer. However, Viagra was soon marketed so as to include virtually all men who might have any insecurity around sexual performance. The definition of erectile dysfunction was expanded to include any erectile difficulties at any age, whether occasional problems or problems with erection quality. While medicalization is often seen in a negative light as a form of social control, 'it should be noted, however, that along with medicalizing sexual performance, Viagra has also helped to de-stigmatize erectile dysfunction, making it a topic men and women could more freely discuss without embarrassment or shame' (Conrad, 2007, p. 44).

Toward Demedicalization?

Despite the influence of psychiatry, not all attempts to medicalize a field of behaviour are necessarily successful. As Conrad (2007) has argued, medicalization is uneven and bidirectional. Just as segments of the medical profession gain exclusive or partial jurisdiction over managing certain behaviour or individuals whom they define as pathological and sick, they also lose jurisdiction. The term **demedicalization**, the reverse of medicalization, denotes that an issue is no longer defined in medical terms and that medical intervention is no longer thought to be appropriate. Masturbation, for example, is a behaviour that has now been demedicalized whereas in the nineteenth century it was considered a disease in need of medical treatment. While not completely demedicalized, childbirth has been transformed. For example, midwifery, once was illegal in Canada. Today it is recognized as a legal and regulated profession in most provinces and territories. The availability of birth centres such as those in Quebec, staffed by midwives who follow a woman through her pregnancy, provide low-tech and more natural alternatives for childbirth. The natural childbirth movement places greater emphasis on the Lamaze method with a partner providing support and acting as a coach through labour. On the other hand, the growth of medical technology has made fetal monitoring and ultrasounds routine even in low-risk cases. The direction over childbirth remains a contested area between medical specialists and advocates of natural childbirth.

Demedicalization does not necessarily indicate that the behaviour in question ceases to be subject to normative evaluation and social control, for example, homosexuality, which arguably has been demedicalized. Through history, male homosexuality has been defined as a sin, as a crime, and during most of the twentieth century, as a medical or psychiatric condition. Some of the medical interventions for homosexuality have included

andropause

Defined as an age-related decline in testosterone levels. It is often considered the male equivalent of menopause.

demedicalization

The reverse of medicalization—that is, when a behaviour once defined in medical terms is no longer defined as such.

hormone therapy, drugs, therapeutic castration, and aversive conditioning using electric shock, while Freudian approaches have emphasized psychoanalysis. The first edition of the DSM in 1952 included the diagnostic label 'homosexuality' as one of several types of 'sexual deviation' within the more general classification of 'sociopathic personality disturbance' (Conrad & Schneider, 1992, pp. 187–193). During the 1970s the gay liberation movement, which was oriented to the rights of gay men, was successful, along with key psychiatrists, in having the category of homosexuality removed from the DSM.

This change did not mean that gay men were no longer subject to discrimination or were no longer viewed as deviant. Despite changing official definitions and the fact that same-sex marriage is legal in places like Canada, there remain people who view homosexuality as immoral and something that should be condemned. The alacrity with which many people have associated gay men and AIDS in Western societies attests to their lack of integration and acceptance. Because of the increasing prevalence of the human immunodeficiency virus (HIV), gay men (as well as intravenous drug users, prostitutes, and others) are subject to increasing medical scrutiny, albeit in a different form. Medical intervention and surveillance aimed at preventing the spread of AIDS do not necessarily confer the sick role. Often the language of law, rather than medicine, is invoked: gay men are viewed as responsible for and therefore guilty of HIV transmission; some view the contraction of AIDS as just deserts for engaging in risk behaviour or for deviating from moral precepts.

Conclusion

Medicalization encompasses broad areas of human life. Psychiatry, through its use of the Diagnostic and Statistical Manual of Mental Disorders, has been engaged over the past century in policing behaviour and remains a powerful instrument of social control. However, the process of medicalization today goes far beyond that of psychiatry. Other branches of medicine and social forces, such as the pharmaceutical industry, consumer rights groups, patients, and health insurance companies are equally critical in promoting the medicalization of all aspects of life. Medicalization has transformed the normal into the pathological, and medical ideologies, interventions, and therapies shape our notions of acceptable behaviour and states of being (Conrad, 2007). Normal events such as aging are constructed as a medical problem or pathology and have led to new ways of thinking about the aging body, whereby medical intervention to slow the aging process is considered necessary and appropriate. The biomedicalization of aging has 'affected our understanding of the nature of late life, individual and societal decision making, and family and medical responsibility. . . . The body [becomes] open to unlimited manipulation, at any age. . .' (Kaufman et al., p. 2). Excessive consumerism is now labelled 'compulsive buying'. It is framed as a psychiatric disorder and can be treated as similar to other disorders, such as obsessive-compulsive behaviour, substance abuse, and depression (Lee & Mysyk, 2004). Shyness is also increasingly defined and managed as a social problem that can and should be treated. Methods of treatment include prescription medications, cognitive-behavioural therapies, and self-help materials (Scott, 2006).

Medicalization focuses on the individual as the source of the problem. As a consequence, the concern is to treat the individual back to what is considered a normal state. Social determinants of health that influence well-being are obscured. Depression, for example, is treated predominantly with psychotropic medications while social environments that feed depression are not altered (Conrad, 2007). Furthermore, what is considered normal or deviant is neither objective nor obvious. Rather, these concepts are constituted in particular social and political contexts and reflect the views of powerful groups in society, be they religious or scientific. Focusing on the individual diverts attention from social, economic, and ideological factors that may either contribute to or cause certain behaviours or illness. Little attention is paid to social factors, cultural differences, or disagreements about what constitutes deviance and normality, or to the fact that these categories are social constructions by which dominant groups can exercise control over others in society. As Caplan states, 'The act of naming is an act of power. To assign a name is to act as though we are referring to something that exists, something real' (cited in Lee & Mysyk, 2004, p. 1716).

There are certain social consequences to medicalization (Conrad, 2007). One benefit is that medicalization extends the sick role to a wider range of ailments and behaviours (ADHD, alcoholism, erectile dysfunction, PMS) and thus reduces individual blame for the problem. Medications have significantly improved the lives of many individuals suffering from various conditions such as depression, bipolar disorder, ADHD, and fibromyalgia. Medical treatments have also helped those dealing with conditions such as obesity and menopause. On the negative side, however, medicalization has transformed many human differences into pathologies: 'The greater danger here is that transforming all difference into pathology diminishes our tolerance for and appreciation of the diversity of human life' (p. 148). *Normal, expected,* and *acceptable* are increasingly being defined by biomedicine and pharmaceutical companies.

Furthermore, the scope and direction of medicalization is intensifying in new ways as a result of the technoscientific revolution. Biomedicine now has the potential to transform biological processes of human life forms, often transforming life itself: 'The scope of biomedicalization processes is thus much broader, including conceptual and clinical expansions through the **commodification of health**; elaboration of risk and surveillance; and innovative clinical applications of drugs, procedures, and other treatments' (Clarke et al., 2005, p. 444). New technologies will pervade even more aspects of everyday life. Clarke et al. go on to suggest that in the biomedicalization era, risk and surveillance practices will be the ways by which health is achieved and maintained. Since all individuals are always at risk of becoming ill, the focus in the biomedicalization era 'is no longer on illness, disability, and disease as matters of fate, but on health as a matter of ongoing moral self-transformation . . . health itself becomes something to work *toward*', not something that we take as a given (p. 447). In the future, it is conceivable that our bodies and lives will be constructed and altered through technoscientific tools to create new social identities.

commodification of health

Treating health as an object or commodity that can be purchased or marketed.

Summary of Main Points

- Normal and deviant are not objective concepts but are socially constructed and reflect the social and the political contexts in which they emerge.
- Medicalization is the process whereby nonmedical problems or phenomena become defined and treated as illnesses, disorders, syndromes, or problems of adjustment.
- More aspects of everyday life are coming under medical scrutiny.
- Medicalization can occur on at least three levels: the conceptual, the institutional, and the interactional.
- The medicalization thesis looks at how medical categories are applied to all parts of life and how people actively internalize these perspectives and seek medical remedies.
- Psychiatry is most often associated with medicalization.
- Psychiatry has always been involved in the identification and regulation of deviance and is the primary example of medical social control.
- The term *social control* refers to the mechanisms that aim to induce conformity or at least to manage or minimize deviant behaviour and to reaffirm norms.
- Medicalization focuses on the individual and diverts attention away from the social environment.
- The pharmaceutical industry, social movements, consumer groups, the media, health insurance companies, and new biotechnological discoveries are important engines of medicalization today.
- Traditionally, women's lives were more subject to medicalization than men's. But we now see the extension of medicalization to men's bodies.
- Medicalization has social consequences that are both positive and negative.
- Demedicalization is the reverse of medicalization and refers to when behaviour is no longer defined in medical terms and is no longer in need of medical intervention.
- Medicalization today is being transformed through developments in technoscientific medicine.

 ## Sociological Reflection: Role of Media in Medicalization

Increasing aspects of life are being medicalized. Behaviour such as shyness and normal processes such as aging are coming under medical scrutiny. For medicalization to be successful, however, people have to buy into the problem as being real. What role do the media play in this process? List some examples from your experience that illustrate the role of the media in medicalization.

Discussion Questions

1. What is the role of psychiatry in the medicalization of deviance?
2. Why has homosexuality successfully been demedicalized?
3. Discuss some similarities in the medicalization of women's and men's bodies.
4. What are some consequences for the individual when new illnesses (such as shyness, excessive shopping, or seasonal affective disorder) become medicalized?
5. Critically examine the proposition that everyday stresses and strains of life are becoming medicalized or that some mental illnesses are becoming normalized.
6. Discuss how biomedical and technological discoveries could alter how we view the normal body and health.
7. Discuss how notions of normal and illness have changed over time. What are the reasons for these changes?
8. Why do some groups or individuals consciously seek medicalization?
9. What are some social consequences of medicalization? Are there times when medicalization is more harmful than helpful? When might that be the case?
10. In what ways could looking at social determinants of health be useful in understanding an illness or behaviour that has been constructed as deviant?

 Further Investigation

1. There is increasing emphasis today on individuals taking responsibility for their own well-being, which parallels the adherence to neoliberal ideology and a decline of the welfare state. What role, if any, does psychiatry play in contemporary society in promoting individual responsibility for one's well-being? If you think it does play a role, explain how you see it doing so.
2. Critically analyze the proposition that psychiatry is one of the most powerful institutions of social control in contemporary societies.

 Further Reading

Conrad, P. (2007). *The medicalization of society.* Baltimore, MD: The Johns Hopkins Press.

Conrad, P., & Schneider, J. (1992). *Deviance and medicalization: From badness to sickness* (2nd ed.). Philadelphia, PA: Temple University Press.

Findlay, D., & Miller, L. (2002). Through medical eyes: The medicalization of women's bodies and women's lives. In B. S. Bolaria & H. Dickinson, H. (Eds.), *Health, illness and health care in Canada* (3rd ed.). Scarborough, ON: Nelson Thomson Learning.

Goffman, E. (1961). *Asylums: Essays on the social situation of mental patients and other inmates.* Garden City, NY: Anchor Press.

Szasz, T. (2007). *The medicalization of everyday life.* Syracuse, NY: Syracuse University Press.

Zola, I. K. (1972). Medicine as an Institution of social control. *Sociological Review, 20,* 407–584.

Web Resources

Canadian Mental Health Association
www.cmha.ca

Centre for ADD/ADHD Advocacy, Canada
www.caddac.ca/

Health Canada, Healthy Living
www.hc-sc.gc.ca/hl-vs/mental/index_
e.html

Mood Disorders Society of Canada
www.mooddisorderscanada.ca/

*Public Health Agency of Canada: Report on
Mental Illnesses*
www.phac-aspc.gc.ca/publicat/miic-mmac/

CHAPTER 10

Constructing Disability and Living with Illness

Jennie Hornosty

Overview

- Do illness and disease differ?
- Are there cultural differences in health beliefs?
- How are illness and disability experienced?
- What are the main theoretical approaches to understanding disability?
- What is the prevalence of disability in Canada?

This chapter discusses the human body as a socio-cultural phenomenon rather than simply a biological one. It examines dominant approaches for understanding disability and the implications of these for social policy. As well, the chapter looks at how chronic illness and disability are socially constructed and can act as barriers to inclusion. It considers the meanings that chronic illness and disability can have for different individuals.

Key Terms

acute illness	illness	sick role
chronic illness	Participation and Activity	social construction
disease	Limitation Survey (PALS)	stigma
the diminished self	the self	systemic discrimination
embodiment	sickness	

Introduction

If asked about the human body most people would describe it in biological terms. This assumption that the body is simply a biological and natural phenomenon is the dominant discourse in medicine and the allied health sciences. Such a perspective does not consider that there is anything social or cultural about the human body, except perhaps such superficial aspects as clothing, hairstyle, and body shape. This biological perspective also fails to recognize that people may experience their bodies differently. Certain aspects of the human body are, of course, given and immutable—for example, all humans are born and must die and all humans experience pain and illness. But as sociologists and anthropologists have pointed out, the ways that people understand and experience their bodies are mediated through social, cultural, and political processes. As we have seen in Chapters 6 and 7, different groups have different beliefs, understandings, and experiences of health and illness. Their interpretations of so-called natural events, such as birth and death, can also vary, sometimes dramatically. There are also social and cultural differences as to what constitutes a healthy body or an ideal body. A sociological approach to the body is the notion that we both are and have a body. In other words, people's bodies are central to their self-identity; it is the thing or container in which we present ourselves to others, and through which we experience the world.

Understanding Illness: It's Not Just Biological

> 'The ideal of health . . . embodies a particular culture's notions of well-being and desired human qualities.'
>
> — *Freund et al., 2003, p. 126*

How do we define *illness*? What makes something an illness? Whose definition is correct? When is depression considered an illness as opposed to being seen as a normal (i.e., healthy) response to a situation? Health and illness are often thought of as medical categories; however, according to sociologists these are also social phenomena that cannot be understood fully by biomedical criteria. It is especially important, therefore, to explore individuals' understanding of their bodies and their health beliefs. Several studies have pointed to the importance of lay health beliefs in people's understandings of the body (see, for instance, Kleinman & Seeman, 2000; Lock, 2000) and have demonstrated how health beliefs may vary between different social and cultural or ethnic groups. These studies note that lay people often adhere to concepts of health, illness, disease, and the body that may differ dramatically from the orthodox medical position. Research involving interviews with older African-American women living in a southern US state, for example, revealed a common belief that a blow to the breast could cause a bruise or a knot that could result in breast cancer. As a result of this belief, some of the women thought that a mammogram could predispose them to developing breast cancer because they found the procedure painful (Wardlow & Curry, 1996).

There is an assumption that people experience pain in a universal way, that pain can be measured objectively, and that, therefore, we can compare magnitudes of pain between individuals. A common question patients are asked in the hospital when they present with pain is this: 'On a scale of one to ten, with one being the least and ten being the highest pain, how would you rate the pain you are currently experiencing?' The answer is undoubtedly helpful to doctors in determining what they should prescribe or what treatment options they should consider to manage the patient's pain. However, an oft-cited study by Zborowski suggests that pain is unique to each individual. In a qualitative study involving patients from four ethno-cultural groups—Jewish, Italian, Irish, and 'Old American stock'—Zborowski (1952) found that there were important cultural differences in both attitudes and reactions to pain. While both Jewish and Italian patients responded with more emotionality, their underlying attitudes were different. Italian patients were more focused on the immediacy of their pain experience and welcomed pain-relieving drugs, whereas Jewish patients were more focused on the symptomatic meaning of their pain for the long term. They were more reluctant to accept pain-relieving drugs because they were concerned with the effects of the drug on their overall health. Those of 'Old American' origin responded to pain in a matter-of-fact way, somewhat akin to a detached observer. Similar to Jewish patients, they also were concerned with the symptomatic significance of their pain. Patients of Irish heritage were more likely to repress their suffering and deny pain.

Social class can also be a factor in how illness is defined. Kenneth Davidson (1969) explored meanings of disease and illness among different social-class groups in a rural northeast community of Nova Scotia. Significant differences existed between the three groups: Class I (those who had achieved high professional, occupational, and educational status); Class II (the majority of wage earners in the community, including trades and small business owners); and Class III (those with little training or education, high seasonal unemployment). Davidson found that many of those in Class III tended to take a stoical view of illness and suffered considerable pain and discomfort before they sought medical help or defined themselves as being ill. By comparison, respondents in Class I and II were much more likely to seek medical attention early on for a wide range of symptoms. Illness behaviours also differed. For example, Class III respondents dismissed childhood diseases, such as measles, mumps, and chicken pox, as a natural part of growing up whereas those in Class I would take their children to a doctor 'over the least little thing' (p. 238). Explanations for illness also differed among the three groups. The majority of people in Class III took a fatalistic approach when explaining their illnesses, attributing it to things such as 'bad luck' or 'God's will' (p. 239) whereas those in Class I and II were more likely to explain most illnesses as the consequence of viruses and other pathogenic agents. Not surprisingly, Davidson found different approaches to treatment and curing among the three groups.

A sociological approach to illness emphasizes that our understandings and definitions of illness are mediated through factors such as culture, class, ethnicity, and age. In other words, illness is not an objective state but is dependent on how individuals define their situation or experience. Put another way, illness is **socially constructed**; that is, our meanings of illness are shaped through our interactions with others. The meanings of illness are also influenced by an individual's identity, time, and place. People may have the same disease, but they may experience it and react to it quite differently (Brown, 2000). For example, a diagnosis of rheumatoid arthritis will have different meanings for a competitive skier than for a writer. Similarly, a 65-year-old would likely think differently than a 22-year-old about such a diagnosis. People's behavioural responses can also vary. An elderly person with a heart condition might severely restrict her physical activity whereas a 30-year-old with a heart problem might change his dietary habits and embark on a

social construction

Refers to the socially created characteristics of human life based on the idea that people actively construct reality, meaning it is neither natural nor inevitable. Therefore, notions of health/illness are subjective human creations that should not be taken for granted.

physical exercise program as a way to manage his condition. To say that illness is socially constructed, however, is not to deny that viruses and diseases objectively exist.

Theory Link
See Chapter 2 for a discussion of the major theoretical perspectives in health sociology.

disease

Refers to a biophysical condition diagnosed by a medical practitioner.

illness

The subjective response to a disease.

embodiment

The lived experience of both being a body and having a body.

sickness

Refers to the actions an individual takes while sick, including taking on the sick role.

sick role

A concept used by Talcott Parsons to describe the social expectations of how sick people should act and of how they are meant to be treated.

While in everyday life the terms **disease** and **illness** are frequently conflated into the term illness, sociologists tend to make a distinction between disease and illness. Simply put, disease is located in the body; it is a biophysical condition, something that doctors diagnose as such, and is treated through biomedical interventions. However, its distribution, as we have seen in Chapters 4, 6, and 7, is also strongly affected by social factors, such as class, race, sex, ethnicity, and education. Illness is a more subjective phenomenon; it is something that people experience when they believe that they are not well and may be considered an **embodied** experience. Illness refers to 'how the sick person and the members of the family or wider social network perceive, live with, and respond to symptoms and disability' (Kleinman, 1988, pp. 3–6, as cited in Freund et al., 2003, pp. 147–149). However, the same social factors that affect the distribution of disease also are evident in people's varying perceptions and experiences of health and illness (Brown, 2000).

A further distinction is **sickness**, which refers to the actions a person takes, as discussed by Parsons in his concept of the **sick role**. While in many cases individuals diagnosed with a disease may think of themselves as being ill and take on the sick role, this is not always the case. As Davidson (1969) found, most respondents in his Class III group treated childhood diseases as a natural part of growing up while respondents in Class 1 sought medical intervention for their children. In other words, respondents from the two groups attached different significance to the same diseases.

Theory Link
See Chapter 2 for a further discussion of the sick role.

Irving Zola (2000) points out that the process by which people construct symptoms as illness is a complex one. Physical symptoms among people are widespread, yet very few are brought to a doctor's attention. Zola argues that neither the obviousness of a symptom, the medical seriousness, nor objective discomfort can account for the point at which a person converts to a patient. Rather, he found that the reason people sought medical treatment was related to their social-psychological circumstances, such as an interpersonal crisis, perceived interference with social or personal relations, or interference with work or physical activity. Furthermore, different ethnic groups showed different patterns of explanation for seeking help. Zola concluded that while the symptoms were there, the perceptions of those symptoms differed considerably: '[T]he very labelling and definition of a bodily state as a symptom as well as the decision to do something about it is itself part of a social process' (pp. 212–213). People bring different world views to the ways in which they frame an etiology.

From both a biomedical and sociological approach a distinction must be made between acute illness and chronic illness. An **acute illness** typically develops quickly, lasts for a short period of time, and often goes away without the use of medications or surgery. It is by definition transitory. Common examples of acute illness are colds, the flu (including H1N1), eye infections, headaches, tonsillitis, appendicitis, pneumonia, and severe acute respiratory syndrome (SARS). Those with an acute illness may take on the sick role. During our lifetime, all of us will experience many acute illnesses; however, our concept of **self** or who we are will not be changed as a result of such illnesses. A **chronic illness**, on the other hand, is ongoing, recurrent, noncommunicable (except for HIV/AIDS), often degenerative, and has no cure (at least not yet). Examples of chronic illness include AIDS, diabetes, arthritis, asthma, cancer, heart disease, stroke, Alzheimer's disease, multiple sclerosis, Parkinson's disease, rheumatoid arthritis, emphysema, and fibromyalgia. Individuals with a chronic illness face a number of common problems in terms of everyday life, including the need to constantly manage their illness. Although from the view of the sufferer an acute illness can be problematic, disruptive, and even life threatening, it does not damage the ill person's sense of self. A chronic illness, on the other hand, is a rupture in our relationship with our body, the self, and the world (Williams, 2004).

A number of reports have shown that chronic disease accounts for a significant portion of morbidity and mortality among Canadians. According to a 2003 report, 16 million individuals and families in Canada live with a chronic illness, with increased prevalence among those in vulnerable communities, such as Aboriginal people and those who are socio-economically disadvantaged (*Canada Report*, 2003). Moreover, cardiovascular disease, type 2 diabetes, and cancer are the leading causes of death and disability in Canada. Over three million Canadians cope with serious respiratory diseases, such as asthma, chronic obstructive pulmonary disease, lung cancer, influenza and pneumonia, bronchiolitis, tuberculosis, cystic fibrosis, and respiratory distress syndrome (Public Health Agency of Canada, 2008a). As well, 1.3 million Canadians report having heart disease diagnosed by a health practitioner and about 300 000 are living with the effects of a stroke (Public Health Agency of Canada, 2009a). In 2005, 695 000 Canadians, or 2.2 per cent of the Canadian population, had received a diagnosis of cancer at some time during the previous 10 years (The Daily, 2009). More than 3 million Canadians have diabetes, of which 90 per cent have type 2 (Canadian Diabetes Association).

Constructing Chronic Illness

> 'Living with a serious illness takes effort and devours time. It also means overcoming stigmatizing judgments, intrusive questions, and feelings of diminished worth.'
>
> — *Charmaz, 1993, p. 2*

Has there ever been a time when you've felt frustrated that you're just not physically well enough or strong enough to do something you wanted to do? Have you wondered how your life would be different if you had multiple environmental sensitivities or constant back pain? Especially when we are young, many of us take our bodies for granted and assume that our bodies will do whatever we want them to do. As the popular expression goes, it is only a matter of 'mind over body'. Being ill is not only inconvenient; experiences of illness remind us of our limitations and our dependencies, and of our ultimate mortality. Our

acute illness

An illness that develops quickly and is short-lived.

the self

A concept used by George Herbert Mead to refer to a core identity. For Mead the self is a social product that emerges through our interaction with others.

chronic illness

An illness that is ongoing, often lasts a lifetime, and has no known cure.

sense of who we are and our social relationships are intimately connected with our bodies and their everyday functioning. Being ill is disruptive and disorderly (Freund et al., 2003). Moreover, Susan Wendell (2001) reminds us that any practical concept of chronic illness has to be patient-centred or illness-centred, rather than simply being based on diagnosis or disease classification. Wendell makes a distinction between 'healthy disabled' and 'unhealthy disabled'. By 'healthy disabled' she is referring to 'people whose physical conditions and functional limitations are relatively stable and predictable for the foreseeable future' and whose impairments may not be apparent (p. 19). 'Unhealthy disabled' are people with obvious impairments that limit their participation in various activities on a regular basis. See Box 10.1 for a story about Katy, who is an example of someone who is 'healthy disabled'.

George Herbert Mead states that the self is a social product that arises only in interaction with others. For Mead, the self is 'that which can be an object to itself'; it is 'reflexive', that is, it can be both subject and object (Mead, 1964/1934, p. 140). Our human uniqueness stems from our ability to reflect on our experiences; the self is not present at birth but evolves through our interaction with others. While in some respects our sense of who we are—that is, our identity—is shaped in the early years through a process of socialization, the self is also fluid. Chronic illness often challenges and disrupts our earlier sense of self. While chronically ill people do experience physical pain and psychological distress, another aspect of the suffering is the loss of self. In the words of Kathy Charmaz, 'chronically ill persons frequently experience a crumbling away of their former self-images without simultaneous development of equally valued new ones. The experiences and meanings upon which these ill persons had built former positive self-images are no longer available to them' (1983, p. 168).

Freund et al. (2003) write that chronic illness often leads to a radical assessment of one's self in relation to one's past and one's future, in light of changed and changing capacities (2003, p. 149). The extent of disruption to the earlier self with the onset of a chronic illness depends on a number of factors, including the severity of the illness, its visibility to others, and its perception by others. Certain chronic illnesses, such as HIV/AIDS, for example, carry a great deal of **stigma**. Advanced stages of multiple sclerosis can mean total dependence on others for assistance with mundane everyday activities. An individual with diabetes can often manage to hide the illness from co-workers; someone with severe rheumatoid arthritis often can not. Nevertheless, people with chronic illnesses face a number of common problems in terms of organizing their social environments, in terms of the attitudes of others, and in terms of their sense of self. Relationships with family members and the individual's wider social network may need to be re-examined. Becoming dependent can mean that normal rules of reciprocity and mutual support may need to be altered or abandoned. Bodily states may need to be closely monitored; time must be devoted to the management of symptoms and medical regimes (Bury, 1982). Having a chronic illness makes a person's life less predictable and controllable: *Will I get worse? Will I be able to go on this planned vacation? If I take on this demanding but interesting project, will I have another heart attack?*

A major consequence of having a chronic illness can be the loss of independence. In a society that prides itself on self-sufficiency and individual responsibility, this loss can threaten the ill person's sense of self because it impairs the ability to participate as an equal in social relationships. Many chronically ill persons subscribe to this ideology and

stigma

A physical or social trait, such as a disability or a criminal record, that results in negative social reactions, such as discrimination and exclusion.

BOX 10.1 Katy's Story[1]

Katy, an accomplished academic in her early 40s, is respected for her ideas, her teaching, and her calm, reasoned approach to issues. As a result, she is often asked to sit on committees at both a national and local level. She is energetic, outgoing, athletic, always cheerful, considerate of others, and eternally optimistic, the kind of person everyone enjoys being around. You would never know from a casual acquaintance with Katy that, on a daily basis, she needs to be vigilant about where she goes, where and how she travels, and what she eats. If she is not careful, she will be physically ill for days. People are often surprised to learn that Katy has multiple environmental sensitivities. Among the many things she reacts to are perfumed scents, smoke, environmental pollution, household and commercial cleaning products, paint, various construction materials, whiteboard markers, and freshly paved asphalt. Her home is the only place that she knows for certain will not make her ill.

Katy lives with unpredictability—she never knows for certain when something will trigger a reaction. She has had to leave concerts before they even began because someone in the audience was wearing a scent. She hesitates to travel to countries where smoking is not banned in public places. In fact, she minimizes her travels as much as possible because the cleaning fluids used in hotel and conference rooms can trigger a severe headache and nausea. On a sunny and warm day she is hesitant to eat on patios in restaurants because someone outside may light up a cigarette. Doctors have told her to eliminate certain foods from her diet to help her immune system so she has to watch carefully what she eats. When travelling, Katy carries a face mask and often an air purifier with her; even during daily walks with her dog, she sometimes wears a mask because roads that are being paved or emissions from the pulp mill 100 kilometres away affect her breathing.

She has sought help from both conventional doctors and alternative health practitioners. In some cases, the seriousness of her condition has been questioned or attributed to psychological factors, such as the possibility of earlier trauma. It has been suggested that maybe her problems are 'all in her head'. Some acquaintances and colleagues were initially skeptical about the seriousness of her illness or the severity of her symptoms if she is exposed to chemicals and pollutants. As one person remarked, 'I didn't really believe it until I saw it [the physical reaction] with my own eyes'.

Does Katy suffer from a chronic illness? The answer is yes and no. Her multiple environment sensitivities profoundly affect her behaviour on a daily basis. However, despite any medical definition, Katy's self-identity, that is, her sense of who she is, has not changed. Occasionally Katy might say with some frustration 'that my body is really starting to wear me down'. But on a daily basis she does not define herself as a person who has a chronic illness or a disability.

---

1. Based on a true story.

view dependency as something negative, as a loss of a so-called normal life. In Charmaz's words, 'Values of independence and individualism combine to intensify the immobilizing effects of chronic illness' (1983, p. 172). As a result, former friendships may become strained or lost altogether; the chronically ill individual may retreat into his or her own world and shun social relationships. For example, the pain from fibromyalgia is more acute at some times than others so individuals with fibromyalgia may not know ahead of time whether they will feel well enough to attend a social function. If they frequently decline social invitations for fear that they may not be able to go, or accept invitations but later need to send regrets, it may only be a matter of time before such invitations are no longer issued. Also, as Freund et al. (2003) explain, for some people pain, requirements of treatment, and lack of access to everyday activities foster isolation; others may socially withdraw because they are unable to deal with the chronic problems, thus setting in motion a spiral of increasing isolation: 'The less one can or wants to do, the less one socializes; but the less one socializes, the more others withdraw, and in turn the more the person with a chronic illness withdraws' (p. 150). In other words, over time the chronically ill individual can become marginalized from social activities, which results in a **diminished self**. However, as we saw in Katy's story in Box 10.1, this is not the experience of everyone with a medically defined chronic illness. Also, there may be gender differences in response to chronic illness: constructions of masculinity that place greater emphasis on autonomy and independence for men may make it more difficult for them to preserve their sense of self (p. 151).

Chronic illness affects not only an individual but it can also have an impact on family members and other close members of the sufferer's social network, who may feel the disruption of the illness (Freund et al., 2003, p. 151). The onset of a chronic illness may lead to financial crises and family strain, and the necessity of giving up paid employment or reducing hours of works can create economic hardships. As a result, the individual or family may be forced to live economically marginal existences or to drastically alter their lifestyles. In situations where a chronically ill person was previously the sole or primary caregiver other arrangements will need to be made. Depending on the circumstances this can be both costly and lead to family strain. One of Charmaz's (1983) interviewees, the older sister of a woman with anorexia nervosa, explained her frustration with the disruption to her life this way: 'it is very hard to keep my life up and positive when I am constantly drained, . . . because it does take a lot out of me to deal with my sister . . . same with my mother, it takes a lot of energy and I do get angry' (p. 179).

Sociologists have argued that people with chronic illnesses need to construct a new sense of self as their former self-images disappear. Our emotions around chronic illness and our definition of self are produced in ongoing social interactions with family, friends, co-workers and health-care providers. Charmaz reminds us that supportive friends and intimates play a major role in bolstering the ill person's self, maintaining ongoing relationships, and minimizing the potential for discrediting experiences. But what happens to people who find themselves in a foreign environment? In her study with Cantonese-speaking immigrant women in Canada, Joan Anderson (1991) shows that multiple factors influence a person's ability to manage chronic illness. She writes that for an immigrant woman, 'the difficulties in living with a chronic illness are exacerbated by the experience of uprooting from her homeland and resettling in a new country. She must deal with her

---

diminished self

The term that Charmaz (1983) uses to refer to the loss of a previously valued identity.

marginality, social isolation and alienation in a foreign culture' (p. 710). People with a chronic illness sometimes feel devalued by others; this feeling arises from a sense of not being taken seriously or not being listened to. For immigrant women, however, this feeling of being devalued was heightened by the migration experience and the feeling of being marginal in a culture that was foreign. Furthermore, the lack of English language skills made it difficult to communicate with English-speaking health professionals.

Theory Link
See Chapter 6 for a discussion of health and ethnicity.

Anselm Strauss and Barney Glaser's (1975) now classic work on chronic illness pointed to the limitations of a biomedical approach for understanding the complexity of chronic illness. They argued as have others that it is important to understand the subjective experience of living with chronic illness. For example, there are certain demands placed on people with chronic illness and their families in terms of managing a medical regime. Medications must be taken at set times; medical appointments need to be organized and scheduled; and arrangements must be made to ensure the individual is able to get to an appointment. People with a chronic illness must deal with uncertainty about their future, they may need to find ways to cope with social isolation, and they must manage relationships with friends and co-workers. Different illnesses, of course, affect people's lives in different ways; it is important, therefore, to look at chronic illness in the context of people's lives. Not all chronic illnesses are accorded the legitimacy of being considered a real illness. A case in point is that of chronic fatigue syndrome. In her interviews with 50 individuals in the Boston area who had sought help for a debilitating fatigue that significantly interfered with their work and home activities, Norma Ware (1992) found that her interviewees regularly reported two types of delegitimizing encounters as a result of their experience with chronic fatigue syndrome. One type stems from the apparent insignificance of the symptoms in the eyes of many people. Since everyone from time to time has aches and pains, feels fatigued, or has feelings of depression, people would dismiss or trivialize the symptoms with comments such as 'You're tired? We're all tired! So what!' The other delegitimizing experience was the result of encounters with doctors. There are no definitive diagnostic tests for the illness, and chronic fatigue syndrome is only just gaining acceptance as a real medical condition. Participants reported that many physicians viewed the illness as psychosomatic— that is, it was considered to be 'all in your head'. Interviewees also complained of being disbelieved or not taken seriously because they didn't look sick (p. 350). This experience of being repeatedly disconfirmed in their definition of reality lead to self-doubt, suffering in silence, and alienation as a result of deciding to keep the illness secret: 'The self-doubt and the threat of stigma, the secrecy and the social isolation that results, the psychological paralysis induced by the ambiguities of the illness, and the shame of being wrong about "really" being sick all contribute to the psychic suffering of the chronic fatigue victim' (p. 355). Delegitimization of one's illness also means that one is not viewed as worthy of sympathy, support, or time off work.

Constructing Disability

'It is often assumed that a disability such as deafness, cerebral palsy, mental retardation or blindness poses an insurmountable barrier to the enjoyment of a normal life, one replete with challenges, joys, success and failure. Life with a disability is perceived as tragic.'

— *Lepofsky, 1985, p. 312, cited in McCoy, 2001, p. 22*

'[T]here are important differences between healthy disabled and unhealthy disabled people that are likely to affect such issues as treatment of impairment . . . , accommodation of disability in activism and employment, identification of persons as disabled, disability pride, and prevention and so-called 'cure' of disabilities.'

— *Wendell, 2001, p. 17*

Since the 1960s various attempts have been made to explain the complex relationship between chronic illness, impairment, and disability (Bury, 2004; Oliver, 2004). As mentioned, a *chronic illness* is recurrent or ongoing and typically lasts over a person's lifetime. It is something that has a physiological basis and can generally be identified by diagnostic procedures. As defined by the World Health Organization (WHO), an *impairment* is a loss or abnormality of psychological, physiological, or anatomical functions, for example, a limb amputation, loss of vision, or paralysis, whereas a *disability* is any restriction or lack of ability to perform an activity in a manner considered normal (Oliver, 2004). That is, a disability is a consequence of impairment, such as the inability to climb stairs, to walk, or to watch television. However, in common parlance, disability and chronic illness are often constructed as being the same. Although some people with chronic illnesses will also have a disability, this is not inevitable. Likewise those with disabilities do not necessarily have a chronic illness. Impairment can be the result of a genetic disorder, accidents, or trauma rather than the result of a chronic illness (Weiss & Lonnquist, 2006). Rioux & Daly (2010) suggest the reason chronic illness and disability are often conflated is due to an individualistic approach to health and a biomedical reading of the disabled body as ill. The reality is, as they point out, that people with disabilities experience periods of good and ill health in the same way that all people do. It is precisely this possibility of fluctuating health, Wendell (2001) suggests, that causes people with chronic illness to appear to be 'unreliable'. Fluctuation in health may disrupt day-to-day tasks, such that one's productivity at work is compromised. Even seemingly simple tasks (answering the phone, attending a meeting) may be difficult on a given day. Whether for a cause an individual believes in or expectations on the job, 'pushing our bodies and minds excessively means something different to people with chronic illness: it means danger, risk of relapse, hospitalization, long-lasting or permanent damage to our capacities to function (as for some people with MS)' (Wendell, 2001, p. 25).

Defining *impairment, disability,* or *illness* is not simply a matter of language or science; it is also a matter of politics (Oliver, 2004). To illustrate this point, Oliver cites the conceptualization of AIDS as an example: while some argued that AIDS was primarily to be understood as a biomedical problem, others argued that it was equally a social and political issue. The discourse one chooses has implications for social policy and how people with AIDS are treated. The same can be said for the two dominant discourses around disability: one is a biomedical approach; the other, a relational or social approach:

. . . how a society defines disability and whom it recognizes as disabled are of enormous psychological, economic and social importance, both to people who are experiencing themselves as disabled and to those who are not but are nevertheless given the label. . . .

There is no definitive answer to the question: Who is physically disabled? We cannot approach chronic illness as having universal meaning across individuals. Disability has social, experiential and biological components, present and recognized in different measures for different people. (Wendell, 1989, p. 108)

Disability as Individual Pathology

A biomedical approach to disability locates the problem within the individual. That is, disability is constructed as an individual condition or pathology that requires ongoing medical intervention to help the individual function as normally as possible. But what is a normal body? And what makes something normal or abnormal? The implicit assumption from this perspective is that people with impairments or disabilities are abnormal. A biomedical perspective focuses on an individual's functional limitations and is concerned with medical diagnosis and treatments for the so-called dysfunction (Rioux & Daly, 2010). Since disabilities are seen as located in individuals' pathologies, the medical profession acts as a gatekeeper to determine who is entitled to certain accommodations, benefits, specialized training, etc., all of which are tied to medical certification. One example of this is student accessibility centres in universities. Students are eligible for accommodations, such as having access to note takers, writing their exams in separate rooms, having extra time to complete exams, or carry a reduced full-time course load (and still be considered a full-time student), only if they are deemed worthy of such accommodations. In certain situations, such as 'learning disabilities', to be eligible for these accommodations requires some form of medical documentation. These accommodations are seen as privileges, not rights, and students have to apply for them on a regular basis. What is not acknowledged in such an approach is the possibility that the problem is not a student's inability to learn but, rather, is a function of the way academic material is traditionally conveyed and the way standardized testing procedures are used to evaluate whether the material has been properly mastered. A variant of the individual pathology model is the functional approach to health, which also views disability as an individual pathology. The focus, from this perspective, is on providing services of a therapeutic nature, including the development of life skills that will enable the individual to become as socially functional as possible (Rioux & Daly, 2010).

Disability as Social Pathology

'For me the social model of disability is concerned with the personal and collective experiences of disabling social barriers and how its application might influence professional practice and shape political action.'

— *Oliver, 2004, p. 287*

The main critique of the individual pathology model of disability is that it fails to look at societal factors and how they prevent certain individuals from leading their lives as they

systemic discrimination

A form of discrimination that arises from the way that organizational structures, policies, practices, and procedures operate (unrelated to the requirements of the job), which while appearing neutral have a discriminatory effect on certain groups of people.

would like. The social model or social pathology approach to disability locates disability within society, not within the individual. From this perspective, disability is not a bodily or mental attribute of the individual but, rather, results from the interaction between person and environment: 'Disability is something imposed on top of our impairments by the way we are unnecessarily isolated and excluded from full participation in society' (Oliver, 1996, quoted in Freund et al., 2003, p. 160). In other words, whether an objective impairment becomes a disability is contingent on people's social environment. If Braille was the main method of written communication, blindness would not be a disability. People in wheelchairs are considered disabled because there are physical barriers to their mobility. Freund et al. (2003) explain that until the 1940s many of the inhabitants of Martha's Vineyard (a community in Massachusetts) were deaf but were not marginalized in any way. The entire community, including those who were able to hear, used sign language as a natural and ordinary form of communication. Those with impaired hearing were treated no differently from those who were not: they worked, married, and were not thought of as being significantly different. These examples suggest that whether something is constructed as a disability is dependent on the physical, social, and cultural environment in which people live, and is influenced by normative practices and people's attitudes. In her 1984 Royal Commission on Equality in Employment, Judge Rosalie Abella makes the same point. Abella identifies four groups of people who have been and are disadvantaged in the workplace as a result of **systemic discrimination**: women, visible minorities, Aboriginal peoples, and people with disabilities. She writes this:

> Persons with disabilities experience some limitation of their work functioning because of their physical or mental impairment. But the extent to which their disability affects their lives on a daily basis—that is, handicaps them—is very often determined by how society reacts to their disability. A disabled person need not be handicapped. (1984, p. 39)

One could also say that someone with a handicap need not be viewed as disabled.

A social pathology perspective challenges the hegemony of a biomedical approach to disability: it suggests instead that the appropriate unit of analysis is the social system. Rioux & Daly (2010, pp. 349–351) suggest that there are two models of disability within the social pathology framework: the environmental approach and the rights-outcome approach. The environmental approach suggests that disability arises from the failure of environments to accommodate people's differences and needs, and the way in which environments are organized constructs disability: public transportation in many cities makes it difficult if not impossible for people relying on wheelchairs to use the service. The lack of elevators in public buildings provides a major obstacle for those who have physical disabilities. Those who are visually impaired can not use automated banking machines without assistance if the keys do not have Braille characters. Rigid workplace policies that fail to provide flexible work options pose problems for people who need longer rest breaks. Standardized methods for assessing learning outcomes put those who learn differently at a disadvantage, and construct those differences as learning disabilities. Imagine how you would fare if suddenly the normal mode of communication was sign language. Imagine what it would be like if physical spaces were designed only for people in wheelchairs; there would be no need for chairs and doorways, and counters and sinks would be closer to the ground. Imagine being in a situation where the primary means of evaluation was your ability to explain in picture form. In other words, the environmental approach highlights the fact that certain people are excluded from the mainstream of social life, not as a result of their individual inadequacies but as a result of the failure of social environments to accommodate people's differences. We live in human-made, artificial spaces that currently have not been adapted to accommodate a wide spectrum of bodies but that could, in fact, be modified to do so (Freund et al., 2003). Policies stemming from the environmental approach, where disability is viewed as difference, not as abnormality, suggest ways to minimize the societal barriers: 'For instance, changes to building codes, employing principles of barrier-free design, adapted curricular, and targeted policy and funding commitments have been usefully employed' (Rioux & Daly, 2010, p. 350).

Building on the recognition that a variety of supports may be necessary to allow all citizens to participate as equal citizens, 'the rights outcome approach moves beyond calls for adaptations to environments, reflecting a shift that has taken place over the past 20 years in the paradigm of disability from a medical welfare model to a human rights model' (Rioux & Daly, 2010, p. 350). Applying a human-rights approach, according to Rioux & Daly, underscores respect for diversity, the right to autonomy and the inherent self-worth of all individuals. Providing necessary accommodations and supports is considered a basic right, not a privilege. This approach argues for the need to eliminate all forms of discrimination, including systemic discrimination, that prevent people with disabilities from having access to the full range of opportunities and benefits available to those without such disabilities. A primary concern is to ensure that principles of human rights are being adhered to and that systemic barriers to equal opportunities are eliminated. This was a major focus of Judge Rosalie Abella's recommendations for removing systemic barriers in employment for people with disabilities as well as the other three disadvantaged groups.

Theory Link
See Chapter 2 for a discussion of a human rights approach.

Within human rights there is an important distinction made between a goal of *equality* and one of *equity*. Unlike the principle of equality where the underlying premise is that everyone must be treated the same, equity is about ensuring fairness through a recognition of difference. The former is concerned only with equal opportunity while the principle of equity addresses equality of outcome or equality of condition as the basis of equality. For example, it is often argued, and is legally the case, that everyone in Canada has the same or equal opportunity to get a good education. However, this ignores that fact that not all Canadians begin at the same starting point; those from privileged backgrounds have many greater advantages than those who live in poverty. To achieve equity requires that the underlying structural or systemic inequalities be addressed first. Similarly, as discussed in Chapter 4, although all Canadians are entitled to the same level of health care not all have the same (or equitable) access to health-care services. To ensure that all people have the same or equal rights may require implementing different provisions for different groups of people. As a result of hearing a claim by three deaf applicants, the 1997 Canadian Supreme Court decision in *Eldridge v. British Columbia* affirmed this when it ruled that the provincial government was discriminatory in its health-care services because it did not include sign-language interpreters as an insured service nor did it require hospitals to provide such services. The court stated that

> to argue that governments should be entitled to provide benefits to the general population without ensuring that disadvantaged members of society have the same resources to take full advantage of those benefits bespeaks a thin and impoverished vision of S 15(1) [the equality provisions in the Canadian Charter of Rights and Freedoms] (cited in Rioux, 2010, p. 103).

For Michael Oliver, author and disability rights activist, disability should be seen as a form of social oppression that arises from definitions and practices that seek to exclude individuals seen to deviate from the socially constructed norms of the 'able bodied' (Bury, 2004, pp. 271–272). Similarly, Wendall (1996) argues that it is our cultural attitudes toward the body and our tendency to view bodies that are different as weak that contribute to the stigma of disability. According to Bury (2004), Oliver sees disability as a product of the labelling process, which categorizes people by virtue of their position in relation to the dominant structures and values of society. Exclusionary practices in a capitalist society designate certain attributes as productive and acceptable, namely those able to meet the needs of economic production and the workplace; those who do not possess these attributes are seen as abnormal or deviant and, hence, of less value. Furthermore, these practices reinforce an ideology of individualism, which tends to portray disability as a feature of the individual. In this context, the state's role is to ensure that social order is maintained by regulating eligibility for state benefits (such as a disability pension).

Most sociologists today reject the biomedical model, which constructs disability as an individual pathology, and there is general acceptance that disability arises in the complex relationship between individuals and their social environments. Greater attention now is focused on how employment, structural, and attitudinal barriers exclude certain groups of people. The social model underscores the connection between the personal and the political, and changed the discourses around disability and provided the foundation upon which people with disabilities began to organize collectively. It became a basis for advocacy to give people with disabilities autonomy and control in their lives (Oliver, 2004). The disability rights movement that emerged in the 1970s further challenged the existing discriminatory attitudes and exclusionary practices toward those with disabilities. See Box 10.2 for a brief history of the disability rights movement in Canada.

Criticisms of the Social Model

Despite the successes that the social model helped foster, the model has also come under scrutiny and critique both from people with disabilities and others working in the field of chronic illness (Oliver, 2004). A criticism that some people with disabilities have made of the social model is that it does not adequately address the personal experiences of impairment. French (1993) argues that her visual impairment imposes certain restrictions—for example, her inability to recognize people, to see colour, or to read nonverbal cues—that cannot be eliminated by applying principles of the social model (cited in Oliver, 2004, p. 284).

BOX 10.2 The Disability Rights Movement in Canada

In Canada and the United States, the disability rights movement began in the 1970s as people with disabilities came together to challenge a society that did not fully recognize their rights. A basic human right is the right to equality in society. Encouraged by the successes of the 1960s social movements, people with disabilities argued for the right to participate as autonomous individuals on the same basis as others in society and to shape their own lives. They rejected the predominant attitude that people with disabilities should be treated as charity cases, and they demanded recognition of their rightful place in Canadian society as citizens with equal rights. They fought against discriminatory policies and practices that placed people with physical and mental disabilities at a disadvantage and lobbied to have their rights included in human-rights legislation and the Canadian Charter of Rights and Freedoms. When the Canadian Human Rights Act passed in 1976–77, it became illegal to discriminate against individuals because of their disability, and thus gave persons with disability the same rights as others.

In 1976, the Coalition of Provincial Organizations of the Handicapped (COPOH) was formed by provincial organizations that came together to form a national organization; in 1994, the organization changed its name to the Council of Canadians with Disabilities (CCD) to reflect a new membership structure and provide a national voice for disability organizations. The organization has lobbied for legal changes, has developed coalitions and organized national forums, and has supported provincial organizations concerned with the rights of persons with disabilities. COPOH was instrumental in developing skills and strategies used by leaders of the Canadian disability rights movement to challenge the federal government's first-draft omission of disability in the Canadian Charter of Rights and Freedoms. One of the most important victories for the disability movement was its success in entrenching the rights of Canadians with disabilities in the Constitution and in the Charter, which became law in 1982. Section 15 (1) of the Canadian Charter of Rights and Freedom reads as follows:

> Every individual is equal before and under the law and has the right to the equal protection and equal benefit of the law without discrimination and, in particular, without discrimination based on race, national or ethnic origin, colour, religion, sex, age or mental or physical disability.

Source: Disability Rights in Canada: A Virtual Museum. (Website). (n.d.). Available from http://disabilityrights.freeculture.ca/index.php

Another criticism is that the social model does not take into account the pain and suffering that accompanies impairment. Jenny Morris (1991) acknowledges the importance of the social model in aiding people to understand the disabling barriers and attitudes that accompany disablement. However, she notes the model has also pushed aside the experiences of disabled people's bodies:

> . . . there is a tendency within the social model of disability to deny the experience of our own bodies, insisting that our physical differences and restrictions are entirely socially created. While environmental barriers and social attitudes are a crucial part of our experience of disability—and do indeed disable us—to suggest that this is all there is to it is to deny the personal experience of physical or intellectual restrictions, of illness, of the fear of dying (quoted in Oliver, 2004, p. 284).

Others have criticized the social model for not adequately incorporating other oppressions, such as racism, sexism, and homophobia.

Canadians with Disabilities

Participation and Activity Limitation Survey (PALS)

A national survey designed to collect information on people whose activities are limited because of a condition or health problem.

According to the **Participation and Activity Limitation Survey (PALS)** (Statistics Canada, 2006c), an estimated 4.4 million Canadians—one out of every seven in the population (14.3 per cent)—reported having a disability, an increase from 2001 when the disability rate was 12.4 per cent. Problems related to pain, mobility, and agility affected the largest number of adults, with pain as the most common form of disability reported by those of working age. For the purposes of the survey, persons with disabilities were defined as those who reported difficulties with daily living activities or those who indicated that a physical or mental condition or a health problem reduced the kind or amount of activities that they could do (The Daily, 2007c). Unlike health measures like the Disability Adjusted Year Life (DALY), which objectively measures how many years of life are lost for a person or population compared to some normative standard of health that equates freedom with disability (Rioux & Daly), PALS uses self-reported measures to determine the prevalence of disability in a population.

Not surprisingly, the survey shows that the disability rate in Canada varies by age and sex. The rates of disability rose from 3.7 per cent for those under age 15 to 22.8 per cent for those between the ages of 55 to 64 to a high of 56.3 per cent for those 75 years and older. Women in general were more likely to report an activity limitation (15.2 per cent) than men (13.4 per cent) except in the age category 0 to 14, where boys were nearly twice as likely to report activity limitations compared to girls. By age 25, the reported rates of disability for women began to be higher than men. A possible explanation for this increase in reported disabilities is the changing demographic structure in Canada. While this accounts for some of the increase, only 40 per cent of the disability rate increase can be explained by population aging. A change in disability profiles and reporting practices or some combination may account for some of the increased rate between 2001 and 2006. Moreover, perceptions of disability vary over time as does the willingness of people to report them; societal understanding of the causes of disability and what is considered an activity limitation may have changed and could explain some of the difference as well.

Rates of reported disability vary across the country: outside the Northwest Territories and Nunavut, Quebec has the lowest reported disability rate at 10.4 per cent whereas Nova Scotia has the highest rate at 20.0 per cent. Of the remaining provinces, those in the East had higher disability rates on average than those in the West. Ontario's reported rate was 15.5 per cent. Some but not all of this difference can be explained by the different demographic makeup of each province.

Types of Disabilities among Children in Canada

According to PALS, 69.8 per cent of children aged 0 to 4 (or 1.2 per cent of all Canadian children under the age of 5) with one or more disabilities had a chronic health-condition-related disability, the most common of which was asthma or severe allergies, attention deficit disorder with or without hyperactivity (ADD/ADHD), and autism. Learning disabilities (69.3 per cent) and chronic health conditions (66.6 per cent) were reported most often among school-aged children. Learning disabilities include such conditions as attention problems, hyperactivity, or dyslexia. The disability rate for school-aged children increased between 2001 and 2006; learning disabilities account for the largest part of the increase. See Table 10.1 for a distribution of the types of disabilities among children.

A significant number of children reported two or more disabilities; 50 per cent of children ages 0 to 4 had two or more disabilities while 74.8 per cent of children ages 5 to 14 reported having two or more disabilities. While the majority of children in Canada who had some activity limitation reported having mild to moderate disability, a significant percentage—41.7 per cent—reported experiencing severe to very severe disability.

Prevalence of Disabilities in Adults in Canada

Problems related to pain, mobility, and agility affected nearly three million adults (15 years and older) in Canada in 2006; 70 per cent of those reporting one of these three disabilities

TABLE 10.1 Types of Disabilities among Children with Disabilities, by Age Group, Canada

Type of Disability	Number of Children	Total Percentage
All categories	202 350	100
Hearing (1)	23 290	11.5
Seeing (1)	19 710	9.7
Speech (2)	78 240	44.8
Mobility (2)	23 160	13.2
Agility (2)	37 240	21.3
Learning (2)	121 080	69.3
Developmental (2)	53 740	30.7
Psychological (2)	60 310	34.5
Delay (3)	17 090	62.1
Chronic (1)	135 570	67.0
Other (1)	8100	4.0

Note: The sum of the categories is greater than the population with disabilities because persons could report more than one type of disability.
(1) Applies to all children under 15
(2) Applies to all children aged 5 to 14
(3) Applies to children aged 0 to 4
Source: Adapted from Statistics Canada. (2006). Participation and Activity Limitation Survey, Analytical Report, p. 23. Available from www.statcan.gc.ca/pub/89-628-x/89-628-x2007002-eng.pdf

were also affected by the other two. A mobility limitation was the disability reported most frequently by seniors (age 65 and over): 76.4 per cent of all seniors with disabilities reported mobility challenges. Of those aged 15 to 64, the most commonly reported disability was pain and discomfort, described by 74.4 per cent. Not surprisingly, most types of disability increase with age, the exceptions being learning disabilities and psychological disabilities. Women more than men frequently reported disabilities related to pain, mobility, or agility: 13 per cent of women in Canada as compared to 9 per cent of men. This gender gap increases with age. As in the case of children, a large number of adults living with disabilities (81.7 per cent) reported having two or more disabilities. The survey found that 1.7 million people or 6.6 per cent of Canadians 15 years and older have a severe or very severe disability. Broken down by sex, we see that women with disabilities reported having more severe and very severe limitations than men: 42.2 percent versus 39.8 per cent, respectively. See Table 10.2 for a distribution of reported disabilities by adults.

Barriers to Inclusion in Canada

Decades ago, persons with disabilities were relegated to the margins, becoming the objects of repulsion and fear. They were thought to be a burden to society and were victims of prejudice and abuse. In Canada, persons with disabilities have had difficulties attaining employment and, if they were employed, tended to be marginalized in low-paying jobs with minimal responsibility and little chance of advancement. Channelled out of the mainstream, they were segregated into special schools, workplaces, or residential facilities; indeed, they were treated as charity cases (McCoy, 2001).

In response to the Abella Report, the Canadian government introduced employment equity legislation that mandated federally regulated employers to identify and remove any systemic barriers to employment for persons with disabilities (as well as for the other

TABLE 10.2 Prevalence of Disabilities in Adults 15 Years of Age or Older by Type of Disability, Canada, 2006

Type of Disability	Number	Per cent
Hearing	1 266 120	5.0
Seeing	816 250	3.2
Speech	479 740	1.9
Mobility	2 923 000	11.5
Agility	2 819 580	11.1
Pain	2 965 650	11.7
Learning	631 030	2.5
Memory	495 990	2.0
Developmental	136 570	0.5
Psychological	589 470	2.3
Other	119 390	0.5

Source: Statistics Canada. (2006). Participation and Activity Limitation Survey, Analytical Report, p. 29. Available at www.statcan.gc.ca/pub/89-628-x/89-628-x2007002-eng.pdf

three disadvantaged groups). The Canadian Human Rights Act prohibits discrimination against people with disabilities; as well, persons with disabilities are protected under the equality section of the Canadian Charter of Rights and Freedoms. In many jurisdictions, efforts have been made to improve accessibility in education and employment. Can we assume, then, that persons with disabilities today participate as equals in society?

According to the Canadian Council on Learning (CCL) a significant number of Canadians with disabilities of working age still experience major barriers to labour-force participation and economic security, from physical barriers that limit mobility to discriminatory hiring practices (Canadian Council on Learning, 2009). Compared to nondisabled Canadians, more than twice the number of Canadians with disabilities are unemployed or not actively seeking employment; in 2006, 51 per cent of persons with disabilities were employed, compared to 75 per cent of those without disabilities. The employment profiles are also different for persons with disabilities compared to other workers; those with disabilities are more likely to be employed part-time and are also much more likely to experience at least one period of unemployment. The failure to provide workplace accommodation is a primary reason that many persons with disabilities are not in the labour force. In many cases this could be addressed through a modification to the workplace structure, such as adding handrails and ramps, making washrooms more accessible, modifying workstations, and improving accessible parking. Further modifications could include adding work aids, such as modified work hours; increasing supports, such as sign-language interpreters or assistants; or providing technical aids, such as a computer with Braille, speech recognition software, and recording devices. It has been estimated that the costs of providing more workplace accommodations is relatively low, that is, under $1500. However, 'employers are still ignorant about what it takes to hire and accommodate a person with a disability' (Canadian Council on Social Development, 2010, p. 219).

An oft-cited reason for persons with disabilities having difficulty finding paid work is inadequate skills and education. The CCL states that Canadians with disabilities have markedly poorer literacy skills than nondisabled individuals, especially for those with learning disabilities, although it is also the case for those with other types of disabilities. Furthermore, the CCL points out that individuals with disabilities often encounter barriers to education, which in turn impedes the development of their literacy skills. These difficulties can discourage such individuals from pursuing further educational opportunities. The main barriers to education and training that learners with disabilities encounter are physical accessibility, i.e. inaccessible classrooms, lack of transportation; financial issues, that is, courses and programs may be costly and learners may finding applying for student aid difficult; and attitudes. Learners with disabilities reported that instructors did not allow the necessary accommodations, such as note-takers, separate rooms at exam time, or additional time for tests. Sometimes teachers had stereotyped views about what sorts of programs children with disabilities should pursue (McCoy, 2001). Although low educational achievement may explain some of the reasons why there are disproportionately fewer persons with disabilities in the paid labour force, it does not appear to be the sole reason. McCoy (2001) notes that if we compare university graduates with disabilities to university graduates without disabilities, those with disabilities are still significantly disadvantaged. One study, for example, found that university-educated persons with disabilities had unemployment rates that were almost 10 times higher than for those without disabilities (McCoy, 2001). Furthermore, even when education is attained, persons with disabilities have often been steered toward entry-level jobs that are low paying and offer little employment security or opportunities for promotion (p. 30).

Barriers to employment and education can lead to poverty and poor health. Studies show that Canadians with disabilities are more than twice as likely to live in poverty as other Canadians (Council of Canadians with Disabilities [CCD], 2010, pp. 228–233). Rates of violence and abuse against people with disabilities are among the highest of any group in Canada. The CCD argues that access to needed supports—whether these are at work, school, or home—'is the central foundation for inclusion and equal participation of Canadians with disabilities' (p. 229). According to McCoy, education and training are insufficient mechanisms to ensure employment equity. He agrees with Rioux (1985, p. 611) 'that changing attitudes is the only real, long term solution to employment of persons with disabilities' (McCoy, 2001, p. 42).

Conclusion

From a sociological perspective, illness and disability can best be understood as social constructions. While in both situations there may be physiological or psychological dimensions, the impact of chronic illness and disability on the individual depends significantly on the society in which she or he lives. Biomedical approaches individualize experiences and are inadequate for explaining the complex relationship between embodiment and socio-cultural processes. To understand what chronic illness or having a disability means to the individual, one needs to understand how people experience their body and how social interaction and societal arrangements impact on peoples' experiences.

Summary of Main Points

- Illness is socially constructed.
- Peoples' socio-cultural beliefs shape views of health and illness.
- Individuals with chronic illnesses and disabilities are often stigmatized.
- Some people with chronic illnesses and disabilities experience a loss of self.
- Chronic illness and disability are not necessarily the same thing.
- The biomedical approach views disability as an individual pathology.
- A social model of disability examines how societal arrangements construct disability.
- Nearly 15 per cent of Canadians report having a disability.
- Persons with disabilities are excluded from participation as equal members of society.

 ## Sociological Reflection: Significance of Body Image

Most societies have idealized notions of the body for women and men. The bodies of persons with disabilities or chronic illnesses are often regarded as abnormal or diseased. Reflect on the following:

- The idealized notion of the body in Canada, in terms of what is socially desirable and what is not.
- In terms of their everyday lives, what might the impact be on persons with a disability or those with a chronic illness?
- What role does stigma play in upholding idealized notions of the body?

 ## Discussion Questions

1. How do people's socio-cultural beliefs about illness affect their illness behaviour?
2. Why are societal arrangements important for an understanding of disability?
3. Are equality rights important for people with disabilities, and, if so, in what specific ways?
4. In what ways might having a chronic illness lead to a loss of self?
5. Thinking about Katy's story (see Box 10.1), which approach is most useful in understanding her situation: a biomedical approach or a social constructionist approach? Explain your answer.

Further Investigation

1. How many people in your community are living with disabilities? What sorts of physical and attitudinal barriers do they encounter? What sorts of changes need to be made to remove these barriers?
2. Research and compare two chronic illnesses. What sorts of different challenges would individuals with these illnesses face? Are there any similarities between individuals who suffer from a chronic illness?

Further Reading

Barton, L., & Oliver, M. (Eds.). (1997). *Disability studies: Past, present and future*. Leeds, UK: The Disability Press.

Charmaz, K. (1993). *Good days, bad days: The self in chronic illness*. New Brunswick, NJ: Rutgers University Press.

Dossa, P. (2009). *Racialized bodies, disabling worlds: Storied lives of immigrant Muslim women*. Toronto, ON: University of Toronto Press.

Lupton, D. (2003). *Medicine as culture: Illness, disease and the body in western societies* (2nd ed.). London, UK: Sage.

Strauss, A., & Glaser, B. (1975). *Chronic illness and the quality of life*. St. Louis, MO: Mosby.

Wendell, S. (1996). *The rejected body: Feminist philosophical reflections on disability*. New York, NY: Routledge.

Web Resources

Canadian Arthritis Network
www.arthritisnetwork.ca

Canadian Cancer Society
www.cancer.ca

Canadian Council on Learning (CCL)
www.ccl-cca.ca

Canadian Council on Social Development (CCSD)
www.ccsd.ca/

Canadian Diabetes Association
www.diabetes.ca/

Council of Canadians with Disabilities (CCD)
www.ccdonline.ca

Chronic Illness Community, Support and Resources
www.healingwell.com

Disabled Peoples' International (DPI)
www.dpi.org/

Disability Rights Promotion International (DRPI)
www.yorku.ca/drpi/

Disability Studies Quarterly (DSQ)
www.dsq-sds.org/

Heart and Stroke Foundation
www.heartandstroke.ca

CHAPTER 11

Aging, Dying, and Death in the Twenty-first Century

Maureen Strazzari & Jennie Hornosty

Overview

- What are the prevailing social attitudes toward aging, death, and dying?
- What are the experiences of the elderly in Canada?
- What is ageism?
- How do individuals experience death and dying?

This chapter is concerned with the social construction of aging, death, and dying today, with a focus on Canada. Experts are involved in institutional policy decisions, some arguing that the aged are a 'social burden', placing a strain on health and other resources as they become frail and immobile. While death, statistically, is postponed until old age for most non-Indigenous Canadians, there is an increased awareness of the risks associated with contemporary living and of ever-emerging new risks, which generate fears of death and suffering, even among the young. Medical life-and-death decisions have become complex as the boundaries between life and death have become blurred. Significantly, these decisions are being made within an environment of economic rationalism, with pressure on medical and health professions to cut health-care costs. Medical, legal, and other discourses associated with the process of dying have provided a contemporary language for discussing death, but these discourses do not address 'ontological insecurity' (Giddens, 1991)—that is, existential concerns that are likely to emerge in the experience of dying.

Key Terms

assisted living
ageism
class
collective conscience
discourse
economic rationalism/
  economic liberalism

ethnicity
euthanasia
gender/sex
globalization
ideology
individualism/
  individualization

medicalization
Medicare
public health/public
  health infrastructure
social construction
social death

Introduction

Biological life and death are not of themselves the reality that people experience and to which they respond. What is perceived as real and normal about events and processes such as aging, dying, and death is **socially constructed**, and depends on the historical, social, and cultural contexts in which they occur and are given meaning. At the beginning of the twenty-first century in Canada, for example, the death of a young person is considered tragic because it is premature. Not too far back in history, however, it was normal for the young to die; to reach old age was extraordinary.

Age structures are shifting radically as populations age, and it is predicted that this phenomenon will continue to have profound implications within the areas of health and medicine, as well as in the broader social, political, and economic spheres. These social processes are deeply connected with people's lives. Anthony Giddens (1991) argues that a characteristic of 'late modernity' (i.e., present-day society) is the interconnection of individual experiences with **globalization**. People may have little, if any, personal contact with death, but television brings into their homes graphic and selected images of death and dying from around the globe. At the institutional level, international agencies influence national policies, which affect individuals. Recommendations of the World Health Organization (WHO), for example, become translated into Canadian health policies. These policies are reflected in health promotion and education activities, which assist people to maintain their health into old age. These are contemporary resources and strategies, and they are replacing traditional relationships (Giddens, 1991).

As Giddens (1991) argues, life in late modernity is profoundly different from life in earlier times. In his analysis, the contemporary social world is forever changing, with an array of novel resources, previously unimaginable, becoming available to individuals to create their own lifestyle, while traditional linkages, such as close family ties, lose significance. Giddens (1991) acknowledges that disadvantaged groups are marginalized or excluded from the new opportunities. Moreover, death, he argues, has been sequestered from social life. Not only has it physically been removed to the hospital, but questions and anxieties arising from the universality of human finitude have, at least until very recently, been repressed. And today, in times of personal crisis—for example, severe illness or bereavement—people are more likely to seek guidance from modern experts, such as doctors or counsellors, than from religious leaders.

The terms *lifespan* and *life cycle* are representative of changes in life as people age. In past eras, the life cycle linked the generations and resonated with the seasonal cycles of nature. The cyclical notion of renewal following death provided death with meaning. No effort was required to believe in life after death, as it appeared to be perfectly natural that this was so. The lifespan, by contrast, is linear. It has a definite beginning and end. In response, people today emphasize what can and ought to be done to improve the quality of the lifespan, and to extend it. As a result, differences, even conflict, between generations are highlighted—for example, between the baby boomers and generation X. The baby boomers, stereotypically, are accused of spending their children's inheritance or, conversely, of becoming the 'sandwich' generation, 'caught between parents who are living longer and children who won't leave home' (Sampson, 2000).

The health and medical care that elderly people can expect to receive is the result of institutional planning and strategies. Other social responses to the aging population come

---

social construction/ constructionism

Refers to the socially created characteristics of human life based on the idea that people actively construct reality, meaning it is neither natural nor inevitable. Therefore, notions of normality/abnormality, right/ wrong, and health/illness are subjective human creations that should not be taken for granted.

globalization

Political, social, economic, and cultural developments—such as the spread of multinational companies, information technology, and the role of international agencies—that result in people's lives being increasingly influenced by global, rather than national or local, factors.

from those experts who contribute to bodies of knowledge that affect experiences of aging and old age. Expert knowledge informs health and medical practices and influences or directly advises government policy-makers. In Canada, people continue to die in hospitals, but hospices and palliative care have come to be associated with dying. **Euthanasia**, although illegal in Canada, is receiving some support as an alternative 'good death' while also generating controversy. Opinions concerning euthanasia are deeply divided among health and medical professionals, which may affect relationships between professional caregivers who are sharing the care of patients. The wider social context within which health and medicine are practised—especially economic and political concerns about escalating **public health** and medical costs—cannot be excluded from consideration. What are the consequences of all these conditions for the ways that aging, death, and dying are experienced?

Aging: A Socially Constructed Process

There are considerable differences in social and cultural responses to old age and hence in meanings and experiences associated with old age, some of which are discussed in this chapter. Subjectively, people have very different views of when old age begins. To children, 30 years of age can seem old but in today's society, where everyone is encouraged to lead a healthy, active lifestyle, many aged people may not feel old. A particular construction of old age that has disappeared is the virtue of 'growing old gracefully' in contrast with what was derided as 'mutton dressed up as lamb'. In today's consumerist society, ageless faces and 'taut and terrific' bodies are displayed in the media as the norm to be desired and achieved. Anti-aging theorists, such as Deepak Chopra, argue that while chronological age (age from birth) cannot be altered, biological age (functioning of body) and subjective, psychological age (how young a person feels) can be changed. Older people can be rejuvenated by means of, for example, meditation, injections, cosmetics, exercise, vitamins, nutrition, detoxing, fasting, and surgery. Nature no longer determines aging processes involved in the diminishing sexual prowess of men, who can now become sexually youthful with the help of pharmaceutical aids.

Growing Old in Canada

In Canada, the age profile of the population is rapidly changing. Today, seniors (those ages 65 and over) constitute the fastest growing population group in Canada. Low fertility, longer life expectancy, and the effects of the baby boomers (those born between 1946 and 1965 —a period of high birth rate) are the major factors contributing to the aging of Canada's population. By 2041, it is estimated that seniors will comprise about 25 per cent of the overall Canadian population (Health Canada, 2002a). Figure 11.1 shows the past and projected growth of the subgroups of seniors in the country. However, keep in mind that seniors are a heterogeneous population in terms of health status, living arrangements, and financial situation, as well as gender, ethnicity, sexual orientation, and Aboriginal status.

Life expectancy in Canada for both men and women has been rising steadily. In 1921, the life expectancy at birth for males was 59 years and for females, 61 years; in 2006, life expectancy for males was 78 years and for females, 83 years (Statistics Canada, 2010). It is predicted that life expectancy at birth will continue to grow, reaching 81 years for men and 86 years for women by 2041. Women form the majority (56 per cent in 2001) of the

euthanasia

Meaning 'gentle death', the term is used to describe voluntary death, often medically assisted, as a result of incurable and painful disease.

public health/public-health infrastructure

Public policies and infrastructure to prevent the onset and transmission of disease among the population, with a particular focus on sanitation and hygiene, such as clean air, water and food, and immunization. *Public-health infrastructure* refers specifically to the buildings, installations, and equipment necessary to ensure healthy living conditions for the population.

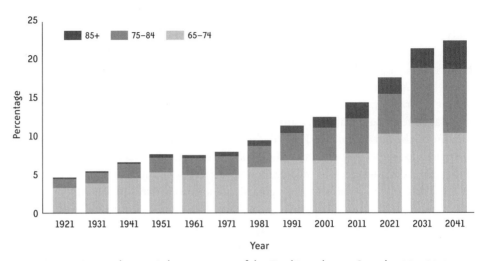

FIGURE 11.1 Seniors by Age Subgroups, as % of the Total Population, Canada 1921–2041

Source: Health Canada. (2002, p. 3). *Canada's Aging Population.* Available from http://dsp-psd.pwgsc.gc.ca/Collection/H39-608-2002E.pdf. Reproduced with the permission of the Minister of Public Works and Government Services Canada, 2011.

population of Canadian seniors, and their proportion increases with age. And since women tend to live longer than men, many women will be alone as they age. In 1996, 46 per cent of senior women in Canada were widowed, a figure that goes up in older age groups.

There are some notable geographical differences across Canada in terms of the seniors' population. The proportion of seniors is lowest in Nunavut (2.6 per cent) and generally low in both other territories compared to the rest of the country. The highest proportion of seniors live in Saskatchewan (14.4 per cent). In Ontario, seniors make up 12.6 per cent and in Quebec, 12.8 percent of the population. In Newfoundland and Labrador, seniors comprise 11.6 per cent of the population. In all the other provinces, the proportion of seniors is somewhere between 13.5 per cent (Manitoba) and 12.9 per cent (New Brunswick). Approximately 75 per cent of all seniors live in a metropolitan or urban area (Health Canada, 2002a).

Although most countries are experiencing a trend toward aging, there continues to be huge discrepancies both between and within countries. In poor countries, life expectancy can be as low as 37 years, with large numbers of children not reaching their fifth birthday (World Bank, 2004). In Canada, Aboriginal seniors (in 1996) comprised only 3.5 per cent of the reported Aboriginal population. However, Aboriginal peoples are living longer and the number of seniors is expected to triple by 2016 (Health Canada, 2002a).

Theory Link
See Chapter 7 for a discussion of some of the reasons for this comparatively low life expectancy of Aboriginal peoples.

Things have changed in Canada since the early twentieth century. Then, old age for men[1] was tied to paid employment. Workers remained in the paid labour force as long as

---

1. Women did not enter the paid labour force in significant numbers until the late 1950s in Canada.

they could or until they were laid off because they were no longer considered productive, and then went to live with family or found other means of support. When the means-tested Old Age Pension Act was first introduced in 1927, it applied to persons 70 years or older. It was only in 1965 with a new federal act that the age of eligibility for pension benefits dropped from 70 to 65. Age 65 was considered the hallmark of a socially defined 'old age' in countries such as Canada and Australia. Since the latter part of the twentieth century, there have been dramatic changes that have made 'old age' an ambiguous term. The social definition of 'old age' is no longer strictly determined by the age of retirement. The workplace has changed dramatically from the time when men were the breadwinners and women the homemakers. Women have entered the workforce, capitalism has globalized, casual work has increased at the expense of full-time work, and workers face constant job insecurity. Many workers are retiring early and in some cases this is not simply a matter of choice. Workers, now referred to as 'human resources', become redundant as their skills become outdated or as companies downsize or shift their production or services offshore. The current global financial crisis has meant massive job losses (especially in the manufacturing and service sectors), reduced household finances, major declines in the stock market, and the shrinking of pension funds. Between the mid 1970s and mid 1990s, the median age of retirement in Canada for men declined by three years (from 64.5 to 61) and by five years for women (from 65 to 60) (Public Health Agency of Canada, 2009c). However, recent job losses, failure of some employer pension plans, and loss of investment income may mean that millions of Canadians are forced to work well into what many had planned would be their retirement years. The elimination of mandatory retirement in most jurisdictions in Canada extends the protection against age discrimination to those over 65 and gives baby boomers an option of when to retire. In an effort to reduce growing government pension costs, however, some Western European countries are now extending the pension age to 67 or 68 years.

Canada, like many European countries, has a compulsory earnings-related retirement pension system, the Canada Pension Plan (CPP)[2]. Every person over 18 must pay into the CPP, with half of the total contributions being paid by the employer. Retirement benefits normally begin at age 65, although one can apply for reduced pension benefits as early as age 60. Combined with Old Age Security (OAS), the CPP provides seniors with a modest base of retirement income. CCP benefits replace about 25 per cent of income earned. It is estimated that about three-quarters of seniors' income comes from the public retirement income system (the OAS and the Canada/Quebec Pension Plans) and from private retirement pensions, including employer registered pension plans (RPPs) and individual registered retirement saving plans (RRSPs) (Public Health Agency of Canada, 2009c). The government also provides a Guaranteed Income Supplement for those with very low incomes, of whom approximately 65 per cent are women (Service Canada, n.d.). However, for over two-thirds of seniors the main source of income comes from the CCP/QPP and the OAS, rather than from private plans. Indeed, fully 60 per cent of the Canadian workforce does not have access to a workplace pension plan (CARP, 2010). Privately managed pension plans are both costly and especially vulnerable to market downturns. Unless there is pension reform, the prospects of economic security for seniors in the future does not seem promising.

---

2. Quebec has its own retirement pension plan called the Quebec Pension Plan.

According to the National Advisory Council on Aging, the economic situation of seniors has improved since the 1980s, although there is still a substantial number of seniors living in poverty, in particular women over 80, seniors living alone, immigrants, and visible minorities. However, since the economic recession beginning in 2008, the number of seniors living in poverty has increased by 25 per cent. Older women overall tend to have lower incomes because their wages were less then men's and because they live longer. An increasing number of seniors are using food banks. In its latest report, Food Banks Canada reports that 7.2 per cent of its users were persons over 65, a nine per cent increase from 2009; in Ontario, senior usage of food banks has increased to 12 per cent and in Manitoba, to 15 per cent in 2010 (Food Banks of Canada, 2010).

In many countries across the globe, including Canada, a current concern associated with increasing aging populations is the looming prospect of fiscal strain on governments, particularly in financing pensions and health care, in what has been characterized as an aging 'tsunami' (Znaimer, 2010). This is occurring at a time when **individualism** and **economic rationalism** have become dominant ideologies. Individuals are expected to be personally responsible for their own retirement income (Macintyre, 1999). The young cannot delay contemplating their old age, and are targeted by financial institutions with the message that they must plan ahead and start saving for their retirement if they wish to maintain a comfortable lifestyle. Concerns are expressed that the younger generation will need to pay higher taxes in order to finance the government pension plan. Caught in the transitionary period of a transforming **ideology**, aging baby boomers, who are heading toward retirement and who had reasonably expected to receive an old-age pension, are being labelled a burden and selfish for not sufficiently planning for their own retirement. Public pressure is mounting on the government to reform the public pension plan to improve pension accessibility and provide an adequate retirement income for all seniors.

In contrast to what occurred during much of the twentieth century, it is likely that experiences of old age in the twenty-first century will be individualized. Not all people have the ability to save for retirement. Growing income inequality in Canada means that some individuals have more disposal income during their working years than others to invest or pay higher levels of superannuation in order to maximize their retirement income. Seasonal workers, minimum-wage workers, casual workers, and homemakers are not in a position to invest for their retirement but will remain solely dependent on the government pension plan. The structure of inequality is further reproduced in the senior years.

How Ageism Is Constructed in Today's Society

Ageism, according to Hepworth (1995), is 'prejudice against older people collectively stereotyped as a section of the population disqualified by reason of their chronological age from making a full contribution to society' (p. 177). A popular belief is that the elderly are not valued in our technological society because the knowledge they have acquired over their lifetime is irrelevant, whereas in bygone days the aged were respected for their wisdom. Historical studies indicate, however, that attitudes toward the elderly have fluctuated over time and between cultures (Bytheway, 1995). The significant question is how ageism is constructed in today's society. The workplace has become ageist. Many workers in their forties and fifties, especially males, are considered too old for retraining after being made redundant.

**individualism/
individualization**

A belief or process supporting the primacy of individual choice, freedom, and self-responsibility.

**economic rationalism/
economic liberalism**

Terms used to describe a political philosophy based on small-government and market-oriented policies, such as deregulation, privatization, reduced government spending, and lower taxation.

ideology

In a political context, refers to those beliefs and values that relate to the way in which society should be organized, including the appropriate role of the state.

ageism

A term, as with *sexism* and *racism*, that denotes discrimination but based on age.

Stereotypical views of old age also contribute to ageism. Old age is associated with memory loss, incontinence, lack of cleanliness, making mistakes, slowness, becoming argumentative or withdrawn, or acting childishly. Old age is considered something to be feared, as it is increasingly associated with becoming demented. This embedded view is in sharp contrast with the contemporary value placed on youth, health, and fitness. There is little wonder that for many, old age has become something to postpone as long as possible. Moreover, aged people may themselves internalize ageist views, their feelings of self-worth diminished by their loss of youth, fitness, and choice.

The current use of the term *agelessness* may be perceived as introducing a positive attitude to old age, but this is questionable. Molly Andrews (1999) cautions that it is a seductive term, allowing us to believe 'we can transcend age' (p. 301). Such an anti-aging stance denies the importance of individuals' biographies in terms of the role played by unique life experiences in the aging process. Agelessness is compatible with secular society by evoking images of an earthly life where aging can be avoided. At the most, agelessness can offer only a temporal transcendence in contrast with traditional religious hope for immortal life beyond the poor health and death that naturally accompany old age.

The mass media, in their variety of forms—television, films, magazines, billboards, and the internet, particularly through advertising—provide different stereotypical images of age. Elderly people may be presented as incompetent. Advertisements promoting retirement financing or housing, on the other hand, are often accompanied by images of a smiling and contented older couple. The media also promote the idea that people can remain ageless; for example, a recent television ad for an anti-inflammatory prescription medication had this as its slogan: Defy aging: Speak to your doctor (the caption listed the name of the medication). The ad itself featured youthful seniors engaged in various sorts of physical activities. As the so-called baby boomers reach old age, they will become increasingly targeted by corporations and it will be interesting to see what marketing images will be used. Old age is attributed to a diverse group of people whose ages range from 50 to over 80, depending on how old age is defined. Stereotypical images oversimplify, being unable to capture the diverse situations of older people or the effects that their different gender and cultural backgrounds or their **class** positions have on their lives.

Ageism can result in the progressive exclusion of elderly people from the social world, a situation for which Mulkay (1993) has coined the term **social death** and which can occur well before biological death. Many people's lives become more restricted as they retire and have less income. Over a period of time they become frail, are marginalized by family members, are visited less frequently, and become socially isolated. Finally they cease 'to exist as an active agent in the ongoing social world of some other party' and become a 'non-person' (Mulkay, 1993, pp. 33–36).

Ironically, stereotypical and ambivalent images of aging and old age are also constructed by experts through bodies of knowledge that are generated in order to provide ways of understanding aging and old age. Specialized forms of knowledge inform the practices of medical and health professions as well as the practices of bureaucrats and others involved with making policies that affect the aged or aged care. Experts define the problems and solutions connected with old age, and policies are developed from the ways that experts define old age. This construction of age by experts establishes images of what is considered normal for particular age groups. The result is contradictory. On the one hand, old age is presented as a burgeoning social problem; as more people live longer

class (or social class)

A position in a system of structured inequality based on the unequal distribution of power, wealth, income, and status. People who share a class position typically share similar life chances.

social death

The marginalization and exclusion of elderly people from everyday life, resulting in social isolation.

they become an economic and social burden. On the other hand, the aged are portrayed as being responsible for their own quality of life, with the potential to remain healthy and active participants in society. For example, the Public Health Agency of Canada (PHAC) publishes numerous pamphlets, tips, and fact sheets informing seniors on how they can take responsibility for remaining healthy and active (Public Health Agency of Canada, 2009). Both approaches are ageist constructions, contributing to stereotypical views.

How Old Age Is Perceived as a Social Burden

Rather than appreciating the longevity of populations as an achievement, both nationally and internationally this trend is being viewed increasingly with dismay. Indeed, current concern about the perceived burden of the aged is said to be reaching the level of hysteria, with a 'sense of impending crisis' pervading several international reports (Walker, 1990, p. 378). There is a prevalent belief that Canada's aging population will wreak havoc on the health-care system. The title of a recent issue of *Maclean's* magazine read 'The Health Care Time Bomb—Our Aging Population Will Make Unthinkable Reforms Inevitable' (April 2010). The writer spoke about the fast-rising health costs and noted that health-care spending is 'skewed toward the old'. In its editorial of May 27, 2010, *The Globe and Mail* refers to two reports that 'put into stark relief changes that will be required to Canada's social safety net with an aging population and a demanding health-care system' (Hui, 2010). In February 2010, Parliamentary budget officer Kevin Page released a report warning that elderly benefits and health-care costs associated with aging will require Ottawa to hike taxes or cut spending by at least $20 billion over the coming decade (Hui, 2010). A symposium at Queen's University in April 2007 also warned that the aging baby-boom generation might implode the health-care system. It was suggested that one of the underlying causes of an acute shortage of beds at Kingston General Hospital 'is that the city has a much higher percentage of seniors than many other communities' (Axworthy, 2007).

Not all agree with the dire predictions, however. Sociologists Susan McDaniel and Monica Boyd both dispute the assumption that aging seniors will be an economic burden. Boyd notes that many elderly people are choosing not to retire immediately; rather than becoming a drain on the system, she suggests the future elderly will be contributing, productive members of the economy. McDaniel argues that the dire predictions are based on incorrect assumptions. The mistake is that policy people think that the health-care needs of the elderly in the future will be the same as those who are 85 today. According to McDaniel, 'people who are 85 now were born in a time when smoking was chic, they sometimes went through the Depression—they're an entirely different person' (quoted in Hui, 2010). The lifestyles of baby boomers and those who will enter retirement in the future is qualitatively different. Today's seniors are more physically active and socially engaged than those in previous generations (Hui, 2010). While it is true that the elderly have more health problems than younger Canadians, which is reflected in higher health-care expenditures, the data need to be interpreted carefully. Znaimer (2010) argues that although statistics show that 90 per cent of seniors visited a doctor in the past 12 months, it is interesting to note the relatively high percentages of Canadians in other age brackets who also consulted a physician within the same period: 82.8 per cent of those aged 45 to 64, 80 per cent in the 35- to 44-year-old bracket, and 85 per cent of children under the age of 12. Since advancing age is associated with declining health, physician visits tend to increase at older ages: 'But when the level of need and the other characteristics were controlled, the relationship between age and physician consultations was less clear' (Health Reports, 2007, p. 27). In a report released by the Canadian Institute for Health Information (CIHI) (2008b), the authors concluded that population aging would add no more than one per cent a year to provincial and territorial government health-care spending between 2002 and 2026. If one takes inflation into account, the pure aging effect, in terms of real per capita spending, would account for a very slight increase of $628.00 over the 24-year period.

Canadians are not only living longer than before, but they also live more of their years in good health. In 1997, according to Health Canada, 78 per cent of seniors who were living at home reported their health as being good, very good, or excellent, while only 6 per cent reported their health as being poor. This perception was similar for both those 65 to 74 and seniors aged 85 or older: 80 per cent of seniors aged 65 to 74 reported their health as good; 70 per cent of those 85 and older reported likewise (Public Health Agency of Canada, 2009). In comparing two cohorts of Canadians aged 50–67 years, Chen and Millar (2000) found that people in their fifties and sixties in 1996/97 were in better health than those in the same age group in 1978/79. There were substantial improvements in health between the two groups; they predicted that the health of baby boomers, who will constitute the senior population in the first half of the twenty-first century, will be as good as or even better than the previous generation's (Chen & Millar, 2000). Although a significant number (25 per cent) of seniors report having an activity limitation, this doesn't necessarily translate into significantly greater health costs. Rather, new technologies and increasing pharmaceutical costs are major contributing factors to growing government health-care expenditures. The fact remains that the majority of older Canadians are healthy and remain active. What is also overlooked is that the majority of seniors contribute significantly to the economy and health costs through their taxes.

Depictions of seniors as major economic burdens foster ageism and ignore certain facts. According to Turcotte and Schellenberg (2007), the financial situation of seniors in Canada has actually improved over the past 25 years. Although a significant number of seniors live below the poverty line, between 1984 and 1999 the median wealth of families headed by someone 65 or older increased 56 per cent. Home ownership is also relatively high among seniors: in 2001, 75 per cent of seniors between ages 65 to 74 owned their own homes (p. 69). More importantly, depictions of seniors as burdens ignores the many contributions they have made during their lifetime and continue to make to society. For example, past contributions to the economy during their working lives, taxes paid during that time, the unofficial caring and financial assistance provided to adult children and grandchildren, and the various volunteer activities they engaged in are all discounted in such a depiction, and the benefit of these services to the well-being of the country is ignored. Further, stereotyping the aged as a collective social burden also has sexist implications because the majority of older people are women. Finally, anxiety about the baby boomers becoming a bourgeoning social burden neglects the growing influence of aged people with disposable income as a market sector for a range of services.

People's experience of aging is complex as power, wealth, and health are unequally distributed among the aged and those who will age in the future. Social class, status, **gender**, and **ethnicity** may be contributing factors in determining whether people retire with

gender/sex

Refers to the socially constructed categories of feminine and masculine (the cultural values that dictate how men and women should behave), as opposed to the categories of biological sex (female or male).

ethnicity

Sociologically, the term refers to a shared cultural background, which is a characteristic of all groups in society.

chronic health problems, resulting from long years of repetitive or heavy manual work, or whether they retain positions of power for many more years as members of boards of directors or as consultants. The growing gap between the rich and the poor, which is likely to continue into people's retirement years, and the neo-liberal agenda of the current federal government will exacerbate these inequalities. With the increase in casual and part-time work at the expense of full-time employment, it will be difficult for many younger people to buy their own home and save for their future retirement. The causes and solutions, however, do not lie with these victims of global capitalism and economic rationalism but with government policies to minimize social inequalities. It is well to remember that terms are never neutral. While experts warn that the aging masses are likely to be a *social burden*, this term is not directed at, say, ex-politicians, most of whom retain substantial benefits at public expense throughout their retirement.

How to Age Successfully

Recognition of the discriminatory effects of ageism, especially in a world that is rapidly aging, has prompted resistance to the notion of the aged as a social burden. This cause has been assisted through Laslett's identification of a stage in life that has become known as the 'third age'. Laslett states that nearly all elderly are, or have the potential to be, healthy and active, and many are highly productive. Conceivably, the length of this period could be extensive as the biological limits of the human lifespan are uncertain, with predictions ranging as high as 120 years or even well beyond (Laslett, 1989, p. 13). Health promotion focuses on the healthy elderly, who age successfully, and offers advice to encourage individual responsibility for maintaining healthy lifestyles into old age. Age is no longer perceived as a barrier to health-promotion activities. It is possible for older people to achieve measurable health improvements and fitness levels. To be healthy has become a moral imperative; to age successfully, a moral duty.

Within this positive view of aging, the continuing rise in life expectancy poses the possibility of life continuing indefinitely. Illness, deterioration, and death do not fit into the construction of positive health. Death cannot, in the end, be denied, but with medical cures and disease prevention it may be postponed, avoided, or resisted. Individuals are encouraged to concentrate on daily healthy living (choosing and eating healthy foods, making time for daily exercise, coping with stressful situations as they arise). They are reassured by the continuing advancement of medical techniques to combat disease (for example, bypass surgery, transplantations, chemotherapy, and so on) and, more recently, by the potential of genetic intervention. The result of the construction of positive or successful aging is the idea of an indefinitely extended and healthy middle age, with death coming quickly at the end of a satisfactory life. Aged people are likely to be more realistic, however, having experienced and continuing to experience losses through their own illnesses or disabilities and through the deaths of those close to them.

A study by Health Canada (2002a) found that seniors in the three age groups—those 65 to 74 years, 75 to 84, and 85 and over—reported having good to excellent health. Despite the fact that over one in four Canadian seniors living at home had a long-term disability that restricted everyday activity and more than 80 per cent of seniors suffered from a chronic health condition, the great majority in all of the above age groups nevertheless considered themselves to be healthy. Most older people appear to appraise their own well-being from the vantage point of those of similar age and circumstances, and in terms of what realistically can be expected rather than aspiring to so-called successful aging and the expectation that they remain healthy and fit for as long as possible.

It is the final stage of life that is one of 'decrepitude and dependency' according to Laslett (1989). He suggests that the repercussions are profound: for personal relations (in terms of time and effort), especially for families, and for national budgets (in terms of supplying hospital and medical care) (Laslett, 1989, p. 13). It is during this final stage, then, that old age is perceived as a social burden. That the last years of a person's life are represented by the term 'social burden' says much about the way old age is constructed by experts in today's society. Measuring and discussing chronic illness and dependence on the services of others in terms of cost ignores personal suffering as well as the right of everyone, regardless of age, to be treated with dignity.

Services for the Aged

It is becoming increasingly important to consider the housing needs of seniors given the rapid aging of the Canadian population. Most aged, even frail aged, manage to remain at home rather than go into institutional care. Since the early 1980s, the number of seniors in Canada living in residential institutions has declined; particularly significant is the decline among seniors aged 85 and older. Two-thirds of long-term care residents are women, which is explained in part by women's higher longevity, higher levels of chronic illness, gender-based poverty, and less access to informal community-based supports (Penning & Votova, 2008). According to the 2001 census, 93 per cent of seniors aged 65 and over live in private households while the remaining seven per cent reside in primary health-care institutions, such as nursing homes and hospitals. Not surprisingly, institutional residence is age-related, from 2 per cent of those aged 65 to 74, to 32 per cent for those aged 85 and over (Statistics Canada, 2007a). Much of the focus of Canada's health-care system has been on acute care; however, the health-related needs of many seniors are for services that are long term. This could mean occasional support and assistance for those who are able to live at home or something like comprehensive residential care. Such care is not available on a universal basis; mostly it falls outside the realm of **Medicare**. As well, provinces vary in the services they offer, eligibility criteria differ, and there is variability in user fees (Canadian Association on Gerontology, 2011).

In 2007, the majority of seniors who received care lived in their own homes; only 22 per cent lived in formal care facilities, from **assisted living** to nursing homes (Cranswick & Dosman, 2008). Community-based home-care services were formally introduced in the 1970s as a way of potentially limiting the number of seniors requiring residential institutional care. They encompass a variety of supportive, therapeutic, and personal health services which make it possible for those with minor physical limitations or social needs to live at home (Penning & Votova, 2009). Responsibility for home-care services rests with the provinces and territories and generally these services are not covered by Medicare. As with residential care, home-care services are delivered by both public and private sources, on both a for-profit and not-for-profit basis. Different provincial and territorial health-care programs cover costs associated with home care and most provinces offer a mix of publicly and privately funded services. For most seniors, however, sources of support and assistance are informal, provided by family members, friends, or others

Medicare

Canada's universal health-care program, which is funded and administered by federal, provincial, and territorial governments.

assisted living

Where individuals live somewhat independently in apartment units but receive assistance with meals, housekeeping, and personal health care.

in the community. Nearly 70 per cent of care was provided by close family members: approximately one in five Canadians 45 years and older provided care to a senior in 2007 (Cranswick & Dosman, 2008). One-third of seniors who resided in care facilities also received personal care as well as assistance with transportation from family and friends. In many cases family members, most often the female members, have multiple caring responsibilities, such as looking after dependent children as well as aged parents, or providing assistance to their adult children and grandchildren, as well as an aged spouse or parent.[3] Many also juggle paid employment with caregiving responsibilities.

An ideology of community has accompanied governmental decisions to rely more on noninstitutional rather than institutional care. Notions of community care carry connotations of neighbourhoods in which people have the time and motivation to help one another and, especially, to be willing to care for the sick and needy in their midst. But the reality for many is quite different. Acutely ill people remain in hospital for only a short time as a result of prevailing budgetary constraints; they are discharged before being able to resume their own care and consequently may require intensive home support services. Services for those with chronic problems may not be a priority, and thus they must fend for themselves, pay for services if they can afford it, or rely on voluntary assistance or family support. The burden of home or community care, to a very large extent, falls back on families and in particular on those in the family who are willing and able to take up and maintain the responsibility of caring for their elderly relatives.

Increasingly, health and health care today are being commodified within a profit-driven health-care marketplace (Coburn, 2004): 'Older adults and other health service users are being encouraged to consume in the name of health, lifestyle, and independence, as well as to "shop for services" and pay privately for care that enables independent living for as long as possible' (Penning & Votova, 2009, p. 359). This is evident in the promotion of self-care, including the emphasis on 'being informed' and taking personal responsibility for one's health.

Dying and Death: How Perceptions Have Changed

Throughout Western history, until relatively recently, it was uncommon for people to live into old age. Little could be done to control epidemics, diseases, infections, and childbirth complications. Historian Philippe Aries (1981) suggests that, because of this, death remained 'tame' throughout most of the long history of Western civilization; it had to be accepted as fate. Fate offered the solace of a better existence in the next world for those who righteously accepted life in this world as a 'vale of tears'. Slowly, people became aware that life conditions were not completely out of their control and that action could be taken to improve some situations. The Enlightenment—an eighteenth-century intellectual movement—marked the beginning of a growing optimism that there were secular answers to life's problems. Causes and, therefore, prevention and cures of illness and disease could be discovered. Medical interventions, such as vaccinations and antibiotics, have generally been credited with the decline in mortality that has occurred in Western societies. Against this, it has been argued that public health measures, introduced earlier through quarantine

---

3. Adults who are raising their own children and at the same time taking care of their parents are referred to as the 'sandwich generation'.

and sanitary reform, were the reason for decline in disease. No doubt both public health measures and medical treatments have contributed to people's living longer. Better standards of living—including working conditions, accommodation, availability and affordability of nutritious food, and education—have also made a significant difference.

The medical profession came to occupy a position of dominance in the health area, symbolized and institutionalized by the establishment of the prestigious modern hospital. Fighting to save lives became a central task of hospitals, which also became the sites at which deaths occurred when the battles were lost. Dying and death were thus removed from the homes and neighbourhoods where they had always resided, thereby becoming separated from everyday life. The idea that death can be avoided or postponed indefinitely is fostered as people live increasingly longer lives, and younger deaths are seen as premature and abnormal. Optimism is invoked by claims that quality of life can be enhanced or maintained by healthy living. A steady stream of media reports inform people of the promising results of new curative or preventive research findings. Medical technology has become very sophisticated and expensive; people can be kept alive through surgical procedures, such as heart bypasses and organ transplantations, as well as through continually updated pharmaceutical drugs and technological therapies. The mapping of the human genome has produced radical promises for eliminating hereditary diseases.

Somewhat paradoxically, in light of these actual and potential achievements aimed at conquering death together with the institutional sequestering of death, dying and death are now returning to everyday life. The limitations of medical technology's endeavour to eliminate diseases are apparent in the chronic, sometimes debilitating, ailments associated with aging. Also, technology blurs the distinction between life and death: is chemotherapy, for instance, prolonging life or prolonging the dying process? With increasing awareness of risk, and of ever-emerging new risks, life seems dramatically less secure. Death may be lurking in unprotected sex, in contaminated food, in the very air we breathe.

Death in Canada

Most people in Canada die sometime after the age of 65; moreover, life expectancy among seniors at the age of 65 has been on an upward trend for several years for both men and women. On average, a 65-year-old woman in 2005 to 2007 could expect to live another 21.3 years, an increase of 1.3 years from the previous decade. A man the same age could expect to live another 18.1 years, an increase of 2.0 years. In 2007, Nunavut had the highest standardized death rate in Canada, followed by the other two territories. The lowest standardized rate occurred in British Columbia, followed by Ontario, Quebec, and Alberta (The Daily, 2007, Deaths). For all age groups, mortality rates vary by factors such as socioeconomic status, ethnic origin, and Aboriginal status. For Aboriginal peoples in Canada, the average age of death is significantly lower than that for the rest of the population. The lowest mortality rates are among the university-educated, the employed, those in professional and managerial occupations, and those in the top income brackets.

Generally, the death of old people is accepted—they are said to have had their 'good innings'—while young deaths are perceived as premature and, therefore, problematic. Some deaths are not caused by disease—for example, accidents, motor vehicle traffic accidents, suicide, and homicide—but cancer, heart disease, and stroke are the main causes of death in Canada. In 2007, these accounted for 58 per cent of all deaths.

How Death Is Now an Ambiguous Process

Death has become an ambiguous process rather than just a natural event. Brain death has become the accepted criterion for death so that an apparently live patient whose heart is still beating but whose brain no longer functions is declared dead, thus becoming a source of fresh body parts for patients who would otherwise die. Medical intervention can retard the advancement of many diseases that once would have killed more quickly so that it is now possible for individuals to continue their normal social activities for months, or even years, after having been diagnosed with a terminal illness, albeit in a state of uncertainty about their future. Patients are now likely to be informed of their dying status and urged to make preparations for the time when they may no longer be competent to make decisions. They can discuss their preferences for their final stages of life and for their death—for example, for their medical treatment and for their funeral. People can draw up living wills or advance directives, and/or they may give an enduring power of attorney to a trusted person to ensure, as much as possible, that even when dying they maintain control over their lives. The underlying assumption is that all people want to be informed that they are dying, that they all have the knowledge, and the will, to plan ahead—i.e., to consider their potential future circumstances and to choose possible alternative ways of dying—and that their wishes will be adhered to.

New ethical issues have arisen in relation to death and dying, for which there is often no easy solution. People are encouraged to donate organs in order to save lives, but executed prisoners in China have their organs taken. In some countries, there is a black market in organs. There is also the question of how patients are selected as organ recipients. How many Aboriginal people, for example, have received organ transplantations? Challenging ethical questions arise in relation to dying: for example, in relation to the withdrawal of treatment, at what stage should patients be taken off ventilators? Who decides, and when, whether the lives of patients who have suffered severe brain trauma will continue to be worthwhile? Is it ever ethical to withdraw nutrition and fluid from a patient? Should euthanasia be legalized in Canada, and if so, what should be the conditions of its legalization? Should priority be given, in terms of health-care costs, research, and expertise, to more sophisticated technology and treatment, or to palliative treatment for the chronically ill and dying?

The Search for a Good Death

medicalization

The process by which nonmedical problems become defined and treated as medical issues, usually in terms of illnesses, disorders, or syndromes.

The ideal so-called good death, prior to its **medicalization** and prior to the secularization of society, was to die at home, surrounded by friends and neighbours, accepting this last earthly suffering as a preparation for eternal life after death. Death often came early and relatively quickly as there was little that medical therapies or the medical profession could do. In the face of the inevitable, the doctor retreated, leaving the priest to perform the last rites. When the hospital became the place where people were sent to be cured, or to die, no longer was the dying person or the person's family in charge of the dying process. The patient became the property of the hospital, with visiting hours restricted and subject to hospital rules for the convenience of hospital organization and staff. The image of dying in hospital became that of patients attached to an arsenal of equipment in a futile attempt to defeat death, and resulting only in the unnecessary prolongation of their suffering. This is likely to have contributed to prevalent fears of experiencing suffering, degradation, and loss of control during a drawn-out dying period. People are made more fearful by descriptive media accounts of dying with cancer, HIV/AIDS, and dementia.

Palliative care and, more recently, euthanasia may be thought of as providing contemporary ideals of a good death. A good death may be envisaged as having a period of time during which the dying individual and relatives prepare for their forthcoming separation, for affairs to be put in order, and for the spiritual side of death to be approached. The aim of palliative care is to alleviate suffering in order to allow for these opportunities. Others may wish to die suddenly and painlessly after living a healthy, active life in old age, and when nature does not oblige, euthanasia or physician-assisted suicide may appear to offer a good death.

Palliative Care

Palliative care is an approach to care for those who are living with a life-threatening illness; the focus is on achieving comfort, ensuring respect, and maximizing quality of life for persons nearing death. In Canada, palliative care is provided in a variety of settings, including hospitals, long-term care facilities, hospices, and in individuals' homes on both a profit and not-for-profit basis. The types of services and funding available vary depending on the community in which an individual lives (Health Canada, 2009b). Canadians living in remote and rural areas or those living with disabilities have very limited access to palliative care services (Living Lessons, 2007). Hospices can provide both in-patient care in special facilities and care to patients in their own homes; doctors and nurses working in hospices specialize in palliative care. The aim is to offer comprehensive support by controlling pain and other symptoms as well as addressing the psychological, social, and spiritual needs of the dying person. The first hospice in Canada opened in November 1974 at St. Boniface General Hospital in Winnipeg, Manitoba (Tomczak, n.d.).

In recent years, the limitations of palliative care have been pointed out. Individuals have their own particular needs, and it is argued that, especially as hospices have become more medicalized and institutionalized, tension has developed between maintaining the ideal of a good death and maintaining the hospice organization (McNamara et al., 1994). Hospices have tended to focus on patients with cancer and, more recently, HIV/AIDS while excluding other types of illness. Palliative care may be restricted to achieving pain relief, which may necessitate rendering patients unconscious. Kellehear (1999), a sociologist and professor of palliative care, argues that palliative care is underdeveloped and should be available to those with life-threatening illnesses rather than only to those in the later stages of terminal illness. Such care should be concerned with promoting the health of the ill as well as wider social aspects of illness. Palliative caregivers whose aim is neither to hasten death nor prolong dying have tended to oppose views supportive of euthanasia.

Euthanasia

Euthanasia and physician-assisted suicide provide the medical means of ending life that is perceived as being unbearable, usually, although not necessarily, in relation to terminal illness. These actions are illegal in most countries; the exceptions are the Netherlands, Belgium, Switzerland, and the state of Oregon in the United States. Opponents of Canada's Criminal Code have challenged the constitutionality of the law that prohibits assisted suicide, of which the most famous case is that of Sue Rodriguez. The 42-year-old

Rodriquez, who had amyotrophic lateral sclerosis (ALS)—also known as Lou Gehrig's disease—asked the Supreme Court in the early 1990s for the right to kill herself with a doctor's help. She argued that the ban on assisted suicide violated the Constitution by curbing her right to personal liberty and autonomy guaranteed under the Charter of Rights and Freedoms. In a narrow 5–4 ruling in 1993 the court rejected her argument. (See M. Smith, 1993, for a review of the case.) Sue Rodriguez committed suicide in 1994 with the help of an anonymous doctor. Her struggle helped to galvanize right-to-die groups, such as the Right to Die Society of Canada whose mandate is to secure or protect the rights to self-determination at the end of their lives, and the legal debate over the right to assisted suicide.

The word *euthanasia* literally means a 'good death' or 'dying well', but within the complex debate that has emerged there are conflicting opinions about what constitutes the practice of euthanasia. The very definition of the term, therefore, is in dispute, and this can cause much confusion when posing the question 'What is euthanasia?' The injection of a lethal drug dose by a doctor with the explicit intention of terminating life at the request of a patient who is competent to make decisions is voluntary euthanasia, sometimes referred to as active euthanasia. When a doctor does not directly cause death but prescribes or provides the substance that causes death, it is regarded as physician-assisted suicide. This is similar to voluntary active euthanasia in that the intention of the doctor and patient is to actively cause the patient's death, but in physician-assisted suicide the patient self-administers the fatal dose.

Withdrawing medical treatment from the terminally ill when such treatment is considered to be useless and providing drugs to the terminally ill to relieve pain knowing that this may result in death, have traditionally been accepted as good medical practices. These measures are sometimes referred to as passive euthanasia. The medical profession has generally accepted that while death may be the side effect of pain relief, the intention is to relieve pain, not to end life. When individuals die after the withdrawal of ineffective treatment, the interpretation is that they are merely being allowed to die naturally from their disease, without having their lives artificially prolonged. Within the current euthanasia debate, however, euthanasia supporters may argue that such practices cannot be divorced from active euthanasia because the end result is the same—death. Euthanasia intentionally administered to patients who are incapable of making decisions (such as the severely demented) or to those who are unable to make their wishes known (for example, the unconscious) is referred to as involuntary euthanasia and is indistinguishable from murder or manslaughter (Library of Parliament, 2008).

Supporters of euthanasia usually focus on arguments for voluntary euthanasia by appealing to the right of individuals to control their own death. The reasoning is that legislation upholding this right will have no impact on others, who can simply refrain from exercising this prerogative. According to this view, legalizing voluntary euthanasia provides justice for all. A law that denies choice is unjust and oppressive to those who decide that life has become unbearable for them or that life has lost any qualities that would make it worthwhile. Euthanasia supporters suggest that the problem of involuntary euthanasia can be overcome by competent people leaving clear instructions of their wishes in a living will as well as appointing an enduring power of attorney to act on their behalf in the case of their becoming incompetent (Baume, 1995).

Opponents of legalized voluntary euthanasia often invoke what is called the 'slippery slope' (or 'thin edge of the wedge') argument to support their case. They assert that it is not simply a matter of individual rights but that changing attitudes could eventually lead to the acceptance of some forms of nonvoluntary euthanasia whereby the quality of life of those considered too socially burdensome may be perceived as being not worthwhile. A case in point is Nazi Germany, where killings sanctioned by the state under Nazi rule were carried out by doctors (Morgan, 1996, pp. 12–14). Various support groups for people with disabilities are particularly active in lobbying against the legalization of euthanasia and assisted suicide for the same reason. While the debate continues, in hospitals ethical decisions are being made daily about whether to continue treatment.

The euthanasia debate has highlighted, and probably provoked, attitudinal divisions among medical and health professionals, but what they do have in common is a paramount aim to relieve the suffering of dying patients. While pain relief is only one factor driving the euthanasia debate, it is a serious factor for those dying patients who suffer uncontrolled pain and for others who fear that such pain will be their fate. The interest of researchers and funding bodies, as well as of appropriately trained medical and health practitioners, is required to bring adequate and sustained pain relief to the dying, which at the same time allows them to retain some control over their lives.

According to most religions, euthanasia and physician-assisted suicide are morally wrong. Religion, according to Émile Durkheim, provides a **collective conscience**—that is, a moral framework that transcends any individual conscience or morality (Durkheim, 1984/1893). Many people, however, no longer accept moral answers based on traditional authority. Giddens (1991) suggests that although traditional authority, including religion, continues to exist, there are many other competing authorities in the modern world of expertise. Individuals are presented with choices from a wide range of contested and changing bodies of expert knowledge and techniques (Giddens, 1991). When making life-and-death decisions during times of illness, medicine, rather than religion, is likely to be regarded as more significant because of the high value that people place on medical knowledge and technology that can save or maintain life. While alternative healing methods have become popular for some, either to complement medical treatment or to replace it when treatment is not achieving a cure or reprieve, medicine remains the area of expertise that controls the knowledge, drugs, and technology associated with health and illness and with the dying process.

collective conscience
A term used to describe shared moral beliefs that act to unify society.

Conclusion

Medical and health professionals are under increasing pressure to find methods to achieve cost efficiencies in distributing funds and setting priorities for the allocation of health services. Medical life-and-death decisions are being made within this environment, and are no doubt influenced by it. Perceived quality of life is an important factor in making such decisions, but *quality of life* is not a neutral term.

Historically, religion has provided a language for speaking about death to the dying, but from the time that death was transferred from home to hospital, and for the first half of the twentieth century, death became something of an embarrassment. It was felt that dying persons should remain unaware of their fate and instead be kept in a state of

discourse

A domain of language-use that is characterized by common ways of talking and thinking about an issue (for example, the discourses of medicine, madness, or sexuality).

hopefulness of a medical cure. Now there are new ways of speaking about death, derived especially from medical and legal **discourses**. Individuals can decide whether they wish to become an organ donor, to appoint an enduring power of attorney, to discuss medical treatment such as chemotherapy, and so on. Such language encourages discussion of end-of-life decisions but does not encourage discussion of existential questions and anxieties that may emerge when individuals are facing their own mortality. For the dying, the reality of everyday life is called into question, and they may face questions about the meaning of their existence, experiencing what Giddens (1991) calls 'ontological insecurity'. Kellehear (1999) stresses the importance of understanding the significance of death's meaning for the dying. Some believe that life begins and ends with material embodiment while others believe in personal survival after biological death. Perhaps all individuals are seekers of immortality, albeit in different ways.

Summary of Main Points

- Our approach to aging, death, and dying is socially constructed.
- People today are living longer, although there are differences both between and within countries. Aboriginal Canadians, for example, have a lower life expectancy than the rest of the Canadian population. Life expectancy also varies by socio-economic status.
- Health, fitness, and youth are dominant values in modern society, and this contributes to ageist attitudes toward those who display characteristics associated with old age.
- Stereotypical views of old age contribute to ageism, that is, discrimination based on age.
- Old age has been constructed in conflicting ways. Within these constructions, the aged are either viewed as a social burden draining scarce resources or as proof that the ills associated with old age can be avoided.
- Medical intervention is postponing and changing the process of dying.
- Within the bioethical construction of euthanasia, the proponents of legalized voluntary euthanasia argue that it will enable individual autonomy in life-and-death decision making. Opponents to legalization argue that it will lead inevitably to some form of nonvoluntary euthanasia and to disregard for human life.
- Medical and health practitioners are making life-and-death decisions at a time when they are under pressure to cut costs.
- The dying may experience ontological insecurity, raising questions about the meaning of life and death.

Sociological Reflection: Living in an Ageless World

Imagine a time when medical science has discovered a cure for aging: a one-shot vaccine has been discovered that makes people virtually immortal. Would you take the vaccine? What would be the ramifications of a world in which no one ever grew old, and aging, dying, and death were things of the past?

Discussion Questions

1. What examples of ageism can you think of?
2. How do you distinguish between people who are old and people who are not old?
3. Why are health, fitness, and youthfulness so highly valued?
4. What does death mean in today's society?
5. Which groups of people do you think are more likely to agree with legalized voluntary euthanasia? Which groups are more likely to disagree? Why?
6. Why is it important to understand the economic and political factors that affect health and medical care?

Further Investigation

1. Extending on the information in this chapter, critically analyze policies that affect the aged in Canada.
2. Are the ethical dilemmas that have emerged in relation to dying and death new dilemmas? Critically discuss this question.
3. Critically discuss whether a good death is possible. What is the meaning of death in the sense of a good death?

 Further Reading

Auger, J. (2000). *Social perspectives on death and dying.* Halifax, NS: Fernwood.

Auger, J., & Tedford-Litle, D. (2002). *From the inside looking out: Competing ideas about growing old.* Halifax, NS: Fernwood.

Chappell, N., & Pennine, M. (2005). Family caregivers: Increasing demands in the context of 21st century globalization. In M. Johnson (Ed.), *The Cambridge handbook of age and aging* (pp. 455–462). New York, NY: Cambridge University Press.

Denton, M., & Kusch, K. (2006). *Well-being through the senior years.* Ottawa, ON: Social Development Canada.

McDaniel, S. (1986). *Canada's aging population.* Toronto, ON: Butterworths.

Northcott, H., & Wilson, D. (2001). *Dying and death in Canada.* Aurora, ON: Garamond.

Snyder, L., & Caplan, A. (Eds.). (2001). *Assisted suicide: Finding common ground.* Indianapolis, IN: Indiana University Press.

 Web Resources

Canadian Hospice Palliative Care Association
http://chpca.net

Canadian Institute for Health Information (CIHI)
www.cihi.ca/cihiweb/dispPage.jsp?cw_page=home_e

Health Canada
www.hc-sc.gc.ca/

Public Health Agency of Canada (PHAC)
www.phac-aspc.gc.ca/index-eng.php

Right to Die Society of Canada
www.righttodie.ca/

Ring of Death: Sociology of Death and Dying
www.trinity.edu/~mkearl/death.html

SocioSite—Death and Dying
www.sociosite.net/topics/health.php#DEATH

Statistics Canada
www.statcan.gc.ca/pub/

PART 3

The Social Organization of Health Care: Politics, Values, and Professions

'That any sane nation, having observed that you could provide for the supply of bread by giving bakers a pecuniary interest in baking for you, should go on to give a surgeon a pecuniary interest in cutting off your leg, is enough to make one despair of political humanity.'

— *George Bernard Shaw, The Doctor's Dilemma*

One way that Canadians distinguish themselves from Americans is through differences in the two health systems. But this was not always the case, so how did these differences emerge? An understanding of the social organization of health care in Canada today requires us to examine issues of power, ideology, and values in shaping health care and health-care institutions. An understanding of health care in Canada also requires an understanding of the relationship between the state and the growing pharmaceutical industry and how economic and political forces have influenced the delivery of health care. A common theme among Chapters 12, 13, 15, and 16 is the influence of the medical profession on health policy, on other health professionals, and on the delivery of health care. The influence of the pharmaceutical industry on health policy is the theme of Chapter 14. The chapters examine key features of the health system—its history, its structure, and the changes underway—to understand why the health system is organized the way that it is and how it could be otherwise organized.

As mentioned, Part 3 is divided into five chapters:

- Chapter 12 traces the development of medicine's dominance of health care and how this dominance is continually the source of challenge and resistance.
- Chapter 13 discusses the history of health care in Canada, the politics that shaped its publicly funded health-care system, and the current debate about the need for reform.
- Chapter 14 examines how the profit motive affects the operation of the pharmaceutical industry and the relationship between the industry and Health Canada.
- Chapter 15 looks briefly at the history of nursing and some of the major challenges and problems that nurses are confronted with today.
- Chapter 16 considers some explanations for the growing population of complementary and alternative medicines.

CHAPTER 12

Medicine, Medical Dominance, and Public Health

Jennie Hornosty & John Germov

Overview

- What are the origins of medicine?
- What is medical dominance?
- How did medicine emerge as the dominant health-care profession?
- In what ways has medical dominance been challenged?
- What is the role of public health and health promotion?

Medicine today is the dominant health profession. However, medicine as we know it is a fairly recent phenomena, dating back only to the late nineteenth century. How did medicine develop, and how has it achieved such dominance? This chapter provides a brief overview of the history of scientific medicine and the underlying assumptions of medicine today. It discusses how medical dominance was established in Canada and looks at some of the challenges to medical dominance. While medical dominance has often been resisted in formal and informal ways, recent challenges, including complementary and alternative medicine, the growth of allied health professionals, the women's health movement, and the involvement of government in the provision of health care, have proved effective in challenging medical power. However, scientific medicine will likely remain the dominant health profession for some time to come. Concern with public health has its roots in the nineteenth century. Although Canada played a leading role in emphasizing the societal roots of health inequities, health policy today is geared primarily toward changing individual lifestyles.

Key Terms

allopathic medicine
biomedicine/biomedical
  model
discourse
epidemiology
feminization
health promotion

hegemony/hegemonic
iatrogenesis
medical dominance
Medicare
Ottawa Charter
patriarchy/patriarchal
primary health care

public health
social determinants of health
state
victim blaming
welfare state
women's health movement

Introduction

It is hard for us to imagine a time when medicine as it is practised today did not exist. Whether for a regular checkup, because we are ill, or because we need a doctor's note to explain our absence from work or for a missed exam, most of us have visited the doctor's office for more than one reason. Many of you will have received vaccinations as children, or more recently against viruses such as H1N1. Some of you will have been to a hospital for X-rays, blood tests, or surgery. Although some people seek out what is referred to as alternative medicine or therapies from time to time, most people still have a great deal of faith in doctors. We look to medicine to come up with cures for such things as heart disease, diabetes, blindness, and cancer. When people are asked why they have such respect for medicine, a common response is that medicine is scientific. A scientific approach to illness is, however, a fairly recent development.

Theory Link
See discussion in Chapter 16 on complementary and alternative health care.

The Origins of Scientific Medicine

'To seek to ease pain is natural.'

— *Silverburg, cited in 'Hippocrates Biography', 1966, p. 16*

People have always sought ways to relieve pain. All known societies have had theories or explanations about disease and illness. Early societies, for example, attributed sickness to spiritual or supernatural causes, such as evil spirits, direct intervention by gods, or the work of a sorcerer. When someone got sick, they turned to shamans, who were seen as intermediaries between the natural and spiritual worlds. Shamans used prayer, incantations, spells, and sacrifices to drive away or appease the gods or spirits thought to be responsible for people's illnesses. They also developed certain skills such as using herbal remedies and setting broken bones (History of Medicine, Shamanism).

Supernatural explanations for disease were first challenged in classical Greece. Hippocrates (460–377 BCE), generally considered the 'Father of Medicine', is credited with laying the foundations of medicine as a science; he rejected superstition and magic and argued that every disease had only natural causes. Hippocrates subscribed to the humoral theory of disease, that is, the belief that each of the four natural elements—air, earth, fire, and water—was associated with a particular humor. He believed that illness resulted when these four humors (blood, phlegm, yellow bile, and black bile) were not in balance and that this could be detected through physical symptoms (Weiss & Lonnquist, 2009).

Early Christianity, however, attributed disease and illness as a punishment for sin or as a test of one's faith and commitment to God. For example, people with disabilities were viewed as sinners or as the offspring of parents who had sinned. This view prevailed until the seventeenth century (Covey, 2005). In the Medieval era, religious dogma dominated explanations of illness and healing practices. Medical practice was initially based in the monastery and controlled by the Church. Although people complemented religious healing with secular healing, physicians represented a form of blasphemy because they did not use religious intervention, such as prayer and penitence, to cure disease. By the second half of the Medieval era, medicine became the responsibility of secular clergy (Weiss & Lonnquist, 2009).

The Renaissance period marks the beginning of a more scientific approach to medical knowledge and practice. This was a period of significant intellectual growth and discovery; the teachings of the Church were being challenged and Christianity began to lose authority and control to the state. The previously accepted humoral theory of disease was rejected, as experimentation, observation, and dissection on the human body led to new discoveries and theories of human anatomy. During this period, medical specialization became more pronounced. Physicians were those who had graduated from a school of medicine, and they provided diagnosis and treatment to the wealthy. Surgery, however, was practised mostly by barbers and had lower status. These *barber surgeons*, who learned their skills in apprenticeship, in many cases on the battlefield, performed surgeries, managed open wounds, and repaired broken bones. Apothecaries, the early pharmacists, dispensed herbs and spices and in the countryside sometimes acted as physicians. The discoveries and advances of this period primarily benefited the wealthy; most people in villages and towns continued to rely on less expensive traditional methods, such as herbal and spiritual healing (Weiss & Lonnquist, 2009; *History of Medicine*, Renaissance Medicine, n.d.). The Scientific Revolution in the seventeenth century was a period of major intellectual change. The writings of such people as Francis Bacon, Galileo Galilei, and René Descartes signalled a revolution in thought and practice that brought about modern science. During this period and the following Age of Enlightenment (in the eighteenth century), science and medical knowledge developed in leaps and bounds; new ideas in physics, astronomy, biology, human anatomy, chemistry, and other sciences replaced the earlier doctrines from Ancient Greece and the Middle Ages. Systematic doubt and empirical verification by experiment became the new paradigm—what we know today as the scientific method. One of the most important medical advancements in the seventeenth century was in physiology and William Harvey's experimental proof that blood is conserved and then circulated through the body by the heart. In the eighteenth century, an Italian physician and professor of anatomy, Giovanni Morgagni, demonstrated that specific diseases could be traced to specific pathology in individual organs—and hence developed the anatomical concept of disease. An Austrian internist, Josef Leopold Auenbrugger, discovered that he could detect fluid in the lungs by tapping on the chest. An English country doctor, Edward Jenner, paved the way for modern immunology with his discovery that persons inoculated with cowpox developed immunity to smallpox, which at the time was a leading cause of death among children. And in the early nineteenth century a French physician named René Laennec invented the stethoscope (Weiss & Lonnquist, 2009; *History of Medicine*, History of Scientific Medicine, n.d.).

In the nineteenth century new discoveries such as improvements in the microscope, X-rays, the discovery of the cell, and the germ theory of disease revolutionized medicine. The *cell theory*, associated with German pathologist Rudolf Virchow, postulated that diseases begin when there are changes in a healthy cell; treatment, therefore, requires restoring the cell to its normal state. The *germ theory* was advanced by French chemist Louis Pasteur. Pasteur, who invented the process known as pasteurization, demonstrated that micro-organisms (germs) were responsible for infectious diseases in humans and animals and for their transmission among them. Building on the work of Pasteur, Robert Koch, a German doctor, identified specific bacteria that caused specific diseases, and formulated a set of rules known as Koch's postulates for determining conclusively whether a particular bacterium was the cause of a particular disease. His work laid the foundations for the science of bacteriology (Weiss & Lonnquist, 2009; *History of Medicine*, The Rise of Scientific Medicine, n.d.). Along with ongoing medical discoveries, there was also a growing interest in social medicine or what is now often referred to as public health. Links were made between the overcrowding in cities, unsanitary living conditions, and poor working conditions and the spread of infectious diseases such as cholera, typhoid fever, diphtheria, and tuberculosis. Those who fell ill were increasingly being treated in hospitals, which also grew in number. By the end of the century, the science of pharmacology was established. Surgery, which had previously been painful and frequently resulted in an infection, became safer with the development of both anesthesia and antiseptics. Nitrous oxide was first used for anesthesia by American dentists in the 1840s. In the mid-1860s, Sir Joseph Lister, a British surgeon, discovered that infection was caused by airborne bacteria and that by applying carbolic acid to the wound, dressings, and surgical instruments, which sterilized them, infection could be prevented (Weiss & Lonnquist, 2009; *History of Medicine*, The Rise of Scientific Medicine, n.d.).

Theory Link
See Chapter 1 for a further discussion of the emergence of interest in social medicine and public health.

By the twentieth century, scientific medicine and the biomedical approach to illness had gained a great deal of legitimacy. Advancements in technology and the discovery of antibiotics and antiviral vaccines were instrumental in encouraging faith in medicine. Most of the medical technology and medications we take for granted today were developed less than 100 years ago. Ultrasound imaging, CT scans, MRIs, endoscopes, heart-lung machines, kidney-dialysis machines, antibiotics, cortisone, and drugs to treat mental illness, for example, are all products of twentieth-century medicine.

Biomedicine/Scientific Medicine

Biomedicine, often referred to as **allopathic** medicine or conventional medicine, is considered to be *the scientific approach* for treating disease and illness. Underlying this approach are certain basic assumptions that have implications for the structure and practice of medicine today. In their book *Wasting Away* (2003), Pat and Hugh Armstrong critically examine five such assumptions that form the basis of allopathic medicine (pp. 18–42), which we will examine next.

1. The Determinants of Illness Are Primarily Biological
An underlying premise is that mind and body are separate, and that each disease has a specific etiology, that is, each disease has a specific cause (germs, cancer cells) that can be diagnosed by specific medical tests. In narrowing a focus on disease to a biological level, it is easy to minimize other aspects of illness.

biomedicine/ biomedical model
The conventional approach to medicine in Western societies, based on the diagnosis and explanation of illness as a malfunction of the body's biological mechanisms. This approach underpins most health professions and health services, which focus on treating individuals, and generally ignores the social origins of illness and its prevention.

allopathic medicine
A name given to conventional biomedicine. Treatment of diseases is by drugs, which have effects opposite to the symptoms.

This assumption also has an impact on the doctor–patient relationship and the way that medicine is practised. Doctors need not ask about social factors or what else is happening in a patient's life. If a patient's complaint has no identifiable biological cause, it may be dismissed as not real or as simply being all in the mind. Hence, doctors generally only spend a limited amount of time with their patients. (In many private practices the usual allotted time is 15 minutes per patient.) Prescriptions and diagnostic tests are typically the modes of treatment. Walk-in clinics operate on the assumption that only diagnoses of physiological symptoms are necessary for effective treatment.

2. Biomedicine Uses the Engineering Model of the Body

Biomedicine operates within a unified paradigm or model that views the body as a machine. That is, the body is approached as if it was composed of a number of different parts that can be separated and analyzed from each other. Since each disease is thought to be caused by a specific germ, diagnosis and treatment is limited to specific causes and specific parts. Accordingly, doctors are frequently encouraged to specialize in one branch of medicine. Nearly half (48.6 per cent) of practising physicians in Canada today are medical specialists (CIHI, 2009c). While specialization is associated with increased expertise in an area, for the patient with a complicated medical problem such as concomitant heart disease and kidney problems, this can mean having to see many different specialists, each one not having a complete understanding of how the treatment for one may affect the other.

The Armstrongs (2003) explain that this approach to the human body, combined with the doctrine of specific etiology, makes possible a fee-for-service payment, whereby each service or task is calculated to be worth a specific amount, and doctors are reimbursed accordingly. Furthermore, an assumption that treatment can be broken down into specific parts makes possible the rationalization of work in hospitals, whereby the amount of time required for each procedure is calculated to improve efficiency. In the process, the social and psychological needs of individuals are ignored.

Theory Link
See Chapter 15 for a discussion of the impact of this approach on nursing.

3. Health Care Is Primarily about Curing Illness or Disability

It is assumed that the primary role of modern medicine is to cure the patient in order to make them 'normal' again. This justifies the provision of the majority of health-care resources to acute-care hospitals with a focus on treating a specific medical condition as quickly as possible. According to Pat and Hugh Armstrong (2003), 'management techniques developed in industry are transferred to health care on the assumption that fixing a care part is not much different from fixing a car part' (p. 21). Patients are treated as cases rather than as unique individuals who may have a range of specific physical and emotional needs; increasingly more surgeries are done on an outpatient basis. Focusing on acute care makes it is possible to ignore the effects of social determinants of health, such as unemployment, poverty, and racism, on health or the importance of public health in preventing disease and illness.

4. Medicine Is Scientific

The alleged superiority of allopathic medicine over other forms of treatment (e.g., homeopathy or naturopathy) stems from its claim to being a science. An assumption is that all surgical procedures, medications, and tests that doctors use have been proven scientifically; that is, they have been evaluated through experiments using double-blind randomized clinical trials, that there is agreement on what constitutes scientific evidence, and that doctors are value neutral in their practice of medicine. Furthermore, there is an assumption that all patients with the same illness will have the same symptoms or will have the same pattern of disease development.

However, all of these assumptions are problematic. In New Brunswick, for example, for moral reasons some doctors refuse to prescribe birth control pills or make referrals for abortion. It has now been established that women and men can have very different symptoms of impending heart attacks, and treatments appropriate for one may not be appropriate for the other. And in Chapter 14, Joel Lexchin demonstrates how the profit motive rather than science sometimes drives the pharmaceutical industry.

5. The Doctor Is the Authority and Expert

Allopathic doctors today are considered the 'master labellers' of illness. That is, they are the ones who have the power to decide what is considered an illness, what the appropriate treatment is, as well as who provides the treatment. Our abiding faith in everything that is deemed scientific as well as doctors' lengthy educational and clinical training and their ability to convince us that the 'doctor is always right' means that most people still look to the doctor as the expert. As a result, patients' views or opinions about their health and health care may be dismissed in the belief that they lack sufficient knowledge. How doctors achieved such dominance is discussed in the next section.

The Ascendancy of Medical Dominance

'There would never be any public agreement among doctors if they did not agree to agree on the main point of the doctor being always in the right.'

— *George Bernard Shaw, The Doctor's Dilemma*

The term **medical dominance** refers to the fact that medicine was, and to some extent still is, the most powerful profession in the health system. It points to the power the medical profession has, despite its limited numbers, to control its own work and that of other health-care workers, and to have influence over health policy and the organization of hospitals. For example, medical doctors in Canada are by no means the largest group of health-care workers. In 2006, doctors comprised fewer than 12 per cent of the total health-care professional workforce, compared with nurses, who made up 54 per cent, and allied health-care workers (including audiologists, dentists, dieticians, medical laboratory technicians, midwives, occupational therapists, optometrists, pharmacists, physiotherapists, psychologists, radiation technologists, respiratory therapists, and speech pathologists), who collectively constituted 29 per cent (Statistics Canada, 2009). A number of significant works have examined the issue of professions, particularly the rise of the medical profession (see Freidson, 1970, 1994; Gillespie, 1991; Johnson, 1972; Larkin, 1983; Larson, 1977; Navarro, 1976, 1986; Starr, 1982; Willis, 1983, 1989b).

medical dominance

A general term used to describe the power of the medical profession in terms of its control over its own work, over the work of other health workers, and over health resource allocation, health policy, and the way that hospitals are run.

One factor in the growing dominance of medicine during the twentieth century was the continual advancement of science. No one can deny that scientific medicine has found effective cures for many diseases, and now with the completion of the Human Genome Project medicine potentially will be able to prevent or ameliorate the suffering from genetically caused illnesses. However, we need also to look at the societal factors that help explain medicine's ability to attain power and political influence. Eliot Freidson (1970), a key author in the field of medical dominance, suggests that the professional dominance of medicine is due to doctors' clinical role of diagnosis and treatment; to the ability of doctors to exert control over the knowledge base and occupational territory of other health professions; to the requirement that doctors request and supervise the work of other health practitioners; and to the unequal public status of medicine compared to other health professions. Similarly, Paul Wolpe (1985) argues that 'a profession's power rests on its consensually granted authority over a specific, cultural tradition', which is its social capital. This is then institutionalized by the institution's retaining of control over licensing procedures, its education, and self-regulation (cited in Weiss & Lonnquist, 2006, p. 29). As Freidson (1970) points out, the key feature of medical dominance is autonomy, which he defines as the 'authority to direct and evaluate the work of others without in turn being subject to formal direction and evaluation by them' (p. 135).

Some of the specific ways where medical power is evident include the following:

- Only doctors can formally diagnose disease and sign birth and death certificates, and they have significant control over access to nonmedical benefits, such as sick leave, workers' compensation, and early retirement due to health reasons.
- Doctors' control of diagnosis and treatment means that they effectively have administrative authority over other health professions. For example, doctors' decisions affect the work of nursing and allied health professionals who are often directly or indirectly responsible to doctor authority, particularly within the hospital system.
- Doctors can control access to a range of therapies through the requirement of a doctor's referral before other health professions can treat a patient.
- Doctors retain the right to set professional standards about treatment, which can affect hospital expenditures and the work of other health-care workers (enacted through licensing laws, which protect medicine from occupational encroachment).
- Doctors control the educational curriculum, as well as the examination and licensing of future doctors.

Another explanation for the ascendancy of medical dominance is found in the writings of Marxists like Vicente Navarro. Navarro's (1988) class analysis leads to his argument that medical dominance occurred in the United States because it served the interest of the dominant class:

> Professional power was and is submerged in other forms of power such as class, race, gender, and other forces that shape the production of the knowledge, practice, and institutions of medicine. The power of the professions is subservient to the powerful forces such as the dominant classes that have an overwhelming influence in medicine. (p. 64)

Although Navarro's analysis is based on the ascendancy of medicine in the United States, his basic points are applicable to the Canadian context.

The Emergence of Medical Dominance in Canada

At the time Canada became a nation in 1867, there were few trained doctors, no medical schools, and no medical associations. During most of the nineteenth century and into the early twentieth century, most people did not consult a doctor when they were sick but, rather, visited the more affordable, accessible, and respectable homoeopaths, chemists, Chinese herbalists, spiritual healers, and midwives. Aboriginal peoples for example, used a variety of natural remedies and spiritual practices to treat diseases and illness. Later, settlers brought with them their informal healing practices that predominated until the latter half of the nineteenth century. During that time, medicine had little connection with science (Torrance, 1998). Physicians were scarce and most of the population relied heavily on lay healers. Home remedies made from roots, bark, leaves, and seeds, in addition to whisky, brandy, and opium were the standard fare for treating such things as respiratory and digestive problems.

In the early nineteenth century, doctors had few cures and little scientific understanding of disease. Most doctors serviced the wealthy, who resided in the major cities and could afford their fees. The general population was highly skeptical of medicine, particularly surgeons, because of the high death rate from post-operative infection (antiseptic only came into use in the 1880s). Although the first hospital in North America was established in Quebec City in the early part of the seventeenth century (Judi Coburn, cited in Armstrong & Armstrong, 2003), it was not until the twentieth century that hospitals became a place for most medical and surgical procedures. Prior to that, hospitals were seen as places for the chronically ill, the poor, and the dying. People viewed hospitals as dangerous places with poor hygienic practices and unqualified practitioners (Armstrong & Armstrong, 2003). Those who were middle class or wealthy were treated at home or in doctor's offices (Torrance, 1998).

There was no cohesive medical profession in the early nineteenth century; rather, there was a continual struggle between the regular (medical practitioners) and irregular (traditional folk) healers, who enjoyed popular support (Blishen, 1991). However, as early as 1795 in Upper and Lower Canada, there were attempts made by physicians, who because of their social origins also had connections to political elites, to restrict who could practise medicine. Licensing legislation was in place by 1870 but physicians were unable to achieve hegemonic control of the medical profession until well into the twentieth century (Torrance, 1998).

Formal educational qualifications are a key aspect of professionalization in order to ensure uniform training, socialize newcomers into accepted professional ideologies, and limit the number of those who can practise the profession. In Canada, the first medical school was established in Montreal in 1824, which five years later became affiliated with McGill University. By the end of the nineteenth century, six other medical schools were established: the University of Toronto, Laval, Queen's University, Dalhousie University, the University of Western Ontario, and the University of Manitoba (*The Canadian Encyclopedia*, Medical Education, n.d.). Today there are 17 university medical facilities in the country. The affiliation with universities both added respectability and served as a means of controlling curriculum and entrance to the profession. In practice, it meant restricting entry to those of higher social class origins and ultimately standardizing curriculum and training (Torrance, 1998, p. 8). As well, the Canadian Medical Association was formed in 1867; this body was given the power to examine would-be practitioners and set curriculum (Blishen, 1991).

'The emergence of medical dominance in Canada took place between the nineteenth century, when medicine lacked power and status, and the early twentieth century, by which time it largely controlled the emerging health means of production' (Coburn, 1988a, p. 94). At a general level, the evolution of medical dominance in Canada followed a pattern similar to that of other capitalist nations at similar levels of economic development. Similar types of institutions were established to provide health care, which included 'a hierarchy of healing occupations and professions under a dominant medical profession; hospitals as key institutions; . . . [and] specialized organizations for the training and socialization of health workers . . . ' (Torrance, 1998, p. 3). Medicine later consolidated its power between the First World War and 1962, the time of the Saskatchewan doctors' strike (Coburn et. al., 1983, p. 407).

To gain dominance, physicians needed to restrict the activities of other health occupations, such as pharmacists, and of healers, such as homeopaths and eclectics, who had popular support among citizens. Pharmacists were regularly sought after for medical advice, were able to counter-prescribe drugs for customers, and were powerful enough initially to resist medical attempts to control their profession (Muzzin et al., 1998, p. 381). However, pharmacists eventually agreed to stop prescribing on the condition that doctors stopped dispensing medications: 'By the early twentieth century, pharmacy's subordination to medicine was complete' (Torrance, 1998, p. 8). The medical profession also succeeded in bringing nursing under medical control and making it a subordinate profession. Similarly, doctors gained exclusive control over pregnancy and childbirth, and midwifery was relegated to isolated and northern regions of the country.

This ability of the medical profession to unify and attain professional dominance over competing health-care occupations was strengthened by its connections to elite groups and the **state**. Because of their social origins, their affiliation with elite educational institutions, and their connections with socially and politically dominant groups, physicians were able, with the help of the state, to achieve and maintain their **hegemonic** position. They succeeded either through absorbing competing professions, marginalizing them, or granting them some legitimacy in exchange for subordinate status (Torrance, 1998, p. 4).

Ongoing tensions between physicians and other health-care providers continued well into the twentieth century; however, the key institutions that helped consolidate the power of allopathic medicine were in place by the beginning of the First World War. The Flexner Report ('Medical Education in the United States and Canada'), which gave rise to modern medical education, was released in 1910. The report, conducted for the Carnegie Foundation, emphasized the need for rigorous academic standards, a curriculum based around biomedicine and scientific evidence, and an apprenticeship system with hands-on clinical training. It 'ensured the "triumph of the specific aetiology paradigm", the one called scientific medicine', which continues to dominate today (Armstrong & Armstrong, 2003, p. 24). Largely as the result of efforts by Dr Thomas Roddick, a celebrated physician

state
A term used to refer to a collection of institutions, including the Parliament (e.g., government and Opposition political parties, the civil service, the judiciary, the police, and the military).

hegemony/hegemonic
Dominance or power of one social group, idea, or discourse over another.

and Member of Parliament, the government passed the Canada Medical Act in 1912, which led to the formation of the Medical Council of Canada. This had the effect of creating a national medical licensing standard and examination procedures across the country.

Medical dominance in Canada, as has been the case elsewhere, was secured and has been maintained by political means. In the Depression years, although doctors suffered a loss of income, the medical profession remained powerful and continued to have a strong influence on developments in health care. In the period of the Second World War, 'government practically integrated its policy and planning with that of the profession' (Coburn, 1988a, p. 100). The close relationship at the time between medicine and the state is well illustrated in a comment made by a medical officer in the Department of Health, who stated 'we do our utmost to maintain at every turn the interests of the practitioners of Canada as well as organized medicine' (cited by Coburn, 1988a, p. 101). By post–World War II, the medical profession was almost a private government and took an even more active role in formulating public policy. In the words of Taylor,

> . . . the private government of the medical profession and the public government of the country have become interlocked and, to some degree, interdependent. . . Organized medicine influences legislative policy with respect to the timing and design of public programmes, guides the choice and structure of administrative agencies, prescribes certain of the administrative procedures, participates in the continuing decisions of administrators, and . . . serves as the governmental agency in the administration of major programmes (cited in Coburn, et al., 1983, p. 417).

Medical hegemony was secured through its control of licensing and medical education and the subordination of other health professionals under the authority of doctors, and by limiting the work of other health workers and restricting competition by denying legitimacy to alternative-health practitioners. The medical profession ensured its dominance through allegiances with the state and the ruling elite until the introduction of government health insurance in the 1960s.

Challenges to Medical Dominance

Medical dominance has never been absolute; there has always been some resistance, whether from other health professions or the working classes in society who were critical of medicine's elitist class position. However, several major countervailing powers in society have also recently challenged and constrained medical influence. The first significant one was the introduction of government-financed and -controlled health insurance plans implemented in Canada in the 1960s.

The Emergence of the Welfare State

The 1930s and 1940s saw the emergence of the **welfare state** in Canada. Saskatchewan elected the first social-democratic government (the Co-operative Commonwealth Federation) in the country in 1944 on its promise to implement a government hospital

welfare state

A system whereby the government assumes primary responsibility for the welfare of its citizens through programs designed to protect and promote the economic and social well-being of its citizens.

insurance plan, which it successfully did in 1947. But it was Saskatchewan's implementation of a government-controlled provincial medical-care plan in 1962 that led to the 23-day doctors' strike. This strike and the subsequent defeat of the doctors was, Coburn et al. (1983) argue, a 'landmark of [a] new era in relationships between the profession and the state' (pp. 418–419); it marked the beginning of a decline in medical dominance. In opposing government health insurance in Saskatchewan and later in the recommendations of the Hall Commission to establish a national plan, 'the medical profession lost substantial ideological and political influence regarding nonclinical matters' (p. 419).

Theory Link
See Chapter 13 for a discussion of the history of Canada's health-care system.

Medicare

Canada's universal health-care program, funded and administered by federal, provincial, and territorial governments.

When the federal government passed the Medical Care Act in 1966, which laid the foundation for **Medicare** in Canada, this diminished some of the power of the medical profession to set wages and the conditions of work. In her discussion of professional power, Elston (1991) argues that economic autonomy, that is, the right of doctors to determine their pay rates, had been an important component of medicine's autonomy. This autonomy was lost with the introduction of government health insurance as doctors now had to negotiate their schedule of fees with their respective provincial or territorial governments. Initially, doctors tried to circumvent some of this control through extra-billing but, ultimately, were unsuccessful; the federal government brought in legislation that made extra-billing illegal.

Theory Link
See Chapter 13 for a further discussion of extra-billing.

Furthermore, state-administered health plans provided an opportunity for government surveillance of physicians' local work and income patterns (Coburn, 1988, p. 103). As well, there were other changes that redefined and delimited the traditional mandate of the medical profession in substantial ways: hospital budgets were closely scrutinized and medical technology was 'rationalized' to avoid duplication, which affected the type of care doctors were able to provide (Coburn, 1988a). Administration and management of hospitals increasingly came under university-trained administrators rather than physicians. Coburn et al. (1983) note that a new class of corporate rationalizers (including health administrators, planners and bureaucrats, medical researchers, and doctors in public health) brought in new managerial strategies that constrained doctors' clinical autonomy. This bureaucratic rationalization of hospitals decreased medicine's direct control over its major workplace; doctors became just another, although still powerful, interest group in a large organization. In some instances, governments required hospitals to put emergency room doctors on salary rather than fee-for-service compensation. In many provinces, health services were regionalized and operated under the direction of district health councils, which included lay and other health-care personnel besides doctors (Coburn et al., 1983; Coburn, 1988a).

Government, through funding, was able to control the number of intern and residency training spots available in any year. For example, in the late 1970s governments were successful in getting medical schools to reduce the number of students they accepted and ensure that general practitioners accounted for about 50 per cent of graduates (Coburn, et al., 1983; Coburn, 1988a). Also in the 1970s and 1980s, there was a shift in government priorities in health to focus more on disease prevention, health promotion, and **social determinants of health** (see Epp, 1986; Lalonde, 1974).

The Professionalization of Other Occupations

In addition to managerial reforms that are exerting control over health care, the medical profession is facing challenges from other health occupations, who want greater autonomy from medicine. Nurses, optometrists, pharmacists, chiropractors, psychologists, dentists, and other health professionals are asking for a share of government monies and are striving to enhance their power and influence in the medical domain. Many of these occupations have professionalized and now have self-governing and licensing bodies. For example, nursing has recently become more critical of the medical profession and has asserted its right to practise independently in the community. Furthermore, today an increasing number of Canadians are choosing alternative therapies instead of, or as an addition to, allopathic medicine. This choice is facilitated by supplementary private health insurance plans, which cover some of the costs of naturopaths, osteopaths, chiropractors, acupuncturists, and massage therapists.

Theory Link
See Chapter 15 for a discussion of nursing in the twenty-first century.

Theory Link
See Chapter 16 for more information regarding complementary and alternative health care.

Women's and consumer groups continue to question traditional technological approaches to childbirth, and they lobby hospitals to provide alternatives, such as family-oriented birthing rooms. The **women's health movement**, long critical of the medicalization of women's bodies, has played an important role in legitimating midwifery as a desirable alternative to physician-managed pregnancy and childbirth. Today, midwives are legal and regulated to practise in most provinces and territories. Advocacy groups such as the Canadian Health Coalition (which includes nurses, health-care workers, including some doctors, seniors, labour groups, churches, and academics) lobby for greater participation by patients and members of the public in health-care reform and an expanded

social determinants of health

Refers to the social and economic environments in which people live and which determine their health. Examples of social determinants include housing, job security, working conditions, education, income, social class, gender, Aboriginal status, and the social safety net. The quality of these determinants is a reflection of how society is organized and how it distributes its economic and social resources.

women's health movement

In Canada, included both formal and informal organizations of women that addressed issues ranging from birth control to poverty. The movement did not have a single voice or leader but, rather, encompassed a variety of groups and activities, collectively known as the women's health movement.

role of non-physician health-care providers. The Canadian Health Coalition criticizes the fee-for-service model and advocates a community-based, multidisciplinary approach to health-care delivery (Canadian Health Coalition, 2011).

Conflicts within Medicine

Heterogeneity within medicine today is another factor that mitigates medical hegemony (Coburn et al., 1983). There are more academic and research physicians whose attitudes, interests, and goals differ from general practitioners and specialists. As well, the orientations of general practitioners often differ from that of specialists, such as those in surgery or cardiology. The latter group tends to focus on acute care and individual treatment, arguing for more money for advanced diagnostic medical technology; doctors in general practice may favour greater decentralization and community-based health care. And there are conflicts within the profession itself. Groups such as the Medical Reform Group of Ontario, formed in the late 1970s as an organization for progressive, socially conscious physicians, advocates for a different model of primary care. For example, the group actively opposed extra-billing and the subsequent doctors' strike in Ontario. It 'destroyed the myth of the unanimity of the medical profession in a very visible and repeated fashion' (A Brief History of the Medical Reform Group of Ontario, 1979–1994).

The Demystification of Medicine

An indirect challenge to medical dominance is the growing public skepticism of medical authority as scientific and infallible. People today have higher levels of education and are better informed about health issues. And, although the information is not always reliable, the internet provides easy access to a vast health literature and a range of health resources, including information on diseases, medications, and suggested therapies. As a result, medicine and medical practice no longer hold the same mystique. The media has also played an important role in demystifying medicine and raising ethical questions about certain medical practices,

Medicine has been criticized for being self-serving—placing self-interest over patient or public interest—in the delivery of health services and the treatment of disease. From the public's perception, this was especially evident during both the Saskatchewan and Ontario doctors' strike, discussed in Chapter 13. Professional self-regulation has been criticized as being unable to effectively address issues of fraud, negligence, misconduct, or incompetence among its members. Media exposés of medical fraud and negligence have made the public increasingly aware of the potentially damaging effects of medical

iatrogenesis

A concept popularized by Ivan Illich that refers to any adverse outcome or harm as a result of medical treatment.

treatment, what Illich (1977) referred to as **iatrogenesis**. Various forms of scientific dishonesty have been exposed over the years—particularly scientific fraud in the form of biased medical research (La Follette, 1992); pharmaceutical fraud, such as the promotion of thalidomide and more recently Vioxx and SSRI medications (Braithwaite, 1984; Healy, 2003); and medical technology fraud, such as the marketing of the Dalkon Shield (Cashman, 1989). In addition, serious questions have been raised about the close relationship between medicine and Big Pharma (see Healy, 1997, 2003). In March 2009, students at Harvard's Medical School exposed the links that a number of professors had with drug companies after a student became concerned when one of his professors promoted the benefits of cholesterol drugs and belittled the student for asking about side effects. Through his investigations, the student found that this full-time member of the medical faculty was a paid consultant to 10 pharmaceutical companies, including 5 who developed cholesterol medications (*New York Times*, March 3, 2009).

Theory Link
See Chapter 14 for more information about the relationship between medicine and Big Pharma.

Media attention to cases of medical error and negligence has added to public skepticism about the scientific validity of diagnostic testing and the trustworthiness of doctors' professional opinions. Such cases raise doubts in people's minds about the quality of care they receive from their doctors. After a patient went public in February 2010, a surgeon at a Windsor, Ontario, hospital was required to stop performing surgeries after it was revealed that she performed a mastectomy as a result of a misdiagnosis on two women who did not have cancer. It appears the doctor misread the initial pathology report (CBC, 2010). In 2008, a New Brunswick pathologist was stripped of his medical license after an investigation found that 18 per cent of the cases he diagnosed were incomplete and 3 per cent of the diagnoses were wrong (CBC, 2008). In Newfoundland, a provincial inquiry found that laboratory errors led to the misdiagnosis and incorrect treatment of 383 patients between 1997 and 2005, resulting in 108 deaths (Furlow, 2008). Another recent high-profile case in Canada relating to medical error was that of Dr Charles Smith, once considered a leading expert in the field of pediatric forensic pathology. When an Ontario coroner reviewed 45 child autopsies in which Dr Smith had attributed the cause of death to either homicide or as being criminally suspicious, it was found that Smith made questionable conclusions of foul play in 20 of the cases, 13 of which resulted in criminal convictions. A subsequent inquiry into Smith's professional conduct found that Smith 'actively misled' his superiors, and 'made false and misleading statements' in court (CBC, 2009).

While it would be unreasonable to assume that any of the incidents mentioned were the result of deliberate negligence, they do highlight the fact that mistakes by health-care providers are not that uncommon. The president of the Canadian Medical Association, Dr Anne Doig, admitted that there are 'outright [medical] errors', and urged patients to 'ask for a second opinion' prior to making momentous life decisions about their health (Nguyen, 2010). According to Dianne Carmichael (president of Best Doctors Canada, a company that retests medical results), initial diagnoses worldwide are incorrect 22 per cent of the time (Nguyen, 2010). In its analysis of patient safety in Canada, the Canadian Institute for Health Information states that 10 per cent of patients with health problems surveyed reported that they had been given a wrong medication or a wrong dose in the past two years; 15 per cent reported a medical mistake in the care they received, of which nearly half stated that this mistake caused a serious health problem (CIHI, 2007b). Increased public access to health research and information, a greater knowledge about health issues, and more scrutiny of medical errors have undermined the basis of doctors' once exclusive claim to medical knowledge and authority.

The Face of Medicine Today

According to a report prepared by the Canadian Institute of Health Information, in 2008 there were 65 440 active physicians in Canada (excluding those who are military, semi-retired, and residents), an eight per cent increase over 2004's figures. For the same period (2004–2008), the Canadian population grew by 4.3 per cent. In the past three decades, with the exception of a few years, the number of doctors (including both Canadian and foreign trained) entering the workforce exceeded the number of those leaving. And student enrolment in Canadian medical schools continues to increase (after a steady decline beginning in 1993 to 1999): in 2007, there were 9640 students enrolled (CIHI, 2009c).

Physicians are quite evenly divided between family medicine and specialty medicine: just over half (51.5 per cent) of all physicians are in family medicine. However, the ratio varies by province; for example, in Prince Edward Island 61 per cent of doctors are in family medicine whereas in Ontario, 48 per cent are in family medicine. The three territories are particularly disadvantaged in terms of the availability of specialists. **Primary health care** is provided predominantly by family physicians and general practitioners working in solo and small-group practices, many of which operate only to share office costs and are reimbursed on a fee-for-service basis. Pat and Hugh Armstrong (2008) point out that such a system 'discourages physicians from spending time with their patients to explore multiple causes of ill health or to identify disease prevention and health promotion strategies . . . it discourages primary care providers from holding team meetings to discuss patient issues' (p. 72). There is little opportunity to share medical knowledge or feedback; there is also little scope to monitor physicians' work.

The medical profession is no longer as homogeneous by class and sex as it was before. Pressures for greater diversity in Canadian universities in the 1970s have had some impact on recruitment to medical schools. However, students in Canadian medical school today still come disproportionately from privileged socio-economic backgrounds. In their survey of first-year medical students in Canada, Dhalla et al. found that 17 per cent of the students had parents with household incomes greater than $160 000 as compared with 2.7 per cent of Canadian households that had an income greater than $150 000. Nearly half of the students came from neighbourhoods with median family incomes in the top quintile (Dhalla et al., 2002). Dhalla et al. also found that while certain minority groups (Chinese and South Asian) were overrepresented, others, like Black and Aboriginal peoples, were under-represented.

The most significant change in the physician workforce is the increased number of women, as women in particular have benefited from the challenge to medicine's **patriarchal** and elitist tradition. Barbara Ehrenreich and Deidre English (1973) were among the first writers to highlight the patriarchal and oppressive role of medicine in the persecution of women healers, who were often accused of being witches. Many scholars have also criticized the patriarchal tradition of medicine for various forms of sexism in the research, diagnosis, and treatment of illness, and in terms of discrimination against female medical students and doctors (see Annandale, 2004; Annandale & Hunt, 2000; Kirk, 1994; Walters, 1994). Although women worked as midwives and nurses in the eighteenth and nineteenth centuries, women in Canada were not allowed to study medicine at university until the late nineteenth century. Dr Emily Stowe, the first Canadian woman to practise medicine in Canada, received her medical training in the United States because

primary health care
Both the point of first contact with the health-care system and a philosophy for delivery of that care.

patriarchal
A system of power through which males dominate households. The term is used more broadly by feminists to refer to society's domination by patriarchal power, which functions to subordinate women and children.

no Canadian medical school would accept her. When she returned to Canada in 1867, she practised unlicensed; as an American-trained doctor she was required to take courses at an Ontario medical school and then write the qualifying exams for an Ontario license. However, again, no Ontario medical school would admit her. Eventually, in 1870, she was admitted to the University of Toronto and in 1880 obtained her medical license from the College of Physicians and Surgeons of Ontario. In 1883, Stowe's daughter, Ann Augusta Stowe-Gullen, following in her mother's footsteps, became the first female doctor to graduate from a Canadian medical school—the Faculty of Medicine at Victoria University ('Famous Canadian Physicians', n.d.). Yet it took nearly 100 years before the Canadian Medical Association chose its first woman president, Dr Bette Stephenson, elected in 1974. Not until 170 years after the first medical school in Canada was opened was a woman finally appointed dean of a medical faculty: in 1999, Dr Noni MacDonald was appointed dean of Dalhousie Medical School (Robb, 1999).

The gradual entry of women into the profession began during the second half of the twentieth century. Women today (2008–2009) comprise 58.1 per cent of medical school enrolment, a significant difference from 1968–1969 when only 14.3 per cent of those enrolled in Canadian medical schools were female. In 1940, only 4.1 per cent of the MDs awarded in Canada went to women. For the next 20 years the percentage of women earning medical degrees fluctuated between 4.1 and 8.7 per cent. It wasn't until 1966 that the proportion of women receiving medical degrees began to increase steadily, reaching 20 per cent in 1974, 36.8 per cent in 1984, and 44.3 per cent in 1994. In 2009, 57.3 per cent of medical degrees awarded by Canadian universities went to women (Association of Faculties of Medicine of Canada, 2009).

The composition of the physician workforce in the country is also changing as women become an increasingly larger proportion of practising doctors. Between 2004 and 2008, the number of male doctors increased by 3.8 per cent, while the number of female doctors grew by 16.3 per cent. In 2008, women accounted for more than half (52.1 per cent) of new general practitioners (GPs) and close to half (45.1 per cent) of new specialists. In that year, almost two out of five (39.6 per cent) GPs and close to one-third (29.4 per cent) of specialists practising in Canada were women. This **feminization** of the physician workforce is expected to continue (CIHI, 2008a).

It is unclear how this feminization will affect the practice of medicine. Some research suggests that female and male physicians bring different professional and personal values and attitudes, which may be reflected in the way they choose to organize and manage their professional practices. It has also been suggested that female physicians are more attuned to psychosocial aspects of patient care and are less likely to accept the status quo in medicine and the technologic focus of the biomedical disease model (Maheux et al., 1990; Williams et al., 1990). Maheux et al. note that the results of their study confirm other findings that suggest that female physicians have more social concerns than male doctors and show more interest in educating and counselling patients about health matters. Furthermore, studies suggest that women physicians are less likely than men to enter specialty practice and prefer group over traditional solo practice. Women physicians tend to work fewer hours and see fewer patients but spend more time with each patient than their male colleagues do. This difference may be explained by the fact that women have responsibilities as child bearers and primary caregivers and organize their practices with these imperatives of family life in mind (Burton & Wong, 2004; Maheux et al., 1990; Williams

feminization

A shift in the gender base of a group from being predominantly male to being increasingly female.

et al., 1990). In a recent qualitative study of female physicians, researchers found a strong link between the choice of specialty and lifestyle issues. Most of the female physicians they interviewed indicated a strong commitment to maintaining a balanced lifestyle, which required certain career decisions (Mobilos et al., 2008). While it is not clear what impact the increased representation of women will have on medical hegemony, it is possible that gender differences in professional attitudes and practice patterns could fragment the profession further (Coburn et al., 1983). This feminization of the profession is also likely to have implications for the delivery of medical services; it appears female physicians on average prefer working in urban areas, have a preference for family medicine, and work fewer hours per week (CIHI, 2008a).

The Role of Public Health and Health Promotion

Canada, like many countries, has broadened its definition of *health*, along the lines of that put forth by the World Health Organization (WHO). Health is now considered to be a state of complete physical, mental, and social well-being, and not just the absence of disease or illness. Current health-care reform in Canada is focusing on **health promotion**, on **public health**, and on prevention in an effort to control health-care expenditures and to reduce health inequities among population groups. According to a recent evaluation report on medical education, the medical curriculum needs to change to better prepare future doctors to respond to Canada's changing health needs, including a focus on prevention and public health. The report acknowledges that the biomedical focus in doctors' education devalues prevention and population health and that there is a need in the curriculum 'to include competencies, skills, and expected outcomes in relation to population health, prevention, promotion, and the social determinants of health' (Association of Faculties of Medicine of Canada, 2010, p. 22).

Concerns about public health and disease prevention, as discussed in Chapter 1, date back to the 1800s. However, such concerns dissipated as medical treatments improved, and it was not until the 1970s that any significant interest in public health was renewed. As the so-called lifestyle diseases or diseases of affluence (i.e., heart disease, cancer, and stroke) became the leading causes of death in developed countries, governments and health professionals turned their attention to disease prevention. Health promotion as a term was popularized through the 1974 Lalonde Report, *A New Perspective on the Health of Canadians*, generally regarded as providing the impetus for global initiatives in health promotion, the major driving force of which has been the World Health Organization (WHO), a United Nations body. WHO has hosted a series of important international health conferences, out of which have emerged a number of highly influential health policy documents. These include the Alma-Ata Declaration of 1978 (WHO, 1978), which was released at its International Conference on Primary Health Care held at Alma-Ata, and the **Ottawa Charter for Health Promotion** of 1986 (WHO, 1986).

The Ottawa Charter, which emerged from the First International Conference on Health Promotion in Ottawa, has been a dominant influence over health promotion approaches in Canada and elsewhere. The model is an attempt to integrate health education and individual behaviour-change strategies, with broader structural strategies that aim to fundamentally

health promotion

Has recently become a goal of health policy in Canada. Any combination of education and related organizational, economic, and political interventions designed to promote individual behavioural and environmental changes conducive to good health, including legislation, community development, and advocacy. Draws attention to a variety of social determinants.

public health

Policies, programs and services designed to keep citizens healthy and to improve the quality of life. The focus is on enhancing the health status and well-being of the general population rather than just looking at the health of individual persons.

Ottawa Charter for Health Promotion

A 1986 document produced by the World Health Organization. It was launched at the first international conference for health promotion, held in Ottawa, Canada.

reorient health-care services and public policies to address the social determinants of health. The Ottawa Charter highlights equity as a prerequisite of health and the need for social policies that foster greater equity as an important goal of health promotion (WHO, 1986). Similarly, the Epp Report (1986) took a broad structural approach to health promotion; it emphasized the need for government policy to focus on reducing inequities between economic groups; it also identified implementation strategies to foster public participation to strengthen community health services (Raphael, 2008, p. 486). The consistent message of these publications is a movement away from focusing on individuals and toward looking at societal factors that influence health. These documents make clear that health professionals and policy-makers not only need to educate people about health matters, but they also need to change the social conditions in which people live and to involve the community in implementing projects to improve health.

An Individualist Approach

However, despite the developments at the national and international level in support of creating healthy communities, much of health promotion funding in Canada has been narrowly focused around educating people to change their lifestyles. On a daily basis, Canadians are bombarded by lifestyle messages from government agencies, public-health agencies, and the media that promote healthy diets, physical activity, and the reduction of tobacco use (Raphael, 2008). Such programs assume that all that is needed is to educate people that they are putting their health at risk by smoking cigarettes, eating unhealthy food, drinking too much, and not exercising enough. In this **discourse**, the problem of illness is conceptualized in terms of individuals' noncompliance with health advice. Some people are said to have 'failed' to give up full-cream milk or butter, for instance. Smokers are said to have 'failed to understand' that lung cancer and coronary heart disease are major risks of smoking (Borland et al., 1994, p. 369). Obesity is blamed on the consumption of too many calories, unhealthy foods, and lack of physical activity (Prince, 2009).

discourse
A domain of language use that is characterized by common ways of talking and thinking about an issue (for example, the discourses of medicine, madness, or sexuality).

Government-produced brochures explain the importance of eating lots of fresh fruits and vegetable and wholesome grains. For example, Canada's Food Guide, now available in 10 languages in addition to English and French, tells individuals how many servings they should eat daily of fruits, vegetables, and dairy products and emphasizes the importance of choosing lean meats (Canada Food Guide, 2007). Canada's Physical Activity Guide, put out by the Public Health Agency of Canada, explains the health benefits of being active and warns of the danger of inactivity.

What is missed is that there are many material impediments to people's ability to put health messages into practice. One example comes from a study of food-buying in Canada, which looked at five low-income women and how they budgeted for food for their families (K. Travers, 1996). The study found that these women were not adhering to a live-for-today mentality, and what determined their food purchases was their low income, which reduced their capacity to select appropriate foods or to shop at more distant locations, where food was cheaper. Another significant factor was the pressure that the women faced from their children, who saw food advertised on television. Travers argued that good food messages are phrased in dogmatic terms and list unfamiliar, often expensive, and not easily available foods. Regular ground beef is significantly cheaper than extra-lean ground beef, for example, but the latter is healthier. Travers concluded that teaching someone to budget does not address the structural inequity created by inadequate welfare allowances (K. Travers, 1996). In relation to diet, '[h]ealthy choices are not usually easy choices for the socially disadvantaged' (McMichael, 1991, p. 10).

Although there is little evidence to suggest that promotion strategies that place the onus on individuals to change their behaviour are successful, the dominant approach of government and nongovernment health agencies (e.g., the Canadian Cancer Society, the Heart and Stroke Foundation) remains that of educating the public. The rhetoric of individual health promotion ignores the political, environmental, and social contexts of people's lives.

Theory Link
Chapter 8 examines in more detail the links between environment and health.

A Materialist/Structuralist Approach

In contrast to the focus on individual responsibility to change behaviour, an increasing number of sociological contributions to health promotion have focused on the social determinants of health behaviour (Raphael, 2009a, b, c). Critics writing from the structuralist perspective argue that the ineffectiveness of the lifestyle approach to health promotion wastes community resources. More importantly, however, they argue that these programs are fundamentally misconceived. The failure of individuals to comply with health warnings is not the problem; the problem is with governments and powerful corporate interests, such as the tobacco lobby, who do not accept responsibility for major diseases in the community. Putting pressure on people to change their lifestyles is, in effect, **victim blaming**, and does nothing to correct the structural causes of ill health (Waitzkin, 1983, p. 215). Structuralists, often from a neo-Marxist or critical political economy perspective, argue that '[t]o focus on individual life-styles is to assume an independence and freedom of the individual that is an illusion' (Navarro, 1986, p. 35). They emphasize that there is a need to examine how social determinants of health influence health both directly and indirectly and how political and economic forces shape the distribution of resources, which in turn influences the quality of resources available to different groups of people (Raphael, 2009c). To address inequities in health, health promotion and public-health policy must do something about the social and material conditions that frame the decisions that individuals make about their health, especially situations such as inadequate incomes and lack of choice of employment and housing.

victim blaming

The process whereby social inequality is explained in terms of individuals being solely responsible for what happens to them in relation to the choices they make and their assumed psychological, cultural, and/or biological inferiority.

Theory Link
See Chapter 4 for a discussion of how social determinants of health influence health.

Public Health in Canada

At the beginning of the twentieth century, contagious diseases, such as scarlet fever, diphtheria, measles, whooping cough, and tuberculosis, were the leading causes of death in Canada. Public-health activities were largely limited to responding to infectious disease outbreaks, although broader public-health initiatives soon emerged. Immunization against smallpox and diphtheria began in Ontario schools; Montreal and Toronto began to pasteurize milk; and some towns began chlorinating drinking water. However, it only was after the First World War that childhood immunization against infectious diseases became commonplace and new scientific discoveries, such as insulin and penicillin, led to treatments for diabetes and infection (Butler-Jones, 2008, pp. 10–12).

The Public Health Agency of Canada (PHAC) was created in 2004, in part as a response to the severe acute respiratory syndrome (SARS) outbreak, to coordinate and establish at a federal level programs to sustain a public-health system that would focus on the following (Public Health Agency of Canada, 2005):

- Promoting programs to encourage healthy living
- Preventing and controlling infectious and chronic illnesses
- Monitoring health and water safety
- Ensuring emergency preparedness

The agency is one of six departments and agencies that make up the Government of Canada's Health Portfolio. Part of its mandate is to strengthen public health 'consistent with a shared understanding of the determinants of health and of the common factors that maintain health or lead to disease and injury' (Public Health Agency of Canada, 2011).

The first annual report of the chief public health officer (Dr David Butler-Jones, 2008) defines public health as 'the organized efforts of society to improve health and well-being and to reduce inequalities in health' (p. i). The report focuses on inequalities in health status, and on how social and economic determinants contribute to these health inequalities. Dr Butler-Jones's view is that 'health inequalities are fundamentally societal inequalities that we can overcome through public policy and individual and collective action' (p. iii). Butler-Jones makes clear that the health status of individuals deteriorates as one moves from the highest to lowest income gradients; that biological health is influenced by physical and social environments; that factors like adequate housing have a profound impact on health; and that 'all Canadians pay a high price by failing to address these issues' (p. 68). There is also recognition that physical and social environments have an impact on the types of choices individuals can make about their health. Social inequalities, Butler-Jones suggests, mediate health and are key factors in the higher rates of heart disease, cancer, and Type 2 diabetes among those least well-off. Addressing child poverty, he suggests, should be a primary focus. This would include consideration of income distribution policies and programs so that all families have the necessary resources for healthy child development, opportunities for early learning, adequate housing and infrastructure, postsecondary education, employment and employment supports (p. 69).

The contents and recommendations of the chief public health officer's report rely more on a materialist/structuralist approach to health status rather than on an individualist one.

Why then, one might ask, does the government continue to spend significant amounts of money on programs and policies targeted at changing individual behaviour? Why, given the extent of social inequalities in Canada, are current population-level prevention strategies mainly composed of individual health promotion and education activities (Prince, 2009)? One suggestion is that individualist approaches continue because they are supported by a range of powerful interest groups, not least a range of medical and allied health professionals. As Alan Petersen (1996) argues, '[health] promotion is not a value-free enterprise. It is enmeshed in power relations' (p. 56). An individualist model has widespread support because it makes governments look authoritative and active while at the same time it avoids confrontations that might prove politically costly (Lupton, 1995). For bureaucrats, the model is appealing because the types of targets set—such as getting 20 per cent more Canadians engaging in physical activity—are quantifiable and seem manageable. The individualist model has the support of the medical profession because it expands medical turf and provides work for **epidemiologists**, health professionals, psychologists, and educationalists, many of whom work within the still-dominant positivist tradition (Beattie, 1991). Pharmaceutical companies also stand to benefit when the focus of ill health is on biology and genetic predisposition. As an example, see Wendy Mesley's CBC documentary, *Chasing the Cancer Answer,* which raises questions about why there is so little research on preventing cancer (such as eliminating carcinogens) compared to the dollars spent on finding a medical cure.

epidemiology

The statistical study of patterns of disease in the population. Originally focused on epidemics, or infectious diseases, it now covers noninfectious conditions, such as stroke and cancer.

Although Canada was a leader in the development of health-promotion approaches that recognize the importance of social and economic factors on health status, the government has done little to implement policies that would address social inequalities. Raphael (2009d) suggests that there are political and economic barriers that explain the failure of the Canadian government to implement structural change, namely the ascendancy of neo-liberalism and the dismantling of the welfare state. Neo-liberal ideology promotes a so-called free market, individualism, and a reduction of spending on social programs: '[N]eo-liberalism and neo-conservative ideologies . . . position societal issues, including health and health promotion, as individual issues beyond the concern of governments and their institutions' (Raphael, 2003, p. 401). As a consequence, there is no support for an agenda that would improve the living conditions of disadvantaged groups through state intervention. Some researchers and health-policy advocates remain committed to the visions articulated in the Ottawa Charter. However, the dominant public-health approach in Canada today is more is keeping with epidemiological and biomedical traditions.

Conclusion

The development of medicine and medical dominance both occurred during specific conjunctures in history. Scientific medicine was made possible by the scientific revolution and the Age of Enlightenment. Medical dominance in Canada came to the fore with the support of the elite classes of the day. Its decline was precipitated by working-class mobilization and government involvement in health insurance. Medical hegemony was also challenged by the growth of allied health professionals, women's groups, and the rationalization and corporatization of health care. Beginning in the 1980s, a new managerial class began to gain control over health care delivery, planning, and funding. Today, it is difficult to write about the medical profession as a single group because it is increasingly fragmented into diverse and sometimes competing factions, such that the profession can no longer claim to speak with a unified voice. Medicine is less homogeneous by class than previously; however, what is most striking today is the feminization of medicine. While scientific medicine is no longer the dominant profession it once was, it still remains the most powerful health occupation. Although there are groups of doctors who espouse progressive policies, ideologically and politically the medical elite remain aligned with conservative values. Medicine continues to struggle against any encroachment on its privileges; however, its fate 'is [ultimately] dependent on the outcome of broader class struggles in Canadian society' (Coburn, 1988a, p. 111).

Concern with public health, sometimes referred to as social medicine, dates back to the nineteenth century. In Canada, public-health initiatives were first implemented in the early part of the twentieth century. However, it wasn't until the mid-1970s and the publication of the Lalonde Report (1974) that there was a renewed awareness of links between social inequalities and health inequalities. The later (1986) Epp Report, Achieving Health for All, and the Ottawa Charter furthered the discussion around social determinants of health and a structural/materialist approach to health promotion. Despite the existence of Canadian research that shows the impact of determinants such as housing, income, unemployment, and poverty on health status, the government has done little to address the underlying structural inequities. Rather, health promotion has focused on changing individuals' habits and lifestyles. This approach is more consistent with an ideology of neo-liberalism, which underpins current government policy.

Summary of Main Points

- Scientific medicine is premised on a number of assumptions about illness.
- Medicine had control over health-care delivery, health policy, and the nature of medical practice.
- Medical dominance was achieved by political means.
- The main challenges to medical dominance include government-controlled health insurance, public skepticism, and divisions within medicine.
- Public health is concerned with prevention and health promotion.
- Health promotion can be categorized into two types: individualist lifestyle approaches, which aim to change behaviour; and structural materialist approaches, which address societal inequities.
- Criticisms of lifestyle health promotion include their ineffectiveness in changing behaviour long-term and their tendency toward victim blaming.
- Although government policy speaks of the importance of social determinants on health status, there has been little effort made to implement social programs that would create greater equity among social groups

 Sociological Reflection: Feminization of Medicine

An important characteristic of medicine today is the number of women enrolled in medical schools and the growing number of women who are practising physicians. What might be some of the reasons for this feminization of medicine? How might it influence medical curriculum and the practice of medicine? Do you think that medicine will fundamentally be changed as a result of this? Why or why not?

 Discussion Questions

1. What are the major assumptions of a biomedical/allopathic approach to health?
2. What are some indicators of medical dominance?
3. How was medical dominance achieved in Canada?
4. By what means has medical dominance been challenged?
5. In what ways has the profession of medicine changed over the past 100 years?
6. How is public health different from allopathic medicine?
7. What are the social determinants of health and why are they considered important?
8. What are the main criticisms that can be made of individualist health promotion?
9. What are the major barriers to structuralist/materialist health promotion?
10. What are some ways (besides lifestyle approaches to health education) to promote health and prevent illness?

Further Investigation

1. What are the differences in how health promotion is understood by the biomedical model compared with the social model of health? Why do these differences exist? Are there limitations to each of these two models? Can the two be reconciled?

2. There is ongoing debate about the degree to which the medical profession has lost its hegemony. To what extent has government emphasis on accountability and the rationalization of health-care delivery challenged the power of medicine? Can the medical profession regain its former power over health care?

 Further Reading

Blishen, B. (1991). *Doctors in Canada: The changing world of medical practice*. Toronto, ON: University of Toronto Press.

Bryant, T. (2009). *An introduction to health policy*. Toronto, ON: Canadian Scholars' Press.

Butler-Jones, D. (2008). *The chief public health officer's report on the state of public health in Canada*. Ottawa, ON: Minister of Health.

Coburn, D., Torrance, G., & Kaufert, J. (1983). Medical dominance in Canadian historical perspective: The rise and fall of medicine? *International Journal of Health Services, 13*, 407–432.

Coburn, D. (1998). State authority, medical dominance, and trends in the regulation of health professions: The Ontario case. In D. Coburn, C. D'Arcy, & G. Torrance (Eds.), *Health and Canadian society: Sociological perspectives* (3rd ed.) (pp. 332–346). Toronto, ON: University of Toronto Press.

Epp, J. (1986) *Achieving health for all: A framework for health promotion*. Ottawa, ON: Health and Welfare Canada.

Freidson, E. (2001). *Professionalism: The third logic*. Cambridge, UK: Polity Press.

Navarro, V. (1988). Professional dominance or proletarianization?: Neither. *The Milbank Quarterly, 66*(2), 57–75.

 Web Resources

Canadian Institute for Health Information (CIHI)
www.cihi.ca

Canadian Medical Association
http://cma.ca

Canadian Policy Research Networks (CPRN)
www.cprn.com

Canadian Public Health Association (CPHA)
www.cpha.ca

Medical Reform Group
http://medicalreformgroup.ca

Public Health Agency of Canada
www.phac-aspc.gc.ca

CHAPTER 13

Power, Politics, and Values: The Canadian Health-Care System

Jennie Hornosty

Overview

- What is the nature of Canada's health-care system?
- Who are the major interest groups and what influence do they have?
- What role do power, politics, and values play in shaping health care?

Most Canadians view government-funded universal health care as a fundamental right of citizenship. However, the Medical Health Act, which became the foundation for Canada's system of Medicare, was only passed in 1966. Its history was fraught with tensions, including two major doctors' strikes. This chapter examines the structure of health care in Canada and the competing interests that shaped its development. It also discusses the growing divide between those who argue for increased privatization of health care and those who defend the basic principles on which Medicare was founded.

Key Terms

allopathic medicine
extra-billing
Canada Health Act
gross domestic product (GDP)

Human Development Index (HDI)
ideology
Medicare
neo-liberalism

primary health care
unalienable human right
welfare state/social welfare state
values

Introduction

In his 'Message to Canadians', the Honourable Roy Romanow, who was appointed in 2001 as sole commissioner to look at the future of health care in Canada, summarized the core values underlying Canada's health-care system as those of equity, fairness, and solidarity. He went on to note, as have others, that Canadians everywhere are deeply attached to these core values underlying **Medicare**. These values reflect the Canadian view that health care is a fundamental right of citizenship and not a privilege of status or wealth (Romanow, 2002; Armstrong & Armstrong, 2003). Medicare as we know it today only became a reality for all Canadians in 1971. Now, however, there is talk of Medicare being in crisis due to escalating costs, an aging population, and long waiting lists. Certain groups in society are raising questions as to whether Canadians can afford Medicare and are advocating for more privatization of health-care services. Others argue that there is no crisis in public health-care costs; rather, the escalating costs are related to services purchased from the private sector, such as drug expenditures (Armstrong & Armstrong, 2003, 2008).

There are competing interests at stake in the current debate about the future of Canada's public health-care system, just as there was earlier when a public health insurance plan was first introduced in Canada. Two of the most powerful groups were and are doctors and politicians. Underlying the debate about costs is a clash in fundamental **values** and **ideology** about whether health care is an **unalienable human right** to which every citizen is entitled or whether it is a commodity in the marketplace where citizens can purchase that which they can best afford. Whose interests are being served if Canada abandons its universal health-care system in favour of more privatization? What political forces are driving the push toward greater privatization of health-care services? This chapter provides an overview of Canada's public health-care system, examines the major historical factors in its development, considers the role of physicians and politicians in shaping health-care policy, and looks at the ideology of neo-liberalism and its impact on health care today.

The Development of Medicare in Canada

> 'As a society, we [Canadians] decided that health is a public good and that the costs of treating illness should be broadly shared. To achieve this goal, we built a system we call "medicare".'
>
> — *National Forum on Health, 1997, p. 4.*

The first initiative to establish some form of government health insurance came in 1919 as part of the platform of the federal Liberal Party under Prime Minister Robert Borden. However, it was not until after the Great Depression that there was renewed interest in a national health insurance plan. During the Depression, doctors' incomes declined dramatically since patients were unable to pay their bills; the government had to institute a medical relief plan to help pay for doctors' salaries and other medical expenses. Health problems among the population worsened as communicable diseases such as tuberculosis, pneumonia, and influenza spread among the population due to inadequate nutrition and poor housing. During the same period, political radicalism, particularly in the Prairie provinces and British Columbia, grew (Torrance, 1998, p. 14).

Medicare

Canada's universal health-care program, funded and administered by federal, provincial, and territorial governments.

values

Important beliefs and ideals shared by members of a culture or society.

ideology

In a political context, refers to those beliefs and values that relate to the way in which society should be organized, including the appropriate role of the state.

unalienable human right

A right considered to inhere in a person as a human being and that cannot be relinquished by government; sometimes referred to as a 'natural right'.

allopathic medicine

A name given to conventional biomedicine. Treatment of diseases is by drugs that have effects opposite to the symptoms.

By the 1930s and 40s, Canadians generally had put their faith in **allopathic medicine**; however, paying for physician and hospital services was difficult for most, including large segments of the working and middle classes. At the time, Canada's health-care system was dominated by private medicine, similar to that in existence in the United States today. Unless people had private insurance or were wealthy, they were forced to rely on charity, sacrifice their life savings, or do without medical treatment: 'Canada trailed most Western European countries, Britain, and New Zealand in making health care economically accessible to most of the population' (Torrance, 1998, p. 11). Although most European nations, including England, had established some form of government-administered health insurance by the end of the First World War, doctors in Canada lobbied against the idea, warning that government insurance plans would undermine the spirit of charity and turn physicians into civil servants (Feldberg & Vipond, 2006).

As was the case in Western European countries, a government-funded health insurance plan was largely brought about as the result of increasing popular pressure for change: 'Channelled through interest groups and political parties of the left, public pressure forced reluctant governments and a mostly resisting medical profession to implement limited reforms' (Torrance, 1998, p. 13). It is not surprising, therefore, that significant government initiatives for a national health plan emerged in Canada in the 1930s. An important player was the Co-operative Commonwealth Federation (CCF) party, which was formed in Calgary 1932. A broad coalition of progressive intellectuals, farmers, and labour groups, the CCF was dedicated to economic reform and to the establishment of a **welfare state**. In 1933, when the party met in Regina, it drafted the Regina Manifesto, which had as one of its key policies state-funded health insurance. The first actual legislation in favour of state medicine was passed in Alberta in 1934 by the United Farmers of Alberta government, but was never implemented by the Social Credit party, which gained power the following year. In British Columbia, the Liberal government was pressured by the CCF to pass a health insurance act. Despite popular support in a plebiscite on the issue, the legislation was never implemented, in part due to opposition from the medical profession and partly because the federal government failed to provide any financial support (Torrance, 1998). However, some years later, in 1947, the CCF government in Saskatchewan, with Tommy Douglas as premier, implemented the first public hospital insurance plan in the country. The plan covered everyone in the province regardless of their ability to pay; money to finance the plan largely came from taxes although those who had the economic means paid premiums (Armstrong & Armstrong, 2008, p. 16).

welfare state/social welfare state

A system whereby the government assumes primary responsibility for the welfare of its citizens through programs designed to protect and promote the economic and social well-being of its citizens.

Ideas for a national health insurance surfaced in both Canada and the United States after the Second World War (Feldberg & Vipond, 2006). World War II reinforced the importance of Keynesian economic theory, which argued for an expanded government role in stimulating the economy and increased government expenditures for social programs to help those in need. This laid the foundation for the **social welfare state**. Canada came out of World War II with a commitment to human rights: 'Increasingly, shared responsibility for what were understood as shared risks was a notion that underlined Canadian government activities, rather than the idea that most people got what they deserved in a market economy and must be held responsible for themselves' (Armstrong & Armstrong, 2008, p. 14). The post-war period was one of economic prosperity; it was also a time when more Canadians demanded that government play a central role in providing basic social services, such as health care, unemployment insurance, and pensions.

In 1945, Prime Minister William Lyon Mackenzie King presented a proposal for national health insurance to the Dominion-Provincial Conference on Reconstruction but failed to get agreement from the provinces. Under the terms of the British North America Act, health care was considered largely a provincial matter; several provinces rejected King's plan because they saw it as encroaching on provincial jurisdiction in health. The tension over provincial–federal jurisdiction continues in discussions over Medicare today, a point which will be discussed later in this chapter. However, the federal government reached an agreement in 1948 with the provinces for a national health grants program, which would cover 50 per cent of the costs for approved hospital construction. This initiative helped establish hospitals as the primary place for medical treatment; at the same time, the costs of hospital care increased significantly. Although hospitals were nonprofit, they still charged for their services and only 40 per cent of the population had some form of hospital insurance. Many could not afford the costs and defaulted on their hospital bills (Armstrong & Armstrong, 2003, p. 49). In response to mounting debts and increased public pressure for a national hospital insurance plan, the federal government implemented the Hospital and Diagnostic Services Act in 1957, which covered half of the costs of specified hospital services, on condition that services were provided to everyone on an equal basis. Coverage included meals and accommodation on a standard ward, medications, laboratory and diagnostic testing, and some outpatient services. Tuberculosis hospitals and sanitoria, institutions for the mentally ill, and care institutions such as homes for the elderly, however, were not covered (Armstrong & Armstrong, 2003, p.50).

Tommy Douglas: Planting the Seeds of Medicare

> 'All my adult life I dreamed of the day when . . . we would have in Canada a program of complete medical care without a price tag.'
>
> — *Tommy Douglas (quoted by Finn, 2007, p. 1)*

Medicare, as we know it today, had its birth in Saskatchewan under the leadership of Tommy Douglas. (See Box 13.1 for a brief overview of Tommy Douglas's life.) During his 1944 provincial campaign as leader of the CCF, Tommy Douglas promised that his party would establish medical, dental, and hospital services 'available to all without counting the ability of the individual to pay' (quoted in Badgley & Wolfe, 1967, p. 17).

In 1947, the first step in Douglas's vision of universal health care was put into place; his government introduced a province-wide public hospital insurance plan, 10 years before the federal government brought in a similar plan. During his first term in government, more than 100 bills were passed, 72 of which were 'aimed at social or economic reform' and included reducing 'the provincial debt by $20 million'. He created new government departments, e.g., the Department of Co-operatives, Department of Labour, and Department of Social Welfare (Tommy Douglas Research Institute, n.d., n.p.).

Influenced by his personal experience with illness and his passionate commitment to values of social justice and human rights, Douglas then continued his fight for a universal health-care program that would further extend health coverage. By 1959, he was confident that financially the government could extend health-care coverage. In a speech that year on 'Prepaid Medical Care', Douglas outlined five basic principles for a proposed comprehensive plan that would cover everyone: prepayment; universal coverage; high-quality service in both urban and rural areas; coverage that was government-sponsored and publically administered; and coverage that was acceptable both to those providing the service and those receiving it (quoted in Badgley & Wolfe, 1967, p. 22). And in 1960, Douglas

---

BOX 13.1 Tommy Douglas: A Visionary

Thomas Clement Douglas, better known as Tommy Douglas, 'the father of Medicare', was born in 1904 in Falkirk, Scotland, but moved with his family to Winnipeg in 1910. His childhood experience of nearly losing a leg helped shape his passionate commitment to social justice and universal health care. His family was not economically well-off, and when he developed a bone disease (osteomyelitis) as a result of an infection, his parents could not afford to pay a bone specialist. Instead, he was put, as a charity patient, in a Winnipeg hospital, where doctors were going to amputate his leg. Had it not been for an orthopedic surgeon who offered to provide the necessary medical treatment (making amputation unnecessary) for free if his students could observe, Tommy's life might have been much different. Later Douglas recalled, 'Had I been a rich man's son instead of the son of an iron molder, I would have had the services of the finest surgeon, and would not have had to depend on charity for a cure' (Finn, 2007, p.1). As noted in *Tommy's Life Story*, 'The treatment [both] saved Tommy's leg—and planted the seed for his vision: universally accessible health care' (Tommy Douglas Research Institute, n.d., n.p.).

Douglas graduated from Brandon College and was ordained as a Baptist minister in 1930. His ministry was shaped by the progressive teachings of the social gospel, which integrated Christianity with struggles for social justice and equality. As a young minister in Weyburn, Saskatchewan, he faced many challenges guiding his congregation through the Great Depression. Through his community work organizing relief programs for local farmers and their families, he saw first-hand the hardships and poverty that many families faced as they struggled to cope with drought and economic depression. Douglas's shift from the pulpit to the political arena arose out of a growing awareness that his relief efforts were incapable of having long-term effects. This was painfully evident when he had to bury two 'young men in their 30's with small families who died because there was no doctor readily available, and they hadn't the money to get proper care' (Palpz, 2004, n.p.).

In 1932, Douglas joined the Saskatchewan Farmer Labour Party (later the Co-operative Commonwealth Federation [CCF]) and in 1935 was elected as one of the first CCF members of Parliament. Seven years later, he resigned his seat to become leader of the Saskatchewan CCF, and in 1944 swept the party to victory under the slogan Humanity First and a promise to implement a universal health care plan, becoming the first social democratic government in North America.

After 17 years as premier of Saskatchewan, Douglas re-entered federal politics as leader of the New Democratic Party (NDP) in 1961, a party formed by a coalition of the old CCF and the Canadian labour movement that he helped found. There, until he resigned his seat to retire in 1979, he continued to promote a national system of health care and his socialist ideals that the common good should supersede private interests (CBC, 2004, *Top Ten Greatest Canadians*). Tommy Douglas died in 1986 of cancer at the age of 82. In 2008 he was voted the Greatest Canadian to have ever lived; his achievements were many and continue to have far-reaching effects.

fought and won the provincial election on a promise to implement a universal medical insurance plan, despite massive opposition from Saskatchewan doctors.

During the 1960 campaign, the Saskatchewan Medical Association (SMA) launched a political campaign to defeat the CCF government and its socialized medicine. The SMA's tactics remind one of the current opposition in the United States to health-care reform proposed by President Obama. Publicity kits distributed to doctors equated the proposed plan as similar to that 'first enunciated by Karl Marx in his Communistic Theories of the last century . . .' (quoted in Badgley & Wolfe, 1967, p. 31). One document warned that a government plan would endanger the doctor–patient relationship and that any emotional problems 'under state medicine [would need to be] referred to a psychiatric clinic or a mental hospital' (p. 33). Four days prior to the election, the SMA placed a full-page advertisement in the daily press that stated, in part,

> Compulsory state medicine has led to mediocrity and a poorer quality of care everywhere it has been put into practice. We believe that compulsory state medicine would be a tragic mistake for this province and it would undermine the high quality of medical care which you now enjoy . . . we refuse to support and service a plan which will lead to a poorer type of medical care (quoted in Badgley & Wolfe, 1967, pp. 34–35).

Doctors supportive of the proposed plan were afraid to speak out for fear of retaliation by the powerful medical lobby (p. 34). Despite the massive efforts of the SMA, however, the CCF government was re-elected. In 1961, the CCF government passed the Saskatchewan Medical Care Insurance Act, based on the five basic principles that subsequently became the model for Canada's Medical Care Act in 1966. The medical profession continued its lobby against the proposed universal health plan even though the electorate endorsed it. Despite the government's willingness to meet with doctors prior to passing the Saskatchewan Medical Care Insurance Act in November 1961, the SMA refused to cooperate or negotiate with the government. It was only in April 1962 that a meeting with the president of the SMA took place; however, the SMA proposals were rejected and negotiations broke down. The physicians described their issues as those of professional autonomy and patient care. Premier Lloyd, who replaced Tommy Douglas, characterized the fundamental disagreement as being 'whether the people of Saskatchewan shall be governed by a democratically elected legislature responsible to the people, or by a small, highly organized group'. He went on to say that the SMA had given notice that unless the act was repealed or doctors were permitted to ignore the act, 'the people of the province will be punished by curtailment of medical services' (cited in Badgley & Wolfe, 1967, p. 56) .

The government refused to back down, and on July 1, 1962, when the act came into effect, the majority of the 725 practising doctors in the province closed their offices and began what was to become a bitter 23-day strike. Although some 250 doctors provided emergency services in centres designated by the medical profession, only 30 or so actively practised under the act. However, these doctors worked with citizens to establish the Community Health Services Association and opened a cooperative health clinic in Saskatoon: the Saskatoon Community Clinic opened with two doctors just three days after the strike began. The clinic's cooperative health model subsequently became an alternative to private-practice medicine.

In anticipation of the doctors' strike, the government had secured doctors from Britain and the United States. The strikers underestimated the extent of pro-Medicare sentiment in the province, and initial public sympathy for the doctors began to dwindle quickly. By July 10, it appeared the profession was having difficulty maintaining the strike. With the help of Lord Taylor, a Labour peer and architect of Britain's national health plan who had been invited to the province by the Saskatchewan government, a settlement with the SMA was signed on July 23. Both the government and the doctors made concessions: 'Doctors . . . had to give way on at least one key principle to reach agreement ending the medical care dispute. This was acceptance of a universal, compulsory medical care plan, long opposed by organized medicine as a threat to doctors' freedom' (cited in Badgley & Wolfe, 1967, p. 72). The government made some amendments to the act, including allowing physicians to opt out and bill patients directly (Frankel et al., 1996, p. 131). In the end, it was clear that the CCF government had triumphed: a universal health plan came to Saskatchewan and the SMA lost some of its power.

Despite the tremendous gains in Saskatchewan for universal health care, Douglas's vision for Medicare has yet to be fully realized. In his view, removing financial barriers was necessary but only the first phase. His vision involved something more comprehensive: a fundamental restructuring of health-care delivery, with a much greater focus on illness prevention, health promotion, and measures to address the social determinants of health, especially poverty and inequality (Campbell & Marchildon, 2007).

Federal Developments

The Saskatchewan plan served as the archetype for the Medical Care Act introduced by the federal government in 1966. Prime Minister John Diefenbaker, with pressure from doctors, appointed a Royal Commission in 1961, chaired by Supreme Court Justice Emmett Hall, to consider options for health care. Although not initially a supporter, Hall recommended a national universal plan covering a full range of health services, including doctor care, for all Canadians in his 1964 report of the Royal Commission on Health Services. The Liberal government of Lester B. Pearson acted quickly on Hall's recommendations and introduced the Medical Care Act in 1966 (Armstrong & Armstrong, 2008, pp. 19–29). Despite strong opposition from the Canadian Medical Association, using similar arguments to those used by Saskatchewan doctors, the bill passed in Parliament by a vote of 177 to 2 (Frankel et al., 1996, p. 133).

The Medical Care Act set out four criteria:

- Universality: health services were to be available to all Canadians on an equal basis.
- Comprehensiveness: all necessary medical services were to be covered.
- Public administration: the plan was to be administered on a nonprofit basis.
- Portability: the benefits were to be portable across provinces, and were to be guided by accessibility.

According to the act, the federal government would reimburse, or cost share, one-half of provincial and territorial costs for medical services provided by a doctor outside hospitals

(Health Canada, 2005d). By 1972, all provinces and territories had established health plans, financed through the cost-sharing formula (P. Rich, 2008).

The implementation of a universal health care, or what became known as Medicare, did not impact negatively on doctors. The plan legitimated allopathic medicine: it maintained the existing model of fee-for-service, private practice, and professional autonomy, and it did not challenge the structure of medical practice or physicians' sole authority to determine care:

> Individual doctors determined what was defined as necessary care and, within the confines of a negotiated agreement with doctors about what should be covered, the governments paid. This power was based on the notion of the doctor as expert, the objective, knowledgeable person who applies proven diagnosis and techniques.' (Armstrong & Armstrong, 2003, p. 55)

Medicare had a significant impact on the everyday lives of most Canadians. It eliminated financial barriers, especially for lower income groups, making access to health-care services more equitable. It went a long way toward fulfilling Tommy Douglas's dream of a health-care system where no one was denied treatment because of inability to pay. However, not all costs are covered; for example, prescription drugs, dental and eye examinations, physiotherapy, and counselling are generally not insured under the plan unless the services are provided in hospitals. Those who can afford it, or who have jobs with health insurance benefits, are able to purchase these and other services through private insurance companies, such as Blue Cross or Manulife. Today, the cost of prescription drugs, in particular, remains a significant obstacle for those living in poverty or in the lower income groups.

Under the Federal-Provincial Fiscal Arrangements and Established Programs Financing Act, 1977 (EPF), the federal government revised its 50–50 cost-sharing agreement with the provinces and replaced it with block funding. This new funding formula involved a combination of cash payments and tax points and meant that provincial and territorial governments would now make the decision of how the health-care dollars would be spent. This new arrangement also meant, however, a cap on cash transfers and required the provinces and territories to shoulder a larger proportion of health-care costs (Armstrong & Armstrong, 2003, p. 56).

According to then federal health minister Marc Lalonde, the intent of this change was to provide flexibility so as to allocate additional resources to preventative medicine (Sawyer, 2006). Regardless, the new funding formula left provincial and territorial governments strapped for cash. A growth in population and an expanded medical-hospital complex in many provinces meant that health-care costs increased dramatically. In response, some provinces implemented **extra-billing** and hospital-user fees (Segall & Chappell, 2000). Citizen groups, such as the Canadian Health Coalition (a not-for-profit, nonpartisan organization formed to protect and expand Canada's public health system), soon raised concerns that such practices were jeopardizing equal access to health care as a fundamental right and that they threatened the very foundation of Medicare (Canadian Health Coalition, 2004) .

To address growing concerns, another federal commission on health care was convened in 1979, chaired by Justice Emmett Hall. The mandate of the commission was to evaluate whether principles of portability, reasonable access, universal coverage, comprehensive

extra-billing
An arrangement that allowed doctors to charge patients over and above the set payment schedule, for which the patient was not reimbursed

coverage, public administration, and uniform terms and conditions were being achieved, one aspect of which were the effects of extra-billing and user fees. In his report, *Canada's National-Provincial Health Program for the 1980s: A Commitment for Renewal*, Justice Hall (1980) recommended eliminating user fees and extra-billing; changing mechanisms for physicians' fees; and setting national standards for portability, comprehensiveness, accessibility, public administration, and universal coverage (Health Canada, 2004a). Hall went on to note that certain practices were threatening to create a two-tier health-care system and would violate a basic principle of equal access.

Canada Health Act

An act passed by Parliament in 1984, which outlined the five principles of Canada's universal, government-funded health-care system.

The federal government acted on Hall's concerns and introduced the **Canada Health Act**. The act passed with unanimous approval in 1984 in both the House of Commons and the Senate, despite strong opposition from the medical lobby. The act sets out the primary objective of Canadian health-care policy, which is *'to protect, promote and restore the physical and mental well-being of residents of Canada and to facilitate reasonable access to health services without financial or other barriers'* (Canada Health Act, 1984, 3, c. 6 s. 3). Under the conditions set out in the act, provincial governments would face dollar-for-dollar penalties if they allowed doctors to extra-bill and hospitals to charge user fees (P. Rich, 2008). The Canada Health Act, it is argued, strengthened Canada's commitment to equity and universal health care as a fundamental right by prohibiting premiums and extra-billing (Feldberg & Vipond, 2006). According to Pat and Hugh Armstrong (2008), the act 'represented a clear defeat of strong physician opposition' (p. 28).

Principles of Equity and Justice

The Canada Health Act institutionalized the belief that health care is a right, not a privilege, and that the costs of treating illness should be shared broadly by society. The act also entrenched the five fundamental principles that were to guide health-care delivery in Canada. The provinces and territories were left with the responsibility to manage, organize, and deliver health services; however, they had to adhere to the five principles in order to qualify for federal funds. These principles make clear that Canada as a society is committed to fundamental principles of equity as the basis for health policy:

> In order that a province may qualify for a full cash contribution . . . for a fiscal year, the health care insurance plan of the province must, throughout the fiscal year, satisfy the criteria described in sections 8 to 12 respecting the following matters:
> - public administration;
> - comprehensiveness;
> - universality;
> - portability; and
> - accessibility. (Canada Health Act, 1984, c. 6, s. 7)

Noncompliance with the act would result in the loss of transfer payments for health-care services. See Box 13.2 for excerpts from the Canada Health Act.

The new act was applauded by citizens' groups like the Canada Health Coalition but strongly opposed by the Canadian Medical Association (CMA); of particular concern was the government's decision to ban extra-billing. Medical associations predicted the act

BOX 13.2 Canada Health Act—Excerpts

(1) In order to satisfy the criterion respecting public administration, the health care insurance plan of a province must be administered and operated on a non-profit basis by a public authority appointed or designated by the government of the province;

(2) In order to satisfy the criterion respecting comprehensiveness, the health care insurance plan of a province must insure all insured health services provided by hospitals, medical practitioners or dentists, and where the law of the province so permits, similar or additional services rendered by other health care practitioners;

(3) In order to satisfy the criterion respecting universality, the health care insurance plan of a province must entitle one hundred per cent of the insured persons of the province to the insured health services provided for by the plan on uniform terms and conditions;

(4) In order to satisfy the criterion respecting portability, the health care insurance plan of a province must not impose any minimum period of residence in the province, or waiting period, in excess of three months before residents of the province are eligible for or entitled to insured health services;

(5) In order to satisfy the criterion respecting accessibility, the health care insurance plan of a province (a) must provide for insured health services on uniform terms and conditions and on a basis that does not impede or preclude, either directly or indirectly whether by charges made to insured persons or otherwise, reasonable access to those services by insured persons; . . . (c) must provide for reasonable compensation for all insured health services rendered by medical practitioners or dentists; and (d) must provide for the payment of amounts to hospitals, including hospitals owned or operated by Canada, in respect of the cost of insured health services.

Source: Canada Health Act, 1984, c. 6, s 8–s 12. Available from http://laws.justice.gc.ca/PDF/Statute/C/C-6.pdf, pp. 6–8.

would 'destroy the fundamental freedoms of all Canadians' (P. Rich, 2008, p. 43). In the words of Dr Everett Coffin, then president of the Canadian Medical Association, 'Surely, the Canada Health Act is a rape of the spirit, if not the legal stipulations, of the Canadian constitution' (cited in Rich, 2008, p. 43). Aware of the potential loss of transfer payments if they did not act, most provinces quickly introduced legislation banning extra-billing. The Ontario Medical Association (OMA), one of the most powerful medical lobby groups in the country, put pressure on the Ontario government to resist such legislation. On June 12, 1986, the OMA escalated its pressure and sanctioned what was to become the longest physicians' strike in Canadian history (Meslin, 1987): approximately 50–60 per cent of doctors closed their offices, withdrew hospital services, cancelled non-emergency surgery and shut down several emergency departments in the province. The OMA argued the proposed Ontario legislation, Bill 94, was discriminatory, that it would undermine the physician–patient relationship, and turn physicians into civil servants. According to Meslin (1987), the real concern was doctors' determination to protect their economic interests. He writes, 'By sanctioning a withdrawal of medical services the Ontario Medical Association sought to make a moral issue out of physicians' right to extra-bill, and to elevate that issue to the same moral plane as the Ontario public's right to universal health care' (p. 13). The Ontario government enacted Bill 94, which eliminated extra-billing, on June 20, 1986; the strike officially ended on July 7, although rotating strikes continued at some hospitals. The Ontario doctors' strike was the second major one in the country in a span of 25 years. The failure of Ontario doctors to force the government's withdrawal of legislation on extra-billing indicated once again that one special interest group would not dictate health-care policy in Canada. The doctors' defeat was another blow to medical dominance.

Universal Health Care under Threat

The early 1990s saw growing concern that Medicare was being eroded. The prime minister of the day, Jean Chretien, proceeded in 1994 to establish an advisory body, the National Forum on Health (Forum), to consult widely with Canadians and advise government on ways to improve Canada's health-care system. The nature of the politics involved is best summed up in the following words from the National Forum on Health's final report:

> Medicare was not born overnight. Nor was it the outcome of calm, reasoned discussions. Its history is fraught with false starts, difficult and sometimes acrimonious federal/provincial relations, and numerous confrontations between governments and health care providers and suppliers. (National Forum on Health, 1997, n.p.)

Like previous bodies, the forum, in its 1997 Final Report, strongly affirmed the necessity of preserving Medicare as outlined in the five principles of the Canada Health Act: they endorsed public funding for medically necessary services, a single-payer model, and a strong federal/provincial/territorial partnership. Moreover, the forum recommended that home care be considered an integral part of publicly funded health services; that government provide full public funding for medically necessary drugs as a means of both controlling pharmaceutical costs and ensuring universal access; and that primary care be restructured to include a greater emphasis on prevention and a gradual elimination of the current fee-for-service structure (National Forum on Health, 1997). None of the recommendations have yet been implemented.

In the mid-1990s, troubled by their large budget deficits, the federal government made huge cuts in transfer payments to the provinces, and provincial governments ended the practice of substantial yearly increases in health-care funding (Canadian Doctors for Medicare). Although subsequent budgets restored much of this money, considerable damage to the health-care system had already occurred. A new funding arrangement in 1995 made it difficult for the federal government to enforce the principles in the Canada Health Act, as did a new framework agreement, the Social Union Framework Agreement (SUFA), drawn up in 1999. When the Alberta government passed legislation that allowed private, for-profit hospitals, the federal government did not take effective measures to reverse this development (Armstrong & Armstrong, 2003).

The Report of the National Forum on Health pointed to the growing chasm between the principles and the reality of Medicare. It noted the growing conflicts between health-care providers and governments; that hospitals were closing; that patients were experiencing longer waiting times for surgery; that health-care expenditures had been reduced; that the private sector was encroaching on health care; and that critics of publicly funded universal health care were arguing that Medicare was no longer sustainable (National Forum on Health, 1997).

Amidst ongoing political controversy, the government established yet another commission in 2001 to review the policies and programs that define Medicare. The Commission on the Future of Health Care in Canada (Romanow Commission), with Roy Romanow as its sole commissioner, tabled the final report, Building on Values, in 2002. Romanow stated unequivocally that a single, publically funded health care was critical to ensuring quality services for all Canadians:

> Canadians have been clear that they still strongly support the core values on which our health care system is premised—equity, fairness and solidarity. These values are tied to their understanding of citizenship. Canadians consider equal and timely access to medically necessary health-care services on the basis of need as a right of citizenship, not a privilege of status or wealth. (Romanow, 2002, pp. xvi)

Medicare, Romanow argued, is as 'sustainable as Canadians want it to be' (p. xvi), but the funding imbalance between the federal and provincial governments needed to change.

While he argued that Medicare had served Canadians well, Romanow also pointed to the serious disparities in both access and health outcomes in some parts of the country that needed to be addressed, especially for Aboriginal peoples and for those in the North. Especially important were his major recommendations for change: the establishment of a new Canadian Health Covenant as a guide for the health-care system; the creation of a Health Council to measure and track the system's performance; the expansion of insured services under the Canada Health Act to include diagnostic services and home care; a dedicated cash-only Canada Health Transfer that would provide stable, predictable, and long-term funding to the provinces/territories; and immediate targeted funds to improve access in rural and remote areas, to improve wait times for diagnostic services, to remove obstacles to primary care, to begin a national home-care plan, and to improve drug coverage for expensive therapies (Romanow, 2002, pp. xxiv–xxv).

Despite these recommendations, little has changed. In 2003, a new Accord on Health Care Renewal was signed with the first ministers to direct new money into primary health-care renewal, and a Health Council to monitor progress was established. The federal government committed to a 10-year plan for stable and increased funding to the provinces but failed to provide sufficient accountability measures or enforce the provisions of the Canada Health Act (Health Council of Canada, 2006).

In the past decade, calls for increased privatization of health care have gained momentum. Two recent past presidents of the Canadian Medical Association came out in favour of privatization of some services, and in 2005 opponents of Medicare received a boost from the Chaoulli decision in Quebec when the Supreme Court, by a 4–3 vote, declared that Quebec's prohibition of private insurance for publicly insured services violated the provincial Charter of Rights (Canadian Health Coalition, n.d.). Legal experts have suggested that this decision is limited in scope to instances where there are unreasonable waiting lists for access to health care; however, *unreasonable* was not clearly defined by the courts. As a result of this decision, Quebec agreed to allow private insurers to provide insurance for those doctors who worked exclusively within the private sector. Alberta has opened the door to a private system parallel to the public one, as has British Columbia. Supporters of Medicare are warning that these developments are opening the door to a two-tier health-care system whereby those with money would be able to purchase faster services.

Nearly 50 years since Medicare was first introduced in Saskatchewan, the tensions, acrimonious relations, and confrontations between governments and special interest groups is as present now as it was when Medicare was born. Now, as was the case then, the debate is not based purely on reason or facts. It is an ideological one between adherents to **neo-liberalism** and those who defend social democratic values. The right to health care as a fundamental right of citizenship is being challenged by those who advocate for a greater role for the private sector, and the future of Canadian health care hangs in the balance. The outcome will depend on whether a coalition of citizen groups, labour, and health-care workers, who share Tommy Douglas's vision of social justice and equality, can once again pressure governments to act in the best interests of all Canadians.

neo-liberalism

A political ideology that advocates the market as the best vehicle for the production and distribution of various resources and an enhanced role for the private sector.

Health-Care System and Delivery

The organization of Canada's health-care system is largely determined by the Canadian Constitution, in which roles and responsibilities are divided between the federal and provincial/territorial governments. Prior to the creation of Medicare, health care in Canada was for the most part privately funded and delivered. Today, however, 70 per cent of expenditures on health care come from public funds. In addition to administering the Canada Health Act and assisting in the financing of provincial/territorial health-care services through fiscal transfers, the federal government is responsible for delivering health-care services to specific groups (e.g., First Nations people living on reserves, members of the Canadian Forces and the Royal Canadian Mounted Police, eligible veterans, refugee protection claimants, inmates in federal penitentiaries). Approximately 1 million people receive **primary** and supplementary **health-care services** directly from the federal government. The federal government also has constitutional authority in some specialized aspects of health care, such as the approval and regulation of prescription drugs and the protection and promotion of health (Health Canada, 2005d).

In accordance with the principles of the Canada Health Act, each provincial/territorial health-care insurance plan provides complete coverage for all necessary hospital and physician services funded through a single-payer insurance system. It has been suggested that the single-payer system not only ensures greater equity but also is more efficient and cost-effective (Stolberg, 2004). The plans are financed through federal, provincial, and territorial taxation, such as personal and corporate taxes, sales taxes,

primary health care

Both the point of first contact with the health-care system and a philosophy for delivery of that care.

payroll levies, and other revenues; services are provided free of charge to individuals without deductible amounts, co-payments, or dollar limits. Most provinces/territories also provide some health services that are not generally covered under Medicare to certain groups, such as seniors, children, and social assistance recipients. The scope and nature of these supplementary health benefits, such as prescription drugs, vision care, dental care, and medical equipment and appliances, vary considerably by province and territory (Health Canada, 2005d).

Most primary health-care services are provided by doctors working in private practice, although an increasing number work as part of health-care professional teams in clinics, community health centres, and group practices. In 2007, physician services accounted for the third-largest health-care expenditure (13 per cent), below that of hospitals (at 28 per cent) and drugs (at 17 per cent) (CIHI, 2008c, p. 5). Over 98 per cent of the expenditures on physician services come from the public sector. Doctors in private practice are paid a fee-for-service according to the reimbursement schedule negotiated between each provincial and territorial government and the medical associations in their respective jurisdictions. Doctors who work in clinics, community health centres, and group practices are generally paid salaries. The first publicly funded community clinics were established in Saskatchewan at the time of the doctors' strike in 1962. Today, Quebec has 146 *centres locaux de services communautaires* (CLSCs), the most extensive network in Canada; these clinics provide coverage to the entire Quebec population. However, only about 20 per cent of Quebec's family physicians and general practitioners work in CLSCs, either full- or part-time. Created in 1972, the CLSCs, comprised of multidisciplinary health teams, provide primary-care medical service as well as mental health, public health, and home-care services on evenings and weekends as well as during the week. Shifting the focus of health-care delivery to multidisciplinary health teams has been suggested as a way of improving access for primary care, directing more resources to preventative care, and containing costs (Health Canada, 2005d; Romanow, 2002; Yalnizyan, 2005). Other provinces have now opened community health centres, but the expansion of such facilities has been slow.

Private-sector expenditures account for approximately 30 per cent of health-care spending in the country and have risen faster than public-sector expenditure over the past three decades: 4.4 per cent versus 3.5 per cent, respectively, on average, per year (CIHI 2006, p. 6). Included are expenses paid through private health insurance plans, either purchased individually or as part of an employee benefit plan, or out-of-pocket expenses for medications, treatments, medical equipment, etc., that either are not covered by private plans or where an individual does not have a supplementary health plan. For example, most dental services, drugs, counselling, and alternative therapies are paid by private supplementary plans or are paid for directly by the individual. Under most provincial and territorial laws, private insurers are restricted from offering coverage that duplicates that of the publicly funded plans, although there are no restrictions on supplementary health services.

Over the years, Canada's universal health-care system has received positive reviews: 'Every successive generation of Canadians [has] enjoyed improved health and physical quality of life' (Yalnizyan, 2005, p. 1). Yet there are serious disparities in health outcomes within the country, mostly notably for Canada's Aboriginal peoples. There are other disparities as well. People who live in remote and rural areas have less access to health-care providers, to medical resources, and to advanced hospital care. Those in the Atlantic region have fewer services available than people living in other parts of Canada. There are, moreover, regional disparities: women in British Columbia, for example, can expect on average to live two years longer (83 years) than women in Newfoundland and Labrador. Disparities also exist in terms of waiting times to see a specialist or for surgery, and primary health-care services are more comprehensive and readily available in the richer and more populated provinces. As well, there are disparities between the supplementary health-care services covered by the various provincial and territorial plans. Economic inequality, linked to other determinants of health, is another form of disparity. The income gap between the rich and poor in Canada is growing. In 2004, the average earnings of the richest 10 per cent of Canadian families were 82 times that earned by the poorest 10 per cent (Yalnizyan, 2007). Many Canadians can not afford to pay for all their health-care needs, such as medications not covered by government plans. Today, Canadians spend more of their own money on prescription drugs than any other category of health expenditure, and those who can not afford prescriptions will do without (Health Canada, 2008a, p. 4). Income disparity is directly linked to health status and has yet to be addressed by Canada's government.

Theory Link
See Chapter 4 & 7 for further discussion of disparities in health-care within Canada.

International Comparisons

Health-Care Expenditures

One of the most contentious issues today concerns the extent that the private sector should be involved in providing health-care services. A common assertion made by the media and by some health policy experts is that spending on health care is spiralling out of control. Canadians are being told that Medicare has become too costly and is no longer economically sustainable (Romanow, 2002). Over the past 40 years, health-care spending has indeed increased in Canada as it has all over the world, both on a per capita basis and as a percentage of the **gross domestic product** (GDP). However, although relatively high in comparison with some other Organisation for Economic Co-operation and Development (OECD) countries, the overall expenditure on health care in Canada is at the level that one would expect given Canada's standard of living (Organization for Economic Cooperation & Development, 2001) and is significantly lower than health expenditures in the United States.

In 2008, Canada spent an estimated $172 billion dollars on health care. However, among the 20 or so richest countries, Canada's spending levels and growth patterns are not unusual. Canada ranks somewhere in the top five to ten countries in terms of both per capita health spending and the proportion of GDP spent on health care. Canada's total heath-care spending as a percentage of GDP in 2007 represented about one-tenth (10.1 per cent) of its GDP. That same year, the United States, by comparison, spent 16.0 percent of its GDP on health care. Although predictions for 2009 suggest a higher ratio of total health

gross domestic product (GDP)
The market value of all goods and services that have been sold during a year.

expenditure to GDP, this is due to the current economic downturn (CIHI, 2009b). For a comparison of selected OECD countries, see Table 13.1.

On a per capita basis, Canada's spending was among the top five of 26 OECD countries. Canada spent $3895 (US dollars) per individual in 2007; on the other hand, the United States, which had the highest expenditure per individual, spent $7290 (CIHI 2009b, p. 58).

In Canada, as in other OECD countries, both the public and private sectors finance health-care services. Public-sector funding includes payments by municipal, provincial/territorial, and federal governments and by worker's compensation boards and other social security programs; private-sector funding consists primarily of health expenditures by individuals and private insurance companies. The proportion of spending on health services by the public and private sectors varies among countries. Since 1997, the share of public sector spending as a proportion of the total health expenditure in Canada has remained relatively stable at about 70 per cent. In 2007, it accounted for 70.3 per cent of total expenditure. This is less than many OECD countries with a comparable standard of living. For example, Denmark, Sweden, Japan, France, Germany, Norway, Austria, Spain, and New Zealand all have higher public-health-care expenditures. By comparison, in the United States the public-sector health expenditure was 45.4 per cent (CIHI, 2009b, p. 63).

Types of service provided for by the public-sector share of health care finances differs among OECD countries. For example, in Canada the public sector pays for most physician services, whereas in France public funds pay around 75 per cent of physician services; however, public funds in France pay 67 per cent of pharmaceuticals and other medical nondurable goods whereas in Canada the portion paid by the public sector is about 38 per cent (CIHI, 2006, p. 7). Canadians rely more heavily than people in most OECD countries on private insurance and direct individual payments for health-care services not covered by its Medicare system (Romanow, 2002, p. 26).

TABLE 13.1 Total Health Expenditure as a Percent of GDP for Selected OECD Countries, 2007

Country	Percentage of GDP
United States	16.0
France	11.0
Switzerland	10.8
Germany	10.4
Canada	10.1
Austria	10.1
Netherlands	9.8
New Zealand	9.2
Sweden	9.1
Australia	8.7
Japan	8.1

Source: Organization for Economic Co-operation and Development, OECD Health Data 2010 June edition, Paris, France. Available from http://secure.cihi.ca/cihiweb/products/National_health_expenditure_trends_1975_to_2009_en.pdf

Canada's health-care costs as a portion of GDP are increasing and the forecast is that they will continue to do so, at least in the near future. Some suggest that this is not sustainable and that, therefore, a greater role should be given to the private sector. Romanow (2002) and others (Armstrong & Armstrong, 2008; Canadian Health Coalition, 2008; Yalnizyan, 2005), however, argue that privatizing health-care services not only undermines the basic values of justice on which Canada's Medicare system was founded but also that it is not the way to reduce overall health-care costs. Prescription drugs are the biggest cost drivers in health care, both in public and private spending (Yalnizyan, 2005). In 2003, just under half (47 per cent) of prescribed drug expenditures were financed from public funds (CIHI, 2006, p. 10). Romanow suggests that in the long run a national pharmacare program would reduce the amount of public spending on drugs. Other suggestions for reducing health-care costs are to restructure the way acute care is delivered, to increase public-health initiatives, and to address the social determinants of health (Armstrong & Armstrong, 2008; Yalnizyan, 2005).

Health Status

Human Development Index (HDI)

Provides a composite measure of three dimensions of human development: living a long and healthy life (measured by life expectancy), being educated (measured by adult literacy and gross enrolment in education), and having a decent standard of living (measured by purchasing power parity and income).

The health status of Canadians compares favourably to most countries in the world. For example, Canada ranks fourth out of 182 countries on the UN's **Human Development Index (HDI)**. By comparison, the United States, a country to which Canada is often compared, ranks thirteenth (Human Development Report, 2009). A number of factors affect an individual's health: biological, socio-economic, and environmental factors, as well as the accessibility of health care. A survey done by the Commonwealth Fund in 2005 asked adults with health problems in six different countries if cost was a determining factor in whether or not they received health services in the preceding two years. The percentage difference between those who responded 'yes' in Canada and the United States was significant (see Table 13.2). These findings suggest that universal accessibility to health care plays an important role in the overall good health status of Canadians.

A common measure of health status is life expectancy at birth. A comparison of WHO's 193 member states indicates that Canada has one of the highest life expectancy rates in the world (WHO, 2008). Since the 1930s, the life expectancy of Canadians at birth has increased 18 years for men and 21 years for women. However, as has been noted previously, Canada's high life expectancy is not shared equally by all Canadians. For a comparison of life expectancy among the G7 countries, see Table 13.3.

TABLE 13.2 Comparison of Responses to Cost Being a Deterrent, in Per Cent, 2005

	Canada	Australia	US
Did not fill prescriptions or skipped doses	20%	22%	40%
Had a medical problem but did not visit a medical doctor	7%	18%	34%
Skipped test, treatment, or followup	12%	20%	33%
Said yes to at least one of the above	26%	34%	51%

Source: The Commonwealth Fund. (2005). International Health Policy Survey. Table condensed from *Health Care in Canada* (CIHI, 2006), p. 11.

TABLE 13.3 Life Expectancy for G7 Countries, 2006

Life Expectancy at Birth (2006)	Males	Females	Both Sexes
Canada	78	83	81
France	77	84	81
Germany	77	82	80
Italy	78	84	81
Japan	79	86	83
United Kingdom	77	81	79
United States	75	80	78

Source: Compiled from data available from WHO Statistical Information Systems, pp. 36–42. Available at www.who.int/whosis/whostat/EN_WHS08_Full.pdf

Theory Link
See Chapter 7 for a discussion of differences in life expectancy within Canada.

The number of years lived in full health is a commonly used measure of a country's health status. This is of special interest to decision makers as many health resources are devoted to reducing the incidence and severity of major diseases that cause morbidity. Health-adjusted life expectancy (HALE) is used as a measure of the quality of life; that is, how many years people, on average, can expect to live in good health. Canada compares favourably on this measure as well. Of the G7 countries in 2006, Japan had the highest HALE of 75 years, followed by Italy with a HALE of 73 years. Canada's HALE was 72 years, while the United States' HALE was 69 years. In all G7 countries, women had a higher health-adjusted life expectancy than men. In Canada, the HALE for women was 74 years compared to 70 years for men. Both sex and income are important for determining HALE. Canadians in higher income groups tend to live longer, healthier lives than those in lower income groups. In 2001, a comparison of HALE across income groups shows, for example, that women in the highest income group have a HALE that is 3.2 years higher than women in the lowest group (Health Canada, 2006a).

Another widely used measure of health status in a country is infant mortality. Infant mortality rates have declined steadily in the Western world. Since the early 1930s, Canada's infant mortality rate has declined from 75.0 per 1000 live births to 5.0 in 2006 (Statistics Canada, 2009, Infant Mortality Rates). This rate is among the lowest in the world: it is not as good as that of Italy and Japan, which both have an infant mortality rate of 3.0, but significantly better than the United States, where the infant mortality rate is 7.0. As with life expectancy, however, within Canada there are major disparities in infant mortality rates. Improvements in areas such as housing, nutrition, sanitation, employment, and education that can account for an improved general standard of living and improved infant mortality have been slow in coming to many Aboriginal communities.

Conclusion

Canada's universal health-care program was implemented during a period that saw the continual growth of a social welfare state. However, in the 1980s Canada's earlier commitment to social and economic equality began to wane as neo-liberalism became the operational framework of successive governments. Neo-liberalism is both a set of economic policies and an ideology. It promotes free enterprise as the means of increasing economic growth; it advocates cutting public expenditures for social services, such as health care; it promotes privatization of public enterprises, such as hospitals; it promotes deregulation of labour and financial markets; and it replaces the concept of 'the common good' by promoting individualism and consumerism (Navarro, 2007). During the 1990s, the Canadian government slashed billions of dollars from social programs, including expenditures for health care (Broadbent, 2009). Despite the principles outlined in the Canada Health Act, the government did little to stop the growth of for-profit health clinics and private surgical facilities.

In the past two decades, income inequality in Canada has grown dramatically. Canada's reduced spending on social programs as a percentage of its GDP (now around 13 per cent) dropped it down to twenty-fifth place among 30 major industrial nations (Finn, 2009). This is bound to have major consequences for people's health: numerous studies have shown that inequality and poverty are decisive factors determining the health of populations. A recent study by Statistics Canada has shown that despite gains in longevity, inequalities in health outcomes across different groups are still pervasive in Canada: men in the highest income decile can expect to live 7.4 years longer than those in the lowest decile. Similarly, women in the highest group can expect to live 4.5 years longer than women who are poor (McIntosh et al., 2009). Not only are poor people less healthy, but inequality harms everyone in society. According to the latest research by Richard Wilkinson and Kate Pickett (2009), there is a gradient to health outcomes: those in the bottom quintile of income fare worse health-wise than those in the middle; those in the middle have poorer health than those in the highest quintile. Overall, more equal societies have better health outcomes for everyone than do countries with greater income inequality. If these findings are correct, one can predict that reducing social spending even further will result in greater health inequalities.

Theory Link
See Chapter 4 for a discussion of class, health inequality, and social justice.

It is within this context of neo-liberalism and reduced spending on social programs that the current debate about the future of Canada's universal health program is taking place. Supporters of Medicare believe that universal and accessible health care for all is a fundamental right of citizenship. Those who advocate for a greater role of the private sector see health care in more individualistic terms; that is, those who can afford private care should have the right to purchase it. As it was nearly 50 years ago when Tommy Douglas first introduced his plan for government-funded health insurance, the struggle over the future of Canada's health system today involves a fundamental conflict over values. It is about power, ideology, and the role of the state in promoting economic equality and social rights.

Summary of Main Points

- Canada's universal health-care system, Medicare, is valued by many Canadians as a fundamental human right.
- A universal health-care program was first established in 1961 by the CCF government of Tommy Douglas in Saskatchewan with popular support from farm and labour groups.
- The Saskatchewan Medical Association strongly opposed government involvement in health services, which culminated in a 23-day doctors' strike. About 30 doctors supportive of the government worked with citizen groups to establish the Saskatoon Community Clinic as an alternative to private practice.
- The Saskatchewan plan served as the archetype for the Medical Care Act introduced by the federal government in 1966; it set the five basic criteria as universality, comprehensiveness, public administration, and portability guided by accessibility.
- Originally, funding for Medicare was cost-shared 50–50 by the federal government and the provincial/territorial governments. Subsequent funding agreements placed greater financial responsibility on the provincial/territorial governments.
- The Canada Health Act, like the Medical Care Act, affirmed the basic principles of Canada's health policy as public administration, comprehensiveness, universality, portability, and accessibility, and listed the conditions to be met to receive federal funding.
- A 25-day strike by the Ontario Medical Association was in opposition to the elimination of extra-billing.
- The National Forum on Health (1994) and the Romanow Commission (2001) on the Future of Health Care strongly endorsed the principles on which Medicare was based and recommended universal health coverage to currently uninsured medical services.
- There is growing support for the privatization of some health-care services; today, private clinics operate in a few provinces.
- Canada's health-care spending costs as a percentage of GDP are similar to that of other G7 countries.
- The health status of Canadians compares favourably to most countries in the world; however, there are serious internal discrepancies.
- The future of Medicare is contested; the debate is shaped by two different sets of values about the role of the state in promoting economic equality and social rights.

Sociological Reflection: Public or Private Health Care?

Consider and outline the arguments for and against privatizing health-care services.

- What is the root of these differences?
- What are the implications of each position for the individual and society?
- Are there ethical concerns?
- If you were asked to appear before a commission reviewing health care, what position would you take and why?

Discussion Questions

1. Saskatchewan's model of publicly funded health insurance laid the foundations for Canadian Medicare. What principles did it establish?
2. Did the Medical Care Act (1984) enhance health care in Canada? If so, in what ways?
3. It has been suggested that the establishment of Medicare affected the position and power of the medical profession. Discuss.
4. What are the possible reasons that Canada developed a universal health-care plan and that the United States has so far failed to do so?
5. What are some explanations for the growing support for privatization of health-care services in Canada?
6. How have values and ideology shaped the debate over the future of Medicare?

Further Investigation

1. Critically evaluate the role of ideology in the development of health policy. Illustrate your answer with examples of specific health policies.
2. Compare the Canadian model of a publically funded universal health-care system with the predominantly private health-care system currently in the United States. What inequities, if any, result from a private, for-profit system?

Further Reading

Armstrong, P., & Armstrong, H. (2008). *Health care: About Canada*. Halifax, NS: Fernwood Publishing.

Armstrong, P., & Armstrong, H. (2003). *Wasting away: The undermining of Canadian health care* (2nd ed.). Toronto, ON: Oxford University Press.

Badgley, R., & Wolfe, S. (1967). *Doctors' strike*. Toronto, ON: Macmillan of Canada.

Canadian Institute for Health Information. (2007). *Health care in Canada*. Ottawa, ON: CIHI.

Hall, Justice E. (1980). *Canada's national-provincial health program for the 1980s: A commitment for renewal*. Ottawa, ON: Government of Canada.

National Forum on Health. (1997). *Canada health action: Building on the legacy: The final report*. Ottawa, ON: Government of Canada.

Romanow, R. (2002). *Building on values: The future of health care in Canada*. Ottawa, ON: Government of Canada.

Web Resources

Canadian Institute for Health Information (CIHI)
www.cihi.ca

Canada Health Act
http://laws.justice.gc.ca/en/c-6/index.html

Canada's Health Care System
www.hc-sc.gc.ca/hcs-sss/alt_formats/hpb-dgps/pdf/pubs/2005-hcs-sss/2005-hcs-sss-eng.pdf

Canadian Health Coalition
www.healthcoalition.ca/

Canadian Doctors for Medicare (CDM)
www.canadiandoctorsformedicare.ca/

Commission on the Future of Health Care in Canada
www.hc-sc.gc.ca/hcs-sss/hhr-rhs/strateg/romanow-eng.php

Health Council of Canada
www.healthcouncilcanada.ca/en/

Weyburn Review: The Greatest Canadian
www.weyburnreview.com/section/weyburn0607

CHAPTER 14

The Pharmaceutical Industry and Health Canada: Values in Conflict?

Joel Lexchin

Overview

- How do pharmaceutical companies operate within a market economy?
- What is the relationship between the pharmaceutical industry and Health Canada?
- What are the values that guide Health Canada?

Pharmaceuticals are an essential element in modern health care but they are produced by companies operating within a capitalist market economy. This chapter explores how the profit motive affects the operation of the pharmaceutical industry. The industry functions within a regulatory structure set by the state. As a result, there are significant interactions between Health Canada and the industry. The values of Health Canada and how they are reflected in Health Canada's interactions is the subject of the second part of this chapter. Finally, the chapter ends with an exploration of whether the relationship between the industry and the government is compatible with democratic values.

Key Terms

appropriate prescribing
association
basic research
Canada's Research-Based
   Pharmaceutical Companies
   (Rx&D)
clientele pluralism
clinical drug trials
Food and Drug Administration
   (FDA)
Food and Drugs Act

gastrointestinal medications
Health Canada
human testing
market failure
neglected diseases
Patented Medicine Prices
   Review Board (PMPRB)
patents
Pharmaceutical Advertising
   Advisory Board (PAAB)
postmarketing surveillance

precautionary principle
prescreen
principal-agent theory
promotional activities
risk management
self-regulation
smart regulation
state
Summary Basis of Decision
transparency
user fees

Introduction

Pharmaceuticals are an essential element of modern medicine and when used appropriately can be of great value in maintaining and restoring health. Medicines for HIV/AIDS have turned what used to be a fatal illness into a chronic one, and drugs have revolutionized the care for some forms of cancer and heart disease. In 2008, there were about 450 million prescriptions dispensed in Canada ('Retail Prescriptions Dispensed in Canada, 2006–2008,' 2009) at a cost of $25 billion (CIHI, 2009).

The importance of pharmaceuticals to health, along with the amount of money being spent on them, makes it imperative to understand the dynamics of the pharmaceutical industry. However, the industry does not stand in isolation; it is intimately intertwined with the **state** through a number of relationships: The public sector does much of the **basic research** that leads to the development of new medicines (United States Senate, 2000). The government has established a set of elaborate regulations that must be met before new medicines are allowed onto the market. A large share of all of the money spent on prescription medicines comes from the public sector (in Canada about 45 cents out of every dollar, or $11.2 billion, is spent by governments) (CIHI, 2009). And, finally, legislation means that only select groups of professionals (doctors, dentists, and in some cases optometrists, nurse practitioners, podiatrists, and midwives) can prescribe medicines, and another professional, a pharmacist, has to dispense them.

Although the pharmaceutical industry is generally not considered a social determinant of health, it nevertheless has an important impact on the health status of Canadians. As we saw in Chapter 13, the cost of prescription medications are not generally covered by provincial and territorial publicly funded heath insurance plans. Individuals who are unable to afford the cost of prescription drugs either do not fill their prescriptions or compromise their efficacy by not adhering to directions prescribed by their doctor. For example, some may take their medications every second day rather than every day so that prescriptions are refilled less frequently. Some people may cut a prescribed pill in half for the same reason. Affordability of prescription drugs is a growing concern for more Canadians as the cost of drugs escalates. This chapter opens with a description of some of the main characteristics of the pharmaceutical industry and then looks at the interaction between the industry and the state in four key areas: **user fees** in drug regulation, **postmarketing surveillance**, **transparency** in the regulatory system, and regulation of company **promotional activities**. Much of the information in this chapter is based on Canadian data, but in some cases it will be necessary to refer to information from the United States and other countries.

Characteristics of the Pharmaceutical Industry

The pharmaceutical industry is no different from any other enterprise in a capitalist economy; the primary motivation for making drugs is profit. The mission statement from **Canada's Research-Based Pharmaceutical Companies (Rx&D)** emphasizes the 'social responsibilities and role to improve the health and social environments that Canadians enjoy' that its members take on (*Code of Conduct—January 2008*, 2008, p. 3). However,

state

A term used to describe a collection of government and government-controlled institutions within a country, including the Parliament (government and Opposition political parties), the public-sector bureaucracy, the judiciary, the military, and the police.

basic research

The research phase where the basic discoveries are made about how cells function and about human physiology. This type of research lays the groundwork for further work in developing new molecules (drugs) that affect these functions.

user fees

A general term applied when an individual, group, company, or organization that benefits from a public service is required to pay part of the cost of that service. With respect to pharmaceuticals, it means that when companies apply to have a new drug approved they must pay a fee to Health Canada. Those fees form part of the revenue that is used to operate the part of Health Canada that deals with medications.

postmarketing surveillance

Refers to all of the activities that are undertaken to monitor the safety and effectiveness of drugs once they have been approved for marketing.

that quotation needs to be balanced against one from a former president of the association, who said 'The pharmaceutical industry has never claimed to be motivated by altruism, but rather by profit for survival' (Garton, May 26, 1980, personal communication).

Profits and Public Values

A couple of Canadian examples (Lexchin, Forthcoming-a) show that when profits and the public interest conflict, companies put their financial interests first. The Canadian Coordinating Office for Health Technology Assessment (CCOHTA, now the Canadian Agency for Drugs and Technologies in Health) prepared an assessment regarding the comparability of the statin group of drugs, drugs used to lower cholesterol. The report concluded that all of the then available statins were equivalent in their benefits. Bristol-Myers Squibb, makers of Pravachol (pravastatin), took CCOHTA to court to stop the release of the report. Although the case was thrown out when it finally was heard by a judge, it delayed the release of the report by a full year and cost CCOHTA 13 per cent of its annual budget on lawyers' fees (Hemminki et al., 1999).

Dr Anne Holbrook of McMaster University was hired by the government of Ontario to produce a report on **gastrointestinal medications**. Her report concluded that AstraZeneca's drug, Losec (omeprazole), was no better than two less expensive products in the same drug class. As a consequence of her conclusion, she received a letter from a law firm representing AstraZeneca claiming that if her report was released she would be contravening Canadian federal law and that 'In the event that you proceed notwithstanding this warning you should assume that our client will take appropriate steps including the commencement of appropriate legal proceedings in order to protect its interests and to obtain compliance with the law' (Shuchman, 1999). AstraZeneca quickly apologized to Dr Holbrook and claimed that the letter had been misdirected to her and should have instead been sent to the Ontario government ('Talking Points Re: Media Reports—Dr. Holbrook and AstraZeneca,' 2002).

This vigorous defense of profits has not gone unrewarded. For over 30 years profit levels in the pharmaceutical industry have outstripped profits in other industries by a wide margin, and that gap has been growing. During the 1970s, drug companies averaged 8.9 per cent profit as a percentage of revenue compared to 4.4 per cent for all Fortune 500 industries. In the 1980s, drug companies increased their margin by earning 11.1 per cent compared to 4.4 per cent for all Fortune 500 companies, and during the 1990s, the gap grew to 15.1 per cent compared to just 4.1 per cent (Public Citizen's Congress Watch, 2002). In the past couple of years, the pharmaceutical industry has fallen from first place in the Fortune 500 rankings but it still outpaces nearly all other industries in profitability ('How the Industries Stack Up: Most Profitable Industries,' 2005). Profits for Canadian subsidiaries are more difficult to obtain since many of them are wholly owned by the parent company and do not publicly release much information. However, Statistics Canada reports indicate that except for a period in the late 1990s when industry profits were exceptionally low, drug companies operating in Canada earn about twice what all manufacturing industries do (Lexchin & Wiktorowicz, 2009).

The pharmaceutical industry uses two main arguments to justify its high profit levels. First, it claims that discovering new drugs is a highly risky venture where only 1 in

transparency

In the context of drug regulation, refers to how much input the public and health-care practitioners have in the decision to approve a new drug and how much public access there is to the clinical information that companies have to submit to Health Canada when they apply to get a drug approved.

promotional activities

All of the methods undertaken by pharmaceutical companies to increase the sales of their products. These include, but are not limited to, advertisements in medical journals, visits by pharmaceutical sales representatives to doctors' offices, medication samples left behind in doctors' offices, and television advertisements about diseases.

Canada's Research-Based Pharmaceutical Companies (Rx&D)

The association that represents the Canadian subsidiaries of the brand-name multinational companies operating in Canada.

gastrointestinal medications

Drugs for stomach and bowel problems.

10 000 chemicals that are initially screened ever makes it to market (Towards Increasing Research and Development in Canada: A New Innovative Pharmaceutical Strategy, 2004). Given this level of risk, so the argument goes, high profits are necessary in order to convince investors to put their money into drug companies as opposed to companies where the risk is much lower. While the overall failure rate cited by the industry may be true, it does not mean that developing drugs is risky. Most of the chemicals that fail to make it to market do so very early on in the process when costs are minimal. By the time that prospective drugs enter the later stages of **human testing**, where 75 per cent of the costs are incurred, the failure rate is much lower—in the order of 1 in 2 or 1 in 3 (Light et al., 2009). Finkelstein and Temin have analyzed the risk involved in drug R&D since 1970 and have concluded that the risk that large drug companies would have diverse fortunes, so evident in the 1970s, disappeared completely after 1980. They all do well. . . . And this trend of doing well appears to continue today . . . The largest drug companies can mitigate the risk at the company level by diversifying it . . . It's the difference between saying that any one house might burn down and saying that the company itself is risky. Investing at the drug company level is a good, solid, and basically riskless proposition [emphasis in original] (Finkelstein & Temin, 2008).

The second argument brought forward by the industry is the cost of developing a new drug. Industry spokespeople cite a figure of over $800 million (US) as the amount it takes to bring a single new drug to market (DiMasi et al., 2003). This figure is heavily debated for a number of reasons detailed in a critique by Light and Warburton (2005). Among other things they point out the following:

- The data used in calculating the $800 million figure came directly from the companies involved and could not be independently verified.
- Although 24 companies were originally asked for information, only 12 responded, and data from 2 of those 12 was not usable.
- The criteria used to select the drugs being studied meant that the sample represented less than one-quarter of all new drug approvals.
- Estimates of company spending on drug development are presented without deducting (or at least identifying) government subsidies, including taxpayer funding from the US National Institutes of Health and other public agencies.
- Amounts are not adjusted for tax deductions and credits for doing research and development, which reduce the final costs by nearly 50 per cent.

DiMasi and colleagues (DiMasi et al., 2005) have vigorously defended their work (using 11 pages to respond to a 4-page critique), but acceptance of their calculations is far from universal.

Research Priorities

For the past few decades, the research priorities of the industry have been driven by a blockbuster mentality whereby in order to deliver the type of returns investors have come to expect the industry needs to produce medicines that will sell in excess of $1 billion annually worldwide. What this approach translates into in terms of research and

human testing

The testing that a drug must go through before it can be approved for marketing in Canada (and virtually all other industrialized countries). In the first stage, drugs are tested in a small number of healthy people to determine the mechanism by which the drug works and to look at whether the number of side effects increases with higher doses. In the second stage, the drugs are tested in about 100–3000 people who have the disease in question in order to evaluate how well the drugs work and to determine side effects and risks. Finally, in stage three the drug is used in several hundred to several thousand people to gather the additional information about its efficacy and safety to more accurately determine the drug's harm-to-benefit ratio.

development (R&D) is that companies are almost exclusively focused on products that can be **patented** and that will be used by large numbers of people with chronic diseases who live in First World countries. These people either have the ability to purchase medicines on their own or, as is more often the case, the cost of medicines is covered publicly. Under these circumstances, most drugs are likely to be profitable and companies are willing to invest in the necessary R&D.

Evidence of **market failure**, that is, the lack of medicines for unprofitable diseases, is not hard to document. Between 1975 and 2004, only 21 out of 1556 marketed new chemical entities were indicated for **neglected diseases** (Chirac & Torreele, 2006). In spring 2001, the 20 top-grossing pharmaceutical companies in the world were surveyed about recent drug development activity for five neglected diseases: Chagas disease, leishmaniasis, malaria, sleeping sickness, and tuberculosis. Eleven companies responded; eight had spent nothing on Chagas disease, leishmaniasis, and sleeping sickness; seven had spent less than 1 per cent of their total R&D budget on any of the five diseases (Drugs for Neglected Diseases Working Group & Campaign for Access to Essential Medicines, 2001). In the ensuing years little changed with respect to industry-initiated R&D for neglected diseases; five out of twelve of the top multinational companies were not conducting any research, and these companies were unwilling to enter this area regardless of any incentives offered to them (Moran et al., 2005). Furthermore, many of the (few) drugs that the industry had developed were of low overall value to developing countries because they were poorly suited to situations in these countries, for example, they needed to be administered within a hospital setting, were not affordable, or had poor efficacy or a poor safety profile (Moran, et al., 2005).

The blockbuster mentality also means that companies tend to copy already successful medicines in the hopes of obtaining a share of the market and the profit for themselves. The end result is that the bulk of these new drugs do not offer any significant therapeutic gain over what is already available. The **Patented Medicine Prices Review Board** evaluates the therapeutic advances of all new medicines marketed in Canada annually. Between 2001 and 2008, there were 177 new medicines that the board looked at. Out of these, 19 (11 per cent) were felt to represent breakthroughs or major therapeutic gains; the rest, except for two that had not been categorized, were categorized as being of moderate, little, or no therapeutic advantage (Annual Report 2008, 2009).

These Canadian figures are echoed by the French drug bulletin, *La Revue Prescrire*, which analyzes the therapeutic value of new drugs (and new indications for older drugs) introduced into the French market. Out of 983 new drugs or new indications for existing drugs marketed between 1996 and 2006, only 4.1 per cent offered major therapeutic gains, and an additional 10.8 per cent had some value but did not fundamentally change present therapeutic practice (see Table 14.1) ('A Look Back at Pharmaceuticals in 2006: Aggressive Advertising Cannot Hide the Absence of Therapeutic Advances,' 2007). Garattini & Bertele (2002) examined 12 new anticancer drugs approved in Europe between 1995 and 2000 that contained new molecular entities or known active principles with new indications and concluded that none of the 12 offered any significant improvement in action. Of the 61 new biotechnology products introduced in Europe between 1995 and 2003 for therapeutic purposes, only 2 were approved on the basis that they were superior to existing therapies using hard clinical endpoints (Joppi et al., 2005).

patents

Medicines typically have two different types of patents—a patent on the process used to make them and a patent on the product itself. While a patent is valid the company owning the product has the exclusive right to sell it. Patents are granted for a 20-year term from the date when the patent application is filed. Patent terms are the same worldwide except for a group of very poor countries.

market failure

The failure of the free-market system to produce results that are socially desirable due to the absence of a sufficient profit motive.

neglected diseases

Diseases that occur in small numbers of people or in people with little to no purchasing power. In these cases the absence of sufficient sales (in dollar value) means that drugs for these illnesses will not be developed by profit-seeking companies.

Patented Medicine Prices Review Board (PMPRB)

A federal Canadian agency that sets a maximum introductory price for any new patented medicine that is marketed in Canada and also limits the rise in the price of patented medicines to the annual rate of inflation. The PMPRB has authority over prices as long as the medication has a valid patent.

TABLE 14.1 Value of New Drugs and New Indications for Existing Drugs Introduced into the French Market, 1996

Category	Number (% of total)
Major therapeutic innovation in an area where previously no treatment was available	2 (0.2)
Important therapeutic innovation but has limitations	38 (3.9)
Some value but does not fundamentally change the present therapeutic practice	106 (10.8)
Minimal additional value and should not change prescribing habits except in rare circumstances	251 (25.5)
May be new molecule but is superfluous because does not add to clinical possibilities offered by previously available products	442 (45.0)
Without evident benefit but with potential or real disadvantages	77 (7.8)
Decision postponed until better data and more thorough evaluation	67 (6.8)
Total	983

Source: Adapted from 'A Look Back at Pharmaceuticals in 2006: Aggressive Advertising Cannot Hide the Absence of Therapeutic Advances.' (2007). Prescrire International, 16, p. 80–6.

Value of Research Done in Canada

clinical drug trials

Testing of drugs on humans. (See *human testing*.)

The research that the pharmaceutical industry conducts in Canada is largely comprised of **clinical drug trials**, considered the development aspect of R&D. Out of the $1.26 billion that companies spent here in 2008, $723 million (57 per cent) went to clinical trials versus $200 million (16 per cent) on basic research (*Annual Report* 2008, 2009). One attempt to explore the value of this clinical research was carried out in 1990 through a survey of 40 key medical figures engaged in pharmaceutical research in Canada (Lexchin & Wiktorowicz, 2009). They were happy about the availability of funding from pharmaceutical companies, but they also expressed a number of misgivings about drug industry funding: 90 per cent foresaw a likely conflict of interest, 80 per cent deemed pharmaceutical clinical research 'me too' research, while 75 per cent saw it as 'might as well' research, and 40 per cent were worried about a potential delay in the publication of unfavourable results (Taylor, 1991).

Research funded by the pharmaceutical industry may leave many questions untouched. Dr Patricia Baird, former chair of the Royal Commission on New Reproductive Technologies, noted that in the area of infertility, drug companies were only likely to fund research that would lead to a new patentable drug, ignoring topics such as behavioural factors involved in the cause and prevention of infertility (Baird, 1996). This research bias described by Baird has important consequences. It focuses the attention of researchers in a particular direction—at therapies directed at the individual rather than looking more broadly at the social causes of many problems. For instance, in the case of infertility much of that is due to sexually acquired diseases that result from unsafe sexual practices; unsafe sexual practices are strongly related to socio-economic class. However, if there is little research funding available to look at the socio-economic construction of sexual practices then researchers will ignore this area.

Drug Promotion

According to data from the US National Science Foundation, in 2004 pharmaceutical companies operating in the US spent $31.4 billion (US) on R&D (National Science Foundation, 2006) but that figure pales beside the $57.5 billion (US) spent on promotion in that same year (Gagnon & Lexchin, 2008). Exact figures for promotion in Canada are not available but estimates are that companies spend between $2.4 and $4.8 billion here annually (CAM Corp International, 2005) or between $35 000 and $70 000 for every doctor in the country. The bulk of that money is spent on the medication samples left behind in doctors' offices and the visits that pharmaceutical company sales representatives make to doctors. There are approximately 5200 sales representatives in Canada (*2002 Detailing Survey*, 2003). In 2000 Merck left behind over 1 million samples of Vioxx (rofecoxib), a drug used for pain and inflammation, with Canadian doctors; there were over 77 000 visits to doctors' offices to promote Celebrex (celecoxib), another drug for pain and inflammation (see Table 14.2) ('Targeting Doctors. Graph: Top 50 Drugs by Promotion Dollars,' 2002).

Besides visiting doctors' offices and leaving samples behind, pharmaceutical companies engage in a variety of other forms of direct and indirect promotion. Direct promotion involves advertising in medical journals and providing hospitality to doctors 'in order to facilitate greater interaction around [the company's] business'. Although the 'hospitality should not be utilized as the primary access to' health-care professionals, it can be used 'as an opportunity to expand the business discussions'. Indirectly, companies will, under certain circumstances, be able to 'provide financial support for a maximum of ten . . . individuals to [attend an] international CHE [continuing health education] event' (*Code of Conduct—January 2008*, 2008). In addition to paying doctors to travel outside Canada to attend medical conferences, between 2000 and 2004, 70 per cent of all the

TABLE 14.2 Promotional Activity in Canada, 2000

Name of Drug	Company Making Drug	Used in Treatment of	Promotional Expenditure ($000)	Number of Advertisement Pages in Medical Journals	Number of Visits by Sales Representatives (000)	Number of Samples Left with Doctors (000)
Vioxx	Merck	Pain and inflammation	6286	1090	48	1060
Celebrex	Pharmacia & Upjohn*	Pain and inflammation	6064	613	77	988
Effexor	Wyeth	Depression	5262	974	48	410
Lipitor	Pfizer	High cholesterol	4385	559	65	513
Baycol	Bayer	High cholesterol	3952	361	54	281

*Later acquired by Pfizer

Source: Adapted from 'Top 50 Drugs by Promotion Dollars,' graph shown on episode entitled 'Targeting Doctors', 2002, CBC-TV program entitled *Disclosure*. Episode air date: March 5, 2002.

association

In statistical terms, means there is a relationship between two items; however, the presence of an association does not prove a cause and effect.

appropriate prescribing

Means only using medications when they are the best type of treatment, selecting the correct medication, understanding the harms and benefits associated with the medication, prescribing it in the correct dose and for the right period of time, informing patients about the nature of their treatment, and monitoring patients to ensure that the drug is having a beneficial effect.

Health Canada

The federal department responsible for helping the people of Canada maintain and improve their health. Within Health Canada the Health Products and Food Branch (HPFB) is responsible for drug, food, and consumer product safety and in the HPFB there are four directorates dealing with medicines. The Therapeutic Products Directorate (TPD) approves and monitors prescription and nonprescription drugs derived from chemical manufacturing and medical devices. The TPD also is responsible for making the decision to remove drugs for safety reasons. The Biologics and Genetic Therapies Directorate (BGTD) is responsible for biological and radiopharmaceutical drugs, including blood and blood products, viral and bacterial vaccines, genetic therapeutic products, tissues, organs, and xenografts. The Marketed Health Products Directorate

continuing medical education programs accredited by the College of Family Physicians of Canada had some funding from the pharmaceutical industry (B. Marlow, 2010, personal communication).

When new drugs are marketed, they are promoted extremely heavily in order to start generating revenue for the company involved. Although the available literature on the effects of promotion can only demonstrate an **association**, the bulk of the studies that have been done show that the more doctors rely on promotion from drug companies as their source of information, the less likely they are to **prescribe appropriately** (Norris et al., 2005; Wazana, 2000). The extensive promotion and its negative influence on prescribing means that drugs are prescribed to a far wider range of people than the group who were exposed to them during the clinical trials. Furthermore, relatively little is known about the overall safety profile of these new drugs compared to drugs that have been on the market for a number of years, meaning that many people are exposed to potentially unsafe products.

Two of the most heavily prescribed drugs in Canada in 2000 (Vioxx and Baycol) were subsequently removed from the market due to safety problems. In the US, Graham and colleagues estimate that in the five years (1999–2004) that rofecoxib was on the market there were between 88 000 and 140 000 excess cases of serious coronary heart disease with 44 per cent of these people dying as a consequence of their heart problems (Graham et al., 2005).

User Fees in Drug Regulation and Their Consequences

Health Canada has traditionally been under-resourced for the activities it is required to undertake with respect to prescription and nonprescription medicines. As a result it operates through a system known as **clientele pluralism** (Atkinson & Coleman, 1989). In such a system the state has a high degree of concentration of power in one agency (Health Canada) but a low degree of autonomy. With respect to pharmaceuticals, in Canada government regulation of drug safety, quality, and efficacy is almost solely the responsibility of Health Canada (Lexchin, 2007a). But the state does not possess the wherewithal to undertake the elaborate clinical and pre-clinical trials required to meet the objective of providing safe and effective medications. Nor is the state willing or able to mobilize the resources that would be necessary to undertake these tasks. Therefore, a tacit political decision is made to relinquish some authority to the drug manufacturers, especially with respect to information that forms the basis on which regulatory decisions are made. In clientele pluralism, the state relinquishes some of its authority to private-sector actors, who, in turn, pursue objectives with which officials are in broad agreement. Not only does the state turn over some of its authority, but the objectives that are being pursued are ones that are often jointly developed between Rx&D and the relevant state bureaucracy, in this case Health Canada.

Since the early 1990s, the relationship between the industry and the regulatory agencies has, if anything, intensified, driven by user fees from industry and an atmosphere of deregulation (Lexchin, 2007a). In Canada in the early 1990s, the federal government, committed to an ideology of neo-liberalism (see Chapters 4 and 13), focused its attention on the budgetary deficit that was running more than $40 billion annually and, in the process, cut funding to many government departments. To make up for the shortfall in revenue, departments, including the TPD, turned to user fees to fund their activities. Pharmaceutical companies are charged a fee for every application that they submit to market a new product, and in addition they pay an annual amount for each drug they have on the market. At present, about one-third of the revenue required to deal with medicines comes from industry (Lexchin, 2006) and the goal is to ultimately raise that to two-thirds (Health Products and Food Branch, 2007a). In 1994, before money was coming from industry, it was taking on average 38 months to approve a new drug and about 50 per cent of applications were receiving a positive decision. Within one year of industry money starting to come into the TPD, approval times were cut in half; by the late 1990s, between 60 and 70 per cent of applications were being approved (Lexchin, 2006). Both of these changes are favourable to the pharmaceutical industry and are consistent with **principal-agent theory**. Prior to the introduction of user fees the principal was the Canadian public and the agent was Health Canada. However since 1994 a new principal has been added—the pharmaceutical industry, which is now providing a substantial fraction of the money needed to run the drug regulatory system. In the case of the approval times, the industry, through its primary organization Rx&D, has consistently emphasized that these need to be faster (Canada's Research-Based Pharmaceutical Companies, 2002) and Health Canada has adopted this goal (Therapeutic Products Directorate, 2004).

Major figures within the drug regulatory system have also made statements in the past indicating that cost recovery has shifted who is regarded as the principal. For example, Dann Michols, director general of the Therapeutic Products Programme (TPP, one of the predecessors of the TPD), circulated an internal bulletin in which he discussed the question of who the TPP's client is. With regard to cost recovery, he advised staff that 'the client is the direct recipient of your services. In many cases this is the person or company who pays for the service'. This one-page bulletin focused on service to industry, relegating the public to the secondary status of 'stakeholder' or 'beneficiary' (Michols, 1997, n.p.).

Regulatory agencies' dependency on user fees may also be compromising drug safety. Carpenter and colleagues looked at the safety of drugs approved by the US **Food and Drug Administration** (FDA), specifically those drugs approved on the cusp of the approval deadline clock (Carpenter, 2008; Carpenter et al., 2008). The FDA has a statutory requirement to complete its review of 90 per cent of new drug applications within specific periods of time. If the FDA fails to meet that obligation, then renewal of legislation that allows it to collect user fees from industry may be endangered. The conclusion reached by Carpenter et al. was that if the deadline is imminent, the FDA does a less thorough job of reviewing drugs in order to avoid crossing the deadline and potentially jeopardizing its revenue from drug companies.

Similarly, revenue to the TPD will also suffer if service standards (completion of reviews of new drug applications within the targeted time) are not met (Lexchin, 2009). If the actual performance in a given fiscal year is more than 110 per cent of the target for a particular fee category (different types of approval applications are subject to different fees), penalties apply for the amount in excess. Fees are then to be reduced for the next reporting year by a percentage equivalent to the performance not achieved, up to a maximum of 50 per cent; so if approvals are 20 per cent, over time fees will drop by 20 per cent (Health Products and Food Branch, 2007b). Faced with the prospect of penalties, it is possible that the TPD might follow the pattern set by the FDA and rush to approve new drugs that are approaching the deadline in order to avoid incurring a financial loss in the next year.

(MHPD) deals with the safety of products already approved for marketing. Finally, the Natural Health Products Directorate (NHPD) approves natural health products.

clientele pluralism

A term that describes the relationship between an agency of the state and the industry that it is charged with regulating, whereby some of the authority of the state is transferred to the industry.

principal-agent theory

Proposes that there is a relationship between a principal, who has a task that needs to be performed, and an agent, who is contracted to do the task in exchange for compensation.

Food and Drug Administration (FDA)

The US equivalent of the Health Products and Food Branch.

Postmarketing Surveillance

According to the **Food and Drugs Act**, Health Canada can order the withdrawal of any medication without first consulting with the company that makes it. However, the only recent situation where this power was actually exercised concerned Adderall XR™, a product used in treating attention deficit hyperactivity disorder (ADHD) in children (Health Canada, 2005, Feb 9). (Adderall XR™ was subsequently allowed back on the market.) In all other situations Health Canada has preferred to negotiate with drug companies prior to removing drugs from sale (Lexchin, 2009).

Negotiating instead of acting can have tragic consequences. Companies are often extremely reluctant to lose products, especially if they are ones that are generating large sales revenue (Lexchin, 2009). In the US, instead of withdrawing the antidiabetic drug Rezulin (troglitazone) from the market as the British did, the FDA and Warner-Lambert, the company marketing the drug, went through a protracted series of negotiations over a period of 29 months that resulted in four labelling changes to the information about troglitazone. When the drug was finally withdrawn, there had been more than 60 deaths due to liver failure. Had the FDA acted when the British did, there would have been fewer than half-a-dozen deaths. Over the time when the drug was sold, Warner-Lambert made $2.1 billion (Willman, 2000). (Troglitazone was approved in Canada but never marketed because the company and the Patented Medicine Prices Review Board could not reach an agreement about the pricing of the drug.)

The most serious deficiency in Health Canada's powers is its lack of the authority to require the manufacturer to undertake any new studies into the product's safety once a drug is on the market (Lexchin, 2009). It can request this type of study but experience in the US indicates that many such requests may never be acted on. In that country, between 2002 and 2005 there were a total of 743 unique postmarketing commitments made by companies. By the end of 2007 just over a third were completed, 91 were delayed, and 200 had not yet started (Booz | Allen | Hamilton, 2008). (Some of the 200 that were pending were not considered delayed since they had not yet passed the original projected beginning date but an unspecified number also did not have FDA-imposed deadlines.) Companies are also required to submit annual reports to the FDA documenting the status of their commitments, but 35 per cent of the 336 reports that were or should have been filed in 2004 were missing entirely or contained no useful information on postmarketing commitments; 39 per cent were missing one or more items of required information (Office of Inspector General, 2006).

In the past five or six years, Health Canada has embraced a concept known as **smart regulation**. (Smart regulation is not unique to Health Canada; this approach to regulation is being widely used within the federal and provincial governments in Canada.) Smart regulation means that Canada should 'regulate in a way that enhances the climate for investment and trust in the markets' and 'accelerate reforms in key areas to promote health and sustainability, to contribute to innovation and economic growth, and to reduce the administrative burden on business' (Department of Finance, 2003, n.p.). While health is not ignored, the emphasis is clearly on creating a business-friendly environment. The federal External Advisory Committee on Smart Regulation explicitly states that **risk management**, as an element of smart regulation, has an essential role in building public trust and business confidence in the Canadian market and regulatory system (External Advisory Committee on Smart Regulation, n.d.).

Theory Link
For a discussion of risk management as it applies to the environment, see Chapter 8.

When applied to drug regulation, risk management means weighing potential negative effects against potential advantages. Potential negative effects are adverse health effects that might occur under reasonably foreseeable conditions (Health Canada, 2003). The shift from the **precautionary principle** to risk management is subtle but unmistakable (Lexchin, 2010). The precautionary principle says that if products cannot be shown to be safe, then they should either not be marketed or be marketed but with significant restrictions; risk management allows products on the market unless they are shown to be harmful. Realigning regulation to conform to the principles of smart regulation would not totally abandon the concept of precaution but would seem to imply that there would have to be a threat of serious or irreversible damage before risk management would come into play.

One indication of Health Canada's view of the importance of drug safety is in its allocation of personnel and money between the TPD, the arm that approves new drugs, and the MHPD, the part that monitors drug safety. In 2004 the TPD was already much more heavily resourced than the MHPD, having almost five times the number of staff and five times the operating budget (Progestic International Inc., 2004). Two years later, in 2006, the allocation of personnel and money between the TPD and the MHPD had only marginally improved; although the MHPD now had 120 staff and a budget of $13 million, the comparable figures for the TPD were 525 employees and $42 million (Manzer, 2006).

In the summer of 2008, Health Canada announced it was allocating $1 million to an independent research network to study the safety of prescription drugs taken by Canadians. This was followed up in January 2009 with an additional $31 million over 4 years and $10 million per year after that. This investment is a much stronger commitment than Health Canada has previously made to drug safety but still falls short of what the new network may need (Silversides, 2008).

Regulatory Transparency

Another manifestation of the clientele pluralist relationship between the state and the pharmaceutical industry is the agreement between the industry and Health Canada that all of the information that companies submit as part of the regulatory approval process is deemed confidential and will not be released without the express consent of the company involved even if an Access to Information request has been filed (Lexchin, 2007a). There is a section of the Access to Information Act that would allow Health Canada to release information 'if that disclosure would be in the public interest as it relates to public health . . . and, if the public interest in disclosure clearly outweighs in importance any financial loss or gain to, prejudice to the competitive position of or interference with contractual or other negotiations of a third party' (Government of Canada, 1985, n.p.). Health Canada has never chosen to utilize this clause.

The level of secrecy in Health Canada has been criticized a number of times, including in a 2000 report by the ad hoc Committee on the Drug Review Process of Health Canada's own Science Advisory Board. The report stated that 'in our view and that of many stakeholders, the current drug review process is unnecessarily opaque. Health Canada persists in maintaining a level of confidentiality that is inconsistent with public expectation and contributes to a public cynicism about the integrity of the process' (Science Advisory Board Committee on the Drug Review Process, 2000, p. 9).

There is no good evidence to show that the interests of companies would be harmed by the disclosure of information about safety and effectiveness (McGarity & Shapiro, 1980). On the other hand, nondisclosure has serious disadvantages for Health Canada, health professionals, and the public. If information submitted to regulatory agencies is never disclosed, then this data will never enter the normal peer review channels and will not, therefore, be subject to scrutiny by independent scientists. Without this type of feedback, TPD reviewers may be more prone to misjudge the accuracy or usefulness of the data submitted; the scientific atmosphere in the agency may be stifled and the professional growth of its staff severely inhibited (McGarity & Shapiro, 1980). Deprived of any independent access to information, health professionals have to accept Health Canada's judgment about the safety and effectiveness of products. In the case of well-established drugs this is probably not much of a concern, but it may be different with new drugs where experience is limited (Lexchin, 2010).

Summary Basis of Decision (SBD)

A document that is released by Health Canada after it has approved a new drug. It outlines the scientific and benefit/risk-based reasons for Health Canada's decision to grant market authorization for a product.

In response to repeated criticism about being overly secretive, in early 2004 Health Canada announced a new initiative termed the **Summary Basis of Decision** (SBD) (Lexchin, 2007b). The SBD is issued after a new drug or medical device is approved and explains the scientific and benefit/risk information that the TPD considered in making its decision (Health Canada, 2004). As far as prescribers and consumers are concerned, the most important section of the SBD is the presentation of the clinical information on the product's safety and efficacy. Do the SBDs contain enough information to allow for the rational prescribing and use of new medications? This question is crucial because within the past few years there have been a number of instances where data held by regulatory agencies was significant in identifying problems with medications that were not apparent by just consulting the published literature. Examples of these problems include cardiovascular risks associated with hormone replacement therapy, safety issues with antidepressants in children and adolescents, and the gastrointestinal safety of Celebrex (celecoxib) versus traditional anti-inflammatory drugs. The absence of key information in the SBDs would have made all of these discoveries impossible. The SBDs lack information about the study protocol, the baseline characteristics of trial participants, the number of participants who withdrew and reasons for their withdrawal, primary and secondary efficacy outcomes, and fatal and nonfatal serious adverse events by treatment arm (Lexchin & Mintzes, 2004).

The approach to releasing the clinical information that companies submit reflects a common understanding between officials in Health Canada and the pharmaceutical industry of medical information as a commodity with commercial value that must be protected. Such information can be 'loaned' to the government for purposes of review but the companies do so with the expectation that the review will produce material gains through marketing of their products. This market based view stands in marked contrast to a view that data on health and safety is something that should be shared directly with the people most affected—those who prescribe and use the products. What we have instead is information filtered through, and protected by, the officials in Health Canada. (Lexchin, 2010)

Regulation of Promotion

The Food and Drugs Act gives the Canadian government the theoretical ability to regulate all forms of drug promotion but under the model of clientele pluralism, the government has turned its authority over to the brand-name pharmaceutical industry (Rx&D) and the **Pharmaceutical Advertising Advisory Board** (PAAB). The latter is an organization with membership from the medical and pharmacy professions, the generic and brand-name industry associations, consumer groups, and organizations representing both medical advertising agencies and medical publications. Rx&D has developed a Code of Conduct (*Code of Conduct—January 2008*, 2008) that governs its members' activities with respect to visits by sales representatives, leaving medication samples with doctors, the sponsorship of continuing medical education activities for health professionals, and gift giving. PAAB also has a Code of Advertising Acceptance (*Code of Advertising Acceptance*, 2009) and **prescreens** all printed material that is either used in advertising of medicines or is produced by pharmaceutical companies and left with doctors. Of significant note, compliance with both codes is voluntary, although Rx&D has made adhering to the PAAB code a condition of membership in the organization.

As Lexchin and Kawachi (Lexchin & Kawachi, 1996) point out, voluntary **self-regulation** seems an attractive option because, lacking government-industry adversariness, it is a flexible and cost-effective option. Government regulators also reason that in a highly competitive industry, the desire of individual companies to prevent competitors from gaining an edge can be harnessed to serve the public interest through a regime of voluntary self-regulation run by a trade association (Ayres & Braithwaite, 1992).

The problem with the foregoing analysis is that industry will always be tempted to exploit the privilege of self-regulation by producing a socially sub-optimal level of compliance with regulatory goals. Experience has repeatedly shown this to be the case in the marketing of pharmaceutical products (Kawachi, 1992). Effective industry control over its own promotional practices in the form of voluntary self-regulation is another reflection of a clientele pluralist relationship between the Canadian government and the pharmaceutical industry.

Under a system of voluntary self-regulation, few trade associations, such as Rx&D, vested with the authority to regulate drug promotion have made systematic efforts to either monitor the advertising practices of their members or to enforce compliance. The problem is that governments and pharmaceutical manufacturers' associations have different missions and goals. The mission of government is to protect public health by encouraging rational prescribing. The mission of trade associations is primarily to increase sales and profit. From the business perspective, self-regulation is mostly concerned with the control of anti-competitive practices. Therefore, when industrial associations draw up their codes of practice, they deliberately make them vague or do not cover certain features of promotion to allow companies a wide latitude. Self-regulation works well when

Pharmaceutical Advertising Advisory Board (PAAB)

An organization with membership from the medical and pharmacy professions, the generic and brand-name industry associations, consumer groups, and organizations representing both medical advertising agencies and medical publications. PAAB evaluates all print advertising directed to medical professionals before it appears in print.

prescreen

Under this system, pharmaceutical companies submit their print advertising to PAAB and only use that advertising when PAAB has given its approval.

self-regulation

The process by which an industry is allowed to regulate its own behaviour.

anti-competitive promotional practices happen to coincide perfectly with government regulators' notions of misleading advertising. Most often, however, the fit is far from perfect because, far from being anti-competitive, many misleading advertising tactics are good for business. Therefore, from the public health perspective, the results of voluntary self-regulation are sub-optimal.

Both the PAAB and Rx&D codes demonstrate the inherent weaknesses in self-regulation. The Rx&D code operates under a reactive as opposed to a proactive style of regulation; that is, action is generally taken only upon receipt of complaints and there is no active monitoring of compliance with the code. Neither code has effective sanctions to levy when breaches have occurred. PAAB has no authority to impose monetary sanctions although it can require companies to pull offending advertisements, but by the time a complaint has been made and a ruling taken, the ad may be near to completing its run in any case. The penalty after a third violation of the Rx&D code in a single year is a $50 000 fine, an insignificant amount for a large pharmaceutical company, and the panel adjudicating whether or not a violation has taken place is composed of a majority of Rx&D officials. Neither code has a predefined period after which it needs to be reviewed or any specific mechanism for revisions.

There is no requirement in the PAAB code for advertisements to devote as much space to safety information as they do to the benefits of the product being promoted, nor does the type size for safety information need to be as large as it is for benefit information. Similarly, the size of the type used for the generic name of the product does not have to be as large as that used for the brand name and the generic name does not have to be mentioned as frequently as the brand name. Furthermore, detailed information about products does not have to be placed directly beside the main display part of the advertisement but can appear at the back of the medical journal.

The Rx&D code does not specifically require sales representatives to provide doctors with information about risks, contraindications, and warnings, and sales representatives do not have to leave a copy of the government-approved official product monograph, which provides detailed information about the drug. Rx&D does not have any system in place to ensure that company sales representatives are following the minimal requirements of its code. According to the Rx&D code, companies are required to 'support, where possible, the principles and practices of CHE [continuing health education]' (Code of Conduct, January 2008, n.p.) but nowhere is it defined what 'where possible' means.

Health Canada has continued its policy of deregulating promotion by drug companies. An example of how Health Canada has abdicated its responsibilities in the area of controlling promotion is the case of direct-to-consumer promotion of prescription drugs. Regulations issued under the Food and Drugs Act only allow companies to advertise prescription drugs to the extent that the name, quantity and price of the product can be displayed. Policy statements in 1996 and 2000 reinterpreted this regulation to mean that companies were allowed to run 'disease awareness' ads as long as the name of a product was not mentioned or firms could name a medication as long as its use was not discussed. The only type of advertising that remained prohibited was one where a product was both named and its use was given (Michols, 1996; Rowsell, 2000). (Lexchin, 2010)

Health Canada has been reluctant to enforce even this loose reinterpretation of its own regulations. An article in the *Canadian Medical Association Journal (CMAJ)* notes that 'Response to complaints tends to be slow, probably reflecting Health Canada's under capacity to regulate DTCA, and, arguably, ineffectual' (Gardner et al., 2003, p. 425). The authors go on to describe how a television advertisement promoting Zyban (bupropion) for smoking cessation was allowed to run for months, even though Health Canada had deemed that it violated the regulations. No penalty of any type was imposed on GlaxoSmithKline, the company responsible for the advertisement ('The Battle Over a Drug Ad,' 2001).

Conclusion

No one should be under any doubt that when properly prescribed and used medicines are an enormous benefit in helping us stay healthy. Similarly, no one should be under any illusion that pharmaceutical companies' primary purpose is not to make the maximum rate of return for their investors. To that end the companies have developed their research strategy, they defend their products against perceived threats, and they devote billions of dollars to making sure that their new and expensive medicines are prescribed as widely as possible. All of these actions are perfectly understandable in a market economy.

What should cause us the utmost concern is that when there is a conflict between private profit and public health, Health Canada seems to be increasingly siding with the pharmaceutical industry:

Private values are antithetical to democracy; they speak to the need to earn a profit, not to protect public health. While the two can at times be synonymous, that happens mostly by coincidence rather than by design. Within the private sector competition and the profit motive may be the best way to get newer and better computers or washing detergent. However, medications are not ordinary consumer products and government is intimately and necessarily involved with almost all aspects of medications because of their importance in health care. When government adopts the values of private industry in drug regulation, it is in essence telling its people that the needs and values of the private sector take precedence over their health. Democracy is not just the right to vote in an election; it means the ongoing and active participation of the citizenry in determining the policies of the government with an expectation that government will acknowledge the views being put forward and incorporate them into its actions. Within the Canadian drug regulatory system, democratic values such as openness, safety and objective information are being championed by organizations reflective of a wide range of the Canadian public (Lexchin, 2008).

Summary of Main Points

- Pharmaceuticals are a key component of modern medicine if prescribed and used appropriately.
- The pharmaceutical industry exists in a market economy and is motivated by profit. Over the past few decades it has been one of the most profitable industries in the world.
- Explanations offered by the industry for the need for large profits—high risk and costs in developing new drugs and low success rates in bringing new drugs to market—do not hold up under analysis.
- In order to enhance its profitability the pharmaceutical industry engages in a variety of activities, including trying to suppress unfavourable opinions about its products, gearing its research activities to areas where the market is largest, not necessarily where the medical need is greatest. As a result, most new medicines do not offer any advantages over existing therapies. Finally, companies heavily promote new drugs in order to start to generate return on investment quickly. The degree of promotion means that people are exposed to potentially risky medicines early on, and the potential for harm is high.
- Health Canada and the pharmaceutical industry exist in a relationship termed clientele pluralism, whereby Health Canada turns over some of its authority to the industry.
- Since the mid 1990s, the industry has been paying for an increasing share of the operating costs of Health Canada; as a result, the relationship between Health Canada and the industry has become closer over the past few decades, with Health Canada adopting some of the industry's values as opposed to those of public health. This shift in Health Canada's values can be seen in its approach to drug approvals, postmarketing surveillance, regulatory transparency, and the way that promotion is controlled.

Sociological Reflection:
Smart Regulation

There is an ongoing debate in regulatory theory between those who argue for a command-and-control approach and those who argue that government should set the rules but leave the day-to-day regulation to the industry. Under the first approach, the government would not only establish the regulations but would employ the people who ensure that the regulations are being followed. Under the second model, industry would be responsible for monitoring its own behaviour by filing periodic reports on its activities; the main task of the government would be to review the reports filed by industry. Those arguing in favour of the first approach maintain that industry cannot be trusted to regulate its own activities if such regulations put its profits at risk. Those arguing in favour of the second approach note that it is less expensive and that industry has a far greater level of expertise than government inspectors and is therefore able to catch problems that would escape government inspection.

- With respect to postmarketing surveillance, discuss which model would better serve to identify new safety problems with medicines and minimize the risk from these problems.

 # Discussion Questions

1. All countries finance part or all of their drug regulatory system from user fees. Why should Canada be any different?
2. There is a tradeoff between studying a drug for a long time before it is marketed in order to identify as many safety problems as possible and getting promising new drugs onto the market quickly so that patients can benefit from them. Where do you fall in this debate and why?
3. How should the government try to ensure that research into new drugs is directed to those areas where the medical need is the highest? What role do companies operating in a free market economy have to play in this regard?
4. How much profit should drug companies be allowed to earn provided that they don't do anything illegal in earning their profits? Is there any limit that should be imposed, and if so, how should that limit be determined?
5. Explain what your position is on whether or not direct-to-consumer advertising of prescription drugs should be legal in Canada.
6. Drugs can never be absolutely safe in every person. What kind of risk is tolerable when drugs are put on the market? Does the level of risk vary depending on what condition is being treated?

 # Further Investigation

1. The drug regulatory system in the United Kingdom is set up differently than the one in Canada. Analyze the UK system and contrast it to the Canadian one.
2. Discuss the pros and cons of risk management versus the precautionary principle as a basis for drug regulation.
3. Look at the history of the patent system in Canada for pharmaceuticals since 1969 and discuss how the changing use of patents has affected the cost of drugs in this country.

 # Further Reading

Abraham, J. (1995). *Science, politics and the pharmaceutical industry: Controversy and bias in drug regulation.* London, UK: UCL Press/Taylor and Francis.

Abramson, J. (2004). *Overdosed America: The broken promise of American medicine.* New York, NY: Harper Collins.

Angell, M. (2005). *The truth about the drug companies: How they deceive us, and what to do about it.* New York, NY: Random House.

Avorn, J. (2005). *Powerful medicines: The benefits, risks, and costs of prescription drugs.* New York, NY: Knopf.

Braithwaite, J. (1984). *Corporate crime in the pharmaceutical industry.* London: Routledge & Kegan Paul.

Brody, H. (2007). *Hooked: Ethics, the medical profession and the pharmaceutical industry.* Lanham, MD: Rowman & Littlefield.

Cohen, J. C., Illingworth, P., & Schüklenk, U. (Eds.). (2006). *The power of pills: Social, ethical & legal issues in drug development, marketing & pricing.* London, UK: Pluto Press.

Davis, P. (Ed.). (1996). *Contested ground: Public purpose and private interest in the regulation of prescription drugs.* New York, NY: Oxford University Press.

Finkelstein, S., & Temin, P. (2008). *Reasonable Rx: Solving the drug price crisis.* Upper Saddle River, NJ: FT Press.

Goozner, M. (2003). *The $800 million pill: The truth behind the cost of new drugs.* Berkeley, CA: University of California Press.

Kassirer, J. (2005). *On the take: How medicine's complicity with big business can endanger your health.* New York, NY: Oxford University Press.

Lexchin, J. (1984). *The real pushers: A critical analysis of the Canadian drug industry.* Vancouver, BC: New Star Books.

Medawar, C., & Hardon, A. (2004). *Medicines out of control? Antidepressants and the conspiracy of goodwill.* Amsterdam: Askant.

Moynihan, R., & Cassel, A. (2005). *Selling sickness: How the world's biggest pharmaceutical companies are turning us all into patients.* Vancouver, BC: Greystone Books.

Mundy, A. (2001). *Dispensing with the truth: The victims, the drug companies, and the dramatic story behind the battle over fen-phen.* New York, NY: St. Martin's Press.

O'Donovan, O., & Glavanis-Grantham, K. (Eds.). (2008). *Power, politics and pharmaceuticals.* Cork: Cork University Press.

Rochon Ford, A., & Saibil, D. (Eds.). (2009). *The push to prescribe: Women and Canadian drug policy.* Toronto, ON: Women's Press.

Shah, S. (2006). *The body hunters: Testing new drugs on the world's poorest patients.* New York, NY: The New Press.

Temple, N. J., & Thompson, A. (Eds.). (2007). *Excessive medical spending: Facing the challenge.* Oxford, UK: Radcliffe Publishing.

Web Resources

Canada's Research-Based Pharmaceutical Companies (Rx&D)
www.canadapharma.org/

Canadian Generic Pharmaceutical Association (CGPA)
www.canadiangenerics.ca/

Canadian Health Coalition
www.healthcoalition.ca

Health Action International
www.haiweb.org

Health Canada: Drug Products
www.hc-sc.gc.ca/dhp-mps/prodpharma/index-eng.php

Healthy Skepticism Inc.
www.healthyscepticism.org/

Hooked: Ethics, Medicine and Pharma
http://brodyhooked.blogspot.com/

IMS Health Inc.
www.imshealth.com/portal/site/imshealth?CURRENT_LOCALE=en_ca

International Federation of Pharmaceutical Manufacturers & Associations (IFPMA)
www.ifpma.org/

Media Doctor Canada
www.mediadoctor.ca/

*Patented Medicine Prices Review Board
(PMPRB)*
www.pmprb-cepmb.gc.ca/

PharmedOut
www.pharmedout.org/

Public Citizen: Drug Projects
www.citizen.org/Page.aspx?pid=4374

Women and Health Protection (WHP)
www.whp-apsf.ca/en/index.html

CHAPTER 15

Nursing in the Twenty-First Century

Jennie Hornosty & Deidre Wicks

Overview

- Why is nursing often depicted in a negative light?
- How did nursing develop in Canada?
- What are some of the major challenges faced by nurses today?
- What has been the impact of financial constraints and downsizing on nurses and nursing practice?

This chapter begins by looking at some of the sociological and theoretical approaches to nursing. It then turns to an examination of the role of nursing in the Canadian health-care system and some of the factors that affect nursing education, recruitment, and retention. This chapter provides a brief history of nursing and analyzes nursing reforms in Canada through a sociological lens. This analysis will also focus on the tension between the values of nursing care and the increasing tendency toward **rationalization** and control of labour in the health-care system.

rationalization
Refers to the standardization of social life through rules and regulations.

Key Terms

agency
biological determinism
class/social class
discourse
doctor/nurse game
ethnography
feminism/feminist
gender/sex
horizontal violence
instrumental approach
licensed practical nurses (LPNs)

materialist analysis
McDonaldization
meta-analysis/meta-narratives
new managerialism
Nightingale tradition
nurse practitioners (NPs)
patriarchy
post-structuralism/postmodernism
racism
rationalization
registered nurses (RNs)

registered psychiatric nurses (RPNs)
sexual division of labour (SDL)
social institutions
social structure
structure–agency debate
theory
time and motion principles

Introduction

Many would argue that nurses are the face of contemporary health care. They play a critical role in the management, delivery, and research of health-care services. They do the majority of caring work in hospitals, nursing/long-term care homes, and community health. Nurses today comprise the largest group of health-care providers in Canada. In 2008, there were 343 100 nurses (including registered nurses, registered psychiatric nurses, licensed practical nurses, and nurse practitioners) as compared to 65 440 physicians (excluding residents) (CIHI, 2008a).

Since the first formal training school for nurses in Canada opened in 1874 in St. Catharines, Ontario, nursing has undergone a number of changes. Then, nursing, traditionally seen as women's work, centred on care; nurses were to provide compassion and comfort for the sick and dying. Unlike physicians, their approach was more holistic. Today, health-care restructuring, managerial ideology, fiscal constraints, and nursing shortages have changed the face of nursing.

Sociological Approaches to Nursing

In the period following World War II, nursing training in Canada was broadened to include both the technological and clinical advances that had occurred as a result of nursing experiences in war. Further expansion of nursing curricula occurred during the 1970s and 1980s to include input from the social sciences, namely psychology and sociology. This was based on a view of nursing that held that nurses needed an understanding of the social context of health-care delivery as well as of their patients' individual psychological needs and perceptions. The sociology introduced at that time, with few exceptions, revolved around the concept of roles and role relationships, such as 'the role of the doctor and nurse in health-care delivery' and 'the role of the patient in hospital care'. As such, sociological theories encouraged an acceptance of existing social relationships and their hierarchies of power and authority. They also, nevertheless, encouraged nursing students to think about social relationships and the impact of those relationships on nursing work and on patient care. As the 1970s progressed, more radical approaches within sociology became popular and were applied to sociology courses within nursing education. New interpretations of nursing history and practice, based on feminist **theory** in particular, began to appear, especially in the new diploma and later degree courses within universities. These courses encouraged a more critical examination of nursing history and practice, as well as a more critical interpretation of the relationship of nursing with other health occupations, especially medicine.

theory
A system of ideas that uses researched evidence to explain certain events and to show why certain facts are related.

Theory Link
See Chapter 2 for an overview of feminist theories.

As well as broadening the understanding of nursing, these new approaches had the unintended effect of presenting nursing in a much more negative light—so much so that

gender/sex
Refers to the socially constructed categories of feminine and masculine (the cultural values that dictate how men and women should behave), as opposed to the categories of biological sex (female or male).

ethnography
A research method that is based on direct observation of a particular social group's social life and culture—of what people actually do.

horizontal violence
A concept derived from Paolo Friere that describes a behaviour common to all oppressed groups, whereby, because of their powerlessness, the oppressed are unable to direct their anger toward their oppressor and, as a result, turn it toward each other, with various degrees of violence and negativity.

class (or social class)
A position in a system of structured inequality based on the unequal distribution of power, wealth, income, and status. People who share a class position typically share similar life chances.

social structure
The recurring patterns of social interaction through which people are related to each other, such as social institutions and social groups.

agency
The ability of people, individually and collectively, to influence their own lives and the society in which they live.

in 1980s sociological writings about nursing presented an almost uniformly negative picture. Repeatedly, nursing was presented as a subordinated occupation and nurses themselves, as passive victims of medical power. While there have been differences in the way that various sociological perspectives view nursing, there has been a consistent theme running through all the interpretations, from social histories of nursing through to more radical feminist accounts. In the historical accounts, it is argued that many of the enduring characteristics of nursing have their roots in nineteenth-century **gender** relations and associated ideas regarding the appropriate behaviour for women in Victorian society. This argument has been a legend in nursing history. For instance, it has been argued that '[t]hese [strategies] replicated within the hospital the existing gender relationships of Victorian society, and did not challenge prevailing male notions of womanly behaviour. Deference to doctors and acceptance of the "handmaiden role" was a cornerstone of this strategy' (Beardshaw & Robinson, 1990).

There is, however, a theoretical and logical flaw in many of the accounts and analyses, which assumed that the political strategy of those in charge and the real-life behaviour of the nurses in question were one and the same. Victorian doctors and administrators may well have desired the nurse to be 'restrained, disciplined and obedient, [carrying] out the orders of doctors in a suitably humble and deferential way' (Davies, 1977). But this did not mean that matrons, nurses, and sisters always cooperated; indeed, there is ample evidence that they frequently did not. For instance, in the earliest era of modern nursing in London, there was an important dispute at Guy's Hospital between Mrs Burt (the matron) and the doctors (Abel-Smith, 1960), and there were also the disputes at St Thomas's Hospital over the timing of medical rounds ('The Doctors versus the Nurses,' 1962). In addition, labour history has documented various forms of industrial action taken collectively by nurses over the past century. Finally, **ethnographic** studies have revealed numerous examples of negotiation, disagreement, subversion, and open conflict as constant elements of nurse–doctor interactions within hospital settings (Game & Pringle, 1983; Hughes, 1988; Porter, 1995; Svensson, 1996; Wicks, 1999). Against this evidence, an orthodoxy has developed within both mainstream and more radical approaches that has focused on the power of doctors, hospitals, and medicine more generally. Nurses were thought to have inherited a tradition of passivity and powerlessness and, worse, a tendency to engage in **horizontal violence** (Roberts, 1983). Indeed, given these characteristics and the twin edifices of **class** and gender, the position of nurses was considered to be all but hopeless (Short & Sharman, 1995). The common thread running through these accounts has focused on the power of **social structure** to shape and control nurses' work, identity, and behaviour and has ignored human **agency**.

Feminist Approaches

Since the 1990s, theoretical developments in feminist theory, and within sociology more generally, have promoted a re-examination of the debate concerning individual choice versus determination by outside forces (**structure–agency debate**) and of the need to understand an issue that has such important implications for politics and social life. Through the influence of **post-structuralism**, there has been a re-emphasis on individual choice and action in the making and re-making of **social institutions**. While some authors think that this trend has gone too far (Walby, 1992), others see it as liberating, challenging the grand narratives that characterized groups such as women as being oppressed by strong and unchanging social structures (Barrett, 1991).

In the early 1970s, two writers from the US—Barbara Ehrenreich and Deirdre English—turned conventional theories on their head with their pamphlet *Witches, Midwives and Nurses: A History of Women Healers* (1973). Their work, with its strong feminist perspective, was a breath of fresh air in a field dominated by conventional histories of medicine. And yet its widespread influence in the decades since its publication has also had a detrimental effect on feminist sociological analyses of nursing. This stems from the way that Ehrenreich and English view the struggle within health care as something that took place in an earlier period between traditional women healers and formal male practitioners. According to their analysis, the defeat of the women healers ushered in an epoch of widespread subordination to organized, scientific male medicine. For instance, they are critical of middle-class reformers, such as Florence Nightingale, and of nineteenth-century feminists who 'did not challenge nursing as an oppressive female role' (1973, p. 38). This analysis overlooks much that is crucial to a dynamic analysis of the historical relationship between nursing and medicine. By viewing the nineteenth-century formation of modern nursing only in terms of capitulation and defeat, the work has had the unintended effect of devaluing contemporary nurses and nursing work.

The most influential piece of writing on nursing and its relationship to medicine is Eve Gamarnikow's 'Sexual Division of Labour: The Case of Nursing' (1978). In this important paper, Gamarnikow challenges accounts of the **sexual division of labour** (SDL) that are based on naturalism or **biological determinism**—that is, the idea that it is natural for women to be nurses in the same way that women are naturally maternal. She argues, rather, for a **materialist analysis**, which locates the SDL as a social relationship that is not inevitable or natural but that has been socially constructed. This was such a significant breakthrough, in an area typified by naturalist explanations, that sociological analysis to this day continues to refer to it to establish a position that runs counter to biological or naturalist accounts of the nurse–doctor relationship (see, for example, Game & Pringle, 1983; Hazleton, 1990; Russell & Schofield, 1986; Short & Sharman, 1995; Willis, 1983). This materialist analysis is still widely regarded as the necessary foundation on which any critical sociological account of nurse–doctor relations must be built.

However, upon closer examination, it is evident that Gamarnikow's account is located squarely within a modernist feminist theoretical model, with its tendency to generalize and universalize. In this case, Gamarnikow generalizes the structural oppression of all nurses by all doctors through a patriarchal ideological structure. While Gamarnikow's approach provides a crucial sense of the strength and pervasiveness of social structure in explanations of the SDL, both Robert W. Connell (1987) and, more recently, Anne Witz (1992) make the point that this approach ignores or at least minimizes the importance of patriarchal practices within the labour market and the workplace itself. The effect of Gamarnikow's emphasis on patriarchal ideology and structure, and that same emphasis in other accounts derived from this analysis, has been the representation of nurses as an undifferentiated bloc of subordinated women. Individual or collective acts of resistance have either been ignored or minimized, being characterized as insignificant or as yet another variant of complaint among nurses (Turner, 1986b). The emphasis on an all-pervasive ideological structure has also had the effect of denying nurses subjectivity (their own identity) because, in accounts based on the power and pervasiveness of structure, the voices of nurses were rarely heard.

structure–agency debate

A key debate in sociology over the extent to which human behaviour is determined by social structure.

post-structuralism/ postmodernism

Often used interchangeably, these terms refer to a broad perspective that is opposed to the view that social structure determines human action, and instead emphasizes a pluralistic world view that explores the local, the specific, and the contingent in social life.

social institutions

Formal structures within society—such as health care, government, education, religion, and the media—that are organized to address identified social needs.

sexual division of labour (SDL)

Refers to the nature of work performed as a result of gender roles. The stereotype is that of the male breadwinner and the female homemaker.

biological determinism

An unproven belief that individual and group behaviour and social status are an inevitable result of biology.

materialist analysis

An analysis that is embedded in the real, actual, material reality of everyday life.

patriarchy

A system of power through which males dominate households. It is used more broadly by feminists to refer to society's domination by patriarchal power, which functions to subordinate women and children.

feminism/feminist

A broad social and political movement based on a belief in equality of the sexes and the removal of all forms of discrimination against women. A feminist is one who makes use of, and may act upon, a body of theory that seeks to explain the subordinate position of women in society.

discourse

A domain of language use that is characterized by common ways of talking and thinking about an issue (for example, the discourses of medicine, madness, or sexuality).

racism

Beliefs and actions used to discriminate against a group of people because of their physical and cultural characteristics.

meta-analysis/ meta-narratives

The big-picture analysis that frames and organizes observations and research on a particular topic.

Gamarnikow's contribution was pivotal, however, for a critical reassessment of the conventional literature on nurse–doctor relations. Indeed, the emphasis on power relationships in general, and on **patriarchy** in particular, opened up the traditional nurse–doctor relationship to a sophisticated and long overdue sociological critique. Nevertheless, an emphasis on structural oppression and on an inferred passivity on the part of nurses also runs the danger of indirectly contributing to the status quo by suggesting that the situation is inevitable and hopeless.

Over the past two decades, there has been what some writers have referred to as a 'paradigm shift' within the founding theoretical principles of modern **feminism** (Barrett & Phillips, 1992). Central to this shift has been a questioning of at least three of the basic assumptions of 1970s feminism: (1) the notion of women's oppression; (2) the assumption that it is possible to specify a cause for the oppression; and (3) consensus that the cause lies at the level of social structure, be it patriarchy, class, ethnicity, or a combination of any or all of the above (Barrett & Phillips, 1992). The new emphasis is on understanding how different women experience different types and degrees of oppression in specific circumstances. This collection of approaches has been heavily influenced by the philosopher and social theorist Michel Foucault. Sociologist Rosemary Pringle (1995) argues that Foucault's emphasis on power as productive (and not merely coercive) has opened up the space for a view of women as active agents rather than as passive recipients of orders from above.

This and other similar approaches have not been without their critics. Feminist theorist Sylvia Walby, for example, has argued that the shift away from structure and toward **discourse** has resulted in a conceptualization of power as highly dispersed rather than as concentrated in identifiable places and groups. She argues further that the concepts of 'woman' and 'patriarchy' are, in fact, essential if we are not to lose sight of the power relations involved and if we are to understand the gendered nature of the social world. In particular, she points out that an analysis of the new international division of labour shows clearly the need to maintain the use of the structural concepts of patriarchy, class, and **racism** (Walby, 1992). While Walby agrees that there were problems with the old **meta-narratives** based solely on class, she holds that the answer is not to discard the concept of social structure. Rather, the answer is to develop better, theoretically richer concepts that are more capable of catching and explaining the theoretical and practical complexities of the operation of power in the social world.

The important point about these theoretical developments and debates is not that there are disagreements but that feminist theory in the twenty-first century is marked not by orthodoxy and homogeneity but, rather, by debate and openness. Directly or indirectly, these developments have encouraged a revival in sociological analyses of nursing and of the division of labour within medicine. Rather than accept old-style assumptions about the patriarchal oppression and medical dominance that are implicit in the **doctor/nurse game**, recent writers, working from a variety of sociological perspectives, have re-examined nurses' and doctors' working relationships and come up with some fascinating and important findings.

Development of Nursing in Canada

David Coburn (1988b) analyzes the development of nursing in Canada in terms of three different time periods. The first period, the emergence of lay nursing, including organization and registration, spans the time period 1870–1930. While some form of nursing care had always been done, it was largely carried out by family members or religious nursing orders. The second era of nursing (1930–1950) saw a move from private nursing to hospital nursing, while the third period of nursing began at the end of the Second World War and brought major changes for nurses and the profession.

The Canadian Encyclopedia (Nursing, n.d.) credits Marie Rollet Hébert as the first person to provide nursing care to the sick after arriving in Quebec in 1617 with her surgeon-apothecary husband. Subsequently, as members of religious orders immigrated to what is now Canada, 'nursing sisters' took on the role of providing nursing care. These nurses, however, were quite different from nurses today; they often served as doctors, making medicines and undertaking surgery; helped establish hospitals; and served as administrators. The Sisters of Charity, more commonly known as the Grey Nuns, were a noncloistered order, founded in 1737 by a Quebec widow, Marguerite d'Youville. From the outset they provided free health care and concentrated their work on home visits to the sick. This predominant group of nursing sisters played an important historical role in the development of health care in the country. Recognizing the importance of segregating the sick, especially during periods of epidemic outbreaks, they spearheaded the creation of a network of hospitals across Canada in the eighteenth and nineteenth centuries, including an orphanage and a home for the aged. Caring for the sick was practised as a devotion to God.

The Emergence of Lay Nursing

The rise and professionalization of nursing is tied to the emergence of hospitals. The formal training of nurses began in the 1870s to provide hospital personnel who would be able to carry out doctors' orders (Wotherspoon, 2009). As new hospitals were established, more nurses were needed to provide care to the sick: 'With a nursing force at hand, public hospitals could shift their image and emphasis from providing a repository for the terminally ill to serving as a centre for treatment and recovery' (p. 105). At the time, nursing was viewed as a supporting occupation concerned primarily with caring and hygiene as compared to that of the curative powers of physicians. In the view of Wotherspoon (p. 105), this medical division of labour reproduced a patriarchal structure whereby men were doctors and women were nurses.

As in Britain, Australia, and the United States, nursing in Canada emerged within the **Nightingale tradition**. Florence Nightingale, born in 1820, was a pioneer in nursing in England who laid the foundation for professional nursing for decades to come. Her impact on the practice of nursing, however, is viewed equivocally. One the one hand, her determination to make nursing a high status profession for women, her holistic approach to health, and her commitment to promoting health rather than simply to nursing illness are viewed as significant achievements. Her prototype for nursing schools, which resulted in a strong female hierarchy in the hands of one female, trained head nurse to protect exploitation, is also considered an important contribution. On the other hand, her strategy to reinforce the status of nursing by promoting an ethos of service had the effect of subordinating nurses, who became viewed as 'handmaidens' to doctors. Indeed, the motto of the first Canadian training school for nurses (1874) founded on Nightingale's principles was 'I see and I am Silent'. It became the watchwords for nurses for the next hundred years (Growe, 1991, p. 47). Summing up Nightingale's legacy, US nurse Marlene

doctor/nurse game

A concept coined by Stein (1967) to refer to the so-called game played out between doctors and nurses, whereby a nurse can be assertive and make suggestions about a patient without appearing to do so, so that nurses' suggestions are provided as prompts for doctors, who can act on them as though they were their own idea.

Nightingale tradition

The view that nursing was a natural extension of women's role as caregivers; nurses were expected to be altruistic and to act with selfless dedication.

Grissum wrote that 'Florence Nightingale may well be given the credit for establishing nursing as we know it—including low pay, long hours, and subservience to men' (cited in Growe, 1991, p. 51).

Hospital administrators quickly recognized the value of nurses in providing inexpensive labour. The number of hospital schools of nursing in Canada grew from 1 in 1874 to 170 in 1909 and to approximately 220 in 1930 (Wotherspoon, 2009, p. 105). The newly trained nurses were taught complete subordination, unquestioning obedience, and loyalty to doctors. A nursing training program accomplished contradictory functions: 'it dampened the hostilities of doctors who scorned nurses as unskilled and uneducated' (Wotherspoon, 2009, p. 105); at the same time, doctors who saw the trained nurse as a potential threat to their livelihood found that they could advance their own interests by getting involved in the nursing training programs. Public health nurses who worked semi-independently in the community were viewed as a special threat. Physicians opposed the founding in 1895 of the Victorian Order of Nurses (VON) and public health nursing in general—wherever they saw nurses doing work that they believed could be done more profitably by doctors (Coburn, 1988b).

By the end of the nineteenth century, trained nurses striving to increase their own status and distinguish themselves from untrained nurses began to lobby and organize: 'Through registration and licensing regulations, nurses sought to obtain a monopoly over the provision of nursing services and to gain higher fees and salaries for themselves. . . .' (Coburn, 1988b, p. 443). Opposition came from both hospital administrators, who feared such power, and doctors. In 1908, the Canadian National Association of Trained Nurses was established; in 1924, with 52 affiliated member organizations, this became the Canadian Nurses Association (CNA) (Wotherspoon, 2009, p. 106). The group focused its energies on establishing registries of trained nurses and by 1922 received legislative recognition in all nine provinces.[1] This institutionalization of nursing, however, Coburn (1988b) argues, was gained at the price of subordination to medicine and to hospital administrators and marked the end of the first era of nursing. Nurses did not attain a monopoly over nursing but only the exclusive right to use the title of nurse or RN (registered nurse). Nursing associations focused on raising standards of care rather than on improving working conditions or pay, but they had no control over who could actually practise nursing. The equation of nursing with qualities of women and motherhood persisted well into the twentieth century: 'Becoming professional meant an altruistic orientation of selfless dedication, the ever-higher education credentialing of nursing, and the placing of as much distance as possible between nurses and lower level hospital workers and between nurses and working-class organizations such as unions' (Coburn, 1988b, p. 445).

Move to Hospital Nursing

The second era of nursing (1930–1950) saw a move from private nursing to hospital nursing. The Depression of the 1930s brought with it high unemployment and economic hardship for a vast number of Canadians. Private-duty nurses, who at the time were in the majority, had a hard time surviving as the demand for their services declined; they

---

1. Newfoundland did not join Canada as its tenth province until 1949.

faced increased periods of unemployment and meager wages. While some left nursing, many moved to the hospitals, which provided more secure employment and better wages, despite poor working conditions. The shift is evident in the following statistics: in 1930, 60 per cent of nurses were in private duty and 25 per cent worked in hospitals or nursing schools; by 1948, 67 per cent were in hospitals or nursing schools, and only 15 per cent were private-duty nurses (Coburn, 1988b).

The Depression also took its toll on hospitals: occupancy rates declined and there was pressure to close schools of nursing and decrease the number of nurse graduates. However, things began to change with World War II, when a large number of nurses went into active service. After the war, improved economic conditions generally meant greater hospital utilization and an increased demand for more nurses. By the end of the war, there was a shortage of nurses in the country. Coburn (1988b) argues that the 1940s and 1950s saw a major shift in the orientation of nursing from a care model rooted in the Nightingale tradition to a more instrumental view that saw nursing as no different from other occupations. There was a growing disparity between the views of the nursing elite, whose interests were in enhancing nurses' professional status through increased education and training, and the majority of ordinary nurses, that is, the 'rank and file',[2] who were more concerned with their working conditions and wages.

After some success in pressing for regulation and licensing, nursing associations focused on improving nursing education and increasing standards. In 1932, Dr George Weir, who had been jointly appointed by a committee of the Canadian Medical Association and the CNA, released a report that called for sweeping changes in nursing education, and he recommended that nursing schools be removed from hospital control and instead be integrated with provincial educational systems (Wotherspoon, 2009). He argued that nurses needed a liberal as well as a technical education. Although there were various external pressures to move the training of nurses away from hospitals, according to Growe (1991), nursing education remained largely under hospital control for another 45 years.

Post-WWII Changes to the Profession

The third period of nursing, beginning at the end of the Second World War, brought major changes for nurses and the profession, including unionization, rationalization of health care, a new managerialism in hospitals, and a move from hospital-based nurse training to colleges and universities. Following the war, there was an expansion of the social welfare state and a growth of the health-care sector in Canada. In 1947, Saskatchewan established the first government-financed hospital insurance plan; a year later, the federal government provided incentives for new hospital construction. By the early 1950s, about one-third of Canadians had private hospital insurance and over one-quarter had some coverage for medical procedures. And in 1958, a federally financed hospital insurance plan was put into place. All these initiatives increased the demand for nurses: between 1941 and 1961, the number of nurses increased from 25 826 to 70 647 (Wotherspoon, 2009, p. 107).

---

2. The term 'rank and file' is frequently used in the labour context to refer to ordinary members who constitute the majority of workers in a group.

Theory Link
See Chapter 13 for a discussion of Saskatchewan's government-financed insurance plan and the development of Medicare.

By the 1950s and 1960s, nurses and nursing associations became more concerned with pay and working conditions. Nurses no longer embraced earlier notions of female obedience and self-sacrifice. Although nursing leaders took a cautious approach to collective bargaining and unionization, the majority of nurses became more vocal about their rights. The fact that most nurses were now employed in hospitals and shared similar experiences also made organizing easier. The move toward union certification and collective bargaining, however, occurred at different times throughout the country. The first group of nurses to negotiate an employment contract was through a professional organization in Quebec in 1939. In 1946, the British Columbia Nursing Association endorsed collective bargaining and the first hospital was certified in that year in Vancouver. However, Ontario nurses did not certify until 1966 (Nursing, n.d.; Coburn, 1988b). In 1973, a Saskatchewan court decision ruled that provincial associations could not act as bargaining agents for nursing employees because it was controlled by management nurses. This led to a separation between all-nurse unions and professional associations; the former engaged in collective bargaining for better wages and working conditions while the latter managed registration, discipline, and standards of practice (Growe, 1991, p. 105).

The Canadian Federation of Nurses Unions (CFNU) was founded in 1981 and is seen as the national voice for unionized nurses. With a membership of around 158 000, it represents nurses unions in nine provinces (all but Quebec), and also has a solid working relationship with Quebec nurses. Over 80 per cent of employed nurses belong to unions (Armstrong et al., p. 111). The CFNU is an active member of the Canadian Health Coalition, protesting against extra-billing, user fees, health cuts, privatization, and the move to a two-tier health-care system. As well, unlike doctors, nurses from the very beginning supported the creation of government-financed hospital and medical insurance. In 1998, the CFNU joined the Canadian Labour Congress (CLC) and works in solidarity with other labour unions to improve the social and economic well-being of workers and defend Canada's social programs. The CFNU has also expanded its ties internationally, i.e., with nurses' unions in other countries, most of whom are facing similar, and sometimes worse, threats to their occupation and to their health-care systems (Canadian Federation of Nurses' Union, 2010a).

Another significant milestone in nurses and nursing in Canada was the move away from hospital-based training first advocated in the 1930s. Change began only after a Royal Commission on Health Services in Canada in the 1960s indicted the nursing education system of the time as educationally unsound and inadequate for the needs of nurses and the health-care system. Besides recommending that nurse training be separated from hospitals, the Royal Commission's report suggested there be coordinated nursing education programs integrated with higher education systems in Canada and the provinces. In 1964, with the cooperation of the Ontario government, a nursing diploma program was established at Ryerson Polytechnic Institute. Just over a decade later, full-time enrolment in community college nursing programs increased dramatically. University degree nursing programs were gradually established. Although the pace of nursing educational reform, particularly at the university level, was initially slow, in part due to the limited commitments by governments and educational institutions, such reform was accelerated by the 1990s through extensive lobbying by the CNA (Canadian Nurses Association, 2000; Wotherspoon, 2009). Today, the educational concerns raised by the Royal Commission have been addressed, and nurses are making significant advances in becoming a university-trained workforce. Colleges and universities across Canada now have a series of collaborative agreements to deliver joint nurse training programs. As well, most provinces in Canada require a baccalaureate in nursing (BN or BScN) to enter the profession (Canadian Nurses Association, 2010). In 2004, nearly one-third of registered nurses had baccalaureate degrees. A number of universities in the country offer masters and doctoral level programs in nursing (Wotherspoon, 2009).

Although the attainment of a university degree represents an increased professional status for nursing, 'it does not guarantee that nurses will gain greater decision-making authority and autonomy' (Wotherspoon, 2009, p. 112). Cutbacks in health-care budgets, restructuring of hospitals to increase efficiency, and a new managerial style committed to applying industrial techniques to the health-care sector have had a significant impact on nursing today (Armstrong & Armstrong, 2003; Coburn, 1988b). Cost-cutting measures have increased managerial control; new scientific techniques based on **time and motion principles** were put into place to monitor care and force nurses to carry out more work in less time. As a means of saving money, nurses' time is rationalized, forcing nurses to give fewer and fewer services to more and more patients faster and faster (Growe, 1991, p. 75). The caring, comforting, and nurturing aspects of their job, which most nurses valued highly, are being undermined. Nursing work has become routinized and increasingly fragmented into discrete tasks that can be allocated to those with fewer qualifications who are paid lower wages. In talking about the impact of new managerial strategies on nursing practice, one nurse put it this way: 'You hit that ward at a run, and you're always having to say to people, "I haven't got time to do that. I'm sorry sir." And it's a horrible way to nurse' (cited in Armstrong et al., 2000, p. 91). Another nurse, explaining why she left hospital nursing, said that 'I was losing that human kind of touch and being able to hold someone's hand and give them that TLC that they need when they're going through a rough time, which you can't do 'cause you're running doing all the tasks' (pp. 95–96). Wendy Austin (2007) in her article, 'The McDonaldization of Nursing?', expressed the frustrations of nurses: 'This is not nursing; it's crowd control. It's like running a marathon, you have very little time to ever stop and breathe. There's not enough time for each person usually. There's never any time to stop either and just talk to the people and treat them like people instead of tasks' (p. 265).

time and motion principles

Introduced by F.W. Taylor in the second decade of the twentieth century to improve industrial efficiency. This involved breaking a job into component parts and measuring the length of time each task would take. It would become the benchmark for how long a particular activity should take.

The Nursing Workforce Today

As discussed in the previous section, nursing underwent major changes from the 1970s through the 1990s. Unionization spread rapidly; nurses went on strike; nursing professional associations actively promoted enhanced credentials and university education as the standard for nurses; nurses opposed medical hegemony and succeeded in gaining occupational autonomy; nurses condemned the 1986 doctor's strike in Ontario and lobbied in favour of the Canada Health Act; the CFNU along with other labour groups

instrumental approach

One in which a job is valued as a means to an end, not for its intrinsic worth.

registered nurses (RNs)

Nurses who coordinate health care, deliver direct services, and support patients in their self-care decisions.

nurse practitioners (NPs)

RNs with additional education qualifications and experience. They may order and interpret diagnostic tests, prescribe medications and other therapies.

licensed practical nurses (LPNs)

Nurses who assess patients and work in health promotion and illness prevention.

registered psychiatric nurses (RPNs)

Nurses who provide services to patients whose primary-care needs relate to mental and development health. They plan, implement, and evaluate therapies and programs on the basis of psychiatric nursing assessments. They are regulated separately from other nursing professionals in four provinces.

joined the Canadian Health Coalition to lobby in support of preserving and enhancing Medicare. Today, Coburn (1988b) argues, nursing is marked by both professional and instrumental orientations. Nursing is now viewed by many nurses as any other service job, and is largely approached in an **instrumental** manner. While a professional orientation based on altruism and dedicated service is still present in nursing, professionalization 'is clearly part of the struggle by nurses to escape hospital and physician control over the nursing labour process' (Coburn, 1988b, p. 452). A look at the nursing labour force today illustrates some of the current challenges that nurses face.

As of 2008 in Canada, the largest group of paid health-care professionals is regulated nurses. With a total workforce of 341 431, they account for one-third of the Canadian health-care workforce. This group is comprised of 261 889 (76.7 per cent) **registered nurses (RNs)**, including **nurse practitioners (NPs)**; 74 380 (21.8 per cent) **licensed practical nurses (LPNs)**; and 5162 (1.5 per cent) **registered psychiatric nurses (RPNs)**. Over the past five years, the annual average growth of the regulated nursing workforce was around 2.0 per cent. The ratio of practising nurses to practising physicians in the country in 2006 was 4.1, slightly lower than that of Japan (4.5) and the United States (4.3) (CIHI, 2010a).

The report prepared by the Canadian Institute for Health Information (CIHI) indicates that nursing remains overwhelmingly a female-dominated profession. In 2008, 94 per cent of registered nurses (RNs) in the country were female, a figure that hasn't changed significantly over the past five years. Male nurses were overrepresented in Quebec and the territories and of those employed in medicine/surgery.

The nursing workforce is aging, with an average age in the mid forties (45.1 for RNs). In 2008, those in the 40–60 age group constituted the majority of the workforce (58.3 per cent of the RN workforce). This is of some concern since there is already a shortage of nurses in the country and the situation is predicted to get worse as more nurses retire. Budget restraints led to restrictions in enrolments in nursing programs such that currently, there are not enough nurses graduating to keep up with the projected demand. The shortage is especially serious in northern, rural, and remote regions in Canada as well as in Aboriginal communities (Canadian Federation of Nurses' Union, 2010b).

Recent changes in funding to the health-care system have had a major impact on nurses' working conditions. Increased workload is one consequence of the government budgetary cutbacks and downsizing, beginning in the 1990s, that reduced the number of nurses graduating and the monies available to hospitals and community services for operating expenses. In an effort to control costs, hospital administrators hired more part-time and casual workers. In 2008, only 58.1 per cent of registered nurses were employed full-time. In some cases, nurses who worked part-time or in casual positions (41.8 per cent) did so by choice, but in other cases, nurses were unable to obtain full-time work. For those with young children, the lack of affordable child care or limited flexibility in the workplace also made full-time employment impossible. In our society, women remain predominantly responsible for family life. Nurses need flexible and innovative schedules that allow a female-dominated workforce to balance home and working lives and to meet unpredictable family-care needs (Canadian Nursing Advisory Committee, 2002). It is not surprising that female registered nurses were more likely than male RNs to have part-time employment (31.3 per cent versus 17.6 per cent, respectively). A substantial number of nurses, especially those employed in part-time or casual positions, work for multiple employers. In many cases the number of hours that part-time nurses work exceed the number of hours full-time nurses work; however, part-time nurses are unlikely to receive overtime rates or the same benefits that full-time nurses receive (Canadian Federation of Nurses' Union, 2010b; CIHI, 2010a). This suggests that rather than creating permanent jobs in response to the nursing shortage, employers are hiring nurses to work more hours (Armstrong & Armstrong, 2003, p. 108). In fact, a survey of Canadian nurses in 2005 found that nearly half of those surveyed reported that they usually worked unpaid overtime, for an average of four hours per week (Shields & Wilkins, 2006).

Reports and studies indicate that the working conditions of nurses today are stressful (Armstrong & Armstrong, 2003; Armstong et al., 2000; Austin, 2007; Canadian Nursing Advisory Committee, Final Report, 2002; Health Canada, 2007a; Shields & Wilkins, 2006). Reasons cited for this include the shortage of nurses, the intensity and complexity of patient care environments, government funding cutbacks, increased workload, fragmentation of nursing work, the increasing use of part-time and casual workers, application of time-motion principles to nursing care, and violence and abuse in the workplace:

> Nurses are working harder, caring for more individuals, and spending less time with each person. What has shrunk in this changing environment is the amount of time they have to assess, monitor and provide appropriate nursing care as well as be teachers, comforters and communicators. (Ontario Nursing Task Force Report 2000, quoted in Canadian Nursing Advisory Committee, 2002, p. 12)

New managerial strategies require nurses to do more in less time or to do more than one thing at a time; nurses end up working long shifts without breaks or working overtime in order to complete their work, which leads to stress and burnout. Over half (54 per cent) of nurses in a Canadian study reported that they often arrived at work early or stayed late in order to get their work done, and 62 per cent reported working through breaks (Shields & Wilkins, 2006). The need to work overtime results in fatigue, a major problem for nurses who work 12-hour shifts. It has been estimated that RNs work the equivalent of 7000 full-time jobs per year in overtime (cited in Canadian Nursing Advisory Committee, 2002, p. 14). Constant pressures in the job have an impact on nurses' physical and psychological health: the result is high absenteeism, burnout, turnover, and inefficiency. Due to illness and injury, the rate of absenteeism among nurses is 80 per cent higher than the Canadian average. Nurses are at a particularly high risk for illness, emotional exhaustion, and musculoskeletal injuries (Greenslade & Paddock, 2007). Over one year, overtime, absentee wages, and replacement for RN absentees cost between $962 million and $1.5 billion (Canadian Nursing Advisory Committee, 2002). Violence on the job (physical and sexual assault, verbal aggression, or emotional abuse) is of increasing concern to nurses: nurses are more at risk for assault than prison guards or police officers, with female nurses considered the most vulnerable, although male nurses were much more likely than female nurses to face physical assaults (Shields & Wilkins, 2006). The International Council of Nurses reported that 72 per cent of nurses did not feel safe from assault in their workplaces, and 95 per cent have been bullied (cited in Canadian Nursing Advisory Committee, 2002, p. 20). For example, Fernandes et al. (1999) found that over half of the staff at a Vancouver emergency department had been physically assaulted in a year and 90 per cent had been verbally abused at least once a week. Furthermore, 68 per cent reported an increased frequency of violence over time, and 60 per cent reported an increased severity. This increase in frequency and severity may be attributed to government funding cuts to hospitals, which has meant fewer doctors and nurses working in emergency departments. As a result, many patients have long waits to see a doctor or to receive treatment, sometimes leading to frustration and hostility. For example, in Fredericton, New Brunswick, it is not unusual to wait eight to ten hours to be seen by a doctor (except in acute situation, such as heart attacks and strokes).

A system-wide fiscal restraint that has restructured health care has meant fewer nurses to do more nursing; at the same time, they are expected to perform non-nursing tasks (Canadian Nursing Advisory Committee, 2002), all of which affects patient care. In a comparative study that included nurses in Canada, 42.9 per cent of Canadian nurses reported doing housekeeping duties; 43.6 indicated that they were unable to speak with and comfort patients because of time restraints (Aiken et al., 2001). As mentioned previously, these pressures have an impact on nurses' well-being. However, a reduced nursing staff and time pressures also have a negative impact on patient care. In their final report, the Canadian nursing advisory committee cites a decade of research that has shown a direct correlation between the ratio of nurses to patients and the health outcomes of those patients (Canadian Nursing Advisory Committee, 2002). Fatigue and understaffing can result in procedural errors. A study in Ontario (Hall et al., 2004), for example, found that the lower the ratio of professional nursing staff to patients in medical and surgical units, the higher the number of medication errors and wound infections. The data from a Canadian survey in 2005 (Shields & Wilkins, 2006) showed that nearly one-fifth of RNs acknowledged that in the year prior, errors in medication for patients in their care had occurred 'frequently' or 'occasionally'. The likelihood of error increased with the level of work overload. Similar findings are reported in an American study (Rogers et al., 2004).

There is little reason for optimism that things will improve in the near future; the economic recession and the dominance of neo-liberal discourse suggest it is unlikely that the current federal and provincial governments will find the necessary additional monies and resources to put into the public health-care sector. According to an interview with Dr Judith Shamian, president of the Canadian Nurses Association, there has been a shift in ideology away from making health care a major priority since the Harper government came into power. Her fear is that 'there's a larger political agenda to take health off the table so provinces can quietly invest less and get out of various health-care services they offer' (Gottlieb, 2009, p. 22). However, the politics surrounding health care are contested by groups such as the Canadian Health Coalition, who call for more government investment in health care.

Theory Link
See Chapter 13 for a discussion of politics and the Canadian health-care system.

Ongoing Tensions

The problems confronting Canadian nurses are not unique. The current shortage of hospital nurses in Western countries is expected to get worse as a result of job dissatisfaction and an aging workforce. It is projected that there will be a shortage of 113 000 RNs by 2016 in Canada (Basu & Gupta, 2007, p. 21). In a national study of nurses in Canada, about 12 per cent of both female and male nurses reported overall job dissatisfaction, compared to 8 per cent in the general employed population. Older nurses were more likely to be dissatisfied than younger nurses (Shields & Wilkins, 2006). A comparison of nurses' work in five countries—Canada, United States, England, Scotland, and Germany—indicates that nurses report similar systems of distress (Aiken et al., 2001). In every country except Germany, at least one-third of nurses reported that they were dissatisfied with their job; a significant percentage (29.4 per cent in Canada) of nurses under 30 were planning to leave their job within the year. A clear majority of nurses in Canada (63.6 per cent) and the United States (83.2 per cent) reported that a major problem, as a result of restructuring in hospitals, was the increased number of patients assigned to them combined with a rise in patient acuity levels. Over 60 per cent of nurses in all five countries reported that there were not enough registered nurses to provide high-quality care. Deterioration in patient care was most frequently reported in Canada and the United States—related, it appears, to the extensive hospital restructuring in both countries. As Aiken et al. (2001) conclude, the re-engineering and restructuring (to emulate industrial models of productivity) that have occurred in the health-care sector have negative outcomes for both nurses and patients.

Conclusion

Nurses are the cornerstone of our health-care system. However, their increasing patient caseload, which includes a greater number of patients who require complex and intensive care, creates major challenges and problems for them. How nursing is practised today is being defined by a **new managerialism** that has reduced nurses' autonomy. Corporate ideologies with an emphasis on efficiency, accountability, quantification, cost-driven decision making, and cutbacks in nursing staff and in other hospital workers impede nurses' everyday work and reduce the quality of patient care. In the view of Bernice Carter (2007), 'Nursing is subtly and insidiously being reformatted, re-engineered, processed to become something which may be efficient and effective in a managerial, commercial and business sense but which is unrecognizable as something nurses or patients genuinely wish to engage with' (p. 270).

A Canadian study by Varcoe et al. (2004, cited by Beagan & Ells, 2009) found that nurses struggled to enact their personal and professional values in a context where they were caught by the need to document and account for their work, discounting those aspects of care that were not quantifiable. Given the institutional emphasis on efficiency, nurses learned to ration their time and their care, but were deeply troubled by this approach to nursing. Nurses cited the health-care system as a constant source of ethical tension for it made them unable to provide the kind of care that compelled them to go into nursing in the first place (Beagan & Ells, 2009). One participant, irritated by the need to quantify everything, commented 'How do you measure emotional support? . . . that's ridiculous' (p. 99).

Critics have referred to the reorganization taking place within nursing as the **McDonaldization** of nursing (Austin, 2007). It is argued that a system that focuses on efficiency, quantification, calculability, predictability, and control to the detriment of individualized care transforms health care into a commodity. This imperative 'requires

new managerialism

A term that arose in the 1980s to describe a shift in the transfer of power from professionals (i.e., doctors) to management. It encouraged the implementation of industrial techniques that emphasized the achievement of measurable objectives, continuous evaluation of performance against defined objectives, rationing of resources using effectiveness criteria, and surveillance of health professionals (Beardwood et al., 1999).

McDonaldization

A term coined by George Ritzer to expand Weber's notion of rationalization; defined as the standardization of social life by rules and regulations, such as increased monitoring and evaluation of individual performance, akin to the uniformity and control measures used by fast-food chains. These principles are now applied to other sectors, both locally and globally.

that nurses, who are educated and committed to care for *people*, are expected to nurse the hospital *organization* (Austin, 2007, p. 266). The corporatization of the hospital entails the transfer of the culture of business to the hospital (Fried et al., 1987, cited in Barbara Beardwood et al., 1999, p. 367). There is even a new business language that frames patient satisfaction as 'customer service', and the chief administrator is now called a CEO. Importantly, this new language reflects a change in the conception of rights: from health care as a social right—that is, based on the collective right of citizenship—to health care as a consumer right (Beardwood et al., 1999, p. 367).

The situation of nursing in Canada must be viewed within a broader socio-economic and political context. It has been argued that the government's economic restraint policies, first implemented in the 1980s, are a major reason for the restructuring of hospitals and nursing care. A neo-liberal ideology held by the federal and provincial governments and the concomitant erosion of the welfare state has led to a reduction in state budgets and spending cuts, including cuts to health care. The results have had an impact on nurses' health and well-being and pose health and safety risks for patients. Dr Judith Shamian, president of the Canadian Nurses Association, fears that as of late 2008 we are entering a new world order with the international economic collapse; this collapse will have a major impact on poverty and other social determinants of health that equally affect health status and health-care systems (Gottlieb, 2009, p. 23). The nursing crisis is expected to continue for some time.

Summary of Main Points

- Historical developments in sociological theory have affected sociological views of nursing.
- Classic sociological and feminist interpretations of nursing have emphasized the overwhelming power of social structure at the expense of an account of nursing agency. Recent developments within sociology in general and feminist theory in particular have led to a refocus—away from structure and toward nursing agency and resistance.
- Changes in nursing must be viewed within a broader socio-economic and political context.
- Nursing emerged within the Nightingale tradition and in Canada has gone through three distinct phases.
- Until the 1960s nurses were educated within hospitals.
- The Canadian Nurses Association played a key role in promoting professionalization and higher credentials for nurses.
- Most nurses today are unionized and are supporters of universal Medicare.
- Cutbacks in health-care budgets in the 1980s led to a decline in nursing enrolments and to hospital restructuring.
- New managerialism has reduced the autonomy of nurses.
- The current shortage of nurses, heavy workloads, and stress on the job are all taking their toll on nurses' health and have negative implications for patient safety.

 ## Sociological Reflection: The Reorganization of Nursing Work

Some have suggested that the way nursing is organized today can be compared to the fast-food industry—i.e., what is referred to as the McDonaldization of nursing.

- Do you think that this is an appropriate analogy? If so, in what ways is it appropriate? Think of some empirical examples from your own experience or from the experience of others.
- If you do not think it is appropriate, why not? Can you give some specific reasons why you do not believe this analogy is accurate?

 ## Discussion Questions

1. How do you understand the term *agency* in the context of nursing work?
2. What social forces affect nursing today?
3. What are the major organizational challenges faced by nurses today?
4. What are the specific hallmarks of each of the three periods of nursing history?
5. How has nursing education changed over the past century?

6. What do you understand by the comment that nursing has been shaped by socio-economic and political forces?
7. Why have nurses supported the creation and retention of universal government-financed Medicare in Canada whereas the majority of doctors have not?
8. What is the impact of privatization on the provision of health care in Canada?

 # Further Investigation

1. In what other areas of health care, besides nursing, has there been a rationalization of health-care resources? Provide some empirical examples.
2. What has been said in the media about the crisis in nursing? Do you detect any bias in the media in terms of reporting on health issues?

 # Further Reading

Armstrong, P., Armstrong, H., & Scott-Dixon, K. (2008). *Critical to care: The invisible women in health services*. Toronto, ON: University of Toronto Press.

Armstrong, P., & Armstrong, H. (2003). *Wasting away: The undermining of Canadian health care* (2nd ed.). Toronto, ON: Oxford University Press.

Armstrong, P, Choiniere, J., & Day, E. (1993). *Vital signs: Nursing in transition*. Toronto, ON: Garamond Press.

Armstrong, P., Armstrong, H., Choiniere, J., Feldberg, G., & White, J. (1994). *Take care (warning signals for Canada's health system)*. Toronto, ON: Garamond Press.

Beardwood, B., Walters, V., Eyles, J., & French, S. (1999). Complaints against nurses: A reflection of 'the new managerialism' and consumerism in health care? *Social Science & Medicine, 48*, pp. 363–374.

Canadian Nursing Advisory Committee. (2002). *Our health, our future: Creating quality workplaces for Canadian nurses*. Health Canada, Ottawa, ON: Government of Canada.

Ehrenreich, B., & English, D. (1973). *Witches, midwives and nurses*. New York, NY: Old Westbury Feminist Press.

Growe, S. J. (1991). *Who cares: The crisis in Canadian nursing*. Toronto, ON: McClelland & Stewart Inc.

Rankin, J., & Campbell, M. (2006). *Managing to nurse: Inside Canada's health care reform*. Toronto, ON: University of Toronto Press.

Roberts, S. J. (1983). Oppressed group behaviour: Implications for nursing. *Advances in Nursing Science, 5*(4), pp. 21–30.

 # Web Resources

Canadian Institute for Health Information
www.cihi.ca/CIHI-ext-portal/internet/EN/Home/home/cihi000001

Canadian Nurses Association (CNA)
www.cna-nurses.ca/cna/

Canadian Federation of Nurses Unions
www.cfnu.ca/

Canadian Centre for Policy Alternatives (CCPA)
www.policyalternatives.ca

Canadian Health Coalition
www.healthcoalition.ca

Health Canada
www.hc-sc.gc.ca

CHAPTER 16

Complementary and Alternative Health Care

Gary Easthope & Jennie Hornosty

Overview

- How does alternative medicine differ from conventional medicine?
- Why is alternative medicine increasingly popular?
- Does alternative medicine work?

Conventional medicine is the dominant form of medicine because, historically, its practitioners organized themselves to lobby governments for special status. However, alternative forms of medical therapies and medicines are becoming increasingly popular, especially among those with higher education and higher incomes. The reasons are related to people's search for meaning, their distrust of science, the preponderance of chronic rather than acute illness, the personal relationship between healers and their clients, and the search for control over one's life. Users of alternative therapies and medicines do not reject conventional medicine but use both. Alternative therapies and medicines can work by changing the relationship of a person to his or her illness or by producing a change in a set of symptoms. There have been few scientific demonstrations using randomized control trials of the efficacy of alternative practices or medicines, but this is also true of most conventional medical practices. Some alternative practices are being incorporated into conventional medicine, and some alternative medical practices are being reclassified as complementary to, rather than alternative to, conventional medicine.

Key Terms

allopathy
apothecary
biomedicine/biomedical
   model
conventional medicine
complementary and
   alternative medicine (CAM)
convergence
eclectic
empirical
holistic/holism

homeopath/homeopathy
iatrogenesis/iatrogenic
integrative medicine/
   integrative health care
lifestyle choices/factors
mesmerism
naturopathic medicine
nosology/nosological
placebo effect
postmodern society/
   postmodernity

psychoneuroimmunology
randomized control trials
   (RCTs)
risk factors
risk society
social closure
social support
state
theodicy

Introduction

This chapter introduces the major arguments about alternative medicine and the **empirical** research conducted on alternative medicine. By the time you have completed reading the chapter, you should be aware that the simplistic distinction between the two medicines that sees the conventional as scientific and the alternative as so-called quackery is wrong. It will also become clear that the distinction between conventional practice and alternative practice has more to do with the relative political power and organization of the two types of medicine than it has to do with any characteristics of their modes of treatment.

The chapter is structured around three questions that are frequently asked by anyone—layperson, doctor, or sociologist—who is at all interested in alternative medicine. The first question—why is alternative medicine considered alternative?—explores what distinguishes alternative medicine from **conventional medicine**.[1] The answer provides a historical and political explanation rather than an explanation in terms of modes of treatment. The next question—why is alternative medicine increasingly popular?—is answered by looking at empirical research on the clients of alternative practitioners and at the market for **complementary and alternative medicine** (CAM) in the context of changes in society and the nature of illness today. An answer to the last question—does alternative medicine work?—requires a discussion of what it means for a treatment to work.

How Does Alternative Medicine Differ from Conventional Medicine?

As we saw in Chapter 12, conventional medicine is a recent social invention. In the early twentieth century, it was only one among a range of medical practices. Its theoretical base was that disease is a result of an imbalance in the body. To restore balance, something must be given or taken away. To decide what was given or taken, the doctor observed the symptoms and prescribed something to produce an opposite effect to those symptoms (a process known as **allopathy**). For example, up until 1884 a patient whose face was suffused with blood would be bled to reduce the blood in the body. Conventional physicians were committed primarily to treating the body (not the minds or spiritual aspects of their patients).

> **Theory Link**
> See Chapter 12 for a discussion of the history of conventional medicine.

Conventional Medicine

The practice base of conventional medicine was broader than its theory. Its practice was developed in the clinic or hospital. Here doctors observed large numbers of patients and began to develop classificatory schemes that grouped sets of symptoms into categories.

---

1. In the literature the term conventional medicine often is used interchangeably with orthodox medicine, allopathic medicine and biomedicine. In this chapter, conventional medicine will be the term generally used.

Sidebar definitions (left margin):

empirical

Describes observations or research that is based on evidence drawn from experience. Such research is, therefore, distinguished from something based only on theoretical knowledge or on some other kind of abstract thinking process.

conventional medicine

The medical practices and institutions developed in Europe during the nineteenth and twentieth centuries that are legally recognized by the state. Central to these practices is the teaching hospital, where all new doctors are inducted into laboratory science, clinical practice, and allopathic biomedicine. These practices and institutions are now dominant in nearly all parts of the world. Conventional medicine is also referred to as orthodox medicine or allopathic medicine.

complementary and alternative medicine (CAM)

Refers to the diagnosis, treatment, and/or prevention that complements mainstream medicine and that satisfies a demand not met by conventional approaches and is not generally reimbursed by health benefit plans. *Complementary medicine* refers to forms of care that are not in opposition to, and often are provided together with, conventional medicine. *Alternative medicine* refers to care used instead of conventional medical care.

Source: Simon Kneebone, reproduced with permission.

Initially such groupings were based upon immediately observable characteristics, and **nosological** schemes were developed that, for example, grouped fevers into different types—dependent on such symptom characteristics as their incidence over time—to produce the categories of continued, intermittent, or remittent fevers. In the nineteenth century, after Koch formulated a set of rules for determining conclusively whether a particular bacterium was the cause of a particular disease, such classifications became more sophisticated, and symptoms were used as indicators of underlying theoretical entities called 'diseases'.

The hospital, as well as providing doctors with large numbers of patients to observe, gave them much more control over their practice. Society physicians in nineteenth century Canada were employed by patrons and had to defer to their patrons' views and treat them accordingly. In the hospital, the doctor was employed by the hospital or the **state** and had to defer to his fellow doctors'[2] clinical judgment rather than that of his patient. In these circumstances, the empirical success of a treatment as judged by fellow doctors was more important than its congruence with allopathic theory.

Allopathy received a great boost in the mid-nineteenth century when Louis Pasteur discovered micro-organisms, thereby vindicating allopathic theory: toxic organisms invaded the body, upsetting its balance and causing symptoms that needed to be treated by attacking the invaders. Following Pasteur's lead, the application of laboratory science to medical practice was an outstanding feature of the development of conventional medicine in the latter half of the nineteenth century and during the early twentieth century. Modern medicine was thus created from a combination of allopathic theory, a focus on the body, empirical clinical experience, and laboratory science. This scientific, clinical, allopathic **biomedicine** became the conventional medicine only in the late nineteenth and early twentieth century. When Canada became a nation in 1867, for example, most people relied on home remedies or sought help from the more affordable and respected homoeopaths, chemists, Chinese herbalists, and spiritual leaders.

Conventional medicine did not become the dominant model because it had a better cure rate than other forms of medicine; rather, its practitioners were better organized and

---

2. Until the late nineteenth century, women in Canada were refused entrance into medical schools.

allopathy

A descriptive name often given to conventional medicine. Allopathy is the treatment of symptoms by opposites.

nosology/nosological

A branch of medicine that deals with the classification of diseases.

state

A term used to describe a collection of institutions, including the Parliament (government and Opposition political parties), the public-sector bureaucracy, the judiciary, the military, and the police.

biomedicine/ biomedical model

The conventional approach to medicine in Western societies, based on the diagnosis and explanation of illness as a malfunction of the body's biological mechanisms. This approach underpins most health professions and health services, which focus on treating individuals, and generally ignores the social origins of illness and its prevention.

more politically astute than practitioners in other forms of medicine, such as homoeopathy. Conventional practitioners successfully restricted or suppressed the activities of the more popular healers, such as **apothecaries**, **homeopaths**, and **eclectics**, and, through their affiliation with elite educational institutions, gained increased respectability that allowed them to restrict entry to the profession.

apothecary

A historical name for a pharmacist, that is, someone who specialized in compounding and distributing medicines and herbs.

homeopath/ homeopathy

An alternative medical practitioner. Homeopathy is a system of natural medicine that uses micro-doses of natural remedies from the plant, animal, and mineral kingdom to stimulate the body's self-healing abilities. It uses a holistic approach to treat the body and mind as a totality (What Is Homeopathy? 2009).

eclectic

A healer who combined various practices and beliefs from different schools to form an individualized therapeutic treatment plan (About Eclectic Therapy, n.d.).

Theory Link
For a more in-depth discussion of the emergence of medical dominance in Canada, see Chapter 12.

Attempts by conventional physicians to restrict who could legally practise medicine began in Canada as early as 1795. However, it was not until the beginning of the twentieth century that medicine consolidated its power over licensing, admittance to medical schools, and educational curriculum. The degree to which conventional doctors were able to control the work of other health practitioners varied among countries, but in most countries only conventional doctors can formally diagnosis disease, recommend medical treatment, and sign birth and death certificates. And generally only certified doctors are able to verify illness for work absence or insurance purposes; directly or indirectly, then, doctors affect the work of other health professionals.

The status of conventional medicine was further boosted by the improved morbidity and mortality rates of the twentieth century. Conventional medicine took credit for these improvements, although we know now that in countries like Canada these were primarily the result of clean drinking water, improved sewerage, and better nutrition rather than due to medical intervention (Butler-Jones, 2008).

Alternative Medicine

Complementary and alternative medicine encompasses a wide spectrum of practices, approaches, and beliefs. Broadly defined, CAM refers to the diagnosis, treatment, and/ or prevention that complements mainstream medicine, and that satisfies a demand not met by conventional approaches and is not generally reimbursed by health benefit plans (Health Policy Research Bulletin, 2003; Millar, 2001). Further, CAM refers to 'healing resources that encompasses all health systems, modalities, and practices and their accompanying theories and beliefs' that are not intrinsic to the dominant health system of a society (cited in York University Centre for Health Studies, 1999, p. 24). Although the boundaries between conventional medicine and CAM are not always fixed, there are some characteristics that are unique to CAM:

holistic/holism

An approach to health that considers all aspects of an individual—physical, emotional, mental, social, spiritual, and lifestyle—as interrelated and must be treated as such.

- It is **holistic**, meaning that all aspects of an individual—physical, emotional, mental, social, spiritual, lifestyle—are interrelated; therefore, treatment requires treating the whole person.
- CAM assumes healing is innate to the human body because it contains self-healing mechanisms; the role of a CAM practitioner is to stimulate this natural healing process.

- The patient is considered an active participant in the management of illness and needs to take personal responsibility for health.

Focus in CAM is on disease prevention and well-being (Smith & Simpson, 2003; York University Centre for Health Studies, 1999, pp. 25–27).

According to Health Canada, there are as many as 4000 different practices, disciplines, or areas catalogued as complementary and alternative health-care approaches (Smith & Simpson, 2003). Other sources suggest there are 200 to 300 different CAM therapies and practices (York University Centre for Health Studies, 1999). These range from complete systems of medicine, such as traditional Chinese medicine and Ayurvedic medicine, to specific interventions, such as craniosacral therapy, reiki, and herbalism. (See Table 16.1 for a list of selected CAMs.) Such diversity makes it difficult to measure CAM usage in a definitive manner since studies sometimes use different definitions and measures

TABLE 16.1 Complementary and Alternative Medicines

Category	Alternative Medicine	
Comprehensive systems	Ayuverdic medicine	Homoeopathy
	Anthroposophy	Naturopathy
	Herbalism	
Spiritual and mental	Faith healers	Past-life regression
	Spiritual healers	Primal regression
	Mental imaging	Transcendental meditation
Energy work	Acupuncture	Reflexology
	Acupressure	Reiki
	Crystal healing	Shiatsu
	Polarity	Therapeutic touch
Dietary therapies	Bach flower remedies	Macrobiotics
	Colonics	Pritikin diet
	Gerson therapy	Vitamin therapy
Manipulation	Alexander technique	Osteopathy
	Chiropractic	Rolfing
	Craniosacral therapy	Tai chi
	Feldenkrais	Trager
	Massage	Yoga
Diagnostics	Applied kinesiology	Kirlian photography
	Biorhythms	Psionics
	Iridology	Radionics
Other	Aromatherapy	Hydrotherapy
	Colour therapy	

Sources: Murray & Shepherd, 1993; Stanway, 1979; Trevelyan & Booth, 1994.

(Andrews & Boon, 2005). However, the general consensus is that CAM use appears to be on the increase.

Natural health products (NHPs) are a large and generally increasing part of the Canadian health-care reality (Simpson, 2003). A 2001 survey found that 75 per cent of Canadians regularly take natural health products, such as nutritional supplements like vitamins and minerals, herbal products, homeopathic medicines, and the like (cited in de Bruyn, 2002, p. 6). Use of NHPs varies depending on the region of the country: it is highest in British Columbia, where 41 per cent of respondents reported using three or more NHPs in the previous six months, as compared with 15 per cent of respondents in the Atlantic provinces (Simpson, 2003). This finding may be partially explained by the ethnic composition of the two regions. Many more people from Asian and South Asian countries, where there is greater receptiveness to complementary and alternative therapies, make British Columbia their home. Women, findings suggest, make greater use of NHPs than men (Simpson, 2003).

Whereas CAM practices are regulated individually and by each Canadian province, NHPs are regulated at the federal level. As a result of federal regulations that came into effect in Canada on January 1, 2004, the manufacture, sale, and importation of NHPs is subject to regulation if they are sold in Canada (Andrews & Boon, 2005). This was a critical development since many consumers and even some practitioners believe that NHPs are always safe, no matter how they are used (Smith & Marles, 2003).

The recognition of the growing use of CAM and NHPs has led policy-makers and conventional health-care practitioners to define these therapies and practices as an important issue for health-care systems. Among the concerns are how to regulate CAM professions and natural health products, how best to incorporate CAM treatments with conventional medicine, and how to protect the public from a wide range of possible CAM-conventional medicine interactions (Boon et al., 2006).

Complementary and alternative medicine use varies by factors such as gender, age, education, income, and number of chronic illnesses (de Bruyn, 2002; McFarland et al., 2002; Millar, 2001; Park, 2005). Surveys suggest that women are more likely to consult CAM practitioners even when the other mentioned factors are taken into account. There is also a gender difference in terms of which types of practitioners are consulted. While both women and men were equally likely to have visited a chiropractor, a much greater percentage of women reported consulting other alternative practitioners (Millar, 2001; Park, 2005). This gender difference may be explained in part by women's unique physiology and reproductive roles, which may lead them to seek natural solutions, such as to relieve nausea during pregnancy when prescription drugs are not an option. Women have been taught to be more health-conscious and are likely to read more health-care magazines where CAM and NHPs are discussed.

Theory Link
See Chapter 5 for gender issues related to health.

Research suggests that people between the ages of 25 to 64 are more likely than others to go to CAM practitioners. Most people in this age group are in the paid labour force and there is a greater likelihood that they have some disposable income or a supplementary private medical plan that would cover some of the costs of CAM. Indeed, ability to pay is a significant factor in determining who can and cannot consult a CAM practitioner (Kelner & Wellman, 1997). Not surprisingly, since provincial health plans do not cover the cost of most CAM treatment, individuals in the highest income groups are more likely to consult CAM practitioners than those in lower income categories: in 2003, 26 per cent as compared with 13 per cent (Kelner & Wellman, 1997). Concerns with appearance among young people, which can promote dieting and body-building, may be a factor that explains the finding that people aged 18 to 24 appear more likely to use natural health products.

There are a number of variables in differentiating CAM use. Those with a university or college degree tended to visit CAM practitioners more often (26 per cent) than those with less than a high school diploma (16 per cent) (Park, 2005). As with the use of NHPs, there are also significant regional differences in the usage of CAM. Use is much higher in Western provinces—British Columbia, Alberta, Saskatchewan, and Manitoba—than in the Atlantic region. Between three and nine per cent of people in the Atlantic region consulted complementary and alternative health care practitioners in 1998/99 compared to 21 to 25 per cent in the Western provinces (Millar, 2001). This variation may be partially explained by the different regulatory policies and different provincial health-care plans (Millar, 2001; Park, 2005). Cultural factors may also account for some of the difference. Another noticeable difference is that individuals' use of CAM practitioners increased as the number of chronic conditions rose. Conventional medicine is successful in dealing with acute illness, but it does not have cures or solutions for most chronic conditions, including chronic pain. Twenty-six per cent of those who suffered from chronic pain had used such CAM services compared with 15 per cent who did not report chronic pain (Millar, 2001, p. 17).

Theory Link
As discussed in Chapter 10, a significant number of Canadians suffer from one or more chronic conditions.

Today, conventional and alternative medicine exist side-by-side, much as they did in the nineteenth century. Although conventional medicine remains powerful and dominant, more people are consulting complementary and alternative medicine (CAM) providers. Conventional medicine has responded in various ways. In some instances, it has attempted to exclude CAM providers by seeking to categorize them as poorly trained quacks compared with conventional doctors. In other instances, conventional doctors use the alternative practices but rename them so that they sound as though they are 'scientific' practices and then restrict who can practise them. Thus, **mesmerism** was reformulated in the United Kingdom as hypnosis in the early years of the twentieth century, and was allowed so long as it was practised solely by certified doctors.

Increasingly, physicians today in Western countries are both tolerant of and interested in CAM. According to Hirschkorn & Bourgeault (2005), a systematic review by Astin et al. (1998) of 25 surveys found that roughly half of physicians believe in the value of at least one modality of CAM. The study revealed that 43 per cent of physicians make referrals for

mesmerism

A therapeutic system of hypnosis believed to be induced by animal magnetism. It was devised by Austrian physician Franz Anton Mesmer.

acupuncture, 40 per cent for chiropractic, and 21 per cent for massage. Some physicians in Canada and other Western countries incorporate alternative modalities into their practice. For example, at least some conventional doctors in British Columbia, Canada, include acupuncture as part of their treatment. The Association of Canadian Medical Colleges has agreed to include CAM content in Canadian undergraduate medical education programs (Caron & Simpson, 2003). A survey of 16 Canadian medical schools in 1999 showed that most schools included CAM in their curricula via lectures as part of a required course (Huang, 2004); as well, recent interviews with academic and community physicians from five regions across Canada all indicated their support for including CAM instruction in medical schools (Mulkins et al., 2006). The physicians interviewed felt that if universities were to train competent doctors, they needed to teach students about CAM since as future physicians they are likely to be confronted every day with questions about CAM from their patients. Since 2003, the medical school at Queen's University in Kingston, Ontario, has implemented a CAM Symposium, a full-day program with a series of lectures covering topics such as principles of traditional Chinese medicine, acupuncture, practices and principles of herbal medicine, chiropractic practice, reflexology, naturopathic medicine, and therapeutic values of meditation (Huang, 2004). The fact that a number of provinces in Canada have passed laws protecting physicians who practise alternative forms of medicine will increase the likelihood that more doctors will become involved with alternative therapies. The College of Physicians and Surgeons of Alberta has already created a system to register doctors who use alternative therapies if they have the required proof of proper training and education in the therapies (Silversides, 2002). New models of integrative health care that combine conventional medicine with CAM are being developed at two Canadian medical clinics (Boon & Kachan, 2008).

On the other hand, some CAM associations are emulating the strategy of conventional doctors to achieve a recognized professional status. Chiropractic has been particularly successful in this: it has set up colleges to train and certify its practitioners and practises usurpatory **social closure** by limiting chiropractic to these certified chiropractors, which it has achieved with the support of private health insurers and the state (Dew, 2000; O'Neill, 1994, 1995). Today, there are over 6500 practising chiropractors in Canada, comprising one of the largest primary-contact health-care professions in the country. Chiropractic treatment is reimbursed generally by private health insurance plans although there is some provincial health plan coverage in two provinces: Manitoba and Saskatchewan. Ontario and Alberta both recently delisted chiropractic from its list of insured services. Like medicine, chiropractic is a self-regulating profession. Each province and the Yukon Territory have a Chiropractic Act that establishes a self-regulatory process, including extensive testing for licensure (Canadian Chiropractic Association, 2011). There are only two accredited chiropractic schools in Canada, one in Ontario and one in Quebec; therefore, most Canadians wishing to become a Doctor of Chiropractic attend schools in the United States.

Naturopathic medicine is also striving for professional recognition through social closure by working to formalize education and qualification standards and thereby limit access to a restricted group of eligible practitioners. Naturopaths, however, are trained in a wide range of therapeutic modalities, which makes it problematic for them to create clear professional boundaries, an important step in the professionalization process (Verhoef el al., 2006). Nonetheless, naturopathic medicine has gained formal recognition, including provincial/territorial regulation, in five Canadian provinces: British Columbia,

social closure

A term first used by Max Weber to describe the way that power is exercised to exclude outsiders from the privileges of social membership (in social classes, professions, or status groups).

naturopathic medicine

A form of alternative medicine that uses natural methods and substances, such as nutritional supplements, exercise, and homeopathy, to support the natural power of the body to establish, maintain, and restore health.

Saskatchewan, Manitoba, Ontario, and Nova Scotia, and is soon to be regulated in Alberta. Other provinces and territories are actively pursing regulation (Canadian Association of Naturopathic Doctors, n.d). Currently there are over 1350 licensed naturopathic doctors in Canada; while some private health insurance companies reimburse patients a limited amount for naturopathic care, naturopathic treatment is not covered by provincial health plans. One of the challenges for naturopaths is to protect their profession from the services of lay natural practitioners and from a powerful biomedical system that is attempting to incorporate aspects of holistic health—e.g., acupuncture and biofeedback—into its own practice (Verhoef et al., 2006, p. 415).

Why Is Complementary and Alternative Medicine Increasingly Popular?

A simple survey of any undergraduate class is likely to find that a large majority of students have used some form of complementary and alternative health care or taken a natural health product in the past few years to treat an illness or injury or to promote well-being. You may have gone to a chiropractor or osteopath, had a massage or acupuncture, consulted a homeopath or naturopath, practised yoga or tai chi, or taken vitamins, herbal medicines, or nutritional supplements. Complementary and alternative medicine (CAM) comprises a wide range of modalities. Its popularity is indexed by the increasing number of people who are using alternative therapies, the increasing number of CAM therapists, the growing market for natural health products and medicines, and the increasing number of tertiary institutions offering training in various CAM therapies.

A section of the population has always used alternative therapies. For example, a survey in the US of 8758 families interviewed between 1928 and 1931 found that one in ten of the families were using alternative therapists (cited in Kaptchuk & Eisenberg, 2001). By the turn of the twenty-first century, 44 per cent of the population in the United States reported using an alternative therapy (Wolsko et al., 2002). A growing number of Canadians also report using natural health products or seeing a CAM practitioner. It is estimated that in 1998 Canadians spent $3.8 billion on CAM-related therapies and products (Simpson, 2003). An analysis of the Canadian National Population Health Survey indicates that 19 per cent of Canadians saw a CAM practitioner in 1998 to 1999, an increase of four percentage points over 1994 to 1995 (Millar, 2001; Simpson, 2003). Park (2005) reported that in 2003 the figure had increased to 20 per cent. CAM is used by some groups more than others. For example, one study in Toronto, Ontario, found that 78 per cent of people with HIV/AIDS had used some form of complementary therapy (Canadian AIDS Society, 1995, cited in Pawluch et al., 2000). This trend toward greater use of alternative medicine is evident in many other countries as well. (For a survey of usage in different places, see Ernst & White, 2000).

Various explanations have been posited for the growing number of people who use complementary and alternative medicine: that it is a search for meaning, that people distrust science, that there is a dissatisfaction with conventional medicine, that healers offer a more personal relationship than doctors, that CAM gives people a feeling of control, and that many illnesses today are not easily treated by conventional medicine because they are chronic or terminal. However, there is no one single reason that can explain why people choose CAM.

The Search for Meaning

Health and illness are fundamental issues that all societies face. Ways of explaining illness, suffering, and death (theodicies) are central to all religions and are a central part of any cosmology or explanation of the universe. In modern Western societies, the traditional religious cosmology that attributed illness to the work of the devil or original sin no longer has institutional support. Conventional medicine, the main institution to deal with illness, has no developed theory to explain illness except allopathy and the theory of germs. In a society in which few become seriously ill through germs but in which many suffer from heart attack or cancer, such conventional explanations have little appeal. Even within the germ theory there is no clear explanation of personal misfortune—why one person gets ill in a flu epidemic and another stays healthy. Under these circumstances, alternative medical theories that explain illness in terms of spiritual forces (spiritualism), the balance of elements in the body (yin and yang, naturopathy), or the development of life force (homoeopathy) have great appeal.

Because of its holistic approach to health, CAM therapies can provide individuals with emotional and psychological support as well as give attention to physical concerns. Patients who are chronically ill speak of their positive experience with CAM in helping them heal emotionally and spiritually, an important dimension of well-being. This is well illustrated in Pawluch et al.'s (2000) research with AIDS patients. Patients told the researchers that their experience with CAM had been transformative and had led to personal growth. As a result, they embraced more philosophical and metaphysical concerns about the meaning of life and death rather than focusing on everyday survival. One patient put it this way: 'It [AIDS] has saved my life . . . My priorities are different. My whole life is different. I'm pretty sure I would have taken a different route if it hadn't been for this gift of AIDS in my life' (Pawluch et. al., 2000, pp. 255–256).

Science has lost its gloss, and scientific medicine has declined in status along with it (Gray, 1999). Science is no longer seen as the solution but instead is frequently seen as part of the problem. The **risk society** (Beck, 1992) is obsessed with the risks created by scientific actions; the environment is seen to be under constant threat from global warming, oil spills, nuclear radiation, and acid rain, all of which are blamed on science and technology. Scientific medicine, moreover, has produced thalidomide as well as the bionic ear. The technological fix is increasingly mistrusted. For example, Fuschia Sirois and Mary Gick (2002) found that dissatisfaction with conventional medicine was one of the best predictors of overall and initial CAM use. Pawluch et al. (2000) found that their respondents described western medicine as 'dangerous', 'powerful', and 'toxic' (p. 257). They saw complementary therapies as less likely to have **iatrogenic** consequences and fewer debilitating side-effects.

risk society

A term coined by Ulrich Beck (1992) to describe the centrality of risk calculations in people's lives in Western society, whereby the key social problems today are unanticipated hazards, such as the risks of pollution, food poisoning, and environmental degradation.

iatrogenesis/iatrogenic

A concept popularized by Ivan Illich that refers to any adverse outcome or harm as a result of medical treatment.

The Personal Healer–Patient Relationship

Closely related to the previous point is the fact that many, although not all, healers provide a personalized service. They spend time listening to their clients and tailor their treatment to the individual client (Easthope, 1985; Lowenberg & Davis, 1994). This is in keeping with their underlying philosophy of holism, which requires treating the whole person (York University Centre for Health Studies, 1999). The patient is also considered an active participant in the management of illness and the healing process. CAM providers can also do this because their clientele are generally paying for the service themselves. In this way, many alternative practitioners are acting as the society physicians did in an earlier age but in a society in which many more people can afford to pay for such personal treatment.

The Search for Control over One's Life

In what some have described as today's **postmodern society**, much of life is felt to be outside the control of the individual. In response, people often search for areas of control. One such area is the self (Giddens, 1991). People seek to control their own bodies through jogging, gymnasiums, vitamins, and alternative therapies. Sirois & Gick (2002) found, for example, that the most frequently endorsed reason for people using CAM is that it allowed them to take a more active role in their health (p. 1032). Healers help people to manage their own disease by giving them the ability to reconstruct themselves. As one healer said in a lecture to his students, 'Be a reflection of the person you're treating . . . to be a more reliable, more secure part of themselves. So, you're the rock, absolutely dependable, absolutely competent, absolutely sure of everything you do and as you're reflecting them, they too can become sure of themselves' (Easthope, 1985, p. 62). This potential of CAM to help people transform their lives is clearly illustrated in the interviews Pawluch et al. (2002) conducted with AIDS patients. The relation between illness and the level of control people have over their life is now also becoming recognized by conventional medicine (see Marmot et al., 1997).

postmodern society/ postmodernity

A disputed term in sociology that broadly refers to a society or social condition following modernity in which many of the key social institutions, including the state, unions, and professions, have lost their power to determine social outcomes as tradition is replaced by a high level of social differentiation and cultural diversity.

The Nature of Illness: Chronic versus Terminal

The success of environmental controls over sewage and water—coupled with immunization, vaccination, and antibiotics—has meant that most illness in modern societies is either chronic or terminal. By definition, neither of these states can be cured. In these circumstances the traditional practice of conventional medicine is relatively useless. Furthermore, its procedures and the mode of payment for those procedures—the clinical examination followed by clinical intervention to produce cure—do not allow for treatment of chronic or terminal illness, both of which require long-term, intermittent intervention rather than one-stop cures. People are therefore turning to those healers who do offer such a long-term relationship: the complementary and alternative practitioners.

Empirical research in Canada (Kelner & Wellman, 1997; Millar, 1997; Pawluch et al., 2000; Sirois & Gick, 2002), the United Kingdom (Ernst & White, 2000; Sharples et al., 2003), New Zealand (Sawyer et al., 1994), Israel (Shmueli & Shuval, 2004), Japan (Yamashita et al., 2002), the US (Bausell et al., 2001; Druss & Rosenhek ,1999; Ni et al., 2002), Italy (Menniti-Ippolito et al., 2002), and Australia (Lloyd et al., 1993; MacLennan et al., 1996; Siahpush, 1998) supports most of these arguments, although different studies focus more on one aspect than another. Those using alternative practitioners are seeking explanations for their health problems. They are worried about the dangers of medical intervention and prefer alternative medicine because it is seen as drug-free and natural, and they appreciate the personal attention they get from alternative practitioners. They also seek control over the methods of dealing with their illness and, when dealing with doctors, want control over treatment decisions. Some look to alternative medicine as a positive choice that offers

lifestyle choices/ factors

The decisions people make that are likely to impact on their health, such as diet, exercise, smoking, alcohol, and other drugs. The term implies that people are solely responsible for choosing and changing their lifestyle.

a natural, holistic approach and a sense of individual responsibility. That is, they see it as a **lifestyle choice** (Lloyd et al., 1993; MacLennan et al., 1996; Thomas et al., 1991).

In brief, then, it appears that individuals use complementary and alternative medicine for many reasons, including a preference for the natural, an appreciation of personal attention, and a desire for control over treatment. Some turn to alternative therapies and medicines when conventional medicine fails to alleviate their symptoms. Users of CAM can not be treated simply as a homogenous group with similar beliefs, motivations, and needs (Sirois & Gick, 2002, p. 1036). In the words of Pawluch et al. (2000), 'there is no simple explanation for the appeal of complementary therapies. The picture is too complex and varied . . . Individuals are attracted to these therapies for a variety of reasons' (p. 262). Although this statement is made in the context of those who have AIDS, the same can be said of all users of CAM. The meanings that individuals ascribe to complementary therapies are shaped by individuals' social characteristics and change over time.

Does Alternative Medicine Work?

The question of whether alternative medicine works is much more complex than it would at first appear. An intervention by a healer can be said to work in three analytically distinct ways (although these ways often overlap empirically):

1. It changes the relationship of individuals to their afflictions so that they feel more comfortable, suffer less pain, and are able to manage their normal daily lives.
2. It produces a clinically observable change in a set of symptoms.
3. It produces a change in a set of symptoms that is scientifically demonstrated to be a function of the intervention.

randomized control trials (RCTs)

A biomedical research procedure used to evaluate the effectiveness of particular medications and therapeutic interventions. *Random* refers to the equal chance of participants being in the experimental or control group (the group to which nothing is done and is used for comparison), and *trial* refers to the experimental nature of the method. It is often mistakenly viewed as the best way to demonstrate causal links between factors under investigation, but it privileges biomedical over social responses to illness.

These three ways of working can be observed in both alternative and conventional medicine. Only a small proportion of conventional medical interventions—estimated as 15 per cent (Coleman, 1994)—have been scientifically tested via **randomized control trials (RCTs)**, and the Cochrane collaboration (Berman et al., 2000) reports that only 21 per cent of conventional medicine's practices have a clearly positive effect. However, an even smaller proportion of complementary and alternative practices has been scientifically tested. Let us look at each of these three ways of working in turn, focusing solely on CAM, and speculate on how CAM works in each instance. In the first instance—in which the individual's relationship to his or her affliction is changed—there is a redefinition of the patient's bodily or mental state as one in which healer and client agree that a healing has taken place. In a study of spiritual healing groups, healings in such groups were seen as

> events that rely on 'rhetorics' of healing that encourage persons to define and redefine problems within idioms that are appropriate to healing [and] that healing must be understood in terms of treatment of lifestyle . . . the realization of meaning attributed to a symptom . . . or the awakening into a religious world view . . . rather than the treatment of a pathology. (Glik, 1990, pp. 162–163).

theodicy

An explanation of suffering, evil, and death.

In these terms, healing works by providing a **theodicy**, an explanation for the affliction, which enables the afflicted to deal with it.

There is little doubt that, in terms of clinical efficacy, many CAM healing practices work. Why they work is unclear, but that is equally true of many conventional healing practices. Two possible explanations of such clinical efficacy have been advanced: the **placebo effect** and the operation of social support (including the activation of the immune response through such support).

The placebo effect is any therapeutic practice that has no clear physiological effect but that nevertheless has an effect on the patient: pain and other symptoms go away ('Sugaring the Pill', 1996). Work on the placebo response has demonstrated that the key features that produce a placebo effect are a feeling of uncertainty in the patient coupled with trust in the authority of the healer. People go to a healer—conventional or alternative—when they are uncertain of their own diagnosis and prognosis and are seeking expert advice and aid. When that healer presents as an authoritative person who gives them personal attention and who is, therefore, someone that patients feel they can trust, a placebo response is very likely. Most alternative practitioners, and many conventional practitioners, present themselves in precisely this way (Easthope, 1985). However, meta-analyses of clinical interventions using acupuncture, herbal remedies, manual therapies, and nutritional therapies have found they are more effective for certain conditions than placebos are—for example, echinacea for relief of cold symptoms (Barrett et al., 1999) and acupuncture for post-operative nausea (Berman et al., 2000). A placebo response is consequently not an adequate explanation for the success of some CAM therapies.

Social support has been proven to be an important variable in illness. It has been implicated in the sociological view of the *causes* of affliction since Émile Durkheim (1951/1897) demonstrated in 1897 that apparently individual acts of suicide produced suicide rates that varied according to the levels of such support (what he called 'social solidarity'). A similar finding was made in a comparative analysis of modern societies (Wilkinson, 1996), which found that social cohesion is a central factor in producing good health for populations. An extensive summary of the literature argued that 'social relationships, or the relative lack thereof, constitute a major **risk factor** for health—rivaling the effects of well-established risk factors such as cigarette smoking, blood pressure, blood lipids, obesity and physical activity' (House et al., 1988, p. 541). It is now also becoming clear that social support may be implicated in the *relief* of affliction. A recently completed meta-analysis of 87 studies on the associations of perceived social support, network size, and marital status with cancer survival concluded that high levels of perceived social support and large social networks reduced the risk for mortality in cancer patients (Pinquart & Duberstein, 2010). Other studies of the survival rates of women with breast cancer also report that social support is an important variable (Maunsell et al., 1995; Waxler-Morrison et al., 1991). David Ornish, an American physician, uses social support (along with diet and exercise) in a regimen that produces changes in the hearts of his patients, which are demonstrable in angiograms (Ornish, 1990; Ornish et al., 1990). A biomedical, rather than a sociological, explanation of these effects is provided by **psychoneuroimmunology (PNI)** (see Vijoen et al., 2003). What the theory of PNI does is to reduce the social to the biological. Proponents of PNI argue that social effects cause changes in the immune system of individuals, and that these changes mean that people are less likely to become ill and more likely to recover when they are ill (see, for example, the study of HIV-positive men by Persson et al., 2002).

There have been few scientific tests of alternative medicine. One reason for this is the different world view held by many alternative practitioners. Many are not concerned

placebo/placebo effect

Any therapeutic practice that has no clear clinical effect. In practice it usually means giving patients an inert substance to take as a medication. When a patient reacts to a placebo in a way that is not clinically explicable, this is called the 'placebo effect'.

social support

The support provided to an individual by being part of a network of kin, friends, or colleagues.

risk factors

Conditions that are thought to increase an individual's susceptibility to illness or disease, such as abuse of alcohol, poor diet, and smoking.

psychoneuroimmunology (PNI)

A study of the interaction between psychological (mental) processes and the body's nervous and immune systems, using an interdisciplinary approach that incorporates a number of scientific and medical disciplines.

with cure but, rather, with healing and thus do not accept the scientific criteria of cure. Further, their strong emphasis on a holistic approach to illness and health means they are unwilling to treat groups of people in exactly the same way, which means that a treatment group cannot be compared with a control group to test a treatment's efficacy. However, the Research Council on Complementary Medicine in the United Kingdom has argued that conventional randomized control trial methodologies can be used to assess alternative therapies (Berman et al., 2000; Mason et al., 2002); some such trials have been undertaken. The journal *Focus on Alternative and Complementary Therapies* (FACT) is using similar methods to the Cochrane collaboration to assess the clinical effectiveness of alternative therapies and medications.

Conclusion: Future Directions

'Canada is home to some of the pathbreaking researchers of CAM' and increasingly more researchers are using a variety of disciplinary perspectives and methods to study CAM in the medical, health professional, and social sciences (Andrews & Boon, 2005, p. 25). The Canadian Interdisciplinary Network for Complementary and Alternative Medicine Research (IN-CAM), funded by the Canadian Institutes for Health Research, was recently established. Andrews and Boon point out that this reflects both government support and priorities. An interesting feature of recent publications on the working of alternative treatment modalities is the increasing interest being shown in such modalities by conventional practitioners in many countries (Astin et al., 1998; Boon & Kachan, 2008; Easthope et al., 2000a, b; Goldbeck-Wood et al., 1996; Hollenberg, 2006; Kelner et al., 2004; Pirotta et al., 2000; Verhoef & Sutherland, 1995a, b).

Conventional doctors are incorporating alternative treatment modalities into their practice of medicine and making judgments of the efficacy and safety of such treatments (Easthope et al., 2000a, b; Hirschkorn et al., 2009; Wong & Neill, 2000). For example, in the 2007 Canadian National Physician Survey, 2.8 per cent of family practitioners/general practitioners indicated that they provided acupuncture to their patients, and 1.8 per cent performed hypnosis as part of their practice (Canadian Medical Association, 2007). In the 2004 survey, in response to a more general question, 6.7 per cent of family practitioners indicated that alternative/complementary medicine was part of their practice (Canadian Medical Association, 2004). Using a random sample of general practitioners in Ontario and Alberta, Verhoef and Sutherland (1995a) found that 54 per cent made referrals to alternative practitioners and 16 per cent practised some form of alternative medicine. In Australia, one in seven GPs uses acupuncture (Easthope et al., 1999), and many doctors are using other complementary therapies or referring patients to other therapists, both medical and nonmedical, for such treatments (Easthope et al. 2000b; Hall & Giles-Corti, 2000; Pirotta et al., 2000). In response to this interest, most medical schools in Canada and the US and over half of those in the United Kingdom now teach their trainee doctors about complementary and alternative medicine (Lewith, 2000; Mulkins et al., 2006; Ruedy et al., 1999; Verhoef et al., 2004), as do many European medical schools (Barberis et al., 2001).

GPs in particular are looking to CAM therapies to re-establish their role, which is being eroded by increased competition for patients among GPs and the development of corporate medicine backed by the state (Strasser, 1992; White, 2000). CAM practices, with their emphasis on holism, are a tempting route for those wishing to avoid this fate. In the marketplace for medical treatment, as in the commercial marketplace, one way to deal with the opposition is to mount a takeover bid (Saks, 1994). Nurses, too, have seen advantages in adopting CAM modalities: the emphasis on care rather than cure, which is a major aspect of CAM, is a means of extending their professional role (Adams & Tovey, 2004).

The result is that complementary and alternative medicine is becoming less and less alternative. Some (Willis, 1989a) have argued that there is a **convergence** between conventional medicine and CAM, but such convergence, if it is occurring in clinical medicine, is very weak (Bombardieri & Easthope, 2000). Rather, for some practitioners, both conventional and otherwise, CAM is being reclassified as complementary medicine—acting as a complement to conventional medicine. A good example of this is the way complementary therapists are used in the Israeli hospital system, where they concentrate on patients' subjective feelings and quality of life, leaving biology to the orthodox practitioners (Shmueli & Shuval, 2004; Shuval et al. 2002). However, if convergence is weak in clinical practice it is very strong in the area of CAM. Where the market is the primary driving force, there has been considerable convergence, with most natural health products/alternative medicines now produced by conventional pharmaceutical companies (Collyer 2004).

One indication that conventional health-care practitioners are less resistant to CAM than earlier is the growing move toward what is being called integrative health care or **integrative medicine**. Among both conventional and CAM practitioners, attention has shifted away from separating therapeutic practices into being either biomedical or alternative toward a focus on merging diverse modalities into a new integrative health system (Boon & Kachan, 2008; Hollenberg, 2006). Both patients and clinicians feel that integrative medicine is the best way to provide optimal health care (Boon & Kachan, 2008). Research at different integrative health-care clinics in Canada suggests that despite some problems and limitations integrative medicine does work (Boon & Kachan, 2008; Hollenberg, 2006). The success of this approach depends on a number of factors, including having credible champions to facilitate programs at an institutional level, having staff members who are receptive to different approaches, and developing trust and respect between the practitioners (Boon & Kachan, 2008).

Despite the use of terms such as *complementary* and *integrative*, it is unlikely that the demarcation between conventional biomedicine and alternative medicine will ever disappear completely. In his study of two recently established integrative health-care clinics in the country, Hollenberg (2006) found that biomedical physicians used exclusionary closure techniques and demarcationary strategies to maintain dominance in health care; similarly, CAM practitioners used usurpationary strategies by evoking esoteric knowledge and credentialism to increase their status. While both biomedical and CAM practices were validated to various degrees in the clinics, conventional medicine continues to maintain its dominance. However, there is no longer a clear battlefront in which doctors are pitted against so-called quacks but, rather, an emerging era of cooperation, in which orthodoxy gradually shades into alternative practice.

convergence

The process, which may or may not be occurring, whereby conventional medicine adopts many of the practices of alternative medicine, and alternative medicine acts to become more conventional by, for example, seeking to license practitioners and make them subject to training.

integrative medicine/ integrative health care

Generally refers to health practitioners with different backgrounds and training working together, although the precise meaning is contested.

Summary of Main Points

- Conventional medicine dominates because, historically, it has been better organized politically than other forms of medicine.
- Complementary and alternative medicine (CAM) is increasingly popular because it provides an explanation of illness, because more people now distrust scientific expertise, and because CAM practitioners appear to cope with chronic and terminal illness better than conventional medicine and they provide more personalized attention. CAM also helps people to believe that they are in control of their illness.
- CAM usage varies by factors such as gender, age, geographical location, and the presence of chronic illness.
- Users of complementary and alternative medicine also use conventional medicine.
- Alternative medicine works by changing the relationship of people to their illnesses through the placebo effect (which is also important in conventional medicine), through the provision of social support, and through other means that are not yet clear (Lewith 1999).
- There have been few scientific tests of the efficacy of CAM, but neither has most orthodox medical practice been subject to scientific testing.
- Many conventional doctors, especially general practitioners, are incorporating CAM treatment methods into their practices and referring patients to CAM practitioners.
- Many natural health products are produced by pharmaceutical companies.
- Integrative medicine, which combines conventional and alternative modalities whereby practitioners work together, is becoming more commonplace.

 ## Sociological Reflection: Alternative or Complementary?

Three health clinics are operating in your town or city. One centre offers the full range of complementary and alternative (CAM) therapies delivered by qualified alternative practitioners. The second is a medical clinic, where doctors practise a number of complementary and alternative therapies, such as spinal manipulation, acupuncture, and naturopathy. The third is an integrative health clinic at which both conventional and CAM health professionals practice side-by-side.

- If you were to use a CAM therapy, which clinic would you visit? Why?
- Have you used CAM therapies? Why or why not?
- Is the process of convergence between conventional medicine and CAM an example of social closure to protect medical dominance or an indication of a more patient-focused medical practice?

Discussion Questions

1. Which complementary and alternative medical practices are most likely to be accepted into conventional medicine? Why?
2. CAM therapies are mainly used by people who have good incomes and can afford to pay the fees. Should the government subsidize some CAM practices so that people on low incomes can use them? If so, which practices should be subsidized, and why?
3. Placebos work even when people know that they are placebos. What are the implications of this for conventional medical practice and for CAM practices?
4. What are the main features of practitioner–client or doctor–patient interaction that would convince afflicted individuals that they are being treated on a personal level?
5. Does CAM provide therapies that could be adopted by nurses or other health workers to improve their practice? If so, which therapies would be most useful?
6. Which CAM therapies (or medicines) would be attractive to different types of people?
7. Do integrative health-care clinics provide better patient care than either conventional medicine or CAM used alone?

 Further Investigation

1. Compare any one complementary and alternative medical therapy (e.g., acupuncture) with any one conventional therapy (e.g., fixing a broken wrist). In making your comparison, you should examine the mode of diagnosis, the role of technology in treatment, the types of therapists involved in treatment, and the institutions in which treatment occurs.
2. Compare and contrast the way conventional medicine and CAM are portrayed in the media. Make comparisons in only one type of media (television, radio, newspapers, or magazines).

 Further Reading

Bombardieri, D., & Easthope, G. (2000). Convergence between orthodox and alternative medicine: A theoretical elaboration and empirical test. *Health, 4*(4), pp. 479–494.

Collyer, F. (2004). The corporatisation and commercialisation of CAM. In P. Tovey, G. Easthope, & J. Adams (Eds.), *The mainstreaming of complementary and alternative medicine.* London, UK: Routledge.

Dew, K. (2000). Apostasy to orthodoxy: Debates before a commission of inquiry into chiropractic. *Sociology of Health and Illness, 22*(3), pp. 310–330.

Health Policy Research Bulletin. (2003, November). *Complementary and alternative health care: The other mainstream?* (Issue 7). Ottawa, ON: Health Canada.

Hollenberg, D. (2006). Uncharted ground: Patterns of professional interaction among complementary/alternative and biomedical practitioners in integrative health care settings. *Social Science & Medicine, 62*, pp. 731–744.

Kelner, M., Wellman, B., Boon. H, & Welsh, S. (2004). Responses of established healthcare to the professionalization of complementary and alternative medicine in Ontario. *Social Science & Medicine 59*, pp. 915–930.

Kelner, M., Wellman, B., Welsh, S., & Boon, H. (2006). How far can complementary and alternative medicine go? The case of chiropractic and homeopathy. *Social Science & Medicine, 63*, pp. 2617–2627.

Pawluch, D., Cain, R., & Gillett, J. (2000). Lay constructions of HIV and complementary therapy use. *Social Science & Medicine, 51*, pp. 251–264.

Siahpush, M. (1998). Postmodern values, dissatisfaction with conventional medicine and popularity of alternative therapies. *Journal of Sociology, 34*, pp. 58–70.

Vincent, C., & Furnham, A. (1998). *Complementary medicine: A research perspective.* Chichester, UK: Wiley.

York University Centre for Health Studies. (1999). *Complementary and alternative health practices and therapies—A Canadian overview.* Prepared for Health Promotion and Programs Branch, Health Canada.

Web Resources

CAMline
www.camline.ca/about/about.html

Canadian College of Naturopathic Medicine (CCNM)
www.ccnm.edu

Canadian Interdisciplinary Network for Complementary & Alternative Medicine Research (IN-CAM)
www.incamresearch.ca/index.php?home&lng=en

Canadian Chiropractic Association
www.chiropracticcanada.ca/en-us/home.aspx

National Center for Complementary and Alternative Medicine (NCCAM)
http://nccam.nih.gov/

Health Canada: Natural Health Products
www.hc-sc.gc.ca/dhp-mps/prodnatur/index-eng.php

The Society of Homeopaths
www.homeopathy-soh.org/

Conclusion

'Freedom is not merely the chance to do as one pleases; neither is it merely the opportunity to choose between set alternatives. Freedom is, first of all, the chance to formulate the available choices, to argue over them—and then, the opportunity to choose. . . . The future is what is to be decided—within the limits, to be sure, of historical possibility. But this possibility is not fixed; . . .'

— C. Wright Mills, *The Sociological Imagination* (1959, p. 174)

Issues of health, illness, and health care are of central concern to Canadians, both at an individual and a societal level. In this book, we have provided you with an introduction to health sociology and with a sample of the diversity of topics and approaches that comprise the general field. The book is divided into three substantive parts plus a general introduction, with each part focusing on somewhat different areas that pertain to the study of health and illness. The Introduction, which includes three chapters, introduces you to the social model of health and different theoretical approaches, concepts, and methodologies sociologists use to study health, illness, and health care. Chapter 1 sets the foundation for understanding and applying a sociological analysis to health-related issues; we introduce you to what C. Wright Mills (1959) calls 'the sociological imagination', an analytical framework for understanding the relationships between individual experience, social structure, and history. The interrelationship between structure and agency as components of human life is emphasized. This entails a critical approach that looks at how our health and health-care systems are influenced by factors outside our immediate control, that is, social, economic, and political forces, yet does not lose sight of the fact that human beings, acting collectively, construct society.

Part 1, comprised of five chapters, examines different social determinants of health and looks at how social inequalities perpetuate other forms of inequality: in particular, health inequalities among different individuals and groups. This approach shows the importance of the social model of health as an alternative to conventional understandings of health and illness drawn from biomedical approaches. Many of the questions raised in this section have been guided by a critical political economy analysis that seeks to understand how health inequalities are produced. How is our society organized and how does it distribute material resources among its members? Why is it that members of some social groups live longer and healthier lives than others? It is suggested that structured inequality produces inequality of conditions and differential opportunities and life chances, which in turn determines one's health status. The focus is on understanding the complexity of illness-inducing and health-enhancing environments, by considering social determinants of health, social contexts, environments, and social relations. Various dimensions of inequality—such as income, gender, Aboriginal status, and racialization, as well as the environment in which one lives—are explored as having significant impacts on health.

In making the case that social inequality is a determinant in health status and experiences of health and illness, sociologists focus on socio-structural factors that influence people's behaviour. However, this is not to suggest a type of social determinism whereby individuals are viewed as puppets. While a critical sociological perspective places individual behaviour, beliefs, and experiences in a social context, it acknowledges equally that it is people who bring about changes in society. The structure–agency debate introduced in

Chapter 1 makes us aware of the interdependence of individuals and their social environments. To paraphrase Karl Marx, 'people make their own history, but they do not make it as they please; they do not make it under self-selected circumstances, but under circumstances existing already, given and transmitted from the past' (Marx, 1869/1959, p. 320). The important thing to remember is that social structures are human creations that are produced, reproduced, and changed by our actions or inactions.

Part 2 looks at the way aspects of human life are socially constructed, that is, the ways people actively make the societies in which they live and the ways they give meaning to their actions. This approach suggests that human life and the way we interact is neither natural nor inevitable and puts more emphasis on the role of human agency in everyday life. How, then, do people perceive, understand, and respond to health- and illness-related events? The three chapters in this section consider topics such as how notions of illness vary over time, the process by which this occurs, and the interpretations people give to their experiences. More specifically, this section examines the concept of medicalization, that is, how nonmedical problems or behaviours once considered part of everyday life come to be defined and treated as medical issues; how illness and disability are socially constructed; and how aging and dying are social processes.

The interrelationship between structure and agency is illustrated again in the final section of the book. Part 3 looks at questions related to the social organization and delivery of health care, and considers the role that values, power, and ideology have played in shaping our health-care systems and options. An underlying question in each of the five chapters is to understand why our health system is organized in a particular way and how it could be otherwise. We see in this section the dominant influence the medical profession has had on health policy, on other health professions, and on health-care delivery. The power and influence of the pharmaceutical industry on health policy and drug approvals is also explored. While this section addresses socio-structural factors in shaping health care, it also points to human agency in bringing about institutional change. Canada's health-care system today is a product of individuals challenging the hegemonic control of medicine over health-care delivery.

Future Trends

Health and health-care delivery remain an enduring societal and governmental concern. There is reason to suggest, however, that future research trends in health sociology will be influenced to a large degree by government priorities. Most of the research today is funded by the Canadian Institute for Health Research (CIHR), a government agency created in 2000 that reports to the minister of health. An indication of CIHR's health research priorities is apparent in the 13 research networks (institutes) it has created to work on particular health issues. In addition to institutes with a biomedical focus, i.e., genetics, cancer research, and circulatory and respiratory health (the three leading causes of death in Canada), there are research networks to address the societal, cultural, and environmental dimensions of health: for example, Aboriginal people's health, gender, and population and public health. Some concerns, however, have been raised that CIHR has pulled social health research toward neo-positivism and that social determinants of health research will become a form of epidemiology, lacking a critical social dimension. At the same time in Canada, we have seen a progressive dismantling of the social welfare state and the emergence of neo-liberalism, which is likely to produce greater health inequalities in the country. The potential effect of globalization on health and illness is also of concern. The impact of these social forces in perpetuating inequalities and inequities, and their affect on health and health care as well as the Medicare debate will continue to be of major interest to critical health researchers working within a political economy tradition. Given Canada's cultural and ethnic diversity and its aging population, health sociology will continue to explore questions of meaning and different people's subjective experiences of illness. Addressing the dismal status of Aboriginal people's health and the impact of racialization and social exclusion on health is certain to be another significant focus in the years to come.

Critical Thinking and Developing Your Sociological Analysis Skills

As we have shown in our consideration of various health-related topics, thinking sociologically requires us to challenge beliefs that are taken for granted, as well as commonsense understandings of reality. The beginning point for a critical sociology is to ask the question 'Why?'. It is to wonder whether things could be otherwise; it frequently requires that we detach ourselves from the prevailing attitudes of the dominant groups to gain a level of understanding that goes beyond conventional perspectives. The following two cases are intended to suggest how you might use some of the sociological skills that you have learned to critically evaluate everyday accounts of two current health-related issues.

Frequent stories in the Canadian media have centred on the question of body weight and obesity. For example, here is a recent front-page headline from *The Globe and Mail* (January 15, 2011), Canada's 'national newspaper': 'How We've Lost the War on Fat'. The featured article centred on a finding from Statistics Canada that half of all adults in the country are either overweight or obese. To address this health concern, the article suggested that the best approach would be to provide people with positive incentives to take charge of their own health. On November 19, 2010, *The Daily Gleaner* (a local New Brunswick paper), reported on comments made by New Brunswick's Wellness, Culture, and Sports minister in response to findings of the latest population health survey: that New Brunswick had the highest obesity rate in the country. The minister suggested that the government needed to change 'people's bad habits' and invest in wellness programming (Bowie, 2010, p. A6).

Is individual choice the key to improving people's health? How might we frame these stories differently from a sociological perspective? Using a social model of health, we could begin by looking at how individual behaviours are influenced by social environments. We would ask questions about whether all people have the same degree of choice about the foods they eat or the leisure and fitness activities in which they participate. We might equally ask if addressing issues of structured inequality might be a better solution to the problem of obesity.

The dominant health-care debate in Canada today centres on the sustainability of a publicly funded universal health-care insurance plan, that is, Medicare. To date, more mainstream media coverage has been given to groups who support for-profit and two-tier health care. As an example, beginning November 6, 2010, *The Globe and Mail* ran a five-part series on whether privatization of some health services 'could help cure medicare' (p. A13). A feature article included an interview with Dr Day, the owner of a privately owned surgery centre in Vancouver and a major spokesperson for private health care. In his view, a two-tier health system is the way of the future and is 'inevitable'. According to Dr Day, 'There is nothing unethical about spending your own money on your own health care, and no one will ever convince me that it is' (Mickleburgh, 2010, p. A13). There was little examination of countervailing views or the underlying value differences between supporters of Dr Day and those who oppose private, for-profit health care. Supporters of Medicare disagree with Dr Day's predictions and his assumptions. They argue that the right to health care is an inalienable human right: that universal, publicly funded health care is a 'moral enterprise, not a business venture' (The Honourable Roy Romanow, 2002).

Using sociological analysis, how do you make sense of this growing debate? Why might mainstream media give greater coverage to one side of the debate? Are there underlying social factors—power, ideology, values, economic resources, etc.—that are driving the debate? Are there particular interests at stake? Whose interests are dominant, and why? Can sociology be useful in helping you decide where you stand and what actions you will take in response to this controversy?

Conclusion

This Canadian edition of *Second Opinion: An Introduction to Health Sociology* has introduced you to some of the key health issues that concern Canadians in the twenty-first century. It has also introduced you to a way of thinking sociologically about health issues and social life in general. In a world where we are constantly bombarded with media images and simplistic slogans, we believe that the perspective of sociology provides a sounding board for a critical analysis of health issues. By studying inequities and inequalities in health status and health care, critical sociology helps us envision a different set of social arrangements. Using the sociological imagination helps us understand how we can construct the world differently to ultimately produce a qualitatively better and healthier life for all.

Glossary

Aboriginal peoples Generally refers to Indigenous peoples in North America and their descendants.

acculturation A process by which newcomers to a country take on the values and behaviours of their host country.

acute illness An illness that develops quickly and is short-lived.

ageism A term, as with *sexism* and *racism*, that denotes discrimination but based on age.

agency The ability of people, individually and collectively, to influence their own lives and the society in which they live.

agribusiness Farming today is part of an integrated larger system that not only includes produce growers but also suppliers, distributors, and food manufacturers.

allopathic medicine A name given to conventional biomedicine. Treatment of diseases is by drugs which have effects opposite to the symptoms.

allopathy A descriptive name often given to conventional medicine. Allopathy is the treatment of symptoms by opposites.

andropause Defined as an age-related decline in testosterone levels. It is often considered the male equivalent of menopause.

apothecary A historical name for a pharmacist, that is, someone who specialized in compounding and distributing medicines and herbs.

appropriate prescribing Means only using medications when they are the best type of treatment, selecting the correct medication, understanding the harms and benefits associated with the medication, prescribing it in the correct dose and for the right period of time, informing patients about the nature of their treatment, and monitoring patients to ensure that the drug is having a beneficial effect.

assimilate/assimilation Refers to the expectation that Aboriginal peoples and immigrants will give up their culture and become indistinguishable from the dominant Canadian majority.

assisted living Where individuals live somewhat independently in apartment units but receive assistance with meals, housekeeping, and personal health care.

association In statistical terms, means that there is a relationship between two items; however, the presence of an association does not prove a cause and effect.

autoethnography An ethnography that focuses on the experience of the researcher.

basic research The research phase where the basic discoveries are made about how cells function and about human physiology. This type of research lays the groundwork for further work in developing new molecules (drugs) that affect these functions.

biological determinism An unproven belief that individual and group behaviour and social status are an inevitable result of biology.

biomedicalization Describes increasingly complex, multi-sited, and multi-directional processes of medicalization.

biomedicine/biomedical approach The conventional approach to medicine in Western societies, based on the diagnosis and explanation of illness as a malfunction of the body's biological mechanisms. This approach underpins most health professions and health services, which focus on treating individuals, and generally ignores the social origins of illness and its prevention.

biopsychosocial model An extension of the biomedical model. It is a multifactorial model of illness that takes into account the biological, psychological, and social factors implicated in a patient's condition. As with the biomedical model, it focuses on the individual patient for diagnosis, explanation, and treatment.

bodies Material constructs, usually talked about as physically separate from the environment but are here understood as shaped by the environment.

Canada Health Act An act passed by Parliament in 1984, which outlined the five principles of Canada's universal, government-funded health-care system.

Canada's Research-Based Pharmaceutical Companies (Rx&D) The association that represents the Canadian subsidiaries of the brand-name multinational companies operating in Canada.

capitalism An economic and social system based on the private accumulation of wealth.

Cartesian dualism Also called mind/body dualism and named after the philosopher Descartes, it refers to a belief that the mind and body are separate entities. This assumption underpins medical approaches that view disease in physical terms and thus ignore the psychological and subjective aspects of illness.

chronic illness An illness that is ongoing, often lasts a lifetime, and has no known cure.

class (or social class) A position in a system of structured inequality based on the unequal distribution of power, wealth, income, and status. People who share a class position typically share similar life chances.

clientele pluralism A term that describes the relationship between an agency of the state and the industry that it is charged with regulating, whereby some of the authority of the state is transferred to the industry.

clinical drug trials Testing of drugs on humans. (See *human testing*.)

collective conscience A term used to describe shared moral beliefs that act to unify society.

colonization/colonialism A process by which one nation imposes itself economically, politically, and socially upon another.

commodification of health Treating health as an object or commodity that can be purchased or marketed.

commodification of health care Treating health care as a commodity to be bought and sold in the pursuit of profit maximization.

complementary and alternative medicine (CAM) Refers to the diagnosis, treatment, and/or prevention that complements mainstream medicine and that satisfies a demand not met by conventional approaches and is not generally reimbursed by health benefit plans. *Complementary medicine* refers to forms of care that are not in opposition to, and often are provided together with, conventional medicine. *Alternative medicine* refers to care used instead of conventional medical care.

context Refers to the social, political, physical, and economic environment.

conventional medicine The medical practices and institutions developed in Europe during the nineteenth and twentieth centuries that are legally recognized by the state. Central to these practices is the teaching hospital, where all new doctors are inducted into laboratory science, clinical practice, and allopathic biomedicine. These practices and institutions are now dominant in all parts of the world. Conventional medicine is also referred to as orthodox medicine or allopathic medicine.

convergence The process, which may or may not be occurring, whereby conventional medicine adopts many of the practices of alternative medicine, and alternative medicine acts to become more conventional by, for example, seeking to license practitioners and make them subject to training.

culturally competent health care Delivery of health-care services in a way that recognizes the cultural beliefs and needs of those they serve.

demedicalization The reverse of medicalization—that is, when a behaviour once defined in medical terms is no longer defined as such.

determinants of health Refers to the social, economic, and physical factors that influence an individual's or a group's health. The term has become widely used in academic and policy circles to indicate that health is structured by more than health services, although the specific determinants on the list vary.

deviance Behaviour or activities that violate social expectations about what is normal.

Diagnostic and Statistical Manual of Mental Disorders (DSM-IV) A manual published by the American Psychiatric Association that lists all mental health disorders for both children and adults. It also indicates causes, types of treatment, and prognosis.

dichotomies Refers to distinctions made between two parts that are understood to be distinct and quite different.

diminished self The term that Charmaz (1983) uses to refer to the loss of a previously valued identity.

disabilities The social model of disabilities understands physical and mental limitations as primarily the result of social conditions while the medical model understands these limitations as primarily the result of bodies.

discourse A domain of language use that is characterized by common ways of talking and thinking about an issue (for example, the discourses of medicine, madness, or sexuality).

disease Refers to a biophysical condition diagnosed by a medical practitioner.

doctor/nurse game A concept coined by Stein (1967) to refer to the so-called game played out between doctors and nurses, whereby a nurse can be assertive and make suggestions about a patient without appearing to do so, so that nurses' suggestions are provided as prompts for doctors, who can act on them as though they were their own idea.

ecological model Derived from the field of human ecology, and when applied to public health, it suggests that an understanding of health determinants must consider the interaction of social, economic, geographic, and environmental factors.

economic rationalism Terms used to describe a political philosophy based on small-government and market-oriented policies, such as deregulation, privatization, reduced government spending, and lower taxation.

education Refers to formal schooling.

embodiment The lived experience of both being a body and having a body.

emotional labour Refers to the use of feelings by employees as part of their paid work. In health care, a key part of nursing work is caring for patients, often by providing emotional support.

empirical Describes observations or research that is based on evidence drawn from experience. Such research is, therefore, distinguished from something based only on theoretical knowledge or on some other kind of abstract thinking process.

endocrine disruptors They mimic natural hormones circulating in the body, either enhancing or blocking the production of these hormones.

environmental racism A term used to describe how disadvantaged communities are disproportionately exposed to environmental health factors and disasters brought about by government and/or industrial policies.

epidemiology/social epidemiology The statistical study of patterns of disease in the population. Originally focused on epidemics, or infectious diseases, it now covers noninfectious conditions, such as stroke and cancer. Social epidemiology is a subfield aligned with sociology that focuses on the social determinants of illness.

ethnic group A group of people who not only share an ethnic background but also interact with each other on the basis of their shared ethnicity.

ethnicity Sociologically, the term refers to a shared cultural background, which is a characteristic of all groups in society.

ethnography A research method that is based on direct observation of a particular social group's social life and culture—of what people actually do.

euthanasia Meaning 'gentle death', the term is used to describe voluntary death, often medically assisted, as a result of incurable and painful disease.

evidence-based medicine (EBM) An approach to medicine that maintains all clinical practice should be based on evidence from randomized control trials (RCTs) to ensure treatment effectiveness and efficacy.

extra-billing An arrangement that allowed doctors to charge patients over and above the set payment schedule, for which the patient was not reimbursed.

feminism/feminist A broad social and political movement based on a belief in equality of the sexes and the removal of all forms of discrimination against women. A feminist is one who makes use of, and may act upon, a body of theory that seeks to explain the subordinate position of women in society.

feminization A shift in the gender base of a group from being predominantly male to being increasingly female.

First Nations Refers to all those people called 'Indian'.

Food and Drug Administration (FDA) The US equivalent of the Health Products and Food Branch.

Food and Drugs Act The federal legislation dealing with medicines.

functional prerequisites A debated concept based on the assumption that all societies require certain functions to be performed for them to survive and maintain social order. Also known as functional imperatives.

gastrointestinal medications Drugs for stomach and bowel problems.

gender Most frequently understood as 'a multidimensional social construct that is culturally based and historically specific, and thus constantly changing' (Johnson, Greaves, & Repta, 2009, p. 6).

gender/sex Refers to the socially constructed categories of feminine and masculine (the cultural values that dictate how men and women should behave), as opposed to the categories of biological sex (female or male).

globalization Political, social, economic, and cultural developments—such as the spread of multinational companies, information technology, and the role of international agencies—that result in people's lives being increasingly influenced by global, rather than national or local, factors.

gross domestic product (GDPs) The market value of all goods and services that have been sold during a year.

grounded theory Usually associated with qualitative methods, it refers to any social theory that is derived from (or grounded in) empirical research of social phenomena.

growth imperative Economic growth that is long term and sustained, supported by government policies that promote free markets.

Health Canada The federal department responsible for helping the people of Canada maintain and improve their health. Within Health Canada the Health Products and Food Branch (HPFB) is responsible for drug, food, and consumer product safety and in the HPFB there are four directorates dealing with medicines. The Therapeutic Products Directorate (TPD) approves and monitors prescription and nonprescription drugs derived from chemical manufacturing and medical devices. The TPD also is responsible for making the decision to remove drugs for safety reasons. The Biologics and Genetic Therapies Directorate (BGTD) is responsible for biological and radiopharmaceutical drugs, including blood and blood products, viral and bacterial vaccines, genetic therapeutic products, tissues, organs, and xenografts. The Marketed Health Products

Directorate (MHPD) deals with the safety of products already approved for marketing. Finally, the Natural Health Products Directorate (NHPD) approves natural health products.

health promotion Has recently become a goal of health policy in Canada. Any combination of education and related organizational, economic, and political interventions designed to promote individual behavioural and environmental changes conducive to good health, including legislation, community development, and advocacy. Draws attention to a variety of social determinants. See also *primary health care* and *public health*.

healthy immigrant effect Refers to the finding that newly arrived immigrants appear to have a health advantage but after a period of time their health status tends to converge toward that of the host population.

hegemony/hegemonic Dominance or power of one social group, idea, or discourse over another.

holistic/holism An approach to health that considers all aspects of an individual—physical, emotional, mental, social, spiritual, and lifestyle—as interrelated and must be treated as such.

horizontal violence A concept derived from Paolo Friere that describes a behaviour common to all oppressed groups, whereby, because of their powerlessness, the oppressed are unable to direct their anger toward their oppressor and, as a result, turn it toward each other, with various degrees of violence and negativity.

Human Development Index (HDI) Provides a composite measure of three dimensions of human development: living a long and healthy life (measured by life expectancy), being educated (measured by adult literacy and gross enrolment in education), and having a decent standard of living (measured by purchasing power parity and income).

human testing The testing that a drug must go through before it can be approved for marketing in Canada (and virtually all other industrialized countries). In the first stage, drugs are tested in a small number of healthy people to determine the mechanism by which the drug works and to look at whether the number of side effects increases with higher doses. In the second stage, the drugs are tested in about 100–3000 people who have the disease in question in order to evaluate how well the drugs work and to determine side effects and risks. Finally, in stage three the drug is used in several hundred to several thousand people to gather the additional information about its efficacy and safety to more accurately determine the drug's harm-to-benefit ratio.

iatrogenesis/social iatrogenesis A concept popularized by Ivan Illich that refers to any adverse outcome or harm as a result of medical treatment.

ideal type A concept originally devised by Max Weber to refer to the abstract or pure features of any social phenomenon.

ideology In a political context, refers to those beliefs and values that relate to the way in which society should be organized, including the appropriate role of the state.

illness The subjective response to a disease.

immigrants First-generation immigrants are those who were born outside of Canada. Second generation refers to those who are Canadian-born and have at least one parent who was born outside Canada. Third generation or more are the offspring of Canadian-born parents (Statistics Canada, 2003).

Indian Act Sets out certain federal government obligations and regulates the management of Indian reserve lands, Indian monies, and other resources. The act defines an Indian as 'a person who, pursuant to this Act, is registered as an Indian or is entitled to be registered as an Indian'.

Indigenous peoples Used interchangeably with the term *Aboriginal peoples.*

individualism/individualization A belief or process supporting the primacy of individual choice, freedom, and self-responsibility.

inequities A term used instead of *inequality* because it implies injustice and because it does not imply the objective of treating everyone the same, as is implied by *equality*. Equitable treatment or conditions require recognizing differences and addressing them in ways that are socially just.

infant mortality Refers to the number of infants who die in the first year after birth per 1000 births.

institutional ethnography (IE) A feminist research strategy associated with Dorothy Smith combining theory and method. It begins from the standpoint of people in the actualities of their everyday world to show how people's social relations are organized by forces outside of them.

instrumental approach One in which a job is valued as a means to an end, not for its intrinsic worth.

integrative medicine/integrative health care Generally refers to health practitioners with different backgrounds and training working together, although the precise meaning is contested.

Inuit Replaces the term *Eskimo* and refers to Aboriginal people who live primarily in Arctic Canada.

licensed practical nurses (LPNs) Nurses who assess patients and work in health promotion and illness prevention.

life chances Derived from Max Weber, the term refers to people's opportunity to realize their lifestyle choices, which are often assumed to differ according to their social class.

lifestyle choices/factors The decisions people make that are likely to impact on their health, such as diet, exercise, smoking, alcohol, and other drugs. The term implies that people are solely responsible for choosing and changing their lifestyle.

McDonaldization A term coined by George Ritzer to expand Weber's notion of rationalization; defined as the standardization of social life by rules and regulations, such as increased monitoring and evaluation of individual performance, akin to the uniformity and control measures used by fast-food chains. These principles are now applied to other sectors, both locally and globally.

manufacturers of illness Corporations who not only manufacture material goods and services—their products can also produce illness and death.

market failure The failure of the free-market system to produce results that are socially desirable due to the absence of a sufficient profit motive.

materialist analysis An analysis that is embedded in the real, actual, material reality of everyday life.

medical dominance A general term used to describe the power of the medical profession in terms of its control over its own work, over the work of other health workers, and over health resource allocation, healthy policy, and the way that hospitals are run.

medical-industrial complex The growth of profit-oriented medical companies and industries, whereby one company may own a chain of health services, such as hospitals, clinics, and radiology and pathology services.

medicalization The process by which nonmedical problems become defined and treated as medical issues, usually in terms of illnesses, disorders, or syndromes.

Medicare Canada's universal health-care program, which is funded and administered by federal, provincial, and territorial governments.

mesmerism A therapeutic system of hypnosis believed to be induced by animal magnetism. It was devised by Austrian physician Franz Anton Mesmer.

meta-analysis/meta-narratives The big-picture analysis that frames and organizes observations and research on a particular topic.

Métis Refers to people of Aboriginal and mixed European ancestry.

morbidity Rates of illness.

mortality Rates of death.

naturopathic medicine A form of alternative medicine that uses natural methods and substances, such as nutritional supplements, exercise, and homeopathy, to support the natural power of the body to establish, maintain, and restore health.

neglected diseases Diseases that occur in small numbers of people or in people with little to no purchasing power. In these cases the absence of sufficient sales (in dollar value) means that drugs for these illnesses will not be developed by profit-seeking companies.

neo-liberalism Economic policies and ideology that advocate a free market for the production and distribution of resources, an enhanced role for the private sector and a reduction of government involvement in the economy.

new managerialism A term that arose in the 1980s to describe a shift in the transfer of power from professionals (i.e., doctors) to management. It encouraged the implementation of industrial techniques that emphasized the achievement of measurable objectives, continuous evaluation of performance against defined objectives, rationing of resources using effectiveness criteria, and surveillance of health professionals (Beardwood, 1999).

Nightingale tradition The view that nursing was a natural extension of women's role as caregivers; nurses were expected to be altruistic and to act with selfless dedication.

nosology/nosological A branch of medicine that deals with the classification of diseases.

nurse practitioners (NPs) RNs with additional education qualifications and experience. They may order and interpret diagnostic tests, prescribe medications and other therapies.

Ottawa Charter for Health Promotion A 1986 document produced by the World Health Organization. It was launched at the first international conference for health promotion, held in Ottawa, Canada.

Participation and Activity Limitation Survey (PALS) A national survey designed to collect information on people whose activities are limited because of a condition or health problem.

participatory action research A more activist approach to research whereby researchers work with local communities, social groups, or individuals to empower the group or its representatives. Often involves participants in formulating the research questions

Patented Medicine Prices Review Board (PMPRB) A federal Canadian agency that sets a maximum introductory price for any new patented medicine that is marketed in Canada and also limits the rise in the price of patented medicines to the annual rate of inflation. The PMPRB has authority over prices as long as the medication has a valid patent.

patents Medicines typically have two different types of patents—a patent on the process used to make them and a patent on the product itself. While a patent is valid the company owning the product has the exclusive right to sell it. Patents are granted for a 20-year term from the date when the patent application is filed. Patent terms are the same worldwide except for a group of very poor countries.

patriarchy/patriarchal A system of power through which males dominate households. The term is used more broadly by feminists to refer to society's domination by patriarchal power, which functions to subordinate women and children.

Pharmaceutical Advertising Advisory Board (PAAB) An organization with membership from the medical and pharmacy professions, the generic and brand-name industry associations, consumer groups, and organizations representing both medical advertising agencies and medical publications. PAAB evaluates all print advertising directed to medical professionals before it appears in print.

placebo/placebo effect Any therapeutic practice that has no clear clinical effect. In practice it usually means giving patients an inert substance to take as a medication. When a patient reacts to a placebo in a way that is not clinically explicable, this is called the 'placebo effect'.

political economy Focuses on how political, economic, and ideological factors influence the distribution of power and other resources in a society, which in turn shapes individual experience and state policies.

positivist research methodologies Research methods that attempt to study people in the same way that physical scientists study the natural world—by focusing on quantifiable and directly observable events. Such research methods focus on the collection of statistical data.

postmarketing surveillance Refers to all of the activities that are undertaken to monitor the safety and effectiveness of drugs once they have been approved for marketing.

postmodern society/postmodernity A disputed term in sociology that broadly refers to a society or social condition following modernity in which many of the key social institutions, including the state, unions, and professions, have lost their power to determine social outcomes as tradition is replaced by a high level of social differentiation and cultural diversity.

post-structuralism/postmodernism Often used interchangeably, these terms refer to a broad perspective that is opposed to the view that social structure determines human action, and instead emphasizes a pluralistic world view that explores the local, the specific, and the contingent in social life.

precautionary principle The principle of taking into account not just known risks, but also potential risks, even if the evidence for those potential risks is weak. In these circumstances, (e.g. a drug) the precautionary principle would say that the product should either not be marketed or should be marketed under significant restrictions.

prescreen Under this system, pharmaceutical companies submit their print advertising to PAAB and only use that advertising when PAAB has given its approval.

primary health care Both the point of first contact with the health-care system and a philosophy for delivery of that care.

principal-agent theory Proposes that there is a relationship between a principal, who has a task that needs to be performed, and an agent, who is contracted to do the task in exchange for compensation.

promotional activities All of the methods undertaken by pharmaceutical companies to increase the sales of their products. These include, but are not limited to, advertisements in medical journals, visits by pharmaceutical sales representatives to doctors' offices, medication samples left behind in doctors' offices, and television advertisements about diseases.

prove harm Scientific proof that a product is harmful.

Prozac A new type of medication (selective serotonin reuptake inhibitor [SSRI]) introduced in 1987 to treat depression.

psychoneuroimmunology (PNI) A study of the interaction between psychological (mental) processes and the body's nervous and immune systems, using an interdisciplinary approach that incorporates a number of scientific and medical disciplines.

public care Refers to health care provided by health-care professionals in a public setting, such as a doctor's office or hospital. Public care is part of Canada's publicly funded, universal health-care insurance policy.

public health-care system Canada's universal, publicly funded health-care system.

public health/public-health infrastructure Policies, programs and services designed to keep citizens healthy and to improve the quality of life. The focus is on enhancing the health status and well-being of the general population rather than just looking at the health of individual persons. *Public-health infrastructure* refers specifically to the buildings and equipment necessary to ensure healthy living conditions for the population.

purposive sampling Refers to the selection of units of analysis to ensure that the processes involved are adequately studied, and where statistical representativeness is not required.

qualitative research Research that focuses on the meanings and interpretations of the participants.

quantitative research Research that focuses on the collection of statistical data.

'race' A term without scientific basis that uses skin colour and facial features to describe allegedly biologically distinct groups of humans. It is a social construction that is used to categorize groups of people and usually implies assumed (and unproven) intellectual superiority or inferiority.

racialized groups The term preferred by those who work with immigrants and refugees when talking about visible minorities. The term captures the fact that certain groups are treated as inferior by the dominant group.

racism Beliefs and actions used to discriminate against a group of people because of their physical and cultural characteristics.

racism/racist *Racism* refers to a set of false beliefs that one racial group is naturally superior to another group based on biological differences. It perpetuates notions of cultural superiority and inferiority and is one basis for social exclusion and discriminatory practices.

randomized control trials (RCTs) A biomedical research procedure used to evaluate the effectiveness of particular medications and therapeutic interventions. Random refers to the equal chance of participants being in the experimental or control group (the group to which nothing is done and is used for comparison), and trial refers to the experimental nature of the method. It is often mistakenly viewed as the best way to demonstrate causal links between factors under investigation, but it privileges biomedical over social responses to illness.

rationalization The standardization of social life through rules and regulations. See *McDonaldization*.

reductionism The belief that all illnesses can be explained and treated by reducing them to biological and pathological factors.

refugees Individuals who flee their country of origin because of a fear of persecution for reasons of race, religion, political opinion, nationality, or membership in a particular social group.

registered nurses (RNs) Nurses who coordinate health care, deliver direct services, and support patients in their self-care decisions.

registered psychiatric nurses (RPNs) Nurses who provide services to patients whose primary-care needs relate to mental and development health. They plan, implement, and evaluate therapies and programs on the basis of psychiatric nursing assessments. They are regulated separately from other nursing professionals in four provinces.

relations of ruling A concept used by Dorothy Smith to refer to social relations in which people are involved and that dominate them, the rational forms of knowledge that are developed, and the organizations that administer and manage these relations.

research methods Procedures used by researchers to collect and investigate data.

rigour A term used by qualitative researchers to describe trustworthy research that carefully scrutinizes and describes the meanings and interpretations given by participants.

risk assessment The process governments use to assess a chemical's potential for injury on humans and on the environment.

risk factors Conditions that are thought to increase an individual's susceptibility to illness or disease, such as abuse of alcohol, poor diet, and smoking.

risk management Taking the known risks and benefits of a drug into consideration before allowing it onto the market. Unless the product has serious known risks, the preference is to allow it to be sold.

risk/risk discourse *Risk* refers to 'danger'; *risk discourse* is often used in health-promotion messages warning people that certain actions involve significant risks to their health.

risk society A term coined by Ulrich Beck (1992) to describe the centrality of risk calculations in people's lives in Western society, whereby the key social problems today are unanticipated hazards, such as the risks of pollution, food poisoning, and environmental degradation.

Royal Commission on Aboriginal Peoples (RCAP) Created by the Canadian government in 1991 to address economic, social, and political issues related to First Nations, Métis, and Inuit peoples in Canada. The commissioners held 178 days of public hearings, visited 96 communities, consulted dozens of experts, and commissioned research studies. They came up with hundreds of recommendations to address the inequities faced by Aboriginal peoples.

ruling class This is a hotly debated term used to highlight the point that the upper class in society has political power as a result of its economic wealth. The term is often used interchangeably with *upper class*.

self-regulation The process by which an industry is allowed to regulate its own behaviour.

sex Most frequently understood as 'a multidimensional biological construct that encompasses anatomy, physiology, genes, and hormones, which together affect how we are labelled and treated in the world' (Johnson, Greaves, & Repta, 2009, p. 5); however, this book challenges the possibility of separating gender from sex.

sexual division of labour Refers to the nature of work performed as a result of gender roles. The stereotype is that of the male breadwinner and the female homemaker.

sickness Refers to the actions a sick individual takes, including taking on the sick role.

sick role A concept used by Talcott Parsons to describe the social expectations of how sick people should act and of how they are meant to be treated.

smart regulation Regulating in a way that enhances the climate for investment and trust in the markets such that the administrative burden is reduced for businesses.

social capital A term used to refer to social relations, networks, norms, trust, and reciprocity between individuals that facilitate cooperation for mutual benefit.

social closure A term first used by Max Weber to describe the way that power is exercised to exclude outsiders from the privileges of social membership (in social classes, professions, or status groups).

social cohesion A term used to refer to the social ties that are the basis for group behaviour and integration. See *social capital*.

social construction/constructionism Refers to the socially created characteristics of human life based on the idea that people actively construct reality, meaning it is neither natural nor inevitable. Therefore, notions of normality/abnormality, right/wrong, and health/illness are subjective human creations that should not be taken for granted.

social control Mechanisms that aim to induce conformity or at least to manage or minimize deviant behaviour.

social Darwinism The incorrect application of Charles Darwin's theory of animal evolution to explain social inequality by transferring his idea of 'survival of the fittest' among animals to explain human inequality.

social death The marginalization and exclusion of elderly people from everyday life, resulting in social isolation.

social determinants of health Refers to the social and economic environments in which people live and which determine their health. Examples of social determinants include housing, job security, working conditions, education, income, social class, gender, Aboriginal status, and the social safety net. This approach shows how society is organized and how it distributes its economic and social resources.

social exclusion A process whereby some groups in society are denied access to material and social resources, thereby excluding their full participation in society. It produces inequality in outcomes.

social iatrogenesis *Iatrogenesis* is a concept popularized by Ivan Illich that refers to adverse effects caused by, or resulting from, medical treatment. *Social iatrogenesis* refers to the process by which biomedicine extends its domain over every stage of life. Illich talked about three dimensions of iatrogenesis: clinical, social, and cultural.

social institutions Formal structures within society—such as health care, government, education, religion, and the media—that are organized to address identified social needs.

social justice A belief system that gives high priority to the interests of the least advantaged.

social model of health Focuses on social determinants of health, such as the social production, distribution, and construction of health and illness, and the social organization of health care. It directs attention to the prevention of illness through community participation and social reforms that address living and working conditions.

social support The support provided to an individual by being part of a network of kin, friends, or colleagues.

social structure The recurring patterns of social interaction through which people are related to each other, such as social institutions and social groups.

socialism/communism *Socialism* is a political ideology with numerous variations but generally refers to the creation of societies in which private property and wealth accumulation are replaced by state ownership and distribution of economic resources. *Communism* represents a vision of society based on communal ownership of resources, cooperation, and altruism to the extent that social inequality and the state no longer exist. Both terms are often used interchangeably.

socialization The process of learning the culture of a society (its language and customs), which shows us how to behave and communicate.

sociological imagination A term coined by C.W. Mills to describe the sociological approach to analyzing issues. We see the world through a sociological imagination, or think sociologically, when we make a link between personal troubles and public issues.

specific etiology The idea that there is a specific cause or origin for each specific disease.

state A term used to describe a collection of government and government-controlled institutions within a country, including the Parliament (government and Opposition political parties), the public-sector bureaucracy, the judiciary, the military, and the police.

stigma A physical or social trait, such as a disability or a criminal record, that results in negative social reactions, such as discrimination and exclusion.

structure–agency debate A key debate in sociology over the extent to which human behaviour is determined by social structure.

Summary Basis of Decision A document that is released by Health Canada after it has approved a new drug. It outlines the scientific and benefit/risk-based reasons for Health Canada's decision to grant market authorization for a product.

systemic discrimination A form of discrimination that arises from the way that organizational structures, policies, practices, and procedures operate (unrelated to the requirements of the job), which while appearing neutral have a discriminatory effect on certain groups of people.

the self A concept used by George Herbert Mead to refer to a core identity. For Mead the self is a social product that emerges through our interaction with others.

theodicy An explanation of suffering, evil, and death.

theory A system of ideas that uses researched evidence to explain certain events and to show why certain facts are related.

time and motion principles Introduced by F.W. Taylor in the second decade of the twentieth century to improve industrial efficiency. This involved breaking a job into component parts and measuring the length of time each task would take. It would become the benchmark for how long a particular activity should take.

total institutions A term used by Erving Goffman to refer to institutions such as prisons and asylums in which life is highly regulated and subjected to authoritarian control to induce conformity.

transparency In the context of drug regulation transparency, refers to how much input the public and health-care practitioners have in the decision to approve a new drug and how much public access there is to the clinical information that companies have to submit to Health Canada when they apply to get a drug approved.

trickle down theory The theory that everyone benefits by allowing the upper class to prosper relatively unfettered. If wealthy capitalists are allowed and encouraged to maximize their profits, it is believed that this increased wealth will eventually 'trickle down' to the workers.

unalienable human right A right considered to inhere in a person as a human being and that cannot be relinquished by government; sometimes referred to as 'natural rights'.

unemployment rate Estimates the proportion of people who are not employed but who are actively looking for work.

user fees A general term applied when an individual, group, company, or organization that benefits from a public service is required to pay part of the cost of that service. With respect to pharmaceuticals, it means that when companies apply to have a new drug approved they must pay a fee to Health Canada. Those fees form part of the revenue that is used to operate the part of Health Canada that deals with medications.

values Important beliefs and ideals shared by members of a culture or society.

verstehen Refers to a process of interpretative and empathetic understanding.

victim blaming The process whereby social inequality is explained in terms of individuals being solely responsible for what happens to them in relation to the choices they make and their assumed psychological, cultural, and/or biological inferiority.

visible minorities A term used by Statistics Canada and other government bodies 'to refer to persons, other than Aboriginal peoples, who are non-Caucasian in race or non-white in colour', as defined by the Employment Equity Act.

welfare state A system whereby the government assumes primary responsibility for the welfare of its citizens through programs designed to protect and promote the economic and social well-being of its citizens.

welfare state/social welfare state A system whereby the government assumes primary responsibility for the welfare of its citizens through programs designed to protect and promote the economic and social well-being of its citizens.

women's health movement In Canada, includes both formal and informal organizations of women that addressed issues ranging from birth control to poverty. The movement did not have a single voice or leader but, rather, encompassed a variety of groups and activities, collectively known as the women's health movement.

References

A Brief History of the Medical Reform Group of Ontario 1979–1994. Retrieved from www.connexions.org/CxLibrary/Docs/CX5209-MRGHistory-1979-1994.htm

A day in the life of a coffee worker. (2010). United States Labor Education in the Americas Project. (USLEAP). Retrieved from www.usleap.org/usleap-initiatives/coffee-worker-justice-initiative/day-life-coffee-worker

A look back at pharmaceuticals in 2006: Aggressive advertising cannot hide the absence of therapeutic advances. (2007). *Prescrire International, 16*, 80–86.

Abbott, A. (1988). *The system of professions: An essay on the division of expert labor.* Chicago, IL: University of Chicago Press.

Abbott, P., & Wallace, C. (1997). *An introduction to sociology: Feminist perspectives* (5th ed.). London, UK: Routledge.

Abella, R. (1984). *Report of the commission on equality in employment.* Ottawa, ON: Minister of Supply and Services.

Abel-Smith, B. (1960). *A history of the nursing profession.* London, UK: Heinemann.

Aboriginal Affairs and Northern Development Canada. (2008). First Nations and Inuit health branch. Retrieved from www.hc-sc.gc.ca/ahc-asc/branch-dirgen/fnihb-dgspni/index-eng.php

———. (2010). Aboriginal peoples and communities. Retrieved from www.ainc-inac.gc.ca/ap/index-eng.asp

Aboriginal Healing Foundation. (n.d.). Mission statement. Retrieved from www.ahf.ca/about-us/mission

Aboriginal Peoples. (2006). Census. Ottawa, ON: Statistics Canada.

About electic therapy (n.d.). The International Association for the Promotion of Eclectic Practice. Available at: www.hstrainingandsupervision.com/?page_id=2

Abramson, B. (2009). Women and health: Taking the matter to heart. In P. Armstrong and J. Deadman (Eds), *Women's health intersections of policy, research, and practice* (pp. 53–60). Toronto, ON: Women's Press.

Access Alliance. (2007). Racialization and health inequalities: Focus on children. Retrieved from http://accessalliance.ca/sites/accessalliance/files/documents/RacializationandHealthInequalities.pdf

———. (2005). Racialized groups and health status: A literature review. Retrieved from http://accessalliance.ca/sites/accessalliance/files/documents/Literature%20Review_Racialized%20Groups%20and%20Health%20Status.pdf

Acharya, M., & Northcott, H.C. (2007). Mental distress and the coping strategies of elderly Indian immigrant women. *Transcultural Psychiatry 44*(4), 614–636.

Acheson, D. (1998). Independent inquiry into inequalities in health. London, UK: Stationery Office.

Adam, B., & Sears, A. (1996). *Experience HIV.* New York, NY: Columbia University Press.

Adam, B., Beck, U., & van Loon, J. (Eds). (2000). *The risk society and beyond: Critical issues for social theory.* London, UK: Sage.

Adams, J., & Tovey, P. (2004). *CAM and nursing: From advocacy to critical sociology.* In P. Tovey, G. Easthope, & J. Adams. (Eds). The mainstreaming of complementary medicine. London, UK: Routledge.

Adelson, N. (2005, Mar/Apr). The embodiment of inequity: Health disparities in Aboriginal Canada. *Canadian Journal of Public Health, 96*, s45–s60.

AFB. (2007, April). Does the 2007 federal budget address inequality and poverty? *Canadian Centre for Policy Alternatives.*

Agnew, V. (Ed) (2009). *Racialized migrant women in Canada. Essays on health, violence and equity.* Toronto, ON: University of Toronto Press.

Agricultural Crop Rotation Act. (2002). Government of Prince Edward Island. Retrieved from www.gov.pe.ca/focus/segment.php3'number=861

Agriculture and Agri-Food Canada. (2007). Blight alert: A simple decision support system for Prince Edward Island potato farmers. Retrieved from www4.agr.gc.ca/AAFC-AAC/display-afficher.do?id=1187716936117&lang=eng. Downloaded January 5, 2010.

———. (2008). Retrieved from www4.agr.gc.ca/AAFC-AAC/display-afficher.do?id=1201189157429&lang=eng#alternate

Ahmad, F., Driver, N., McNally, M-J, & Stewart, D. (2009). Why doesn't she seek help for partner abuse? An exploratory study with South Asian immigrant women. *Social Science & Medicine, 69*, 613–622.

Aiken, L., Clarke, S., Sloane, D., Sochalski, J., Busse, R., Clarke, H., . . ., & Shamian. (2001, May/June). Nurses' reports on hospital care in five countries. *Health Affairs, 20*(3), 43–53.

Alasuutari, P. (1995). *Researching culture: Qualitative method and cultural studies.* London, UK: Sage.

Albritton, R. (2009). *Let them eat junk: How capitalism creates hunger and obesity.* Winnipeg, MB: Arbeiter Ring Publishing.

Alexander, J.C. (Ed). (1985). *Neofunctionalism.* Beverly Hills, CA: Sage.

Alexander, J.C. (1998). *Neofunctionalism and after.* Oxford, UK: Blackwell.

Ali, J.S., S. McDermott, & R.G. Gravel. (2004, May–June). Recent research on immigrant health from Statistics Canada's population survey. *Canadian Journal of Public Health,* 9–13.

Allen, D. (2001a). *The changing shape of nursing practice.* London, UK: Routledge.

———. (2001b). Review article: Nursing and sociology: An uneasy marriage. *Sociology of Health & Illness, 23*(3), 386–396.

Allotey, P. (1998). Travelling with 'excess baggage': Health problems of refugee women in western Australia. *Women and Health, 28*(1), 63–81.

———. (Ed). (2003). *The health of refugees: Public health perspectives from crisis to settlement.* Melbourne: Oxford University Press.

Allotey, P., Manderson, L., & Grover, S. (2001). The politics of female genital surgery in displaced communities. *Critical Public Health, 11*(3), 189–201.

American Psychiatric Association. (1994). *Diagnostic and statistical manual of mental disorders* (4th ed.). Washington, DC: APA.

Anderson, J. (1991). Immigrant women speak of chronic illness: The social construction of the devalued self. *Journal of Advanced Nursing*, 16, 710–717.

Anderson, L., Scrimshaw, S., Fullilove, M., Fielding, J., Normand, J., and the Task Force of Community Preventive Services. (2003). Culturally competent healthcare systems: A systematic review. *American Journal of Preventative Medicine, 24*(3S), pp. 68–79.

Andrew, C., Armstrong, P., Armstrong, H., Clement, W., & Vosco, L. (Eds). (2003). *Studies in political economy: developments in feminism.* Toronto, ON: Women's Press.

Andrews, G., & Boon, H. (2005). CAM in Canada: Places, practices, research. *Complementary Therapies in Clinical Practice*, 11, 21–27.

Andrews, M. (1999). The seductiveness of agelessness. *Ageing and Society*, 19, 301–318.

Angus, Mariel. (2009, Winter). To benefit us all: Childcare in Canada. *The Catalyst 32*(1), 1–4. Retrieved from www.cpj.ca/en/content/benefit-us-all-childcare-canada

Annandale, E., & Clarke, J. (1996). What is gender? Feminist theory and the sociology of human reproduction. *Sociology of Health and Illness, 18*(1), 17–44.

Annandale, E., & Hunt, K. (Eds). (2000). Gender inequalities and health. Buckingham, UK: Open University Press.

Annandale, E. (2004). Feminist theory and the sociology of health and illness. London, UK: Routledge.

Annual report, 2008. (2009). Ottawa, ON: Patented Medicine Prices Review Board.

Archer, J. (1995). *Bad medicine.* Sydney: Simon & Schuster.

Aries, P. (1981). *The hour of our death.* (H. Weaver, Trans.). New York, NY: Knopf Publishers.

Armstrong, D. (1983). *Political anatomy of the body: Medical knowledge in Britain in the twentieth century.* Cambridge: Cambridge University Press.

Armstrong P., & Armstrong, H. (2003). *Wasting away: The undermining of Canadian health care* (2nd ed.). Don Mills, ON: Oxford University Press.

———, & ———. (2008). *Health care: About Canada.* Halifax, NS: Fernwood Publishing.

Armstrong P., & Armstrong, H. (2010). *The double ghetto: Canadian women and their segregated work.* (Updated 3rd ed.). The Wynford Project. Toronto, ON: Oxford University Press.

Armstrong, P., Amaratunga, C., Bernier, J., Grant, K., Pederson, A. and Willson, K. (Eds) (2002). *Exposing privatization: Women and health care reform.* Aurora, ON: Garamond Press.

Armstrong, P., Armstrong, H., Bourgeault, I., Choiniere, J., Mykhalovskiy, E., & White, J. (2000). 'Heal thyself': Managing health care reform. Aurora, ON: Garamond Press.

Armstrong, P., Armstrong, H., Choiniere, J., Feldberg, G., & White, J. (1994). *Take care: Warning signals for Canada's health system.* Toronto, ON: Garamond Press

Armstrong, P., Armstrong, H., & Coburn, D. (Eds). (2001). *Unhealthy times: Political economy perspectives on health and care in Canada.* Don Mills, ON: Oxford University Press.

Armstrong, P., Choiniere, J., Day, E. (1993). *Vital signs: Nursing in transition.* Toronto, ON: Garamond Press.

Armstrong, P., Armstrong, H., & Scott-Dixon, K. (2008). *Critical to care: The invisible women in health services.* Toronto, ON: University of Toronto Press.

Armstrong, P., & Silas, L. (2009). Taking power: Making change. Nurses' unions in Canada. In M. McIntyre and C. McDonald (Eds), *Realities of Canadian nursing: Professional, practice, and power issues* (3rd ed.) (pp.316–336). Philadelphia, PA: Lippincott, Williams & Wilkins.

Armstrong, S. (2002). The emergence and implications of a mental health ethos in juvenile justice. *Sociology of Health & Illness*, 24, 599–620.

Ashley, L. (2008, Nov.). Giving nurses a voice in patient safety. *The Canadian Nurse*, 104–109.

Ashton, J., & Seymour, H. (1988). *The new public health: The Liverpool experience.* Open University Press, Milton Keynes.

Assembly of First Nations. (2002, May). Fact Sheet: Top misconceptions about Aboriginal peoples. Retrieved from http://tricitiesecd.citysoup.ca/NR/rdonlyres/DBF1E6EF-66A7-4357-A3A5-50E1473FD3DE/68643/FACTSandMisconceptions.pdf

———. (2009). Background. http://64.26.129.156/article.asp?id=2845

Association of Faculties of Medicine of Canada. (2010). The future of medical education in Canada (FMEC): A collective vision for MD education. Retrieved from www.afmc.ca/fmec

———. (2009). Canadian medical education statistics. Retrieved from www.afmc.ca/pdf/cmes/CMES2009.pdf

Astin, J.A. (1998). Why patients use alternative medicine: Results of a national study. *Journal of the American Medical Association*, *279*(19), 1548–1553.

Astin, J.A., Marie, A., Pelletier, K.R., Hansen, E., & Haskell, W.L. (1998). A review of the incorporation of complementary and alternative medicine by mainstream physicians. *Archives of Internal Medicine*, 158, 2303–2310.

Atkinson, M.M., & Coleman, W.D. (1989). *The state, business, and industrial change in Canada.* Toronto, ON: University of Toronto Press.

Au, W.W., Lane, R.G., Legator, M.S., Whorton, E.B., Wilkinson, G.S., & Gabehart, G.J. (1995). Biomarker monitoring of a population residing near uranium mining activities. *Environmental Health Perspectives, 103*(5), 466–470.

Auditor General of Canada. (1999). Ozone layer protection: The unfinished journey. Report of the Auditor General of Canada to the House of Commons, 1997. Retrieved from www.statcan.gc.ca/edu/power-pouvoir/ch5/casestudy-edudedecas/5214797-eng.htm

Auger, J. (2000). Social perspectives on death and dying. Halifax, NS: Fernwood.

Auger, N., & Alix, C. (2009). Income, income distribution, and health in Canada. In D. Raphael (Ed) *Social determinants of health* (2nd ed.) (pp.61–73). Toronto, ON: Canadian Scholars' Press.

Auger, J., & Tedford-Litle, D. (2002). *From the inside looking out: Competing ideas about growing old.* Halifax, NS: Fernwood.

Austin, W. (2007). The McDonaldization of nursing. *Health: An Interdisciplinary Journal for the Social Study of Health, Illness and Medicine, 11*(2), 265–272.

Axworthy, T. (2007, April 22). Canada's looming acute-care crisis. *Toronto Star.* Retrieved from www.thestar.com

Ayres, I., & Braithwaite, J. (1992). *Responsive regulation: transcending the deregulation debate.* New York, NY: Oxford University Press.

Badgley, R., & Wolfe, S. (1967). *Doctors' strike.* Toronto, ON: Macmillan of Canada.

Baggott, R. (2000). *Public health: policy and politics.* Basingstoke, UK: Palgrave.

Baird, P.A. (1996). Funding medical and health-related research in the public interest. *Canadian Medical Association Journal, 155,* 299–301.

Barberis, L., De Toni, E., Schiavone, M., Zicca, A., & Ghio, R. (2001). Unconventional medicine teaching at the universities of the European Union. *Journal of Alternative and Complementary Medicine, 7*(4), 337–343.

Barrett, B., Kiefer, D., & Rabago, D. (1999). Assessing the risks and benefits of herbal medicine: An over-view of scientific evidence. *Alternative Therapies in Health and Medicine, 5*(4), 40–50.

Barrett, M., & Phillips, A. (1992). *Destabilizing theory: Contemporary feminist debates.* Cambridge, UK: Polity Press.

Barrett, M., & Roberts, H. (1978). Doctors and their patients. In C. Smart & B. Smart. (Eds.) *Women, sexuality and social control* (pp. 41–52). London, UK: Routledge.

Barrett, M. (1991). *The politics of truth: From Marx to Foucault.* Cambridge, UK: Polity Press.

Bartky, S.L. (1990). *Femininity and domination: Studies in the phenomenology of oppression.* London, UK: Routledge.

———. (1998) Foucault, femininity, and the modernization of patriarchal power. In R. Weitz (Ed) *The politics of women's bodies: Sexuality, appearance and behavior.* New York, NY: Oxford University Press.

Bartley, M., Martikainen, P., Shipley, M., & Marmot, M. (2004). Gender differences in the relationship of partner's social class to behavioural risk factors and social support in the Whitehall II Study. *Social Science & Medicine, 59*(9), 1925–1936.

Barton, L., & Oliver, M. (Eds). (1997). *Disability studies: Past, present and future.* Leeds, UK: The Disability Press.

Basu, K., & Anil Gupta, A. (2007, Feb.). Nursing shortages: Where and why. *Health Policy Research Bulletin, 13* (pp. 21–25). Ottawa, ON: Health Canada.

Baum, F. (1996). Community health services and managerialism. *Australian Journal of Primary Health, 2*(4), 31–41.

———. (2002). *The new public health* (2nd ed.). Melbourne: Oxford University Press.

———. (2003). Primary health care: Can the dream be revived? *Development in Practice, 13*(5), 515–519.

Baum, F., Kalucy, E., Lawless, A., Barton, S., & Steven, I. (1996). *Medical practice and women's and community health centres in South Australia.* Adelaide: SACHRU.

Baum, F., Palmer, C., Modra, C., Murray, C., & Bush, R. (2000). Families, social capital and health. In I. Winter. (Ed) *Social capital and public policy in Australia* (pp. 250–275). Melbourne: Australian Institute of Family Studies.

Baum, F., & Sanders, D. (1995). Can health promotion and primary health care achieve health for all without a return to their more radical agenda? *Health Promotion International, 10*(2), 149–160.

Baume, P. (1995). Voluntary euthanasia: Mercy or sin. *New Doctor, 63,* 13–14.

Bausell, R.B., Lee, W., & Berman, B. (2001). Demographic and health-related correlates of visits to complementary and alternative medical providers. *Medical Care, 39*(2), 190–196.

Baxter, J., Emerson, M., & Western, J. (Eds). (1991). *Class analysis and contemporary Australia.* South Melbourne: Macmillan.

Beagan, B., & Ells, C. (2009). Values that matter, barriers that interfere: The Struggle of Canadian nurses to enact their values. *Canadian Journal of Nursing Research, 41*(1), 86–107.

Beaglehole, R., & Bonita, R. (1997). *Public health at the crossroads.* Cambridge, UK: Cambridge University Press.

Beardshaw, V., & Robinson, R. (1990). *New for old: Prospects for nursing in the 1990s.* London, UK: King's Fund.

Beardwood, B., Walters, V, Eyles, J., French, S. (1999). Complaints against nurses: A reflection of 'the new managerialism' and consumerism in health care. *Social Science & Medicine,* 48, 363–374.

Beasley, C. (1999). *What is feminism anyway?* Sydney: Allen & Unwin.

Beattie, A. (1991). Knowledge and control in health promotion: A test case for social policy and social theory. In J. Gabe, M. Calnan, & M. Bury. (Eds) *The sociology of the health service* (pp. 162–202). London, UK: Routledge.

Beck, U. (1992). *Risk society: Towards a new modernity.* London, UK: Sage.

———. (1999). *World risk society.* Malden, MA: Polity Press.

Becker, H.S. (1963). *Outsiders: Studies in the sociology of deviance.* New York, NY: Free Press.

Beiser, M. (2005, Mar/Apr). The health of immigrants and refugees in Canada. *Canadian Journal of Public Health,* 96, s30–s44.

Beiser, M., & Hou, F. (2001). Language acquisition, unemployment and depressive disorder among Southeast Asian refugees: A 10-year study. *Social Science & Medicine, 53*(10), 1321–1334.

Beiser, M., & Stewart, M. (2005, Mar/Apr). Reducing health disparities. *Canadian Journal of Public Health,* 96, 54–55.

Bell, S. (1987). Changing ideas: The medicalization of menopause. *Social Sciences and Medicine,* 24, 535–542.

Belle, D., (1990, Mar). Poverty and women's mental health. *American Psychologist, 45*(3), 385–389.

Bennett, C., & Shearman, R. (1989). Maternity services in New South Wales: Childbirth moves towards the 21st century. *Medical Journal of Australia,* 150, 673–676.

Benzeval, M., Judge, K., & Whitehead, M. (Eds). (1995). *Tackling Inequalities in Health: An agenda or action.* London, UK: King's Fund.

Berenson, C., Miller, L., & Findlay, D. (2009). Through medical eyes: The medicalization of women's bodies and women's lives. In S. Bolaria, & H. Dickinson (Eds), *Health, illness, and health care in Canada* (4th ed.) (pp. 239–258). Toronto, ON: Nelson Education Ltd.

Berger, P.L. (1966). *Invitation to sociology: A humanistic perspective.* Harmondsworth, UK: Penguin.

Berger, P.L., & Luckmann, T. (1967). *The social construction of reality.* Harmondsworth, UK: Penguin.

Berman, B.M., Swyers, J.P., Hartnoll, M., Sigh, B.B., & Bausell, B. (2000). The public debate over alternative medicine: The importance of finding a middle ground. *Alternative Therapies in Health and Medicine, 6*(1), 98–101.

Bertell, R. (1999). A pollution primer. In M. Wyman (Ed), *Sweeping the earth: Women taking action for a healthy planet* (pp. 35–55). Charlottetown, PEI: Gynergy Books.

Bierman, A. (2007, Dec. 4). Sex matters: Gender disparities in quality and outcomes of care. *Canadian Medical Association Journal, 177*(12). Retrieved from www.cmaj.ca/cgi/content/full/177/12/1520'

Bierman, A.S., Angus, J., Ahmad, F., Degani, N., Vahabi, M., Glazier, . . . Manuel, D. (2010). Access to health care services (Ch. 7). POWER Study, ECHO. Retrieved from www.powerstudy.ca/the-power-report/the-power-report-volume-1/access-to-health-ca

Biggs, B., & Skull, S.A. (2003). Refugee health: Clinical issues. In P. Allotey. (Ed), *The health of refugees: Public health perspectives from crisis to settlement* (pp. 54–67). Melbourne: Oxford University Press.

Birch, L. (1999). Development of food preferences. *Annual Review of Nutrition, 19,* 41–62

Bischoff, A., Bovier, P.A., Isah, R., Francoise, G., Ariel, E., & Loutan, L. (2003). Language barriers between nurses and asylum seekers: Their impact on symptom reporting and referral. *Social Science & Medicine, 53*(3), 503–512.

Bissonnette, F. et al. (2007, June 14). Incidence and complications of multiple gestation in Canada: Proceedings of an expert meeting. *Reproductive Biomedecine Online, 6,* 773–790. Retrieved from www.ncbi.nlm.nih.gov/pubmed/17582911.

Bittman, M. (1991). *Juggling time: How Australian families use time.* Canberra: Office of the Status of Women.

Blaxter, M. (1997). Whose fault is it? People's own conceptions of the reasons for health inequalities. *Social Science & Medicine, 44*(6), 747–756.

Blight Alert, A Simple Decision Support System for Prince Edward Island Potato Farmers. 2007. Agriculture and Agri-Food Canada. www4.agr.gc.ca/AAFC-AAC/display-afficher. do?id=1187716936117&lang=eng

Blishen, B. (1991). *Doctors in Canada: The changing world of medical practice.* Toronto, ON: University of Toronto Press

Bloom, A.L. (2000). *Health reform in Australia and New Zealand.* Melbourne: Oxford University Press.

Bloom, S. (2002). *The word as scalpel: A history of medical sociology.* New York, NY: Oxford University Press.

Bolaria, S., & Bolaris, R. (Eds). (1994). *Women, medicine and health.* Halifax, NS: Fernwood.

Bolaria, S., & Dickinson, H. (Eds). (2009). Health, illness, and health care in Canada (4th ed.). Toronto, ON: Nelson Education Ltd.

Bombardieri, D., & Easthope, G., (2000), Convergence between orthodox and alternative medicine: A theoretical elaboration and empirical test. *Health, 4*(4), 479–494.

Boon, H., & Kachan, M. (2008). Integrative medicine: A tale of two clinics. Biomed Central, BMC complementary and alternative medicine (pp. 1–8). Retrieved from www.biomedcentral.com/content/pdf/1472-6882-8-32.pdf.

Boon, H., Verhoef, M., Vanderheyden, L., & Westlake, K. (2006). Complementary and alternative medicine: A rising healthcare issue. *Healthcare Policy, 1*(3), 19–30.

Booz|Allen|Hamilton. (2008). *Postmarketing commitments study final report.* Washington, DC: Food and Drug Administration.

Bordo, S. (1993). *Unbearable weight: Feminism, western culture, and the body.* Berkeley, CA: University of California Press.

Borland, R., Donaghue, N., & Hill, D. (1994). Illnesses that Australians most feared in 1986 and 1993. *Australian Journal of Public Health, 18,* 366–369.

Boscoe, M., Basen, G., Alleyne, G., Bourrier-Lacroix, B., & White, S. (2004). The women's health movement in Canada. Looking back and moving forward. *Canadian Women's Studies, 24*(1), 7–14.

Boston, P. (1999). Cultural responsive cancer care in a cost-contained work-classification system. *Journal of Cancer Education, 14*(3), 148–153.

Bourdieu, P. (1984). *Distinction: A social critique of the judgement of taste.* London, UK: Routledge & Kegan Paul.

———. (1986). The forms of capital. In J. Richardson (Ed), *Handbook of theory and research for the sociology of education* (pp. 241–258). New York, NY: Greenwood Press.

Bourgeault, I. (2006). Sociological perspectives on health and health care. In D. Raphael, T. Bryant, & M. Rioux (Eds), *Staying alive, critical perspectives on health, illness, and health care* (pp. 35–57). Toronto, ON: Canadian Scholars' Press Inc.

Bowie, A. (2010, Nov. 19). Changing bad habits critical for NBers' health–minister. *The Daily Gleaner,* p. A6.

Boyd, M., & Vickers, M. (2009). The ebb and flow of immigration in Canada. In E. Grabb, & N. Guppy (Eds), *Social inequality in Canada* (5th ed.) (pp. 237–252). Toronto, ON: Pearson Prentice Hall.

Braithwaite, J. (1984). *Corporate crime in the pharmaceutical industry.* London, UK: Routledge & Kegan Paul.

Briar, Celia. (Ed) (2009). *Health hazards in women's work.* Wellington: Dunmore Publishing.

Broadbent, E. (2009, May 1). Barbarism lite. The Monitor, *Canadian Centre for Policy Alternatives.*

Broom, D. (1991). *Damned if we do: Contradictions in women's health care.* Sydney: Allen & Unwin.

———. (1997). *There should be more: Women's use of community health facilities.* Canberra: National Centre for Epidemiology and Population Health.

Broom, D.H., & Woodward, R.V. (1996). Medicalisation reconsidered: Toward a collaborative approach to care. *Sociology of Health and Illness, 18*(3), 57–78.

Brown, K., Kenny, S., & Turner, B.S. (2000). *Rhetorics of welfare: Uncertainty, choice and voluntary associations.* Basingstoke, UK: Macmillan.

Brown, P. (1995). Naming and framing: The social construction of diagnosis and illness. *Journal of Health and Social Behavior,* extra issue, 34–52.

———. (Ed). (2000). *Perspectives in medical sociology* (3rd ed.). Illinois: Waveland Press Inc.

———. (2000). Naming and framing: The social construction of diagnosis and illness. In P. Brown (Ed), *Perspectives in medical sociology* (3rd ed.) (pp. 74–103). Illinois: Waveland Press.

Brown, P., & Ferguson, F.T. (1995). 'Making a big stink': Women's work, women's relationships and toxic waste activism. *Gender & Society, 9*(2), 145–172.

Brown, P., & Mikkelsen, E.J. (1997). *No safe place: Toxic waste, leukemia and community action.* Berkeley, CA: University of California Press.

Brown, W., & Redman, S. (1995). Setting targets: A three-stage model for determining priorities for health promotion. *Australian Journal of Public Health,* 19, 263–269.

Browne, A., & Fiske, J. (2001, March). First Nations women's encounters with mainstream health. *Western Journal of Nursing Research, 23*(2), 126–147.

Brownridge, D.A., & Halli, S.S. (2002). Double jeopardy: Violence against immigrant women in Canada'. *Violence and Victims,* 17, 455–471.

Bryant, T. (2009). *An introduction to health policy.* Toronto, ON: Canadian Scholars' Press Inc.

Bryant, T., Raphael, D., & Rioux, M. (Eds) (2010). *Staying alive: Critical perspectives on health, illness and health care* (2nd ed.). Toronto: Canadian Scholars' Press Inc.

Buhler, S. (2008, Summer). Gender, poverty and HIV/AIDS among women in Ontario: Exploring intersections across three sectors. OWHN E-Bulletin, 1–14. Retrieved from www.owhn.on.ca/ebulletin.htm#a. Downloaded March 2010.

Burton, K., & Wong, I. (2004, April 27). A force to contend with: The gender gap closes in medical schools. *Canadian Medical Association Journal, 170*(9), 1385–1386.

Bury, M., (1982). Chronic illness as biographical disruption. *Sociology of Health and Illness, 4*(2), 167–182.

———. (2004). Defining and researching disability. In M. Bury, & J. Gabe (Eds), *The sociology of health and illness* (pp. 266–276). London, UK: Routledge Press.

Bury, M., & Gabe, J. (2004). (Eds). *The sociology of health and illness.* London, UK: Routledge Press.

Butler, J. (1990). *Gender trouble: Feminism and the subversion of identity.* London, UK: Routledge Press.

Butler-Jones, D. (2008). *The chief public health officer's report on the state of public health in Canada.* Ottawa, ON: Minister of Health.

Bytheway, B. (1995). *Ageism.* Buckingham, UK: Open University Press.

CAM Corp International. (2005). *Worldwide pharmaceutical promotion overview.* New Jersey.

Campbell, B., & Marchildon, G. (2007, Nov. 19). *Completing Tommy's vision.* Ottawa, ON: Canadian Centre for Policy Alternatives.

Canada Health Act. (1984). Retrieved from http://laws.justice.gc.ca/PDF/Statute/C/C-6.pdf

Canada Report. (2003). *Chronic diseases in Canada.* Canada report presented to the *CARMEN* Directing Board Meeting. San Juan, Puerto Rico. June 30, 2003.

Canada Year Book. (2007). Aboriginal Peoples. Ottawa, ON: Statistics Canada. Retrieved from www.statcan.gc.ca

Canada's Aboriginal Action Plan. (1998). Gathering strength: Canada's Aboriginal action plan. Retrieved from www.ahf.ca/downloads/gathering-strength.pdf

Canada's Food Guide, 2007. Health Canada. Retrieved from www.hc-sc.gc.ca/fn-an/alt_formats/hpfb-dgpsa/pdf/food-guide-aliment/print_eatwell_bienmang-eng.pdf

Canada's Research-Based Pharmaceutical Companies. (2002). *Improving health through innovation: a new deal for Canadians.* Ottawa, ON.

Canadian Association on Gerontology. (2011). Home care in Canada. Retrieved from www.cagacg.ca/publications/552_e.php

Canadian Association of Naturopathic Doctors. (n.d). Education and regulation: Regulated provinces. Retrieved from www.cand.ca/index.php?40

Canadian Business Online. (2007). The rich 1000: Canada's wealthiest people. Retrieved from www.canadianbusiness.com

Canadian Cancer Society. (2011). Prince Edward Island Cancer Stats. Retrieved from www.cancer.ca/Prince%20Edward%20Island/About%20cancer/Cancer%20statistics/PEI%20Canadian%20Cancer%20Statistics.aspx?sc_lang=en%3e.

Canadian Chiropractic Association. (2011). Facts and FAQ. Retrieved from www.chiropracticcanada.ca/en-us/FactsFAQs.aspx

Canadian Community Health Survey. (2010). Retrieved from www.statcan.gc.ca/cgi-bin/imdb/p2SV.pl'Function=getSurvey&SDDS=3226&lang=en&db=imdb&adm=8&dis=2

Canadian Council for Refugees. (2007). Refugee claimants: Some facts. Retrieved from www.ccrweb.ca/documents/claimsfacts07.htm

Canadian Council of Social Development. (2010). Employment and persons with disabilities in Canada. In D. Raphael (Ed), *Health promotion and quality of life in Canada.* Toronto, ON: Canadian Scholars' Press Inc.

Canadian Council on Learning. (2009, Oct. 7). Strategies for overcoming barriers to training and education for Canadians with disabilities. Retrieved from www.ccl-cca.ca/pdfs/LessonsInLearning/10_07_09.pdf

Canadian Council on Social Development. (2001, Nov. 15). Equality, inclusion and the health of Canadians. Ottawa, ON: CCSD.

Canadian Diabetes Association. (n.d.). Diabetes - Fact sheet. Retrieved from www.diabetes.ca/files/Diabetes_Fact_Sheet.pdf

Canadian Doctors for Medicare. (n.d.). The case for Medicare. Retrieved from www.canadiandoctorsformedicare.ca/the-case-for-medicare.html

Canadian Encyclopedia, The. (n.d.). Medical education. Retrieved from www.thecanadianencyclopedia.com/index.cfm?PgNm=TCE&Params=A1ARTA0005196

Canadian Environmental Law Association. (2008, Sept. 3). Press release: Environmental organizations issue criticism of Federal government for refusal to phase out cancer causing substances. Retrieved from www.cela.ca/newsevents/media-release/environmental-organizations-issue-criticism-federal-government-refusal-phas

Canadian Federation of Nurses' Union (CFNU). (2010a). International solidarity. Retrieved from www.nursesunions.ca/international-solidarity

———. (2010b, Jan.). The nursing workforce fact sheet. Retrieved from www.nursesunions.ca

Canadian Health Coalition. (2004 Oct.) Canadian healthcare manager: The verdict on Medicare. Retrieved from www.healthcoalition.ca/archive/chm.pdf

———. (2008, Oct. 6). Eroding public Medicare: Lessons and consequences of for-profit health care across Canada. Retrieved from www.healthcoalition.ca/archive/OHCPCR.pdf

Canadian Health Coalition. (2010). S.O.S Medicare 2: Looking forward (building on Tommy Douglas' vision of Medicare. Retrieved from http://healthcoalition.ca/wp-content/uploads/2010/02/looking-forward.pdf

Canadian Health Coalition. (2011). Retrieved from http://healthcoalition.ca/main/resources/a-call-to-care

Canadian Medical Association. (2004). National physician survey 2004: Results for family physicians. Retrieved from www.nationalphysiciansurvey.ca/nps/results/PDF-e/SP/Specialty/Family_Med/CCFP_C.pdf

———. (2007). National physician survey 2007: National results by FP/GP. Retrieved from www.nationalphysiciansurvey.ca/nps/2007_Survey/Results/ENG/National/pdf/Q28/Q28d_NON.CORE.only.pdf

Canadian Nurses Association. (2000). Strengthening the voice–The ninth decade of the Canadian Nurses Association. Retrieved from www.cna-aiic.ca/cna/documents/pdf/publications/ninth_decade_e.pdf

———. (2005, Jan.). Nursing staff mix: A key link to patient safety. *Nursing Now, Issues and Trends in Canadian Nursing.*

———. (2010). Nursing in Canada: Becoming a Registered Nurse. Retrieved from www.cna-aiic.ca/CNA/nursing/becoming/default_e.aspx

Canadian Nursing Advisory Committee. (2002). Final report: Our health, our future: Creating quality workplaces for Canadian nurses. Retrieved from www.hc-sc.gc.ca/hcs-sss/alt_formats/hpb-dgps/pdf/pubs/2002-cnac-cccsi-final/2002-cnac-cccsi-final-eng.pdf

Canadian Press. (2008). Walkerton study finds sharply higher risk of kidney disease. *CBC Online.* Retrieved from www.cbc.ca/health/story/2008/10/16/walkerton-study.html

Cant, S.L., & Sharma, U. (1999). *A new medical pluralism: Alternative medicine, doctors, patients and the state.* London, UK: Routledge.

Caplan, P. (1995). *They say you're crazy: How the world's most powerful psychiatrists decide who's normal.* MA: Perseus Books.

Capra, F. (1982). The turning point: Science, society and the rising culture. New York, NY: Simon & Schuster.

Care and conflict: Vietnamese medical beliefs and the Australian health care system. (1985). In I. Burnley, S. Encel, & G. McCall (Eds), *Immigration and ethnicity in the 1980s* (pp. 248–260). Melbourne: Longman Cheshire.

Caron, I., & Simpson, J. (2003, Nov.). Who's doing what? *Health Policy Research Bulletin, 7,* 28–29.

CARP. (2010, June10). *Open letter to Canada's finance ministers.* Retrieved from www1.carp.ca/PDF/Pension%20Open%20Letter%20Final%20June%2010%20Finance%20Ministers.pdf

Carpenter, D. (2008). Drug-review deadlines and safety problems. *New England Journal of Medicine, 359,* 96–98.

Carpenter, D., Zucker, E.J., & Avorn, J. (2008). Drug-review deadlines and safety problems. *New England Journal of Medicine, 358,* 1354–1361.

Carroll, W. (1984). The individual, class and corporate power in Canada. *Canadian Journal of Sociology, 9,* 245–268.

———. (2004). *Corporate power in a globalizing world: A study in elite social organization.* Toronto, ON: Oxford University Press.

———. (2009). Corporate Canada, globalization, and neoliberal democracy. In E. Grabb, & N. Guppy (Eds), Social inequality in Canada: Patterns, problems and policies (5th ed.) (pp. 29–43). Toronto, ON: Pearson Prentice Hall.

Carson, R. (1962). *Silent spring.* Cambridge, MA: The Riverside Press.

Carter, B. (2007). Reformatting nursing: The invidious effects of the growth of managerialism. *Health: An Interdisciplinary Journal for the Social Study of Health, Illness and Medicine, 11*(2), 265–272.

Cashman, P. (1989). The Dalkon Shield. In P. Grabosky, & A. Sutton. (Eds), *Stains on a white collar.* Sydney: Hutchinson.

Castles, S. (1992). Australian multiculturalism: Social policy and identity in a changing society. In G. Freeman & J. Jupp (Eds), Nations of immigrants: Australia, the United States, and international migration (pp. 184–201). Melbourne: Oxford University Press.

Castles, S., & Miller, M. (1998). *The age of migration* (2nd ed.). London, UK: Macmillan.

Castles, S., Foster, W., Iredale, R., & Withers, G. (1998). Immigration and Australia: Myths and realities. Sydney: Allen & Unwin.

CBC. (2008, May 12). A Miramichi pathologist under the legal microscope. Retrieved from www.cbc.ca/news/canada/new-brunswick/story/2008/05/12/f-pathologist-inquiry.html

———. (2009). Dr. Charles Smith: The man behind the public inquiry. Retrieved from www.cbc.ca/news/canada/story/2009/12/07/f-charles-smith-goudge-inquiry.html

———. (2010). Windsor hospital probes other cases of concern. Retrieved from www.cbc.ca/canada/windsor/story/2010/02/24/windsor-second-mastectomy-100224.html'ref=rss).

———. (2011, Jan.). Canadians not as healthy as they think: Poll. Retrieved from www.cbc.ca/health/story/2010/12/31/canada-weighs-in-poll-health-myths.html

———. (2004). Top ten greatest Canadians. Tommy Douglas: The greatest of them all. Retrieved from www.cbc.ca/10th/timelineContent/20041129_greatest.html

Chappell, N., & Penning, M. (2005). Family caregivers: Increasing demands in the context of 21st century globalization. In M. Johnson (Ed), *The Cambridge handbook of age and ageing* (pp. 455–462). New York, NY: Cambridge University Press.

———, & ———. (2009). *Understanding health, health care, and health policy in Canada.* Don Mills, ON: Oxford University Press.

Charman, K. (2006). Brave nuclear world (second of two parts). *World Watch Magazine, 19*(4).

Charmaz, K. (1983). Loss of self: A fundamental form of suffering in the chronically ill. *Sociology of Health and Illness, 5*(2), 168–195.

———. (1993). *Good days, bad days: The self in chronic illness.* New Brunswick, NJ: Rutgers University Press.

———. (1994). Identity dilemmas of chronically ill men. *The Sociological Quarterly,* 35, 269–288.

Chatterjee, P. (1996). Who is stealing our future: Industry's toxic addiction to estrogen mimickers & endocrine disruptors. *CAQ,* 15, 16–23.

Chen, J., & Millar, W. (2000, May 29). Are recent cohorts healthier than their predecessors? *Health Reports.*

Chen, J., Wilkins, R., & Ng, E. (1996, Winter). Health expectancy by immigrant status, 1986 and 1991. *Health Reports,* 8.

Chernobyl: Assessment of Radiological and Health Impact. (2002). *Update of Chernobyl: ten years on.* Retrieved from www.oecd-nea.org/rp/chernobyl/c01.html

Chirac, P., & Torreele, E. (2006). Global framework on essential health R&D. *Lancet,* 367, 1560–1561.

Chung, L. (2006, June 6). Education and earnings. *Perspectives on Labour and Income,* 7. Retrieved from www.statcan.gc.ca/english.freepub/75-001-x20061089291perspectivesonlabourandincome

CIHI. (2004). *Giving birth in Canada: Providers of infant and maternity care.* Ottawa, ON: CIHI.

———. (2006). *Health care in Canada.* Ottawa, ON: Statistics Canada.

———. (2007a). *Health care in Canada.* Ottawa, ON: CIHI.

———. (2007b, Aug. 14). Patient safety in Canada: An update. *Analysis in Brief.* Ottawa, ON: CIHI.

———. (2008). Health care expenditures, health care in Canada. Ottawa, ON: CIHI.

———. (2008a). Canada's health care providers 2008: Provincial profiles: A look at 24 health occupations. Retrieved from http://secure.cihi.ca/cihiweb/products/provincial_profiles_2010_e.pdf

———. (2008b). Health care in Canada, Health care expenditures. Retrieved from http://secure.cihi.ca/cihiweb/products/HCIC_2008_e.pdf

———. (2008c). Health care in Canada. Ottawa, ON: Statistics Canada.

———. (2009). Drug expenditure in Canada, 1985 to 2008. Ottawa, ON: CIHI.

———. (2009a). Health care in Canada 2009: A decade in review. Ottawa, ON: CIHI. Retrieved from http://secure.cihi.ca/cihiweb/products/HCIC_2009_Web_e.pdf

———. (2009b). National health expenditure trends, 1975–2009. Ottawa, ON: CIHI. Retrieved from http://secure.cihi.ca/cihiweb/products/National_health_expenditure_trends_1975_to_2009_en.pdf

———. (2009c). Supply, migration and distribution of Canadian physicians. Ottawa, ON: CIHI. Retrieved from www.cihi.ca/cihiweb/dispPage.jsp?cw_page=home_e

———. (2010). Health indicators 2010. Ottawa, ON: CIHI.

———. (2010a). Regulated nurses: Canadian trends, 2004–2008. Ottawa, ON: CIHI.

CIHR. (2006). Research finding solutions to HIV/AIDS. Retrieved from www.cihr.ca/e/documents/wad_brochure2%281%29.pdf

———. (2006). Child health. Retrieved from www.cihr-irsc.gc.ca/e/documents/child_health_mpkit_2005_e.pdf

———. (2011). The facts: Research about Aboriginal health. Retrieved from www.cihr-irsc.gc.ca/e/43377.html

Clark, J. (2008). *Health, illness and medicine in Canada* (5th ed.). Don Mills, ON: Oxford University Press.

Clarke, J., Gewirtz, S., & McLaughlin. E. (Eds). (2000). *New managerialism, new welfare.* London, UK: The Open University and Sage.

Clarke, A., Shim, J., Mamo, L., Fosket, J., & Fishman, J. (2005). Biomedicalization: Technoscientific transformations of health, illness and U.S. biomedicine. In P. Conrad (Ed), *The sociology of health and illness: Critical perspectives* (7th ed.) (pp. 442–455). New York, NY: Worth Publishers.

Clement, W. (1975). *The Canadian corporate elite.* Toronto, ON: McClelland and Stewart.

Cleveland, G., & Krashinsky, M. (1998). *The economic rationale for public investment in young children: A policy study.* Toronto, ON: Child Care Advocacy Association of Ontario.

———. (2003). *Fact and fantasy: Eight myths about early childhood education.* Toronto, ON: Childcare Resources and Research Unit, University of Toronto.

Coburn, D. (1988a). Canadian medicine: Dominance or proletarianization. *The Milbank Quarterly,* 66(2), 92-116.

———. (1988b). The development of Canadian nursing: Professionalization and proletarianization. *International Journal of Health Services,* 18(3), 437–456.

———. (1998). State authority, medical dominance, and trends in the regulation of health professions: The Ontario case. In D. Coburn, C. D'Arcy, & G. Torrance (Eds), *Health and Canadian society: Sociological perspectives* (3rd ed.) (pp. 332–46). Toronto, ON: University of Toronto Press.

———. (2000). Income inequality, social cohesion and the health status of populations: The role of neo-liberalism. *Social Science & Medicine,* 51(1), 135-46.

———. (2001). Health, health care, and neo-liberalism. In P. Armstrong, H. Armstrong, & D. Coburn (Eds), *Unhealthy times: Political economy perspectives on health and care in Canada* (pp. 45–65). Toronto, ON: Oxford University Press.

———. (2004). Beyond the income inequality hypothesis: Globalization, class, and health inequalities. *Social Science and Medicine,* 58, 41–56.

———. (2006). Health and health care: A political economy perspective. In D. Raphael, T. Bryant, & M. Rioux (Eds), *Staying alive: Critical perspectives on health illness, and health care* (pp. 59–84). Toronto, ON: Canadian Scholars' Press Inc.

Coburn, D., D'Arcy, C., & Torrance G. (Eds). (1998). *Health and Canadian society (sociological perspectives)* (3rd ed.). Toronto, ON: University of Toronto Press.

Coburn, D., Torrance, G, & Kaufert, J, (1983). Medical dominance in Canadian historical perspective: The rise and fall of medicine. *International Journal of Health Services,* 13, 407–432.

Coburn, D., & Willis, E. (2000). The medical profession: Knowledge, power, and autonomy. In G. L. Albrecht, R. Fitzpatrick, &

S. C. Scrimshaw (Eds), *Handbook of social studies in health and medicine* (pp. 377–393). London, UK: Sage.

Cockerham, W.C. (2004). *Medical sociology* (9th ed.). Englewood Cliffs, NJ: Prentice Hall.

Cocozza, J.J., & Steadman, H.J. (1978). Prediction in psychiatry: An example of misplaced confidence in experts. *Social Problems, 25,* 265–76.

Code of Advertising Acceptance. (2009). Pickering: Pharmaceutical Advertising Advisory Board.

Code of Conduct: January 2008. (2008). Ottawa, ON: Rx&D.

Code, L. (1993). Feminist theory. In S. Burt, L. Code, & L. Dorney. (Eds) *Changing patterns: Women in Canada.* (2nd ed.). (pp. 19–58). Toronto, ON: McClelland & Stewart Inc.

Cohen, R. (1991). Women of color in white households: Coping strategies of live-in domestic workers. *Qualitative Sociology 14*(2), 197–215.

Colborn, T., Dumanoski, D., & Myers J.P. (1996). *Our stolen future: Are we threatening our fertility, intelligence, and survival?* Dutton: Penguin

Coleman, J. (1988). Social capital in the creation of human capital. *American Journal of Sociology*, 94, 95–120.

Coleman, V. (1994). Betrayal of trust. *British Medical Journal*, 42, 9602.

Collins, J. (1991). *Migrant hands in a distant land* (2nd ed.). Sydney: Pluto Press.

———. (1996). The changing political economy of Australian racism. In E. Vasta & S. Castles (Eds), *The teeth are smiling: The persistence of racism in multicultural Australia* (pp. 73–96). Sydney: Allen & Unwin.

Collins, J., Noble, G., Poynting, S., & Tabar, P. (2000). *Kebabs, kids, cops and crime: Youth, ethnicity and crime.* Sydney: Pluto Press.

Collins, M., Bradley, C.P., O'Sullivan, T., & Perry, I.P. (2009). Co-self-care coping strategies in people with diabetes: A qualitative exploratory study. *BMC Endocrine Disorders, 9*(6). doi: 10.1186/1472-6823-9-6.

Collins, R. (1975). *Conflict sociology: Towards an explanatory science.* New York, NY: Academic Press.

Collyer, F. (2004). The corporatisation and commercialisation of CAM. In P. Tovey, G. Easthope, & J. Adams (Eds), *The mainstreaming of complementary medicine.* London, UK: Routledge.

Cone, M. (2008, Nov. 10). Prescription drugs can deliver high doses of phthalates. *Environmental Health News.* Retrieved from www.environmentalhealthnews.org/ehs/news/prescription-drugs-can-deliver-high-doses-of-phthalates

Connell, R.W. (1977). *Ruling class, ruling culture.* Cambridge, UK: Cambridge University Press.

———. (1983). *Which way is up: Essays on sex, class and culture.* Sydney: Allen & Unwin.

———. (1988). Class inequalities and 'just health'. *Community Health Studies, 12*(2), 212–217.

———. (1987). *Gender and power.* Sydney: Allen & Unwin.

Connell, R. W., & Irving, T. H. (1992). *Class structure in Australian history: Poverty and progress* (2nd ed.). Melbourne: Longman Cheshire.

Conrad, P. (1992). Medicalization and social control. *Annual Review of Sociology*, 18, 209–232.

———. (1997). Public eyes and private genes: Historical frames, news constructions and social problems. *Social Problems, 44*(2), 139–154.

———. (Ed). (2005). *The sociology of health & illness (critical perspectives)* (7th ed.). New York, NY: Worth Publishers.

———. (2007). *The medicalization of society.* Baltimore, MD: Johns Hopkins University Press.

Conrad, P., & Gabe, J. (1999). Introduction: Sociological perspectives on the new genetics: An overview. *Sociology of Health and Illness, 21*(5), 505–516.

Conrad, P., & Potter, D. (2000). From hyperactive children to ADHD adults: Observations on the expansion of medical categories. *Social Problems, 47*, 559–582.

Conrad, P., & Schneider, J. (1992). *Deviance and medicalization: From badness to sickness* (2nd ed.). Philadelphia, PA: Temple University Press.

Cooley, C.H. (1964/1906). *Human nature and the social order.* New York, NY: Scribner's.

Cooper, N., Stevenson, C., & Hale, G. (Eds). (1996). *Integrating perspectives on health.* Buckingham, UK: Open University Press.

Council of Canadians with Disabilities. (2010). A call to combat poverty and exclusion of Canadians with disabilities. In D. Raphael (Ed), *Health promotion and quality of life in Canada* (pp. 228–233). Toronto, ON: Canadian Scholars' Press Inc.

Covey, H. (2005). Western Christianity's two historical treatments of people with disabilities or mental illness. *The Social Science Journal, 42*(1), 107–114.

Cox, D.R. (1989). *Welfare practice in a multicultural society.* Sydney: Prentice Hall.

Craib, I. (1992). *Modern social theory* (2nd ed.). London: Harvester Wheatsheaf.

Cranswick, K., & Dosman, D. (2008). Eldercare: What we know today. *Canadian Social Trends.* Ottawa, ON: Statistics Canada.

Creatore, M., Moineddin, R., Booth, G., Manuel, D., DesMeules, M., McDermott, S., & Glazier, R. (2010, May 18). Age-and sex-related prevalence of diabetes mellitus among immigrants to Ontario, Canada. *Canadian Medical Association Journal*, 781–791.

Crompton, R. (1998). *Class and stratification: An introduction to current debates* (2nd ed.). Cambridge: Polity Press.

Crompton, R., Devine, F., Savage, M., & Scott, J. (Eds). (2000). *Renewing class analysis.* Oxford, UK: Blackwell Publishers.

Crompton, S. (2000, Winter). Health. *Canadian Social Trends.* Statistics Canada, 59, 12–17.

———. (2010). Living with disability series: Life satisfaction of working-age women with disabilities. *Canadian Social Trends, Statistics Canada*, 24–32.

Crotty, M., Germov, J., & Rodwell, G. (Eds). (2000, Apr. 27–28). A race for a place: Eugenics, Darwinism and social thought and practice in Australia. *Proceedings of the History & Sociology of Eugenics Conference.* Newcastle, UK: University of Newcastle, Faculty of Arts and Social Science.

Crotty, P., & Germov, J. (2004). Food and class In J. Germov & L. Williams, L. (Eds), *A sociology of food and nutrition: The social appetite* (2nd ed.). Melbourne: Oxford University Press.

Cuff, E.C., Sharrock, W.W., & Francis, D.W. (2005). Perspectives in Sociology, 5th edn, Routledge, London.

Curry-Stevens, A. (2009). When economic growth doesn't trickle down: The wage dimensions of income polarization. In D. Raphael (Ed), *Social determinants of health* (2nd ed.) (pp. 41–60). Toronto, ON: Canadian Scholars' Press Inc.

CWHN. (2006). Maternity care for rural women: A thing of the past. *Network 8*(3/4), 11.

DND denies blame for cancer in Shannon, Que. (2010, Jan. 29). Retrieved from www.cbc.ca/canada/montreal/story/2010/01/29/qc-gvt-defense-shannon-water.html

Dahrendorf, R. (1959). *Class and class conflict in industrial society.* Stanford: Stanford University Press.

Daly, J., Kellehear, A., & Glicksman, M. (1997). *The public health researcher.* Melbourne: Oxford University Press.

Daniel, A. (1998). *Scapegoats for a profession: Uncovering procedural injustice.* Amsterdam: Harwood Academic.

Davidson, K. (1969). Conceptions of illness and health practices in a Nova Scotia community. *Canadian Journal of Public Health, 61,* 232–241.

Davies, C. (1977) Continuities in the development of hospital nursing in Britain. *Journal of Advanced Nursing, 2,* 479–493.

Davies, J. (2009). The distribution of wealth and economic inequality. In E. Grabb, & N. Guppy (Eds), *Social inequality in Canada: Patterns, problems and policies* (5th ed.) (pp 92–105). Toronto, ON: Pearson Prentice Hall.

Davis, D. (1996) The cultural construction of the premenstrual and menopause syndromes. In C. Sargent, & C. Bertrell (Eds), *Gender and health: An international perspective.* Toronto, ON: Pearson.

Davis, R. (2000). Refugee experiences and Southeast Asian women's mental health. *Western Journal of Nursing Research, 22*(2), 144–168.

Daw, J. (2002, Oct.). Is PMDD real? *Monitor on Psychology, 33*(9), 58-59, American Psychological Association.

De Bruyn, T. (2002). *A Summary of national data on complementary and alternative health care. Current status and future development: A discussion paper.* Ottawa, ON: Health Canada.

Delaney, J. (2006, Mar. 23). Potato farms a hotbed for cancer. *The Epoch Times.* Retrieved from http://english.epochtimes.com/news/6-3-23/39627.html

DeLeo, M. (Director). (2003). *Chernobyl heart: The dark side of nuclear power.* [Motion picture]. United States: Home Box Office Production.

Denton, M., & Kusch, K. (2006). *Well-being through the senior years.* Ottawa, ON: Social Development Canada.

Denton, M., & Walters, V. (1999). Gender differences in structural and behavioral determinants of health: An analysis of the social production of health. *Social Science and Medicine,* 48, 1221–1235.

Denton, M., & Zeytinoglu, I. (2010, Mar.). Editorial: An introduction to context, practice, and policy in caring for an aging population. *Canadian Journal of Aging, 29*(1), 1–4.

Denzin, N. (1997). *Interpretive ethnography.* London, UK: Sage.

Department of Finance, C. (2003). Building the Canada we want. Budget 2003: Investing in Canada's health care system. Retrieved from www.fin.gc.ca/budget03/booklets/bkheae.htm

Department of Health and Social Security (DHSS). (1980). *Inequalities in Health.* Report of a working group chaired by Sir Douglas Black. London, UK: Author. DHSS.

Dew, K. (2000). Apostasy to orthodoxy: Debates before a commission of inquiry into chiropractic. *Sociology of Health and Illness, 22*(3), 310–330.

Diebel, L. (1997). Ground coffee practically enslaved workers in Guatemala, Workers in Guatemala pay a high price for coffee. *Toronto Star.* 28 September: F1.

Dhalla, I., Kwong, J., Streiner, D., Baddour, R., Waddell, A., & Johnson, I. (2002, Apr. 16). Characteristics of first-year students in Canadian medical schools. *Canadian Medical Association Journal, 166*(8).

DiMasi, J.A., Hansen, R.W., & Grabowski, H.G. (2003). The price of innovation: New estimates of drug development costs. *Journal of Health Economics,* 22, 151–185.

———. (2005). Reply: Extraordinary claims require extraordinary evidence. *Journal of Health Economics,* 24, 1034–1044.

Dossa, P. (2009). *Racialized bodies, disabling worlds: Storied lives of immigrant Muslim women.* Toronto, ON: University of Toronto Press.

Douglas Coldwell Foundation. (n.d.). T.C. 'Tommy' Douglas: The Greatest Canadian, 1904–1986. Retrieved from www.dcf.ca/en/tommy_douglas.htm

Doyal, L. (1995). *What makes women sick: Gender and the political economy of health.* New Brunswick, NJ: Rutgers University Press.

Drugs for Neglected Diseases Working Group, & Campaign for Access to Essential Medicines. (2001). Fatal imbalance: The crisis in research and development for drugs for neglected diseases. Geneva: M'decins Sans Frontieres.

Druss, G., & Rosenhek, A. (1999). Association between use of unconventional therapies and conventional medical services. *Journal of the American Medical Association, 282*(7), 651–656.

Dubos, R. (1959). *Mirage of health: Utopias, progress, and biological change.* New York, NY: Harper & Row.

Duckett, S.J. (2000). *The Australian health care system.* Melbourne: Oxford University Press.

Duffy, A., & Mandell, N. (2010). The growth of poverty and social inequality: Losing faith in social justice. In V. Zawilski (Ed), *Inequality in Canada* (2nd ed.) (pp. 251–265). Toronto, ON: Oxford University Press.

Dunning, E., & Mennell, S. (Eds). (2003). *Norbert Elias* (4 volumes). London, UK: Sage.

Durkheim, E. (1984/1893). *The division of labor in society.* (W. Halls, Trans.). New York, NY: Free Press.

———. (1951/1897). Suicide. New York, NY: Free Press.

Dyck, R., Osgood, N., Hsiang, T., Gao, A., & Stang, M.R. (2010, Jan.). Epidemiology of diabetes mellitus among First Nations and non-First Nations adults. *Canadian Medical Association Journal,* 19, 1–8.

Easthope, G. (1985). Marginal healers. In K. Jones. (Ed), *Sickness and sectarianism* (pp. 51–71). Aldershot: Gower.

Easthope, G., Beilby, J., Gill, G., & Tranter, B. (1998). Acupuncture in Australian general practice: Practitioner characteristics. *Medical Journal of Australia, 169*(4), 197–200.

Easthope, G., Gill, G., Beilby, J., & Tranter, B. (1999). Acupuncture in Australian general practice: Patient characteristics. *Medical Journal of Australia, 170*(6), 259–262.

Easthope, G., & Julian, R. (1996). Mental health and ethnicity. In M. Clinton & S. Nelson (Eds), *Mental health and nursing practice* (pp. 121–137). Sydney: Prentice Hall.

Easthope, G., Tranter, B., & Gill, G. (2000a). General practitioners' attitudes toward complementary therapies. *Social Science & Medicine*, 51, 1555–1561.

Easthope, G., Tranter, B., & Gill, G. (2000b). The normal medical practice of referring patients for complementary therapies among Australian general practitioners. *Journal of Complementary Therapies in Medicine, 8*(4), 241–247.

Easthope, G., Tranter, B., & Gill, G. (2001). The incorporation of an alternative therapy by Australian general practitioners: The case of acupuncture. *Australian Journal of Primary Health-Interchange*, 7, 1.

Egan, C., & Gardner, L. (1999). Racism, women's health and reproductive freedom. In E. Dua and A. Robertson (Eds), *Scratching the surface: Canadian anti-racist feminist thought*. Toronto, ON: Women's Press.

Ehrenreich, B., & English, D. (1973). *Witches, midwives and nurses*. New York, NY: Old Westbury Feminist Press.

———, & ———. (1974). *Complaints and disorders: The sexual politics of sickness*. London, UK: Compendium.

———, & ———. (1979). *For her own good: 150 years of experts' advice*. London, UK: Pluto Press.

Eisenberg, D.M., Davis, R.B., Ettner, S.L., Appel, S., Wilkey, S., Van Rompay, M., & Kessler, R.C. (1998). Trends in alternative medicine use in the United States, 1990–97. *Journal of the American Medical Association, 289*(18), 1569–1575.

Elias, B., O'Neil, J.D., & Yassi, A. (1997). Wollaston Lake: The uranium mining industry and the perceptions of risk. Centre for Aboriginal Health Research. Retrieved from www.umanitoba.ca/centres/cahr/researchreports/WOLLASTON%20LAKE.pdf

Ellis, C. (1995). *Final negotiations: A story of love, loss, and chronic illness*. Philadelphia, PA: Temple University Press.

———. (1998). Exploring loss through autoethnographic inquiry. In J. Harvey (Ed), *Perspectives on loss: A sourcebook*. New York, NY: Brunner/Mazel.

Elston, M.A. (1991). The politics of professional power: Medicine in a changing health service. In J. Gabe, M. Calnan, & M. Bury (Eds), *The sociology of the health service* (pp. 58–88). London, UK: Routledge.

Emke, I. (2002). Patients in the new economy: The 'sick role' in a time of economic discipline. *Animus: The Canadian Journal of Philosophy and Humanities*, 7. Retrieved from www.swgc.mun.ca/animus

Engel, G.L. (1977). The need for a new medical model: A challenge for biomedicine. *Science*, 196, 129–136.

———. (1980). The clinical application of the biopsychosocial model. *American Journal of Psychiatry, 137*(5), 535–544.

Engels, F. (1958/1845). *The condition of the working class in England*. (W.O. Henderson & W.H. Chaloner, Trans.). Oxford, UK: Basil Blackwell.

Environment Canada. (2009). Clean air on line. Retrieved from www.ec.gc.ca/cleanair-airpur/Health_Concerns-WSC8A1FE65-1_En.htm

Environmental Research Foundation. (1996, April). *Risk assessment package*. Annapolis, MD: Author.

Epp, J. (1986). *Achieving health for all: A framework for health promotion*. Ottawa, ON: Health and Welfare Canada.

Ernst, E., & White, A. (2000). The BBC survey of complementary medicine use in the UK. *Journal of Complementary Therapies in Medicine, 8*(1), 32–36.

Este, D. (2007). Cultural competency and social work practice in Canada: A retrospective examination. *Canadian Social Work Review, 24*(1), 93–104.

Estroff, S. (1995). Whose story is it anyway? Authority, voice, and responsibility in narratives of chronic illness. In S. Toombs, D. Barnard, & R. Carson (Eds), *Chronic illness: From experience to policy*. Bloomington, IN: Indiana University Press.

Ethno-Racial People with Disabilities Coalition of Ontario and the Ontario Women's Health Network. (2008). *Ten+ years later: We are visible*. Toronto, ON: OWHN.

External Advisory Committee on Smart Regulation. (n.d.). Risk management. Retrieved from www.smartregulation.gc.ca/en/05/01/i4-01.asp

Exworthy, M., & Halford, S. (Eds). (1999). Professionals and the new managerialism in the public sector. Buckingham, UK: Open University Press.

Ezzy, D. (2000a). Illness narratives: Time, hope and HIV. *Social Science & Medicine*, 50, 605–617.

———. (2000b). Fate and agency in job loss narratives. *Qualitative Sociology, 23*(1), 121–134.

———. (2001). *Qualitative analysis*. Sydney: Allen & Unwin.

Fadiman, A. (1997). *The spirit catches you and you fall down*. New York, NY: Farrar, Straus and Giroux.

Famous Canadian Physicians. (n.d.). Library and Archives Canada. Retrieved from http://www.collectionscanada.gc.ca/physicians/030002-2500-e.html

Fathers Involvement Research Alliance. (2010). Child care (parental and non-parental care). Retrieved from www.fira.ca/article.php'id=88

Fausto-Sterling, A. (2005). The bare bones of sex: Part 1. 'Sex and Gender' *Signs 30*(2), 1491–1528.

———. (2008, Oct.). The bare bones of race. *Social Studies of Science*, 38/5, 657–694.

Feldberg, G., & Vipond, R. (2006). Cracks in the foundation: The origins and development of the Canadian and American health care systems. In D. Raphael, T. Bryant, & M. Rioux (Eds), *Staying alive, critical perspectives on health illness, and health care* (220–239). Toronto, ON: Canadian Scholars' Press Inc.

Fenta, S., Hyman, I., & Noh, H. (2007). Health service utilization by Ethiopian immigrants and refugees in Toronto. *Journal of Minority Health*, 9, 349–357.

Ferndandes, C., Bouthillette, F., Raboud, J., Bullock, L., Moore, C., Christenson, . . . Way, M. (1999, Nov. 16). Violence in the emergency department: A survey of health care workers. *Canadian Medical Association Journal*, 161(10), 1245–1248.

Ferrari, L., & Drew, L. (2005). *Different minds: Living with Alzheimer disease*. Fredericton, NB: Alzheimer Society of New Brunswick.

Findlay, D., & Miller, L. (2002). Through medical eyes: The medicalization of women's bodies and women's lives. In B.S. Bolaria, & H. Dickinson (Eds), *Health, illness and health care in Canada* (3rd ed.). Scarborough, ON: Nelson Thomson Learning.

Finkelstein, S., & Temin, P. (2008). *Reasonable Rx: solving the drug price crisis*. Upper Saddle River, NJ: FT Press.

Finn, E. (2007). The fateful summer of '62. Canadian Centre for Policy Alternatives. Retrieved from www.policyalternatives.ca/publications/monitor/july-2007-fateful-summer-62

———. (2009). Oh, Oh, Canada. *The Monitor*. Ottawa, ON: Canadian Centre for Policy Alternatives.

Firestone, S. (1979/1970). *The Dialectic of Sex; the case for feminist revolution*. Toronto, ON: Women's Press.

Flavin, Christopher. (2006). Nuclear revival: Don't bet on it! *World Watch Magazine*, 19, 4. Retrieved from www.worldwatch.org/node/4107

Flexner Report, The. (1910). Medical education in the United States and Canada.

Flynn, R. (2002). Clinical governance and governmentality. *Health, Risk & Society*, 4(2), 155–173.

Food Banks Canada. (2010). Hunger count. Retrieved from www.foodbankscanada.ca/documents/HungerCount2010_

Forbes. (2007, Mar. 8). The world's billionaires. *Forbes Online*. Retrieved from www.forbes.com/2007/03/07/billionaires-worlds-richest_07billionaires_cz_lk_af_0308billie_land.html

Foucault, M. (1975). *The birth of the clinic: An archaeology of medical perception*. (A.M. Sheridan, Trans.). New York, NY: Vintage Books.

———. (1979). *Discipline and punish*. Harmondsworth, UK: Penguin.

———. (1988). *Madness and civilization: A history of insanity in the age of reason*. (R. Howard, Trans.). New York, NY: Vintage Books.

Ford-Gilboe, M., Wuest, J., Varcoe, C., Davies, L., Merritt-Gray, M., Campbell, J., & Wilk, P. (2009). Modelling the effects of intimate partner violence and access to resources on women's health in the early years after leaving an abusive partner. *Social Science & Medicine*. 68(6). (pp. 1021–1029).

Ford-Gilboe, M., Wuest, J., Varcoe, C., & Merritt-Gray, M. (2006). Developing an evidence based health advocacy intervention to support women who have left abusive partners. *Canadian Journal of Nursing Research*, 38(1), 147–168.

Fowler, N. (1998). Providing primary health care to immigrants and refugees: The North Hamilton experience. *Canadian Medical Association Journal* 159, 388–391.

Fox, M., Dwyer, D.J., & Ganster, D.C. (1993). Effects of stressful job demands and control on physiological and attitudinal outcomes in a hospital setting. *Academy of Management Journal*, 36, 289–318.

Fox, N.J. (1993). *Postmodernism, sociology and health*. Buckingham, UK: Open University Press.

Franco, E., Duarte-Franco, E., & Ferenczy, A. (2001, Apr. 3). Cervical cancer: Epidemiology, prevention and the role of human papillomavirus infection. *Canadian Medical Association Journal*, 164(7).

Frankel, G., Speechley, M., & Wade, T. (1996). *The sociology of health and health care: A Canadian perspective*. Toronto, ON: Copp Clark.

Freidson, E. (1970). Profession of medicine. New York, NY: Harper & Row.

———. (1986). *Professional powers: A study of the institutionalisation of formal knowledge*. Chicago, IL: University of Chicago Press.

———. (1988). *Profession of medicine: A study of the sociology of applied knowledge*. Chicago, IL: University of Chicago Press.

———. (1994). *Professionalism reborn: Theory, prophecy and policy*. Cambridge, UK: Polity Press.

———. (2001). *Professionalism: The third logic*. Cambridge, UK: Polity Press.

Freund, P., McGuire, M., & Podhurst, L. (2003). *Health, illness, and the social body: A critical sociology* (4th ed.). New Jersey: Prentice-Hall.

Fuhrer, R., Stansfeld, S.A., Chemali, J., & Shipley, M.S. (1999). Gender, social relations and mental health: Prospective findings from an occupational cohort (Whitehall II study). *Social Science and Medicine*, 48(1), 77–87.

Furlow, B. (2008, Sept.). Special report: Cancer inquiry unveils Canada's troubled health system. *The Lancet*, 9. Retrieved from www.thelancet.com/ocology

Gabe, J., Kelleher, D., & Williams, G. (Eds). (1994). *Challenging medicine*. London, UK: Routledge.

Gagnon, M.-A., & Lexchin, J. (2008). The cost of pushing pills: A new estimate of pharmaceutical promotion expenditures in the United States. *PLoS Medicine*, 5, e1.

Galabuzi, G-E. (2001). Canada's creeping economic apartheid. Toronto, ON: CJS Foundation. Retrieved from www.socialjustics.org

———. (2009). Social exclusion. In D. Raphael (Ed), *Social determinants of health* (2nd ed.) (pp. 252–279). Toronto, ON: Canadian Scholars' Press Inc.

Gamarnikow, E. (1978). Sexual division of labour: The case of nursing. In A. Kuhn & A. M. Wolpe (Eds), *Feminism and materialism* (pp. 96–123). London, UK: Routledge & Kegan Paul.

Game, A., & Pringle, R. (1983). *Gender at work*. Sydney: Allen & Unwin.

Garattini, S., & Bertele, V. (2002). Efficacy, safety, and cost of new anticancer drugs. *BMJ*, 325, 269–271.

Gardner, D. M., Mintzes, B., & Ostry, A. (2003). Direct-to-consumer prescription drug advertising in Canada: Permission by default. *Canadian Medical Association Journal*, 169, 425–428.

Garfinkel, H. (1967). *Studies in ethnomethodology*. Englewood Cliffs, NJ: Prentice Hall.

Gathering strength: Canada's Aboriginal action plan. (1998). Minister of Indian Affairs and Northern government. Retrieved from www.ahf.ca/downloads/gathering-strength.pdf

Geddes, J. (2010, April 12). The health care time bomb—Our aging population will make unthinkable reforms inevitable. *Macleans Magazine*. Retrieved from www2.macleans.ca/2010/04/12/the-health-care-time-bomb/

Germov, J., & Williams, L. (Eds). (2004). *A sociology of food and nutrition: The social appetite* (2nd ed.). Melbourne: Oxford University Press.

Germov, J. (1993, Oct.). The waiting list bypass. *Health Forum, 27*, 23–24.

Gesensway, D. (2001). Reasons for sex-specific and gender-specific study of health topics. *Annals of Internal Medicine, 135*, 935–938.

Gibbs, L. M. (1998). *Love Canal: The story continues*. Gabriola Island, B.C: New Society Publishers.

Giddens, A. (1984). *The constitution of society: Outline of the theory of structuration*. Cambridge, UK: Polity Press.

———. (1986). *Sociology: A brief but critical introduction* (2nd ed.). London, UK: Macmillan.

———. (1991). *Modernity and self-identity: Self and society in the late modern age*. Stanford, CA: Stanford University Press.

———. (1996). In defence of sociology. Cambridge, UK: Polity Press.

———. (1997). *Sociology* (3rd ed.). Cambridge, UK: Polity Press.

Gillespie, J.A. (1991). *The price of health: Australian governments and medical politics 1910–1960*. Melbourne: Cambridge University Press.

Gillespie, R., & Gerhardt, C. (1995). Social dimensions of sickness and disability. In G. Moon & R. Gillespie (Eds), *Society and health: An introduction to social science for health professionals* (pp. 79–94). London, UK: Routledge.

Gilligan, C. (1993). *In a different voice*. Boston, MA: Harvard University Press.

Gionet, L. (2008, Nov. 26). Inuit in Canada: Selected findings of the 2006 Census. *Canadian Social Trends*. Ottawa, ON: Statistics Canada.

———. (2009a, May 12). First Nations people: Selected findings of the 2006 Census. *Canadian Social Trends*. Ottawa, ON: Statistics Canada.

———. (2009b, Jan. 20). Métis in Canada: Selected findings of the 2006 Census. *Canadian Social Trends*. Ottawa, ON: Statistics Canada.

Glik, D. 1990, The redefinition of the situation: The social construction of spiritual healing experiences. *Sociology of Health and Illness, 12*(2), 151–168.

Globe and Mail, The. (2005, 31 Oct.). *Running from the shadows of despair*. Retrieved from http://m.theglobeandmail.com/news/national/article853643.ece?service=mobile

———. (2010, 27 May). The costs of sustainability.

Glover, J., Harris, K., & Tennant, S. (1999). *A social health atlas of Australia* (2nd ed.). Adelaide: Public Health Informational Development Unit.

Goar, Carole. (2009, Sept. 9). Quebec shows the way on poverty. *Toronto Star*.

Goffman, E. (1961). *Asylums: Essays on the social situation of mental patients and other inmates*. Harmondsworth, UK: Penguin.

———. (1963). *Stigma: Notes on the management of spoiled identity*. New York, NY: Simon & Schuster.

Goldbeck-Wood, S., Dorozynski, A., Lie, L.G., Yamauchi, M., Zinn, C., Josefson, D., & Ingram, M. ((1996, July 20). Complementary medicine is booming worldwide. *British Medical Journal, 313*, 131–133.

Goldthorpe, J. (1996). Class and politics in advanced industrial societies. In D.J. Lee & B.S. Turner. (Eds). *Conflicts about class*. London, UK: Longman.

Gorey, K., Holowaty, E., Fehringer, G., & Laukkanen, E. (1997). An international comparison of cancer survival: Toronto, Ontario, and Detroit, Michigan, metropolitan areas. *American Journal of Public Health, 87*(7), 1156–1163.

Gottlieb, L. (2009). Putting health care during the past decade in context: An interview with Dr. Judith Shamian. *Canadian Journal of Nursing Research, 41*(1), 21–29.

Government of Canada. (1985). Access to information act.

Grabb, E. (1990). Who owns Canada: Concentration of ownership and the distribution of economic assests, 1975–1968. *Journal of Canadian Studies, 25*, 72–93.

———. (2007). *Theories of social inequality* (5th ed.). Toronto, ON: Thomas Nelson.

———. (2009). Conceptual issues in the study of social inequality. In E. Grabb, & N. Guppy (Eds), *Social inequality in Canada: Patterns, problems and policies* (5th ed.) (pp. 1–16). Toronto, ON: Pearson Prentice Hall.

Grabb, E., & Guppy, N. (Eds). (2009). *Social inequality in Canada: Patterns, problems and policies* (5th ed.). Toronto, ON: Pearson Prentice Hall.

Grabb, E., & Hwang, M. (2009). Corporate concentration, foreign ownership, and state involvement in the Canadian economy. In E. Grabb, & N. Guppy (Eds), *Social inequality in Canada: Patterns, problems and policies* (5th ed.) (pp. 19–28). Toronto, ON: Pearson Prentice Hall.

Graham, D.J., Campen, D., Hui, R., Spence, M., Cheetham, C., Levy, G., . . . Ray, W.A. (2005). Risk of acute myocardial infraction and sudden cardiac death in patients treated with cyclo-oxygenase 2 selective and non-selective non-steroidal anti-inflammatory drugs: Nested case-control study. *Lancet, 365*, 475–481.

Grant, K.R., Amaratunga, C., Armstrong, P., Boscoe, M., Pederson, A., & Willson, K. (Eds). (2004). *Caring for/caring about: Women, home care and unpaid caregiving*. Aurora, ON: Garamond.

Gray, D., Saggers, S., Sputore, B., & Bourbon, D. (2000). What works: A review of alcohol misuse interventions among Aboriginal Australians. *Addiction, 95*(1), 11–22.

Gray, D., Sputore, B., Stearne, A., Bourbon, D., & Strempel, P. (2002). *Indigenous drug and alcohol projects: 1999–2000*. Canberra: Australian National Council on Drugs.

Gray, J.A. (1999, Oct.). Postmodern medicine. *Lancet, 354*, 153–155.

Green, J. (1998). Commentary: Grounded theory and the constant comparative method. *British Medical Journal, 316*(7137), 1064–1065.

Green, R.J., Williams, P., Johnson, L., Shanthi, C., & Blum, I. (2008). Can Canadian seniors on public pensions afford a nutritious diet. *Canadian Journal on Aging, 27*(1), 69–79.

Greenslade, M.V., & Paddock, K. (2007, Feb.). Working conditions of nurses: A cause of concern. *Health Policy Research Bulletin,* 13, 13-16. Ottawa, ON: Health Canada.

Growe, S.J. (1991). *Who cares: The crisis in Canadian nursing.* Toronto, ON: McClelland & Stewart Inc.

Guarnaccia, P. (2000). Introduction: The contribution of medical anthropology to anthropology and beyond. *Medical Anthropology Quarterly, 15*(4), 423–428.

Guberman, N. (1999). *Caregivers and caregiving: New trends and their implications for policy.* Ottawa, ON: Health Canada.

Gupta, S., & Ross, N. (2007, Nov.). Under the microscope: Health disparities within Canadian cities. In Health Canada, People, place and health, *Health Policy Research Bulletin,* 14, 23–28. Retrieved from www.hc-sc.gc.ca/sr-sr/alt_formats/hpb-dgps/pdf/pubs/hpr-rps/bull/2007-people-place-gens-lieux/2007-people-place-gens-lieux-eng.pdf

Hackett, P. (2005, Jan/Feb). From past to present: Understanding First Nations health patterns in a historical context. *Canadian Journal of Public Health,* s17–s21.

Hage, G. (1998). *White nation: Fantasies of white supremacy in a multicultural society.* Sydney: Pluto Press.

Hall, Justice Emmett. (1964). *Report of the Royal Commission on Health Services.* Ottawa, ON.

———, (1980). *Canada's national-provincial health program for the 1980's: Commitment for renewal.* Ottawa, ON.

Hall, K., & Giles-Corti, B. (2000). Complementary therapies and the general practitioner: A survey of perth GPs. *Australian Family Physician, 29*(6), 602–606.

Hall, L., & Huyskens, M. (2002). Finding joy: An exploration of the necessity of leisure in the resettlement process for two refugee women. *Mots Pluriels,* 21. Retrieved from www.arts.uwa.edu.au/MotsPluriels/MP2102hh.html

Hall, L., & Kiesners, D. (2005). A narrative approach to understanding the nursing work environment in Canada. *Social Science & Medicine,* 61, 2482–2491.

Hall, L., Doran, D., & Pink, G., (2004). Nurse staffing models, nursing hours, and patient safety outcomes. *Journal of Nursing Administration, 34*(1), 41–45.

Halpern, S.A. (1992). Dynamics of professional control: Internal coalitions and crossprofessional boundaries. *American Journal of Sociology, 97,* 994–1021.

Halpin, B. (2009). Of the first water: The rights and roles of First Nations in source protection and water quality. *Canadian Water Treatment,* July/August: 18–21.

Hamilton, R., & Barrett, M. (1986). *The politics of diversity: Feminism, Marxism and nationalism.* London, UK: Verso Books.

Hancock, T. (1985, Nov.). The mandala of health: A model of the human ecosystem. *Family and Community Health,* 1–10.

Hankivsky, O., & Christoffersen, A. (2008, Sept.). Intersectionality and the determinants of health: A Canadian perspective. *Critical public health, 18*(3), 271–283.

Hankivsky, O., Morrow, M., & Varcoe, C. (Eds). (2007). *Women's health in Canada: Critical perspectives on theory and policy.* Toronto, ON: University of Toronto Press.

Harding, S. (1991). *Whose science? Whose knowledge?: Thinking from women's lives.* Ithaca, NY: Cornell University Press.

Harris, E., Sainsbury, P., & Nutbeam, D. (Eds). (1999). *Perspectives on health inequity.* Sydney: Australian Centre for Health Promotion, University of Sydney.

Harrison, S., & Ahmad, W.I. (2000). Medical autonomy and the UK state 1975 to 2025. *Sociology, 34*(1), 129–146.

Hazleton, M. (1990). Medical discourse on contemporary nurse education: An ideological analysis. *Australian and New Zealand Journal of Sociology, 26*(1), 107–125.

Healey, E. (1996). Welfare benefits and residential concentrations amongst recently arrived migrant communities. *People and Place, 4*(2), 20–31.

Health Canada. (1996). Family violence in Aboriginal communities: An Aboriginal perspective. National Clearing House on Family Violence. Retrieved from http://dsp-psd.pwgsc.gc.ca/Collection/H72-22-19-1997E.pdf

———. (1999a). *Canadian Research on Immigration and Health: An Overview.* Ottawa, ON: Author.

———. (1999 b). *Intersectoral action…towards population health: Report of the Federal, Provincial and Territorial Advisory Committee on Population Health.* Ottawa, ON: Author.

———. (1999c). *Toward a healthy future. Second report on the health of Canadians.* Ottawa, ON: Author.

———. (2002a). Canada's Aging Population, Division of Aging and Seniors, Ottawa, ON: Retrieved from http://dsp-psd.pwgsc.gc.ca/Collection/H39-608-2002E.pdf

———. (2002b). *Health care system, 'our health, our future': Creating quality workplaces for Canadian nurses.* Ottawa, ON: Author.

———. (2002c). Income inequality as a determinant of health. Retrieved from www.phac-aspc.gc.ca/ph-sp/oi-ar/pdf/02_income_e.pdf

———. (2003). *Improving Canada's regulatory process for therapeutic products: Building the action plan: Multistakeholder consultation: Public Policy Forum.* Ottawa, ON: Author.

———. (2003a, March). Closing the gaps in Aboriginal health. *Health Policy Research Bulletin,* 5. Ottawa, ON: Author.

———. (2003b, Nov.). Who's doing what. *Health Policy Research Bulletin,* 7. Ottawa, ON: Author.

———. (2004). *Issue analysis summary: Summary basis of decision-draft 7.* Ottawa, ON: Author.

———. (2004a). Health services review. Retrieved from www.hc-sc.gc.ca/hcs-sss/com/fed/hs-ss-79-eng.php

———. (2005, Feb. 9). Health Canada important safety information on ADDERALL XR' (amphetamine salts). Retrieved from www.hc-sc.gc.ca/dhp-mps/medeff/advisories-avis/prof/_2005/adderall_xr_hpc-cps-eng.php

———. (2005a, Jan.). *First Nations comparable health indicators.* Ottawa, ON: Author.

———. (2005b). First Nations, Inuit and Aboriginal health, health transfer. Retrieved from www.hc-sc.gc.ca/fniah-spnia/pubs/finance/_agree-accord/10_years_ans_trans/3_transfert-eng.php

———. (2005c). Mandate and priorities, First Nations and Inuit health branch. Retrieved from www.hc-sc.gc.ca/ahc-asc/branch-dirgen/fnihb-dgspni/mandat-eng.php

———. (2005d). Canada' s health care system, 2005. Retrieved from www.hc-sc.gc.ca/hcs-sss/alt_formats/hpb-dgps/pdf/pubs/2005-hcs-sss/2005-hcs-sss-eng.pdf

———. (2006a). Healthy Canadians–A federal report on comparable health indicators 2006. Retrieved from www.hc-sc.gc.ca/hcs-sss/pubs/system-regime/2006-fed-comp-indicat/index-eng.php

———. (2006b). Healthy Canadians, measuring performance. Retrieved from www.hc-sc.gc.ca/hcs-sss/alt_formats/hpb-dgps/pdf/pubs/2006-fed-comp-indicat/2006-fed-comp-indicat-eng.pdf

———. (2007a). The working conditions of nurses: Confronting the challenges, 2005 national survey of the work and health of nurses. *Health Policy Research Bulletin*. Ottawa, ON: Author.

———. (2007b). Indian health policy 1979. Retrieved from www.hc-sc.gc.ca/ahc-asc/branch-dirgen/fnihb-dgspni/poli_1979-eng.php

———. (2007c, Nov.). People, place and health. *Health Policy Research Bulletin*, 14. Retrieved from www.hc-sc.gc.ca/sr-sr/alt_formats/hpb-dgps/pdf/pubs/hpr-rps/bull/2007-people-place-gens-lieux/2007-people-place-gens-lieux-eng.pd

———. (2008a). *Healthy Canadians, a federal report on comparable health indicators*. Ottawa, ON: Author.

———. (2008b). Statistical profile on the health of First Nations in Canada, self-rated health and selected conditions, 2002–2005. Retrieved from www.hc-sc.gc.ca/fniah-spnia/alt_formats/pdf/pubs/aborig-autoch/2009-stats-profil-vol3/2009-stats-profil-vol3-eng.pdf

———. (2008c). Fact Sheet. First Nations and Inuit Health Branch (FNIHB). Retrieved from www.hc-sc.gc.ca/ahc-asc/branch-dirgen/fnihb-dgspni/index-eng.php

———. (2009a). *A statistical profile on the health of First Nations in Canada: Determinants of health 1999 to 2003*. Ottawa, ON: Author.

———. (2009b). Delivery of palliative and end-of-life care services. Retrieved from www.hc-sc.gc.ca/hcs-sss/palliat/services/index-eng.php

———. (2010). Canada's health care system (Medicare). Retrieved from www.hc-sc.gc.ca/hcs-sss/medi-assur/index-eng.php

———. (2011). First Nations, Inuit and Aboriginal health. Retrieved from www.hc-sc.gc.ca.

Health Council of Canada. (2005, Jan.). *The health status of Canada's First Nations, Métis and Inuit Peoples*. Toronto, ON: Author.

———. (2006). *Health care renewal in Canada: Clearing the road to quality*. Ottawa, ON: Author.

Health Policy Research Bulletin. (2003, Nov. 7). *Complementary and alternative health care: The other mainstream*. Ottawa: Health Canada.

Health Products and Food Branch. (2007a). *Cost recovery framework: Consultation document*. Ottawa, ON: Health Canada.

———. (2007b). *Cost recovery framework: Official notice of fee proposal for human drugs and medical devices*. Ottawa, ON: Health Canada.

Health Reports. (2007). *Physician consultations*. 18 (1). Ottawa, ON: Statistics Canada.

Healy, D. (2003). *Let them eat Prozac*. Toronto, ON: James Lorimer & Company Ltd.

———. (1997). *The anti-depressant era*. Cambridge Mass: Harvard University Press.

Hemminki, E., Hailey, D., & Koivusalo, M. (1999). The courts—A challenge to health technology assessment. *Science*, 285, 203–204.

Hepworth, M. (1995). Positive ageing: What is the message. In R. Bunton, S. Nettleton, & R. Burrow. (Eds), *The sociology of health promotion*. London, UK: Routledge.

Hill Collins, P. (2000). *Black feminist thought: Knowledge, consciousness and the politics of empowerment.* (2nd ed.). New York, NY: Routledge.

Hippocrates Biography: His Influence on Modern Medicine (n.d.). Retrieved from www.allsands.com/science/hippocratesbiog_rtb_gn.htm

Hirschkorn, K, Andersen, R., & Bourgeault, I. (2009). Canadian family physicians and complementary/alternative medicine: The role of practice setting, medical training, and province of practice. *Canadian Review of Sociology, 46*(2), 143–159.

Hirschkorn, K., & Bourgeault, I.L. (2005). Conceptualizing mainstream health care providers' behaviours in relation to complementary and alternative medicine. *Social Science and Medicine*, 61. 157–170.

History of Medicine (n.d.). History of scientific medicine: The scientific revolution. Retrieved from www.planetseed.com/node/17132

———. (n.d.). Renaissance medicine. Retrieved from www.planetseed.com/node/17101

———. (n.d.). Shamanism: Healing by supernatural means. Retrieved from www.planetseed.com/node/17120

———. (n.d.). The rise of scientific medicine: The nineteenth century. Retrieved from www.planetseed.com/node/17133

Hoffenburg, R. (1996). Live and let die. In J. Morgan. (Ed), *An easeful death*. Annandale, NSW: Federation Press.

Hofrichter, R. (Ed). (2003). *Health and social justice: Politics, ideology, and inequity in the distribution of disease*. San Francisco, CA: Jossey-Bass.

Hollenberg, D. (2006). Uncharted ground: Patterns of professional interaction among complementary/alternative and biomedical practitioners in integrative health care settings. *Social Science & Medicine* 62, 731–744.

Holloway, G. (1994). Susto and the career path of the victim of an industrial accident: A sociological case study. *Social Science & Medicine*, 38(7), 989–997.

Holstein, J., & Gubrium, J. (1995). *The active interview*. Beverly Hills, CA: Sage.

hooks, b. (1984). *Feminist theory from margin to center*. Boston, MA: South End Press.

Horkheimer, M. (1972). *Critical theory*. New York, NY: Herder and Herder.

Hornosty, J., & Doherty, D. (2003). Responding to wife abuse in farm and rural communities: Searching for solutions that work. In R. Blake & A. Nurse. (Eds), *The trajectories of rural life: New perspectives on rural Canada* (pp. 37–53). Regina, SK: Canadian Plains Research Centre.

———, & ———. (2004). Resistance and change: Building a framework for helping abused rural women. In B. Cheers, R.

Clews, A.M. Powers & L. Carawan. (Eds), Beyond geographical and disciplinary boundaries: Human services in rural communities. *Journal of Rural Social Work,* 9, 106–117.

Hossay, Patrick. (2006). *Unsustainable: A primer for global environmental and social justice.* New York, NY: Zed Books.

Hothschild, A.R. (1979). Emotion work, feeling rules and social structure. *American Journal of Sociology, 85*(3), 551–575.

Hou, F., Balakrishnanen, T.R., & Jurdi, R. (2009). The economic integration of visible minorities in contemporary Canadian society: Revisited. In E. Grabb, & N. Guppy (Eds), *Social inequality in Canada* (5th ed.). Toronto, ON: Pearson Prentice Hall.

House, J.S., Landis, K.R., & Umberson, D. (1988). Social relationships and health. *Science,* 241, 121–124.

How the industries stack up: Most profitable industries. (2005, April 18). *Fortune,* 151, F-28.

Huang, V. (2004, Spring). A brief overview of the teaching of complementary and alternative medicine in the undergraduate medical education curriculum. *Queen's Health Sciences Journal, 7*(2), 39–43.

Hughes, D. (1988). When nurse knows best: Some aspects of nurse/doctor interaction in a casualty department. *Sociology of Health and Illness, 10*(1), 51–63.

Hughes, D., & Light, D.W. (Eds). (2002). *Rationing: Constructed realities and professional practices.* Oxford, UK: Blackwell.

Hui, A. (2010, May 26). Nearly one-quarter of Canadians will be seniors by 2036. *The Globe and Mail.*

Human Development Report. (2009). Summary: Overcoming barriers. United Nations. Retrieved from http://hdr.undp.org/en/media/HDR_2009_EN_Summary.pdf

Hunt, K., & Emslie, C. (2001). The prevention paradox in lay epidemiology: Rose revisited. *International Journal of Epidemiology,* 30, 442–446.

Hunter, K., & Giardino, I. (2007, Feb.). A question of patient safety. *Health Policy Research Bulletin,* 13, 26-29. Ottawa, ON: Health Canada.

Hutchison, B., Abelson, J., & Lavis, J. (2001). Primary care in Canada: So much innovation, so little change. *Health Affairs,* 20, 3.

Hyman, I. (2001). Immigration and health. Health Canada working paper 01–05. Canadian Research on Immigration and Health: An Overview. Ottawa, ON: Health Canada.

———. (2004, May-June). Setting the stage: Reviewing current knowledge on the health of Canadian immigrants. *Canadian Journal of Public Health,* 95, 4–8.

Illich, I. (1976). *Limits to medicine.* Toronto, ON: McClelland & Stewart.

———. (1977). *Limits to medicine, medical nemesis: The exploration of health.* Harmondsworth, UK: Penguin.

Indian Health Policy. (1979). Retrieved from www.hc-sc.gc.ca/ahc-asc/branch-dirgen/fnihb-dgspni/poli_1979-eng.php

Ingleby, D. (1985). Mental health and social order. In S. Cohen & A. Scull. (Eds). *Social control and the state* (pp. 52–75). Oxford, UK: Basil Blackwell.

Innis, H. (1999/1930). *The fur trade of Canada.* Toronto, ON: University of Toronto Press.

International Plastics Task Force. (2009). Retrieved from www.ecologycenter.org/iptf/

Jackson, B., Pederson, A., & Bosco, M. (2006). Gender-based analysis and wait times: New questions, new knowledge. Research Paper. *Women and health care reform group.* Ottawa: Health Canada.

Jagger, A. (1983). *Feminist politics and human nature.* NJ: Rowman & Allanheld.

Janz, T., Seto, J., & Turner, A. (2006). *Aboriginal peoples survey, 2006, An overview of the health of the Métis population, analytical paper.* Ottawa, ON: Statistics Canada.

Jayasuriya, L. (1992). The facts, policies and rhetoric of multiculturalism. In T. Jagtenberg & P. D'Alton. (Eds), *Four dimensional social space: Class, gender, ethnicity and nature* (2nd ed.) (pp. 215–220). Sydney: Harper Educational.

Jayasuriya, L., Sang, D., & Fielding, A. (1992). *Ethnicity, immigration and mental illness: A critical review of Australian Research.* Canberra: AGPS.

Johansen, B.E. (2002). The Inuit's struggle with dioxins and other organic pollutants. *American Indian Quarterly, 26*(3), 479–490.

Johnson, J.L., Greaves, L., & Repta, R. (2009). Better science with sex and gender: Facilitating the use of a sex and gender-based analysis in health research. *International Journal of Health Equity.* Published on-line. 10.1186/1475-9276-8-14

Johnson, T. (1972). *Professions and power.* London, UK: Macmillan.

Joppi, R., Bertele, V., & Garattini, S. (2005). Disappointing biotech. *BMJ,* 331, 895–897.

Judge, K., Mulligan, J., & Benzenval, M. (1998). Income inequality and population health. *Social Science & Medicine,* 46(4-5), 567–579.

Jupp, J. (2002). *From white Australia to Woomera: The story of Australian immigration.* Cambridge: Cambridge University Press.

Kaplan, G.A., Pamuk, E., Lynch, J.W., Cohen, R.D., & Balflour, J.L. (1996). Income inequality and mortality in the United States. *British Medical Journal,* 312, 999–1003.

Kaptchuk, T.J., & Eisenberg, D.M. (2001). Varieties of healing: Medical pluralism in the United States. *Annals of Internal Medicine, 135*(3), 189–195.

Kaufert, P., & Gilbert, P., (1987). Medicalization and the Menopause. In D. Coburn, C. D'Arcy, G. Torrence, & P. New (Eds). *Health and Canadian society: Sociological perspectives.* (2nd ed.). Markham, ON: Fitzhenry & Whiteside.

Kaufman, S., Shim, J., & Russ, A. (2004). Revisiting the biomedicalization of aging: Clinical trends and ethical challenges. NIH Public Access Author Manuscript. Retrieved from www.ncbi.nlm.nih.gov/pmc/articles/PMC2367129/

Kavanagh, A., & Broom, D. (1997). Women's understanding of abnormal cervical smear test results: A qualitative interview study. *British Medical Journal,* 314, 1388–1392.

Kawachi, I. (1992). Six case studies of the voluntary regulation of pharmaceutical advertising and promotion. In P. Davis. (Ed), *For health or profit* (pp. 269–287). Auckland: Oxford University Press.

Kawachi, I., & Kennedy, B. (2002). *The health of nations: Why inequality is harmful to your health.* New York, NY: New Press.

Kawachi, I., & Berkman, L. (2000). Social cohesion, social capital, and health. In L. F. Berkman & I. Kawachi. (Eds), *Social epidemiology* (pp. 174-190). New York, NY: Oxford University Press.

Kellehear, A. (1993). *The unobtrusive researcher.* Sydney: Allen & Unwin.

———. (1999). *Health promoting palliative care.* Melbourne: Oxford University Press.

Kelly, K., & Van Vlaenderen, H. (1996). Dynamics of participation in a community health project. *Social Science & Medicine, 43*(8), 1235–1246.

Kelner, M., & Wellman, B. (1997). Health care and consumer choice: Medical and alternative therapies. *Social Science and Medicine, 45*(2), 203–212.

Kelner, M., Wellman, B., Boon. H, Welsh, S. (2004). Responses of established healthcare to the professionalization of complementary and alternative medicine in Ontario. *Social Science & Medicine,* 59, 915–930.

Kelner, M., Wellman, B., Welsh, S., & Boon, H. (2006). How far can complementary and alternative medicine go: The case of chiropractic and homeopathy. *Social Science & Medicine,* 63, 2617–2622.

Kennedy, B.P., Kawachi, I., & Prothrow-Stith, D. (1996). Income distribution and mortality: Cross-sectional ecological study of the Robin Hood index in the United States. *British Medical Journal,* 312, 1004–1007.

King, M., Smith, A., & Gracey, M. (2009). Indigenous health part 2: The underlying causes of the health gap. *The Lancet,* 374, 76–85.

Kinnon, D. (1999). *Canadian research on immigration and health.* Ottawa, ON: Health Canada.

Kirk, J. (1994). Gender inequality and medical education. In S. Bolaria & R. Bolaria (Eds), *Women, medicine and health.* Halifax, NS: Fernwood.

Kirmayer, L., Weingeld, M., Burgos, G., du Fort, G., Lasry, J-C., & Young, A. (2007). Use of health care services for psychological distress by immigrants in an urban multicultural milieu. *The Canadian Journal of Psychiatry, 52*(5).

Kittrie, N.N. (1971). *The right to be different: Deviance and enforced therapy.* Baltimore, MD: Penguin.

Kleinman, A. (1988). *The illness narrative: Suffering, healing and the human condition.* New York: Basic Books.

Kleinman, A., & Seeman, D. (2000). Personal experience of illness. In G. Albrecht, R. Fitzpatrick, & S. Scrimshaw. (Eds), *The handbook of social studies in health & medicine* (pp. 230–242). London, UK: Sage.

Klimidis, S., & Minas, I. H. (1995). Migration, culture and mental health in children and adolescents. In C. Guerra & R. White. (Eds), *Minority youth in Australia* (pp. 85–99). Hobart: National Clearing House for Youth Studies.

Kobayashi, K. (2003). Do intersections of diversity matter: An exploration of the relationship between identity markers and health for mid-to later-life Canadians. *Canada Ethnic Studies, 35*(3), 85–98.

Kobayashi, K., Prus, S., & Lin, Z. (2008, Apr.). Ethnic differences in self-rated and functional health: Does immigrant status matter. *Ethnicity & Health, 13*(2), 129–147.

Kopec, J., Williams, I., To, T., & Austin, P. (2001). Cross-cultural comparisons of health status in Canada using the health utilities index. *Ethnicity and Health, 6*(1), 41–50.

Kornelsen, J., & Grzybowski, S. with Anhorn, M., Cooper, E., Galvin, L., Pederson, A., & Sullivan, L. (2006). Rural women's experiences of maternity care: Implications for policy and practice. Retrieved from www.swc-cfc.gc.ca/pubs/pubspr/0662407997/index_e.html

Kramer, B., & Thompson, E. (Eds). (2005). *Men as caregivers.* Amherst, NY: Prometheus.

La Follette, M.C. (1992). *Stealing into print: Fraud, plagiarism and misconduct in scientific publishing.* Berkeley, CA: University of California Press.

Laduke, W. (1999). *All our relations: Native struggles for land life.* Cambridge: South End Press.

Lai, D. (2004, Dec.). Impact of culture on depressive symptoms of elderly Chinese immigrants. *Canadian Journal of Psychiatry, 49*(12), 820–827.

Laidlaw, S. (2000, Oct. 9). Spuds and pesticides hot potato in P.E.I.: Farmers learn a hard lesson on Crop rotation. *Toronto Star.*

Lalonde, M. (1974). *A new perspective on the health of Canadians.* Ottawa, ON: Government of Canada.

Lam, R.W., Levitt, A., Levitan, R., Enns, M., Morehouse, R., Michalak. E., & Tam, E. (2006, May). The Can-SAD study: A randomized controlled trial of the effectiveness of light therapy and fluoxetine in patients with winter seasonal affective disorder. *American Journal of Psychiatry,* 163, 805–812.

Lancet, The. (1998, July 18). High death rates linked to income inequality. 352, 206.

Langston, N. (2008). The retreat from precaution: Regulating diethylstilbestrol (DES), endocrine disruptors and environmental health. *Environmental History, 13*(1). Retrieved from www. historycooperative.org/cgibin/justtop.cgi'act=justtop&url=www. historycooperative.org/journals/eh/13.1/langston.html#FOOT4

Larkin, J., Flicker, S., Mintz, S., Dagnino, M., Kolezar-Green, R., & Mitchell, C. (2007). HIV risk, systemic inequities and Aboriginal youth: Widening the circle for HIV prevention programming. *Canadian Journal of Public Health,* 98, 179–182.

Larkin, G. (1983). *Occupational monopoly and modern medicine.* London, UK: Tavistock.

Larkin, M. (1995). Estrogen: Friend or foe. *FDA Consumer, 29*(3), 25–29.

Larson, M.S. (1977). *The rise of professionalism: A sociological analysis.* Berkeley, CA: University of California Press.

Laslett, A. (1989). The demographic scene: An 0verview. In J. Eekelaar & D. Pearl (Eds), *An aging world* (pp. 1-10). Oxford, UK: The Clarendon Press.

Law, D., & Boyce, R.A. (2003). Beyond organisational design: Moving from structure to service enhancement. *Australian Health Review, 26*(1), pp. 175–185.

Lawson, J.S., & Forde, K. (1995). Medicare related payments to Australian medical practitioners. *Australian Health Review, 18*(4), 353–370.

Lawson, J.S. (1991). *Public health Australia: An introduction.* Sydney: McGraw-Hill.

Le Fanu, J. (1986). Diet and disease: Nonsense and non-science. In D. Anderson (Ed), *A diet of reason: Sense and nonsense in the healthy eating debate* (pp. 109-124). London, UK: The Social Affairs Unit.

———. (1999). *The rise and fall of modern medicine.* London, UK: Abacus.

Leduc, N., & Proulx, M. (2004, Jan.). Patterns of health services utilization by recent immigrants. *Journal of Immigration Health, 6*,(1), 15–27.

Lee, S., & Mysyk, A. (2004). The medicalization of compulsive buying. *Social Science & Medicine*, 58, 1709–1718.

Lepofsky, D. (1985). Equality and disabled persons. In R. Abella, & R. Rothman (Eds), *Justice beyond Orwell* (pp. 309–332). Montreal, QC: Editions Y. Blais.

Lewith, G. (1999). The homeopathic conundrum revisited. *Alternative Therapies in Health and Medicine, 5*(5), 32–35.

———. (2000). Complementary and alternative medicine: An educational, attitudinal and research challenge. *Medical Journal of Australia*, 172, 102–103.

Lexchin, J. (2001). Pharmaceuticals: Politics and policy. In P. Armstrong, H. Armstrong & D. Coburn (Eds). *Unhealthy times: Political economy perspectives on health and care in Canada.* (pp. 31–44). Toronto, ON: Oxford University Press.

———. (2006). Relationship between pharmaceutical company user fees and drug approvals in Canada and Australia: A hypothesis-generating study. *Annals of Pharmacotherapy*, 40, 2216–2222.

———. (2007a). Drug regulation: Two paradigms in conflict. In N. J. Temple & A. Thompson. (Eds), *Excessive medical spending: Facing the challenge* (pp. 53–62). Oxford, UK: Radcliffe Publishing.

———. (2007b). The secret thing belong unto the lord our god: Secrecy in the pharmaceutical arena. *Medicine and Law*, 26, 417–430.

———. (2008). New directions in Canadian drug regulation: Whose interests are being served. In O. O'Donovan & K. Glavanis-Grantham. (Eds), *Power, politics and pharmaceuticals* (pp. 153–170). Cork: Cork University Press.

———. (2009). *Drug safety and Health Canada: Going, going, gone.* Ottawa, ON: Canadian Centre for Policy Alternatives.

———. (2010). Pharmaceutical policy: The dance between industry, government and the medical profession. In D. Raphael, T. Bryant & M. Rioux. (Eds), *Staying alive: Critical perspectives on health, illness, and health care* (2nd ed.). (pp. 371–393). Toronto, ON: Canadian Scholars' Press Inc.

———. (Forthcoming). Medicines and money: The corruption of clinical information. In R. Burke, E. Tomlinson & C. Cooper (Eds), *Crime and corruption in organizations: Why it happens and what to do about it.* London, UK: Gower.

Lexchin, J., & Kawachi, I. (1996). Voluntary codes of pharmaceutical marketing: Controlling promotion or licensing deception. In P. Davis (Ed), *Contested ground: Public purpose and private interest in the regulation of prescription drugs* (pp. 221–235). New York, NY: Oxford University Press.

Lexchin, J., & Mintzes, B. (2004).). Transparency in drug regulation: Mirage or oasis. *Canadian Medical Association Journal*, 171, 1363–1365.

Lexchin, J., & Wiktorowicz, M. (2009). Profits first: The pharmaceutical industry in Canada. In B. S. Bolaria & H. Dickinson. (Eds), *Health, illness, and health care in Canada* (4th ed.) (pp. 437–457). Toronto, ON: Nelson.

Library of Parliament. (2008). *Euthanasia and assisted suicide in Canada.* Revised July 17, 2008. Prepared by Tiedemann, M., & Valiquet, D. Retrieved from www.parl.gc.ca/Content/LOP/ResearchPublications/919-e.pdf

Lien, O. (1992). The experience of working with Vietnamese patients attending a psychiatric service. *Journal of Vietnamese Studies*, 5, 95–105.

Light, D.W. (2000). The medical profession and organizational change: From professional dominance to countervailing power. In C. Bird, P. Conrad, & A. M. Fremont (Eds), *Handbook of Medical Sociology* (5th ed.). Englewood Cliffs, NJ: Prentice Hall.

Light, D.W., & Warburton, R.N. (2005). Extraordinary claims require extraordinary evidence. *Journal of Health Economcis*, 24, 1030–1033.

Light, D.W., Andrus, J.K., & Warburton, R.N. (2009). Estimated research and development costs of rotavirus vaccines. *Vaccine*, 27, 6627–6633.

Lincoln, Y. (1995). Emerging criteria for quality in qualitative and interpretive research. *Qualitative Inquiry*, 1, 275-289.

Living Lessons. (2007). Hospice palliative care fact sheet. Retrieved from www.living-lessons.org/main/hospice.asp

Lloyd, G., & Norris, C. (1999). Including ADHD. *Disability & Society, 14*(4), 505–517.

Lloyd, P., Lupton, D., & Donaldson, C. (1991). Consumerism in the health care setting: An exploratory study of factors underlying the selection and evaluation of primary medical services. *Australian Journal of Public Health*, 15, 194–201.

Lloyd, P., Lupton, D., Wiesner, D., & Hasleton, S. (1993). Choosing alternative therapy: An exploratory study of sociodemographic characteristics and motives of patients resident in Sydney. *Australian Journal of Public Health*, 17, 135–144.

Lock, M. (1993). The politics of mid-life and menopause: Ideologies for the second sex in North America and Japan. In S. Lindenbaum & M. Lock (Eds), *Knowledge, power and practice: The anthropology of medicine and everyday life* (pp. 330–363). Berkeley, CA: University of California Press.

———. (2000). Accounting for disease and distress: Morals of the normal and abnormal. In G. Albrecht, R. Fitzpatrick, & S. Scrimshaw (Eds), *The handbook of social studies in health & medicine* (pp. 259–276). London, UK: Sage.

López-Abente, G., Aragonés, N., Pollán, M., Ruiz, M., & Gandarillas, A. (1999). Leukemia, lymphomas, and myeloma mortality in the vicinity of nuclear power plants and nuclear fuel facilities in Spain. Cancer *Epidemiology, Biomarkers and Prevention, 8*, 925–934.

López-Abente, G., Aragonés, N., & Pollán S. (2001). Solid-tumor mortality in the vicinity of uranium cycle facilities and nuclear power plants in Spain. *Environmental Health Perspectives, 109*(7),

721–729.

Lopez, J., & Scott, J. (2000). *Social Structure*. Buckingham, UK: Open University Press.

Lorber, J. (2000). *Gender and the social construction of illness*. New York, NY: Altamira Press.

Lorber, J., & Moore, L. (2002). *Gender and the social construction of illness* (2nd ed.). New York, NY: AltaMira Press

Lowenberg, J.S., & Davis, F. (1994). Beyond medicalization/demedicalization: The case of holistic health. *Sociology of Health and Illness, 16*(5), 579–600.

Lupton, D. (1995). *The imperative of health: Public health and the regulated body*. London, UK: Sage.

———. (1996). *Food, the body and the self*. London, UK: Sage.

Luxton, M., & Maroney , J. (Eds). (1987). *Feminism and political economy: Women'swork, women's struggles*. Toronto, ON: Methuen Press.

Lynch, J. (2000). Income inequality and health: Expanding the debate. *Social Science & Medicine, 51*(3), 1001-5.

Lynch, J.W., Kaplan, G., Pamuk, E.R., Cohen R., Heck, K., Balfour, J. and Yen, I. (1998, July). Income inequality and mortality in metropolitan areas of the United States. *American Journal of Public Health, 88*(7), 1074-80.

Macintyre, C. (1999). From entitlement to obligation in the Australian welfare state. *Australian Journal of Social Issues, 34*(2), 103–129.

Macintyre, S. (1997). The Black report and beyond: What are the issues. *Social Science & Medicine, 44*(6), 723–745.

Mackenzie, C.A., Lockridge, A., & Keith, M. (2005). Declining sex ratio in a First Nation community. *Environmental Health Perspectives, 113*(10), 1295-8.

Mackenzie, H. (2010, Jan.). *A soft landing: Recession and Canada's 100 highest paid CEO's Growing Gap*. Ottawa, ON: Canadian Centre for Policy Alternatives.

———. (2010). *A soft landing*. Ottawa, ON: Canadian Centre for Policy Alternatives.

MacKinnon, M., & Howard., L. (2010). Affirming immigrant women's health: Building inclusive health policy immigrant women's health. In V. Zawilski (Ed), *Inequality in Canada: A reader on the intersections of gender, race, and class* (2nd ed.) (194–210). Toronto, ON: Oxford University Press.

Macleans Magazine. (2010). The health care time bomb: Our aging population will make unthinkable reforms inevitable. April 12.

MacLennan, A.H., Wilson, D.H., & Taylor, A.W. (1996). Prevalence and cost of alternative medicine in Australia. *Lancet, 347*, 569–573.

———, ———, & ———. (2002). The escalating cost and prevalence of alternative medicine. *Preventive Medicine, 35*(2), 166–173.

MacMahon, B., & Pugh, T.F. (1970). *Epidemiological principles and methods*. Boston, MA: Little Brown.

MacMillan, M., MacMillan, A., Offord, D., Dingle, J. (1996, Dec. 1). Aboriginal health. *Canadian Medical Association Journal*, 1569–1578.

Maggi, J., & Tamara, D. (2006). Gender matters: Understanding the emotional and social support needs of women with HIV/AIDS.

Research Bulletin. Retrieved from http://findarticles.com/p/articles/mi_6860/is_2_5/ai_n28426149/

Maheux, B., Dufort, F. Beland, F., Jacques, A., & Levesque, A. (1990, Jan.). Female medical practitioners: More preventive and patient oriented. *Medical Care, 28*(1), 87–92.

Malacrida, C. (2004). Medicalization, ambivalence and social control: Mothers' descriptions of educatiors and ADD/ADHD. *Health: An Interdisciplinary Journal for the Social Study of Health, Illness and Medicine, 8*(1), 61–80.

Manderson, L., & Mathews, M. (1981). Vietnamese attitudes towards maternal and infant health. *Medical Journal of Australia, 1*, 69–72.

Manderson, L., & Reid, J.C. (1994). What's culture got to do with it. In C. Waddell & A.R. Petersen (Eds), *Just health: Inequality in illness, care and prevention* (pp. 7–25). Melbourne: Churchill Livingstone.

Manning, N. (2000). Psychiatric diagnosis under conditions of uncertainty: Personality disorder, science and professional legitimacy. *Sociology of Health & Illness, 22*, 621–639.

Manzer, J. (2006, Dec. 22). Damage control: It's on the market, so now what. *Ottawa Citizen*, p. A6.

Markens, S. (1996). The problematic of 'experience': A political and cultural critique of PMS. *Gender and Society, 10*, 42–58.

Marmot, M. (1999). Introduction. In M. Marmot & R. Wilkinson (Eds), *Social determinants of health*. Oxford, UK: Oxford University Press.

———. (2000, Apr. 17). Social determinants of health: From observation to policy. *Medical Journal of Australia, 172*, 379–382.

———. (2004). Status syndrome: How your social standing directly affects your health and life expectancy. Oxford, UK: Bloomsbury.

Marmot, M., Bosma, H., Hemingway, H., Brunner, E., & Stansfeld, S. (1997, July 26). Contribution of job control and other risk factors to social variations in coronary heart disease incidence. *Lancet, 350*(9073), 235–239.

Marmot, M.G., Davey Smith, G., Stansfield, S., Patel, C., North, F., Head, J., . . . Feeney, A. (1991). Health inequalities among British civil servants: The Whitehall II study. *Lancet, 337*(8754), 1387-93.

Marmot, M.G., Siegrist, J., Theorell, T., & Feeney, A. (1999). Health and the psychosocial environment at work. In M. Marmot & R. Wilkinson (Eds), *Social determinants of health*. Oxford, UK: Oxford University Press.

Marmot, M., & Wilkinson, R. (Eds). (1999). *Social determinants of health*. Oxford, UK: Oxford University Press.

Marmot, M., & Wilkinson., R. (Eds). (2006). *Social determinants of health* (2nd ed.). Oxford, UK: Oxford University Press.

Martin, E. (1987). *The woman in the body: A cultural analysis of reproduction*. Boston, MA: Beacon Press.

Marx, K. (1964/1844). *The economic & philosophic manuscripts of 1844*. New York, NY: International Publishers.

———. (1967/1867). *Capital, volume 1*. New York, NY: International Publishers.

———. (1970/1845). *The German ideology*. New York, NY: International Publishers.

———. (1959/1869). The eighteenth brumaire of Louis Bonaparte. In L. Feuer (Ed), *Marx & Engels: Basic writings on politics & philosophy*. Garden City, NY: Anchor Books, Doubleday & Company.

Mason, S., Tovey, P., & Long, A. F. (2002). Evaluating complementary medicine: Methodological challenges of randomised controlled trials. *British Medical Journal, 325,* 832–834.

Mathers, C., Vos, T., & Stevenson, C. (1999). *The burden of disease and injury: Summary report.* Canberra: Australian Institute of Health and Welfare.

Maticka-Tyndale, E., McKay, A., & Barrett, M. (2001). Teenage sexuality and reproductive behavior in developed countries. *Occasional Report 4.* New York, NY: The Alan Guttmacher Institute.

Maunsell, E., Brisson, J., & Deschenes, L. (1995). Social support and survival among women with breast cancer. *Cancer, 76*(4), 631–637.

Maxwell, D.M., MD. (2008). Cancer, genetic defects are uranium's legacy: An interview with Dr. David Maxwell. Environmental Health Association of Nova Scotia. Retrieved from www .environmentalhealth.ca/fall08legacy.html

May, C. (1992). Nursing work, nurses' knowledge, and the subjectification of the patient. *Sociology of Health and Illness, 14*(4), 472–487.

May, C., & Sirur, D. (1998). Art, science and placebo: Incorporating homeopathy in general practice. *Sociology of Health and Illness, 20*(2), 168–190.

McBane, M. (2005). *Ill-health Canada: Putting food and drug company profits ahead of safety.* Ottawa, ON: Canadian Centre for Policy Alternatives.

McCarthy, M. (1998, July 18). High death rates linked to income inequality. *The Lancet,* p. 206.

McClelland, A. (1991). In fair health: Equity and the health system. *Background Paper 3.* Canberra: AGPS.

McCoy, R. (2001). Employing an individual with a disability: Does this have an effect on employers' attitudes' (MA thesis). University of New Brunswick, Fredericton, NB.

McCrea, E. (1983). The politics of menopause: The discovery of a deficiency disease. *Social Problems.* 31(1), 111–123.

McCurdy, H. (2001). Africville: Environmental racism. In L. Westra, & B. Lawson (Eds), *Faces of environmental racism: Confronting issues of global justice* (pp. 95–112). Lanham, MD: Rowman & Littlefield Publishers.

McDaniel, S. (1986). *Canada's aging population.* Toronto, ON: Butterworths.

McDonald, T., & Kennedy, S. (2004). Insights into the 'healthy immigrant' effect: Health status and health service use of immigrants in Canada. *Social Science and Medicine 59*(8), 1613–1627.

———, & ———. (2007). Cervical cancer screening by immigrant and minority women in Canada. *Journal of Immigrant Minority Health, 9*(4), 323-34.

McDonough, P. (2001). Work and health in the global economy. In P. Armstrong, H. Armstrong, & D. Coburn (Eds), *Unhealthy times: Political economy perspectives on health and care in Canada* (pp. 195–222). Toronto, ON: Oxford University Press.

McElroy, A., & Jezewski, M.A. (2000). Cultural variation in the experience of health and illness. In G. Albrecht, R. Fitzpatrick, & S. Scrimshaw (Eds), *The handbook of social studies in health & medicine* (pp. 191–209). London, UK: Sage.

McFarland, B., Bigelow, D., Zani, B., Newsom, J., & Kaplan, M. (2002, Oct.). Complementary and alternative medicine use in Canada and the United States. *American Journal of Public Health, 92*(10), 1616–1618.

McGarity, T. O., & Shapiro, S. A. (1980). The trade secret status of health and safety testing information: Reforming agency disclosure policies. *Harvard Law Review,* 93, 837–888.

McGibbon, E. (2009). Health and health care: A human rights perspective. In D. Raphael (Ed), *Social determinants of health* (2nd ed.) (pp. 318–335). Toronto, ON: Canadian Scholars' Press Inc.

McIntosh, C., Fines, P., Wilkins, R., & Wolfson, M. (2009, Nov.). Income disparities in health: Adjusted life expectancy for Canadian adults, 1991–2001. *Health Reports, 20*(4). Ottawa, ON: Statistics Canada.

McKay, A. (2006). Trends in teen pregnancy in Canada with comparisons to U.S.A. and England/Wales. *The Journal of Human Sexuality 15* (3–4), 157–161.

McKeown, T. (1976). *The role of medicine: Dream, mirage or nemesis.* London, UK: Nuffield Hospital Trust.

———. (1979). *The role of medicine: Dream, mirage or nemesis.* Oxford, UK: Basil Blackwell.

———. (1988). *The origins of human disease.* Oxford, UK: Basil Blackwell.

McKinlay, J.B., & McKinlay, S.M. (1977). The questionable effect of medical measures on the decline of mortality in the United States in the twentieth century. *Milbank Memorial Fund Quarterly,* 55, 405–428.

McKinlay, J.B., & Stoeckle, J.D. (1988). Corporatization and the social transformation of doctoring. *International Journal of Health Services, 18*(2), 191–205.

McKinlay, J. (2005). A case for refocusing upstream: The political economy of illness. In P. Conrad (Ed), *The sociology of health and illness* (7th ed.) (pp. 551–565). New York, NY: Worth Publishing.

McLeod, K. S. (2000). Our sense of snow: The myth of John Snow in medical geography. *Social Science & Medicine,* 50, 923–935.

McMichael, A.J. (1991). Food, nutrients, health and disease: A historical perspective on the assessment and management of risks. *Australian Journal of Public Health,* 15, 7–13.

McMullin, J. (2010). *Understanding social inequality: Intersections of class, age, gender, ethnicity and race in Canada.* Toronto, ON: Oxford University Press.

McNamara, B., Waddell, C., & Colvin, M. (1994). The institutionalization of a good death. *Social Science & Medicine,* 39(11), 1501–1509.

Mead, G.H. (1964/1934). *Mind, self and society.* Chicago, IL: University of Chicago Press.

Meadows L.M., Thurston W.E., & Berenson C.A. (2001). Health promotion and preventive measures: Interpreting messages at midlife. *Qualitative Health Research, 11*(4), 450–463.

Menniti-Ippolito, F., Gargiulo, L., Bologna, E., Forcella, E., & Raschetti, R. (2002). Use of unconventional medicine in Italy: A nation-wide survey. *European Journal of Clinical Pharmacology,* 58, pp. 61–64.

Mesley, W. (2006, March 5). *Chasing the cancer answer* [Television broadcast]. Toronto, ON: CBC Marketplace.

Meslin, E. (1987, Aug.). The moral costs of the Ontario physicians' strike. *Hastings Center Report, 17*(4), 11–13.

Messing, K. (1998). *One-eyed science: Occupational health and women workers*. Philadelphia, PA: Temple University Press.

Michols, D. (1996). *The distinction between advertising and other activities*. Ottawa, ON: Health Canada, Therapeutics Products Programme.

———. (1997). *Drugs and medical devices programme quality initiative bulletin #2*. Ottawa, ON: Health Protection Branch.

Mickleburgh, R., (2010, Nov. 6). The outspoken surgeon medicare advocates love to hate. *The Globe and Mail*, pp. A12–A13.

Mikkonen, J., & Raphael, D. (2010). Social determinants of health, the Canadian facts. Retrieved from www.thecanadianfacts.org/The_Canadian_Facts.pdf).

Millar, W.J. (1997). Use of Alternative health care practitioners by Canadians. *Canadian Journal of Public Health, 88*(3), 154–158.

Millar, W. (2001, Dec.). Patterns of use: Alternative health care practitioners. *Health Reports, 13*(1). Ottawa, ON: Statistics Canada, Catalogue 82–003.

Mills, C.W. (1959). *The sociological imagination*. New York, NY: Oxford University Press.

Milner, N. (1989). The denigration of rights and the persistence of rights talk: A cultural portrait. *Law and Social Inquiry*, 14, 631–675.

Minister of Indian Affairs and Nortern Government. (1998). Gathering strength: Canada's Aboriginal action plan. Retrieved from www.ahf.ca/downloads/gathering-strength.pdf

Mintzes, B., & Jureidini, H. (2009, Spring). Exposure to SSRI antidepressants in pregnancy. *Women and Environments*, 80/81, 29–32.

Mishra, G.D., Ball, K., Dobson, A.J., & Byles, J.E. (2004). Do socioeconomic gradients in women's health widen over time and with age. *Social Science & Medicine*, 58, 1585–1595.

Mitchinson, W. (1993). The medical treatment of women. In S. Burt, L. Code, & L. Dorney, L (Eds). *Changing Patterns: Women in Canada*. (2nd ed.). pp. 391–421, Toronto, ON: McClelland & Stewart Inc.

Mittlestaedt, M. (2006, Dec. 6). Pesticides are what is killing our kids. *The Globe and Mail*. Retrieved from http://v1.theglobeandmail.com/servlet/story/RTGAM.20061206.wxcancerenviro06/BNStory/cancer/home

Mobilos, S., Chan, M., & Brown, J. (2008, Sept.). Women in medicine: The challenge of finding balance. *Canadian Family Physician*, 54, 1285-6.e1–5

Montague, P. (2004). The chemical wars', part 1, 2 and 3. *Rachel's Environment & Health News*, #798, 799, 780.

Moran, M., Ropars, A.-L., Guzman, J., Diaz, J., & Garrision, C. (2005). *The new landscape of neglected disease drug development*. London, UK: Wellcome Trust.

Morgan, J. (1996). Easeful death: Culture and medicine in the debate on death, dying and euthanasia. In John Morgan (Ed), *An easeful death*. Annandale: Federation Press.

Morris, M. (2004). What research reveals about gender, home care and caregiving: Overview and policy implications. In K.R. Grant, C. Amaratunga, P. Armstrong, M. Boscoe, A. Pederson & K. Willson (Eds), *Caring for/caring about: Women, home care and unpaid caregiving* (pp.91–146). Aurora, ON: Garamond.

Moss P., & Dyck, I. (2003). *Women, body and illness*. Oxford, UK: Roman and Littlefield.

Moss, P., & Teghtsoonian, K. (Eds). (2007). *Contesting illness processes and practices*. Toronto, ON: University of Toronto Press.

Mulkay, M. (1993). Social death in Britain. In D. Clark (Ed), *The sociology of death* (pp. 31–49). Cambridge, UK: Blackwell.

Mulkins, A., O'Beirne, M., Brundin-Mather, R., & Verhoef, M. (2006, May). Do academic and community physicians recognize a role for CAM in undergraduate medical education. *University of Toronto Medical Journal, 83*(3), 184–187.

Muntaner, C., & Lynch, J. (1999). Income inequality, social cohesion, and class relations: A critique of Wilkinson's neo-Durkheimian research program. *International Journal of Health Services, 29*(1), 59–81.

Muntaner, C., Lynch, J., & Davey Smith, G. (2001). Social capital, disorganized communities and the third way: Understanding the retreat from structural inequalities in epidemiology and public health. *International Journal of Health Services, 31*(2), 213–237.

Murray, C., & Chen , L. (1992, Sept.). Understanding morbidity change. *Population and Development Review, 18*(3).

Murray, J., & Shepherd, S. (1993). Alternative or additional medicine: An exploratory study in general practice. *Social Science & Medicine, 37*(8), 983–988.

Murray, R., Bell, K., Grant, M., & Wronski, I. (2003). Aboriginal health and the policy process. In S. Couzos & R. Murray (Eds), *Aboriginal health care: An evidenced based approach* (2nd ed.). Melbourne: Oxford University Press.

Muzzin, L. (2001). Academic capitalism and the hidden curriculum in the pharmaceutical sciences. In P. Armstrong, H. Armstrong, & D. Coburn (Eds), *Unhealthy times: Political economy perspectives on health and care in Canada* (pp. 97–120). Toronto, ON: Oxford University Press.

Muzzin, L., Brown, G., & Hornosty, R. (1998). Professional ideology in Canadian pharmacy. In C. Coburn, C. D'Arcy, & G. Torrance (Eds), *Health and Canadian society: Sociological perspectives* (3rd ed.). (pp. 379–398). Toronto, ON: University of Toronto Press.

Najman, J. (1980). Theories of disease causation and the concept of general susceptibility. *Social Science & Medicine*, 14A, 231–237.

National Clearing House on Family Violence. (n.d.) Family violence in Aboriginal communities: An Aboriginal perspective. Retrieved from www.phac-aspc.gc.ca/ncfv-cnivf/familyviolence/pdfs/aborigin.pdf

National Council of Welfare. (2009). Retrieved from www.ncwcnbes.net/documents/researchpublications/ResearchProjects/PovertyProfile/2009/Poverty Profile 1 2007 E.pdf

National Forum on Health. (1997). Volume 1, Canada health action: Building on the legacy: The final report of the national forum on health. Ottawa, ON: Author. Retrieved from www.hc-sc.gc.ca/hcs-sss/pubs/renewal-renouv/1997-nfoh-fnss-v1/index-eng.php#tphp

National Health Strategy (NHS) (1993). *Removing cultural and language barriers to health.* Issues Paper, No. 6, Canberra, AU: AGPS.

National Physician Survey. (2007). Retrieved from www.nationalphysiciansurvey.ca/nps/2007_Survey/2007nps-e.asp

National Science Foundation. (2006). U.S. industrial R&D performers report increased expenditures for 2004. Retrieved from www.nsf.gov/statistics/infbrief/nsf07304/#notes

Navarro, N. (2004, June). Inequalities are unhealthy. *Monthly Review, 56*(2).

Navarro, V. (1976). *Medicine under capitalism.* New York, NY: Prodist.

———. (1986). *Crisis, health and medicine: A social critique.* London, UK: Tavistock.

———. (1988). Professional dominance or proletarianization: Neither. *The Milbank Quarterly,* 66, Supplement 2, 57–75.

——— . (1998). Book review of private medicine and public health: Profits, politics and prejudice in the American health care enterprise by Lawrence D. Weiss. *Contemporary Sociology, 27*(4), 419–420.

———. (Ed). (2001). *Political economy of social inequalities: Consequences for health and quality of life.* Amityville, NY: Baywood Publishing Company, Inc.

———. (Ed). (2004). *The political and social contexts of health.* Amityville, NY: Baywood Publishing Company, Inc.

———. (Ed). (2007). *Neoliberalism, globalization and inequalities: Consequences for health and quality of life.* Amityville, NY: Baywood Publishing Company, Inc.

———. (2007). *Neoliberalism as class ideology. In V. Navarro (Ed), Neoliberalism, globalization, and inequalities: Consequences for health and quality of life.* Amityville, NY: Baywood Publishing Company, Inc.

———. (2008). Neoliberalism and its consequences: The world health situation since Alma Ata. *Global Social Policy,* 8, 152–155.

Navarro, V., & Muntaner, C. (2004). (Eds) *Political and economic determinants of population health and well-being: Controversies and developments.* Amityville, NY: Baywood Publishing Company, Inc.

Neff, J.A., McFall, S.L., & Cleaveland, T.D. (1987). Psychiatry and medicine in the US: Interpreting trends in medical specialty choice. *Sociology of Health and Illness, 9*(1), 45–61.

Nelson, S., & Gordon, S. (Eds). (2006). *The complexities of care. Nursing reconsidered.* Ithica, NY: Cornell University Press.

Newbold, K.B. (1998). Problems in search of solutions: Health and Canadian Aboriginals. *Journal of Community Health, 23*(1), 59–73.

———. (2005). Self-rated health within the Canadian immigrant population: Risk and the healthy immigrant effect. *Social Science & Medicine,* 60, 1359–1370.

———. (2009). The short-term health of Canada's new immigrant arrivals: Evidence from LSIC. *Ethnicity & Health, 14*(3), 315–336.

Newbold, K.B & Danforth, J. (2003). Health status and Canada's immigrant population. *Social Science & Medicine,* 57, 1981–1995.

Ng, W., Wilkins, R., Gendron, F., & Berthelot, J-M. (2005a). *Dynamics of immigrants' health in Canada: Evidence from the national population health survey.* Ottawa, ON: Statistics Canada.

Ng, E., Wilkins, R., Gendron, F., & Berthelot, J-M. (2005b, Autumn). The changing health of immigrants. *Canadian Social Trends.* Ottawa, ON: Statistics Canada.

Ngowi, V., Maeda, D.N., Wesseling, C., Partanen, T.J., Sanga, M.P., & Mbise, G. (2001). Pesticide-handling practices in agriculture in Tanzania: Observational data from 27 coffee and cotton farms. *International Journal of Occupational and Environmental Health,* 7, 326–332.

Nguyen, L. (2010, Aug. 4). Patients should be 'unafraid' to seek second opinion. Retrieved from www.canada.com/health/Patients+should+unafraid+seek+second+opinion/2640644/story.html

———. (2010, Aug. 24). Patients should be 'unafraid' to seek second opinion: Top MD. *Times Colonist.* Retrieved from www.timescolonist.com/story_print.html'id=2640644&sponsor

Ni, H., Simile, C., & Hardy, A.M. (2002). Utilization of complementary and alternative medicine by United States adults. *Medical Care, 40*(4), 353–358.

Norris, P., Herxheimer, A., Lexchin, J., & Mansfield, P. (2005). *Drug promotion: What we know, what we have yet to learn. Reviews of materials in the WHO/HAI database on drug promotion.* Geneva: World Health Organization and Health Action International.

Northcott, H., & Wilson, D. (2001). *Dying and death in Canada.* Aurora, ON: Garamond.

Nuckolls, C. (1997). Allocating value to gender in official American psychiatry, part I: The cultural construction of the personality disorder classification system. *Anthropology & Medicine,* 4, 45–66.

Nursing. (n.d.). In The Canadian Encyclopedia online. Retrieved from http://thecanadianencyclopedia.com/index.cfm?PgNm=TCE&Params=A1ARTA0005851

Oakley, A. (1980). *Women confined.* Oxford, UK: Martin Robertson.

Office of Inspector General. (2006). *FDA's monitoring of postmarketing study commitments.* Washington: Department of Health and Human Services.

Oliver, M. (1996). *Understanding disability.* London, UK: Macmillan Press.

———. (2004). Defining impairment and disability. In M. Bury, & J. Gabe (Eds), *The sociology of health and illness* (pp. 277–290). London, UK: Routledge Press.

Oliver, V. (2010). Homesick: A political economy of the health experiences of homeless young women. (Doctoral thesis). York University, Toronto, Ontario.

O'Neill, A. (1994). *Enemies within and enemies without: Educating chiropractors, osteopaths, and traditional acupuncturists.* Melbourne: La Trobe University.

———. (1995). Daylight at noon: Alternative health battles. In H. Gardner (Ed), *The politics of health* (2nd ed.) (pp. 482–452). Melbourne: Churchill Livingston.

Ontario Council of Agencies Serving Immigrants. (2005). Immigrant women and health. Retrieved from www.ocasi.org/index.php'qid=785&catid=115

Organization for Economic Cooperation and Development (OECD). (2001). Policy Brief *OECD health at a glance: How Canada compares.* Retrieved from www.oecd.org/dataoecd/5/25/2465559.pdf

Ornish, D. (1990). *Reversing heart disease.* London, UK: Century.

Ornish, D., Brown, S.E., Scherwitz, L.W., Billings, J.H., Armstrong, W.T. Ports, T.A., . . . Gould, K. L. (1990). Can lifestyle changes reverse coronary heart disease. *Lancet, 336,* 129–133.

Ornstein, M. (2006). *Ethno-racial groups in Toronto, 1971-2001: A demographic and socio-economic profile.* Toronto, ON: Institute for Social Research, York University.

Orona, C. (1990). Temporality and identity loss due to Alzheimer's disease. *Social Science & Medicine, 30*(11), 1247–1256.

Orwell, G. (1945). *Animal farm.* London, UK: Secker & Warburg.

Osberg, L. (2006, Apr-May). Pulling apart—The growing gulfs in Canadian society. *Policy Options.*

———. (2008). *A quarter century of economic inequality in Canada: 1981–2006, Growing Gap.* Ottawa, ON: Canadian Centre for Policy Alternatives.

Ostry, A., Shannon, T., Dubois, S., & Tasnim, N. (2003). The interplay of public health and economics in the early development of nutrition policy in Canada. *Critical Public Health, 13*(2), 171–185.

Ottawa Charter for Health Promotion. (1986). WHO. Retrieved from www.phac-aspc.gc.ca/ph-sp/docs/charter-chartre/pdf/charter.pdf

Palpz. (2004). The honourable Thomas Clement Douglas, greatest Canadian of all time, 1904–1986. Retrieved from http://everything2.com/user/Palpz/writeups/Tommy+Douglas

Paltiel, F. (1997). State initiatives; Impetus and effects. In C. Andrew and S. Rogers (Eds), *Women and the Canadian state* (pp. 27–51). Montreal, QC: McGill-Queens University Press.

Pan American Health Organization. (2007). Health in the Americas, volume 11, Countries, Canada. Retrieved from www.paho.org/hia/archivosvol2/paisesing/Canada%20English.pdf

Panitch, L. (1977). *The Canadian state: Political economy and political power.* Toronto, ON: University of Toronto Press.

Park, J. (2005, March). Use of alternative health care. *Health Reports, 16*(2). Ottawa, ON: Statistics Canada.

Parsons, T. (1951a). Illness and the role of the physician: A sociological perspective. American *Journal of Orthopsychiatry, 21,* 452–466.

———. (1951b). *The social system.* New York, NY: Free Press.

Pawluch, D., Cain, R., & Gillett, J. (2000). Lay constructions of HIV and complementary therapy use. *Social Science & Medicine, 51,* 251–264.

Pendergrast M. (1999). *Uncommon grounds: The history of coffee and how it transformed our world.* New York, NY: Basic Books.

Penning, M.J., & Votova, K. (2009). Aging, health and health care: From hospital and residential care to home and community care. In S. Bolaria and H. Dickinson (Eds), *Health, illness and health care in Canada* (4th ed.). Toronto, ON: Nelson.

Pérez, C. (2002). Health status and health behaviour among immigrants. Supplement to *Health Reports,* 13. Ottawa, ON: Statistics Canada.

Perfecto, I., Rice, R, Greenberg, R., & Van Der Voort, M.E. (1996). Shade coffee: A disappearing refuge for biodiversity. *Bioscience* 46:598–608.

Perkel, Colin, N. (2002). *Well of lies: The Walkerton water tragedy.* Toronto, ON: McClelland & Stewart Ltd.

Perspectives on Labour and Income. (2009, Summer). Work absences rates. *Perspectives on Labour and Income, 21* (2), 59–68.

Persson, L., Osgergren, P.O., Hanson, B.S., Lindgren, A., & Naucler, A. (2002). Social network, social support and the rate of decline of CD4 lymphocytes in asymptomatic HIV-positive homosexual men. *Scandinavian Journal of Public Health, 30*(3), 184–190.

Petersen, A. (1996). Risk and the regulated self: The discourse of health promotion as politics of uncertainty. *Australian and New Zealand Journal of Sociology,* 32, 44–57.

Petersen, A., & Lupton, D. (1996). *The new public health: Health and self in the age of risk.* Sydney: Allen & Unwin, and London: Sage.

Petersen, K. (2008). Boiling point. *The Dominion: News from the grassroots,* 53. Retrieved from www.dominionpaper.ca/articles/1944

Pim, L.R. (1981). *The invisible additives: Environmental contaminants in our food.* Toronto, ON: Doubleday Canada Ltd.

Pinto, P.C. (2009). Women, disability and the right to health. In P. Armstrong & J. Deadman (Eds), *Women's health. Intersections of policy, research and practice* (pp. 119–130). Toronto, ON: Women's Press.

Pinquart, M., & Duberstein, P. (2010, Aug.). Associations of social networks with cancer mortality: A meta-analysis. *Critical Reviews in Oncology/Hematology, 75*(2), 122-137.

Pirotta, M.V., Cohen, M.M., Kotsirilos, V., & Farish, S.J. (2000). Complementary therapies: Have they become accepted in general practice. *Medical Journal of Australia,* 172, 105–109.

Pittaway, E. (1999). Refugee women: The unsung heroes. In B. Ferguson & E. Pittaway. (Eds), *Nobody wants to talk about it: Refugee women's mental health* (pp. 1–20). Sydney: Transcultural Mental Health Centre, University of New South Wales.

Poovey, M. (1988). Feminism and deconstruction. *Feminist Studies.* 14 (1), 52–65.

Porter, R. (1997). *The greatest benefit to mankind: A medical history of humanity from antiquity to the present.* London, UK: HarperCollins.

Porter, R., & Porter, D. (1988). *In sickness and in health: The British Experience 1650–1850.* London, UK: Fourth Estate.

Porter, S. (1992). The poverty of professionalization: A critical analysis of strategies for the occupational advancement of nursing. *Journal of Advanced Nursing,* 17, 720–726.

———. (1995). *Nursing's relationship with medicine.* Aldershot:, UK: Avebury.

Power, E. (2008, March/April). Conceptualizing food security. *Canadian Journal of Public Health, 99*(2).

Powles, J. (1973). On the limitation of modern medicine. *Science, Medicine and Man, 1*(1), 1–30.

Powles, J. (1988). Professional Hygienists and the health of a nation. In R. MacLeod (Ed), *The commonwealth of science: ANZAAS and the scientific enterprise in Australasia 1888–1988* (pp. 292–307). Melbourne: Oxford University Press.

Prince, P. (2009). A population health approach to obesity in Canada: Putting the problem back into context. *Transdisciplinary Studies in Population Health Series, I*(I), 22–33.

Pringle, R. (1988). Secretaries talk: Sexuality, power and work. Sydney: Allen & Unwin.

———. (1995). Destabilising patriarchy. In B. Caine & R. Pringle. (Eds), *Transitions: New Australian feminisms* (pp. 198–211). Sydney: Allen & Unwin.

———. (1998). *Sex and medicine: Gender, power and authority in the medical profession.* Cambridge, UK: Cambridge University Press.

Probert, A., & Poirier, R. (2003, Mar.). The health status of First Nations people in Canada. *Health Policy Research Bulletin*, 5. Ottawa, ON: Health Canada.

Progestic International Inc. (2004). *Final report for the financial models project.* Ottawa, ON: Health Canada.

Prudham, S. (2004). Poisoning the well: Neoliberalism and the contamination of municipal water in Walkerton, Ontario. *Geofrum*, 35, 343–359.

Public Citizen's Congress Watch. (2002). *America's other drug problem. A briefing book on the Rx drug debate.* Washington, D.C.: Public Citizen.

Public Health Agency of Canada. (2001). What determines health. Retrieved from www.phac-aspc.gc.ca/ph-sp/determinants/determinants-eng.php#healthychild

———. (2005). Report: A public health agency for Canada—Working group. Retrieved from www.phac-aspc.gc.ca/publicat/phawg-aspgt-noseworthy/index-eng.php#toc

———. (2006) The state of the HIV/AIDS pandemic. Retrieved from www.phac-aspc.gc.ca/media/nr-rp/2006/2006_05bk1-eng.php

———. (2008). The social determinants of health. Retrieved from www.phac-aspc.gc.ca/ph-sp/oi-ar/index-eng.php

———. (2008a). Chronic disease facts and figures. Retrieved from www.phac-aspc.gc.ca/cd-mc/facts_figures-faits_chiffres-eng.php

———. (2008b). History. Retrieved from www.phac-aspc.gc.ca/about_apropos/history-eng.php

———. (2009). Aging & seniors. Retrieved from www.phac-aspc.gc.ca/seniors-aines/index-eng.php

———. (2009a). Tracking heart and stroke disease in Canada. Retrieved from www.phac-aspc.gc.ca/publicat/2009/cvd-avc/pdf/cvd-avs-2009-eng.pdf

———. (2009b). *What mothers say: The Canadian maternity experiences survey.* Ottawa, ON: Author.

———. (2009c). Who are Canada's seniors. Retrieved from www.phac-aspc.gc.ca/seniors-aines/publications/public/various-varies/papier-fed-paper/fedreport1-eng.php

———. (2011). About the Agency. Retrieved from www.phac-aspc.gc.ca/about_apropos/index-eng.php

Putnam, R. (1993). *Making democracy work: Civic traditions in modern Italy.* Princeton, NJ: Princeton University Press.

———. (2000). *Bowling alone: The collapse and revival of American community.* New York: NY: Simon & Schuster.

Pyper, W. (2004, Nov.). Employment trends in nursing. *Perspectives*, 5. Ottawa, ON: Statistics Canada.

Radiation health effects. (2007). Radiation Effects Research Foundation: A Cooperative Japan-US Research Organization. Retrieved from www.rerf.jp/radefx/index_e.html

Radley, A. (Ed). (1993). Worlds of illness: Biographical and cultural perspectives on health and disease. London, UK: Routledge.

Raffensperger, C., & Tickner, J. (Eds). (1999). *Protecting public health & the environment: Implementing the precautionary principle.* Washington, DC: Island Press.

Rankin, J.M., & Campbell, M. (2006). *Managing to nurse: Inside Canada's health care reform.* Toronto, ON: University of Toronto Press.

———, & ———. (2009, May). Institutional ethnography (IE): Nursing work and hospital reform: IE's cautionary analysis. Qualitative Social Research Volume 10(2), (8).

Raphael, D. (1999). Health effects of economic inequality. *Canadian Review of Social Policy*, 44, 25–40.

———. (2000). Health inequalities in Canada: Current discourses and implications for public health action. *Critical Public Health*, 10(2), 193–215.

———. (2001). From increasing poverty to societal disintegration: How economic inequality affects the health of individuals and communities. In P. Armstrong, H. Armstrong, & D. Coburn (Eds), *Unhealthy times: Political economy perspectives on health and care in Canada* (pp. 223–246). Don Mills, ON: Oxford University Press.

———. (2002). *Poverty, income inequality and health in Canada.* Toronto: CSJ Foundation for Research and Education. Retrieved from www.povertyandhumanrights.org/docs/incomeHealth.pdf

———. (2003). Barriers to addressing the societal determinants of health: Public health units and poverty in Ontario, Canada. *Health Promotion International*, 18(4), 397–405.

———. (2006). Social determinants of health: An overview of concepts and issues. In D. Raphael, T. Bryant, & M. Rioux (Eds). (2006). *Staying alive: Critical perspectives on health, illness, and health care.* (pp. 115–138). Toronto, ON: Canadian Scholars' Press Inc.

———. (2008, Dec.). Grasping at straws: A recent history of health promotion in Canada. *Critical Public health*, 18(4), 483–495

———. (Ed). (2009a). *Social determinants of health* (2nd ed.). Toronto, ON: Canadian Scholars' Press Inc.

———. (2009b). Social determinants of health: An overview of key issues and themes. In D. Raphael (Ed), *Social determinants of health* (2nd ed.) (pp. 2–19). Toronto, ON: Canadian Scholars' Press Inc.

———. (2009c). Social structure, living conditions and health. In D. Raphael (Ed), *Social determinants of health* (2nd ed.) (20–36). Toronto, ON: Canadian Scholars' Press Inc.

———. (2009d). Escaping from the phantom zone: Social determinants of health, public health units and public policy in Canada. *Health Promotion International*, 24(2), 93–198.

———. (Ed). (2010). *Health promotion and quality of life in Canada.* Toronto, ON: Canadian Scholars' Press Inc.

Raphael, D., Bryant, T., & Rioux, M. (Eds). (2006). *Staying alive: Critical perspectives on health illness, and health care.* Toronto, ON: Canadian Scholars' Press Inc.

Ratcliffe, J., Wallack, L., Fagnani, F., & Rodwin, V. (1984). Perspectives on prevention: Health promotion vs health protection. In J. de Kervasdoue, J. R. Kimberley, & G. Rodwin. (Eds), *The end of an illusion: The Future of health policy in western industrialized nations* (pp. 56–84). Berkeley, CA: University of California Press.

Rawls, J. (1970). *A theory of justice*. Oxford, UK: The Clarendon Press.

Reid, J., & Trompf, P. (Eds). (1990). *The health of immigrant Australia: A social perspective*. Sydney: Harcourt Brace Jovanovich.

Reid, R., Maag, J., & Vasa, S. (1993). Attention deficit hyperactivity disorder as a disability category: A critique. *Exceptional Children, 60*, 198–215.

Reinharz, S. (1992). *Feminist methods in social research*. New York, NY: Oxford University Press Inc.

Relman, A.S. (1980). The new medical-industrial complex. *New England Journal of Medicine, 303*(2), 963–970.

Researchers find link between chemical, cancer in Shannon, Que. (2009). Retrieved from www.cbc.ca/news/health/ story/2009/01/29/mtl-tce-shannon-researchers-0129.html

Retail prescriptions dispensed in Canada, 2006-2008. (2009). Retrieved from www.imshealth.com/deployedfiles/imshealth/ Global/Americas/North%20America/Canada/StaticFile/ Trends01_En_09.pdf

Reynolds, C. (1995). *Public health law in Australia*. Leichhardt: Federation Press.

Reynolds, H. (1995). *Aboriginal resistance to the European invasion of Australia* (2nd ed.). Ringwood, NJ: Penguin.

Reynolds, H. (2000). *Hmong women and reproduction*. Westport, CT: Bergin & Garvey.

Rice, P.L. (Ed). (1994). Asian mothers, Australian birth: Pregnancy, childbirth and childrearing: The Asian experience in an English-speaking country. Melbourne: Ausmed Publications.

Rice, P.L., & Ezzy, D. (1999). *Qualitative Research methods: A health focus*. Melbourne: Oxford University Press.

Rice, P.L., Ly, B., & Lumley, J. (1994). Childbirth and soul loss: The case of a Hmong woman. *Medical Journal of Australia, 160*, 577–578.

Rice, R., & Ward, J. (1996). *Coffee conservation, and commerce in the western hemisphere: How individuals and institutions can promote ecologically sound farming and forest management in Northern Latin America*. Washington, DC: Natural Resources Defense Council and Smithsonian Migratory Bird Center.

Rich, E. (2006). Anorexic dis. (connection): Managing anorexia as illness and an identity. *Sociology of Health & Illness, 28*(3), 284–305.

Rich, P. (2008, Jan./Feb.). The Canada Health Act. *Canadian Health Magazine*. Retrieved from www.canadian-health.ca/2_1/42 _e.htm

Richards, E. (1988). The politics of therapeutic evaluation: The vitamin C and cancer controversy. *Social Studies of Science, 18*, 653–701.

Richardson, L. (1994). Writing: A method of inquiry. In N. Denzin & Y. Lincoln. (Eds), Handbook of qualitative research. Thousand Oaks, CA: Sage.

Riessman, C. (1983). Women and medicalization: A new perspective. *Social Policy, 14*(1), 3–18.

———. (1993). *Narrative analysis*. Newbury Park, CA: Sage.

Rioux, M. (1985). Labelled disabled and wanting to work. In R. Abella, *Research studies of the commission on equality in employment* (pp. 611–640). Ottawa, ON: Minister of Supply and Services Canada.

———. (2006). The right to health: Human rights approaches to health. In D. Raphael, T. Bryant, & M. Rioux (Eds), *Staying alive, critical perspectives on health, illness, and health care* (pp. 85–110). Toronto, ON: Canadian Scholars Press, Inc.,

———. (2010). The right to health. In T. Bryant, D. Raphael, & M. Rioux (Eds), *Staying alive, critical perspectives on health illness , and health care* (2nd ed.) (pp. 93–119). Toronto, ON: Canadian Scholars' Press Inc.

Rioux, M., & Daly, T. (2010). Constructing disability and illness. In T Bryant, D. Raphael, & M. Rioux (Eds), *Staying alive, critical perspectives on health illness, and health care* (2nd ed.) (pp. 347–369). Toronto, ON: Canadian Scholars' Press Inc.

Ristovski-Slijepcevic, S., Bell, K., Chapman, G., & Beagan, B. (2010). Being 'thick' indicates you are eating, you are healthy and you have an attractive body shape: Perspectives on fatness and food choice amongst black and white men and women in Canada. *Health Sociology Review, 19*(3), 317–329.

Ritzer, G. (1993). *The McDonaldization of society*. Thousand Oaks, CA: Pine Forge Press.

———. (1996). *Sociological theory* (4th ed.). New York, NY: McGraw-Hill.

———. (1997). *Postmodern social theory*. New York, NY: McGraw-Hill.

———. (2000). *The McDonaldization of society* (3rd ed.). Thousand Oaks, CA: Pine Forge Press.

———. (2008). *The McDonaldization of society* (5th ed.). Los Angeles, CA: Pine Forest Press.

Ritzer, G., & Goodman, D. J. (2004). *Sociological theory* (6th ed.). New York, NY: McGraw-Hill.

Roach Anleu, S.L. (1993). Reproductive anatomy: Infertility, deviance and conceptive technology. *Law in Context, 11*, 17–40.

———, S.L. (1999). *Deviance, conformity, and control* (3rd ed.). Melbourne: Longman.

Robb, N. (1999, April 6). Canada has its first female dean—170 years after first medical school opened. *Canadian Medical Association Journal, 160*(7), 1042.

Roberge, R., Berthelot, J-M., & Wolfson, M. (1995, Summer). Health & socio-economic inequalities. *Canadian Social Trends*. Ottawa, ON: Statistics Canada.

Roberts, G.L. (1994). *Domestic violence victims in a hospital emergency department*. Queensland: University of Queensland, Department of Psychiatry.

Roberts, S.J. (1983). Oppressed group behaviour: Implications for nursing. *Advances in Nursing Science, 5*(4), 21–30.

Rochon Ford, A., & Saibil, D. (Eds). (2010). *Push to prescribe. Women and Canadian drug policy*. Toronto, ON: Women's Press.

Rogers, A., Hwang, W., Scott, L., Aiken, L., & Dinges, D. (2004, July/ August). The working hours of hospital staff nurses and patient safety. *Health Affairs, 23*.

Romanow, Honourable Roy. (2002). *Building on values: The future of health care in Canada*. Ottawa, ON: Government of Canada.

Rose, H. (1994). *Love, power and knowledge: Towards a feminist transformation of the sciences*. Cambridge: Polity Press.

Rosen, G. (1972). The evolution of social medicine. In H. E. Freeman, S. Levine, & L. G. Reeder (Eds), *Handbook of medical sociology* (2nd ed.) (pp. 30–60). Englewood Cliffs, NJ: Prentice Hall.

———. (1993). *A history of public health*. New York, NY: Johns Hopkins University Press.

Rosenberg, H. (1990). The home is the workplace: Hazards, stress and pollutants in the household. In M. Luxton, & H. Rosenberg (Eds), *Through the kitchen window*. Toronto, ON: Garamond.

———. (2000, Feb. 16). Gender ideology, power and crisis at Love Canal. Lecture presented at University of Memphis, Department of Anthropology, Memphis, TN.

Rosenhan, D.L. (1973). Being sane in insane places. *Science*, 179, 250–258.

Rowland, D.T. (1991). *Pioneers again: Immigrants and ageing in Australia*. Canberra: Bureau of Immigration Research and AGPS.

Rowsell, L. (2000). *Advertising campaigns of branded and unbranded messages*. Ottawa, ON: Health Canada, Therapeutic Products Directorate.

Royal Commission on Aboriginal Peoples. (1996a). *Highlights from the report of the royal commission on Aboriginal peoples (People to people, nation to nation)*. Ottawa, ON: Indian and Northern Affairs. Retrieved from www.ainc-inac.gc.ca/ap/pubs/rpt/rpt-eng.asp

———. (1996b). *Report of the royal commission on Aboriginal peoples*. Ottawa, ON: Indian and Northern Affairs.

Ruedy, J., Kaufman, D., & MacLeod, H. (1999, June). Alternative and complementary medicine in Canadian medical schools: A survey. *Canadian Medical Association*, 50, J816–817.

Russell, C., & Schofield, T. (1986). *Where it hurts: An introduction to sociology for health workers*. Sydney: Allen & Unwin.

Rx&D. (2002). Talking points re: Media reports—Dr. Holbrook and AstraZeneca. (2002). Retrieved March 1, 2003, from www.canadapharma.org/Media_Centre/Backgrounders/Holbrook99_e.html

———. (2004). *Towards increasing research and development in Canada: A new innovative pharmaceutical strategy*. Ottawa, ON: Author.

Ryan, W. (1971) *Blaming the victim*. New York, NY: Vintage.

Sackett, D. (1981). How to read clinical journals, V: To distinguish useful from useless or even harmful therapy. *Journal of the Canadian Medical Association*, 124, 1156–1162.

Saks, M. (1994). The alternatives to medicine. In J. Gabe, D. Kelleher, & G. Williams (Eds), *Challenging medicine* (pp. 84–103). London, UK: Routledge.

———. (2003). *Orthodox and alternative medicine: Politics, professionalization and health care*. London, UK: Sage.

Sampson, A. (2000, Sept. 19). How the boomers are being skinned. *Sydney Morning Herald* (Insight), p. 7.

Sawyer, E. (2006). *Guarding Canada's health system: The history of the Canadian Healthcare Association, 1931 to 2006*. Ottawa, ON: CHA Press.

Sawyer, M. G., Gannoni, A. F., Toogood, T. R., Antoniou, G., &

Rice, M. (1994). The use of alternative therapies by children with cancer. *Medical Journal of Australia*, 160, 320–322.

Schabas, Richard. (2002). Public health: What is to be done? *Canadian Medical Association Journal, 166*(10), 1282–1283.

Schanfarber, L. (2007). Interview with Dr. Jay Wortman. Retrieved from www.alive.com/6201a15a2.php

Schapiro, M. (2007). *Exposed: The toxic chemistry of everyday products and what's at stake for American power*. White River Junction, Vermont: Chelsea Green Publishing.

Scheff, T.J. (1966). *Being mentally ill: A sociological theory*. Chicago, IL: Aldine.

Schlosser, E. (2002). *Fast food nation: The dark side of the all-American meal*. New York, NY: Perennial.

Schmidt, K., Jacobs, P.A., & Barton, A. (2002). Cross-cultural differences in GPs' attitudes towards complementary and alternative medicine: A survey comparing regions of the UK and Germany. *Complementary Therapies in Medicine, 10*(3), 141–147.

Schneider, J., & Conrad, P. (1983). *Having epilepsy: The experience and control of illness*. Philadelphia: Temple University Press.

Schutz, A. (1972/1933). *The phenomenology of the social world*. London, UK: Heinemann.

Science Advisory Board Committee on the Drug Review Process. (2000). *Report to Health Canada*. Ottawa, ON.

Scott, D., & Stiver, A. (2009). Methyl mercury exposure and women's bodies. In B. Clow, A. Pederson, M. Haworth-Brockman, & J. Bernier (Eds), *Rising to the challenge. Sex and gender-based analysis in health planning, policy and research in Canada*. Halifax, NS: Atlantic Centre of Excellence for Women's Health.

Scott, K. (1977). Madness and segregative control: The role of the insane asylum. *Social Problems*, 24, 337–351.

———. (2002). *Income inequality as a determinant of health*. Ottawa, ON: Health Canada.

Scott, S. (2006). The medicalization of shyness: From social misfits to social fitness. *Sociology of Health & Illness, 28*(2), 33–153.

Scull, A.T. (1975). From madness to mental illness: Medical men as moral entrepreneurs. *Archives Européennes de Sociologie*, 16, 218–261.

———. (1977). Madness and segregative control: The role of the insane asylum. *Social Problems*, 24, 337–351.

Seale, C & Pattison, S. (Eds). (1994). *Medical knowledge: Doubt and certainty*. Buckingham, UK: Open University Press.

Sefa Dei, G. (1999, Sept.). Knowledge and politics of social change: The implication of anti-racism. *British Journal of Sociology of Education, 20*(3), 395–409.

Segall, A. (1997). Sick role concepts and health behaviour. In D. Gochman (Ed). (pp. 289-301). *Handbook of health behaviour research I: personal and social determinants*. New York, NY: Plenum Press.

Segall, A., & Chappell, N. (2000). *Health and health care in Canada*. Toronto, ON: Prentice-Hall.

Selbourne, D. (1994). *The principle of duty*. London, UK: Sinclair-Stevenson.

Senzilet, L. (1930). *Back to Methuselah*. London, UK: Constable.

Senzilet, L. (2007, Nov.). Health variations across Canada: A snapshot. In Health Canada, People, place and health. *Health Policy Research Bulletin,* 14. Retrieved from www.hc-sc.gc.ca/sr-sr/alt_formats/hpb-dgps/pdf/pubs/hpr-rps/bull/2007-people-place-gens-lieux/2007-people-place-gens-lieux-eng.pdf

Service Canada. (n.d.) Services for Canada. Retrieved from www.servicecanada.gc.ca/eng/audiences/seniors/index.shtml

Sharples, F.M.C., van Haselen, R., & Fisher, P. (2003). NHS patients' perspective on complementary medicine: A survey. *Complementary Therapies in Medicine, 11*(4), 243–248.

Shaw, G.B. (1908). *The doctor's dilemma.* London, UK: Constable.

Shields, M., & Wilkins, K. (2006). *Findings from the 2005 National Survey of the Work and Health of Nurses.* CIHI, Ottawa, ON: Statistics Canada.

Shilling, C. (2003). *The body and social theory* (2nd ed.). London, UK: Sage.

Shmueli, A., & Shuval, J. (2004). Use of complementary and alternative medicine in Israel: 2000 vs. 1993. *Israeli Medical Association Journal, 6*(1), 3–8.

Short, S.D., & Sharman, E. (1995). The nursing struggle in Australia. In G. M. Lupton & J. Najman (Eds), *Sociology of health and illness: Australian readings* (2nd ed.) (pp. 236–251). Melbourne: Macmillan.

Shuchman, M. (1999, Nov. 17). Drug firm threatens suit over MD's product review. *The Globe and Mail,* p. A1.

Shuval, J.T., Mizrachi, N., & Smetannnikov, E. (2002). Entering the well-guarded fortress: Alternative practitioners in hospital settings. *Social Science & Medicine,* 55, 1745–1755.

Siahpush, M. (1998). 'Postmodern values, dissatisfaction with conventional medicine and popularity of alternative therapies. *Journal of Sociology,* 34, 58–70.

———. (1999). Why do people favour alternative medicine. *Australian and New Zealand Journal of Public Health, 23*(3), 266–271.

Silversides, A. (2002, Feb. 5). More provinces protecting MDs who practice alternative medicine. *Canadian Medical Association Journal,* 166, 367.

———. (2008). Health Canada's investment in new postmarket drug surveillance network a 'pittance'. *Canadian Medical Association Journal,* 179, 412–413.

Simich. L., Beiser, M., Stewart, M., & Mwakarimba, E. (2005, Oct.). Providing social support for immigrants and refugees in Canada: Challenges and directions. *Journal of Immigrant Health, 7*(4), 259–268.

Simpson, J. (2003, Nov.). Utilization patterns and trends. *Health Policy Research Bulletin,* 7. Ottawa, ON: Health Canada.

———. (2010, Feb. 4). Playing a dirty game: Exporting asbestos. *The Globe and Mail,* p. A5.

Simpson, J.L., Genel, M., Carlson, A.S., Ferris, E., de la Chapelle, A., Ehrhardt, A.A. (2000). Gender verification in the Olympics. *Journal of the American Medical Association,* 284, 1568–1569.

Sinding, C. (2010, Dec.). Using institutional ethnography to understand the production of health care disparities. *Qualitative Health Research, 20*(12), 1656–1663.

Singh, M., & de Looper, M. (2002). Australian health inequalities: 1 Birthplace. Bulletin 2, AHIW Cat. AUS 27, Canberra: AIHW.

Sirois, F., & Gick, M. (2002). An investigation of the health beliefs and motivations of complementary medicine clients. *Social Science & Medicine* 55, 1025–1037.

Sirois, F., & Purc-Stephenson, R. (2008). When one door closes, another door opens: Physician availability and motivations to consult complementary and alternative medicine providers. Complementary Therapies in Clinical Practice, 14, 228–236.

Smith, A., Williams. L., Lyons, M., & Lewis, S. (2005). Pilot testing a multiprofessional learning module: Lessons learned. *Focus on Health Professional Education,* 6, 3.

Smith, B., & Hutchinson, B. (2004). *Gendering disability.* New Brunswick, NJ: Rutgers University Press.

Smith, D. (1987/1974). Women's perspective as a radical critique of sociology. In S. Harding (Ed), *Feminism and methodology.* Bloomington, IN: Indiana University Press.

———. (1987). *The everyday world as problematic: A feminist sociology.* Toronto, ON: University of Toronto Press.

———. (1993). *Texts, facts and femininity: Exploring the relations of ruling.* New York, NY: Routlege.

Smith, D.E., & David, S. (Eds). (1975). *Women look at psychiatry.* Vancouver, BC: Press Gang.

Smith, M. (1993, Oct.). The Rodriguez case: A review of the Supreme Court of Canada decision on assisted suicide. Ottawa, ON: Government of Canada, Law and Government Division. Retrieved from http://dsp-psd.pwgsc.gc.ca/Collection-R/LoPBdP/BP/bp349-e.htm

Smith, M., & Marles, R. (2003, Nov.). It's natural, so it can't hurt me—right? In *Health Policy Research Bulletin,* 7, Ottawa, ON: Health Canada.

Smith, M., & Simpson, J. (2003, Nov.). Alternative practices and products: A survival guide. *Health Policy Research Bulletin,* 7. Ottawa, ON: Health Canada.

Smith, R. (1987). *Unemployment and health: A disaster and a challenge.* Oxford, UK: Oxford University Press.

Smylie, J. (2009). The health of Aboriginal Peoples. In D. Raphael (Ed), *Social determinants of health* (2nd ed.) (pp. 281–299). Toronto, ON: Canadian Scholars' Press, Inc.

Smylie, J., & Anderson, M. (2006, Sept.). Understanding the health of Indigenous peoples in Canada: Key methodological and conceptual challenges. *Canadian Medical Association Journal, 12*(6), 175.

Smythe Dallas, W. (1981). *Dependency road: Communications, capitalism, consciousness and Canada.* Norwood, NJ: Ablex Publishing.

Snow, J. (1936/1855). *On the mode of communication of cholera* [reprinted as *Snow on cholera*]. New York, NY: Hafner.

Snyder, L., & Caplan, A. (Eds). (2001). *Assisted suicide: Finding common ground.* Indianapolis, IN: Indiana University Press.

Social and Aboriginal Statistics Division, Aboriginal Peoples Survey. (2006). *An overview of the health of the Métis population: Fact sheet.* Ottawa, ON: Statistics Canada.

Spack, T. (2003). The importance of culture. *Health Policy Research Bulletin*, 5, 20–22.

Spade, J. Z., & Valentine, C. G. (2008). *The kaleidoscope of gender. Prisms, patterns and possibilities.* Thousand Oaks, CA: Sage.

Sparling, D., & Laughland, P. (2008). Are large farms really different. Vista: On the agri-food industry and the farm community. Statistics Canada Catalogue 21-004-X. Retrieved from www.statcan.gc.ca/pub/21-004-x/21-004-x2007001-eng.pdf. (PDF Version, 123 kb).

Spills lead to fisheries Act convictions. (2000). *Toxic Chemicals Update: An Environment Canada Atlantic Region Newsletter, 4*(1). Retrieved from http://atlantic-web1.ns.ec.gc.ca/epb/newsletters/toxchem/Default.asp'lang=En&n=42EF7454-1#spills

Stanway, A. (1979). *Alternative medicine: A guide to natural therapies.* Adelaide: Rigby.

Starr, P. (1982). *The social transformation of American medicine: The rise of a sovereign profession and the making of a vast industry.* New York, NY: Basic Books.

Statistics Canada. (1995). *Earnings of women and men.* Ottawa, ON: Industry Canada.

———. (1996). *Earnings of women and men.* Ottawa, ON: Industry Canada.

———. (1999). *Statistical report on the health of Canadians.* Retrieved from www.statcan.gc.ca/pub/82-570-x/82-570-x1997001-eng.pdf

———. (2002). Mental health of Canada's immigrants. Supplement to *Health Reports*, 13. Ottawa, ON.

———. (2003). *Ethnic diversity survey: Portrait of a multicultural society.* Ottawa, ON: Author.

———. (2006a). Aboriginal Peoples highlight tables. Retrieved from www12.statcan.ca/census-recensement/2006/dp-pd/hlt/97-558/index.cfm?Lang=E

———. (2006b). Disability rights in Canada: A virtual museum. Retrieved from http://disabilityrights.freeculture.ca/index.php

———. (2006c). Participation and activity limitation survey, 2006 analytical report. Retrieved from www.statcan.gc.ca/pub/89-628-x/89-628-x2007002-eng.pdf

———. (2006d). *Women in Canada.* Ottawa, ON: Ministry of Industry.

———. (2007). The South Asian community in Canada. Retrieved from www.statcan.gc.ca/pub/89-621-x/89-621-x2007006-eng.htm

———. (2007, Feb.). Important health and healthcare issues in Canada. *Health Reports, 18*(1). Retrieved from www.statcan.gc.ca/ads-annonces/82-003-x/index-eng.htm

———. (2007a). A portrait of seniors. Retrieved from www.statcan.gc.ca/pub/89-519-x/89-519-x2006001-eng.pdf

———. (2008a). Aboriginal peoples in Canada in 2006: Inuit, Métis and First Nations, 2006 Census. Ottawa, ON: Author.

———. (2008b). Canadian demographics at a glance. Retrieved from www.statcan.gc.ca/pub/91-003-x/91-003-x2007001-eng.pdf

———. (2008c). Canada's ethnocultural mosaic: 2006 Census. Retrieved from http://dsp-psd.pwgsc.gc.ca/collections/collection_2010/statcan/CS97-562-2006-1-eng.pdf

———. (2008d). 2006 Census Canada. All occupations. Ottawa, ON: Industry Canada.

———. (2009). *Health care professionals and official minorities in Canada 2001 and 2006.* Ottawa, ON: Author.

———. (2009). Infant mortality rates. Retrieved from www65.statcan.gc.ca/acyb02/1947/acyb02_19470143004a-eng.htm and www40.statcan.ca/l01/cst01/health21a-eng.htm

———. (2009). *Perspectives on Labour and Income.* 10 (3). Ottawa, ON.

———. (2010). Life expectancy at birth, by sex, by province. Retrieved from www40.statcan.ca/l01/cst01/health26-eng.htm

Stein, L. (1967). The doctor/nurse game. *Archives of General Psychiatry*, 16, 699–703.

Steingraber, S. (1998). *Living downstream: A scientist's personal investigation of cancer and the environment.* New York, NY: Vintage Books.

Stockholm Convention on Persistent Organic Pollutants. (2009). The convention. Retrieved from http://chm.pops.int/Convention/tabid/54/language/en-GB/Default.aspx

Stolberg, H.O. (2004, Sept.). Canadian health care system: Past, present, and future. *Journal of the American College of Radiology, 1*(9).

Strasser, R.D. (1992). The gatekeeper role of general practice. *Medical Journal of Australia*, 156, 108–110.

Strauss, A., & Corbin, J. (1990). *Basics of qualitative research.* London, UK: Sage.

Strauss, A., & Glaser, B. (1975). *Chronic illness and the quality of life.* St. Louis, MO: Mosby.

Strong, P.M. (1979). Sociological imperialism and the profession of medicine: A critical examination of the thesis of medical imperialism. *Social Science & Medicine*, 13A(2), 199–215.

Sugaring the Pill, (1996, January 27). *New Scientist*, pp. 27–29.

Sutherns, Rebecca. (2009, Spring). Human resources and the environment of birth in Canada. *Women and Environments*, 80/81, 19–21.

Sutton, J.R. (1991). The political economy of madness: The expansion of the asylum in progressive America. *American Sociological Review*, 56, 665–678.

Svensson, R. (1996). The interplay between doctors and nurses: A negotiated order perspective. *Sociology of Health and Illness, 18*(3), 379–398.

Swan, S.H., Main, K.M., Fan, L., Stewart, S.L., Kruse, R.L., Calafat, A.M., . . . Teague, J.L. (2005). Decrease in anogenital distance among male infants with prenatal phthalate exposure. *Environmental Health Perspectives, 113*(8), 1056–1061.

Sydie, R.A. (1987). *Natural women, cultured men: A feminist perspective on sociological theory.* Toronto, ON: Methuen Publications.

Szasz, T.S. (1960). The myth of mental illness. *The American Psychologist*, 15, 113–118.

———. (1961). *The myth of mental illness: Foundation of a theory of personal conduct.* New York, NY: Holber-Harper.

———. (1973). *Ideology and insanity: Essays on the psychiatric dehumanization of man.* London, UK: Colder & Boyars.

———. (2007). *The medicalization of everyday life.* Syracuse, NY: Syracuse University Press.

Szreter, S. (1988). The importance of social intervention in Britain's mortality decline c. 1850-1914: A re-interpretation of the role of public health. *Society for the Social History of Medicine*,1 (1), 1–37.

Talking points re: media reports. Dr. Holbrook and AstraZeneca. (2002). Retrieved March 1, 2003, from www.canadapharma.org/Media_Centre/Backgrounders/Holbrook99_e.html

Tang, S., & Browne, A. (2008, April). 'Race' matters: Racialization and egalitarian discourses involving Aboriginal people in the Canadian health care context. *Ethnicity & Health, 13*(2), 108–127.

Targeting doctors. Graph: top 50 drugs by promotion dollars. (2002), *CBC-TV Disclosure.*

Taube, G. (2009). An interview with Ana Soto. *Science Watch.com*: Tracking trends & performance in basic research. Retrieved from http://sciencewatch.com/ana/st/bis/09sepBisSoto/

Taylor, K.M. (1991). The impact of the pharmaceutical industry's clinical research programs on medical education, practice and researchers in Canada: A discussion paper. *Canadian pharmaceutical research and development: Four short-term studies.* Ottawa, ON: Industry, Science & Technology Canada.

The battle over a drug ad. (2001). CBC-TV. *Undercurrents.*

The Daily. (2006, Feb. 9). Predictors of death in seniors. *Health Reports.* Ottawa, ON: Statistics Canada.

The Daily. (2007a, Feb. 27). *A portrait of seniors.* Ottawa, ON: Statistics Canada.

———. (2007b). Deaths. Ottawa, ON: Statistics Canada. Retrieved from www.statcan.gc.ca/daily-quotidien/100223/dq100223a-eng.htm

———. (2007c, Dec. 3). *Participation and activity limitation survey.* Ottawa, ON: Statistics Canada.

———. (2007d, December). *2006 Census: Immigration, citizenship, language, mobility and migration.* Retrieved from www.statcan.gc.ca/daily-quotidien/071204/dq071204a-eng.htm

———. (2009, Mar. 18). Study: Cancer prevalence in the Canadian population. Retrieved from www.statcan.gc.ca/daily-quotidien/090318/dq090318b-eng.htm

The Doctors versus the Nurses. (1962, June 15). *Nursing Times*, pp. 783–784.

The New York Times. (2009). *Harvard medical school in ethics quandary.* March 3. Retrieved from www.nytimes.com/2009/03/03/business/03medschool.html

The Perfect Potato. (2002, October 25). CTV. *W5.* Retrieved from http://healthcoalition.ca/archive/W5.pdf

The Source: Women's Health Data Directory. (2009). Maternal mortality. Retrieved from www.womenshealthdata.ca/category-aspx'catid

Theorell T., Ahlberg-Hulten, G., Jodko, M., Sigala, F., de la Torre, B. (1993). Influence of job strain and emotion on blood pressure in female hospital personnel during work hours. *Scandinavian Journal of Work, Environment and Health*, 19, 313–318.

Therapeutic Products Directorate. (2004). *Business transformation progress report.* Ottawa, ON: Health Canada.

Thomas, K.J., Carr J., Westlake, L., & Williams, B.T. (1991). Use of non-orthodox and conventional health care in Great Britain. *British Medical Journal*, 302, 207–302.

Tiedemann, M. (2006, Apr. 26). Bill C-5: Public Health Agency of Canada Act. Retrieved from www2.parl.gc.ca/Sites/LOP/LegislativeSummaries/Bills_ls.asp'lang=E&ls=c5&source=library_prb&Parl=39&Ses=1

Tjepkema, M. (2002). The health of the off-reserve Aboriginal population. Supplement to *Health Reports,* 13. Ottawa, ON: Statistics Canada.

Tjepkema, M.l. (2007). Adult obesity in Canada: Measured height and weight. Nutrition: Findings from the Canadian Community Health Survey Statistics Canada. Catalogue 82-620-MWE. Retrieved from www.statcan.gc.ca/cgi-bin/af-fdr.cgi'l=eng&loc=./.pdf/4224906-eng.pdf

Tomczak, J. (n.d.). A short history of hospice and palliative care. Retrieved from www.myseniorsite.ca/eldercare-tomczak27.htm

Tommy Douglas Research Institute. (n.d.). Tommy's life story. Retrieved from www.tommydouglas.ca/?page_id=21

Tong, R.P. (1998). *Feminist thought: A comprehensive introduction* (2nd ed.). Sydney: Allen & Unwin.

Toronto Star. (2009, Oct. 5). Canada 4th in UN ranking. Retrieved from www.thestar.com/news/world/article/705518--canada-4th-in-un-ranking

Torrance, G. (1998). Socio-historical overview: The development of the Canadian health system. In D. Coburn, C. D'Arcy & G. Torrance (Eds), *Health and Canadian society* (3rd ed.). Toronto, ON: University of Toronto Press.

Torrance, G., & Kaufert, J. (1983). Medical dominance in Canada in historical perspective: The rise and fall of medicine. *International Journal of Health Services.*

Towards increasing research and development in Canada: a new innovative pharmaceutical strategy. (2004). Ottawa: Rx&D.

Townsend, P., & Davidson, N. (Eds). (1982). *Inequalities in health: The Black report.* Harmondsworth, UK: Penguin.

Townsend, P., Davidson, N., & Whitehead, M. (Eds). (1992). *Inequalities in health: The Black report and the health divide.* London, UK: Penguin.

Townson, M. (2004). September 2004: A new 'social architecture' for Canada. *The Monitor.* Ottawa, ON: Canadian Centre for Policy Alternatives.

———. (2009). *Women's poverty and the recession.* Ottawa, ON: Canadian Centre for Policy Alternatives.

Tran, H. (1994). Antenatal and postnatal maternity care for Vietnamese women. In P. L. Rice (Ed), *Asian mothers, Australian birth, pregnancy, childbirth and childrearing: The Asian experience in an English-speaking country* (pp. 61–76). Melbourne: Ausmed Publications.

Trautmann, N. M., Porter, K. S., Wagenet, R. J. (n.d). Modern agriculture: Its effects on the environment. Pesticide Safety Education Program, Cornell University Cooperative Extension. Retrieved from http://pmep.cals.cornell.edu/facts-slides-self/facts/mod-ag-grw85.aspx

Travers, A. (2009). The health and well-being of sexual and gender minority women: Still struggling with silence and invisibility. In P. Armstrong and J. Deadman (Eds), *Women's health. Intersections of policy, research and practice* (pp.151–163). Toronto, ON: Women's Press.

Travers, K. (1996). The social organization of nutritional inequities. *Social Sciences and Medicine*, 43, 543–553.

Tremblay, M., Shields, M., Laviolette, M., Craig, C., Janssen, I., & Gorber, S. (2010, Mar. 1). Fitness of Canadian children and youth: Results from the 2007–2009 Canadian health measures survey. *Health Reports*, 21, 7–20.

Trevelyan, J., & Booth, B. (1994). *Complementary medicine for nurses, midwives and health visitors*. London, UK: Macmillan.

Trewin, D., & Madden, R. (2003). *The health and welfare of Australia's Aboriginal and Torres Strait Islander peoples*. Canberra: Australian Bureau of Statistics.

Tuffs, A. (2002). Three out of four Germans have used complementary or natural remedies. *British Medical Journal*, 325, 990.

Tulandi, T., Martin, J., Al-Fadhi, R., Kabli, N., Forman, R., Hitkari, J., . . . Casper, R.F. (2006). Congenital malformation among 911 newborns conceived after infertility treatment with letrozole or clamiphene citrate. *Fertility and Sterility 85*(6), 1761–1765.

Turcotte, M., & Schellenberg. (2007). A portrait of seniors 2006. Ottawa, ON: Statistics Canada. Retrieved from www.statcan.gc.ca/pub/89-519-x/89-519-x2006001-eng.pdf

Turner, B.S. (1987). *Medical power and social knowledge*. London, UK: Sage.

———. (1992). *Regulating bodies: Essays in medical sociology*. London, UK: Routledge.

———. (2004). *The new medical sociology*. New York, NY: W.W. Norton.

———. (1986a). *Citizenship and capitalism: The debate over reformism*. London, UK: Allen & Unwin.

———. (1986b). The vocabulary of complaints: Nursing professionalism and job context. *Australian and New Zealand Journal of Sociology, 22*(3), 368–386.

Turner, B.S., & Samson, C. (1995). *Medical power and social knowledge* (2nd ed.). London, UK: Sage.

Turner, G.W. (Ed.) (1987). *Australian concise oxford dictionary*. Melbourne: Oxford University Press.

Turner, J., & Grieco, M. (2000). Gender and time poverty: The neglected social policy implications of gendered time, transport and travel. *Time and Society 9*(1), 129–136.

Turrell, G., & Mathers, C.D. (2000, May). Socioeconomic status and health in Australia. *Medical Journal of Australia*, *172*(1), 434–438.

Turrell, G., Oldenburg, B., McGuffog, I., & Dent, R. (1999). *Socioeconomic determinants of health: Towards a national research program and a policy and intervention agenda*. Brisbane: Centre for Public Health Research, School of Public Health, Queensland University of Technology.

United States Senate, J.E.C. (2000). The benefits of medical research and the role of the NIH. Washington, DC: Author.

United Nations General Assembly. (2007). United Nations Declaration on the Rights of Indigenous Peoples. Geneva: United Nations. Retrieved from www.iwgia.org/sw248.asp

Unruh, A.M., Ritchie, J., & Merskey, H. (1999). Does gender affect appraisal of pain and pain coping strategies. *The Clinical Journal of Pain*, 15(1), 31–40.

Urmetzer, P., & Guppy, N. (2009). Changing income inequality in Canada. In E. Grabb, & N. Guppy (Eds), *Social inequality in Canada: Patterns, problems and policies* (5th ed.) (pp. 82–91). Toronto, ON: Pearson Prentice Hall.

Usdin, S. (2007). *The no-nonsense guide to world health*. Toronto, ON: Between the Lines.

Vachon, D. (2005, May & June). Doctor John Snow blames water pollution for cholera epidemic. *Old News 16*(8), 8–10. Retrieved from www.ph.ucla.edu/epi/snow/fatherofepidemiology.html

Vågerö, D., & Illsley, R. (1995). Explaining health inequalities: Beyond Black and Barker. *European Sociological Review*, 11, 219–241.

Valverde, M., & White-Mair, K. (1999). 'One day at a time' and other slogans for everyday life: The ethical practices of Alcoholics Anonymous. *Sociology*, 33, 393–410.

Vancouver Coastal Health. (n.d.). Aboriginal health: Aboriginal health facts. Retrieved from http://aboriginalhealth.vch.ca/facts.htm

Varcoe, C. (2009). Inequality, violence, and women's health. In S. Bolaria & H. Dickinson (Eds). *Health, illness, and health care in Canada* (4th ed.). (pp. 259–282). Toronto, ON: Nelson Educational Ltd.

Veenstra, G. (2009). Social inequality and health. In E. Grabb, & N. Guppy (Eds), *Social inequality in Canada: Patterns, problems, and policies* (5th ed.) (pp. 353–366). Toronto, ON: Pearson Prentice Hall.

Verhoef, M., & Sutherland, L. (1995a, June). Alternative medicine and general practitioners. *Canadian Family Physician*, 41, 1005–1011.

Verhoef, M., & Sutherland, L. (1995b). General practitioners' assessment of an interest in alternative medicine in Canada. *Social Science & Medicine, 41*(4), 511–515.

Verhoef, M., Boon, H., & Mutasingwa, D. (2006). The scope of naturopathic medicine in Canada: An emerging profession. *Social Science & Medicine, 63*, 409–417.

Verhoef, M., Brundin-Mather, R., Jones, A., Boon, H., & Epstein, M. (2004, June). Complementary and alternative medicine in undergraduate medical education. *Canadian Family Physician*, 50.

Vijoen, M., Panzer, A., Roos, J.L., & Bodemer, W. (2003). Psychoneuroimmunology: From philosophy, intuition and folklore to a recognized science. *South African Journal of Science, 99*(7–8), 332–336.

Waldfogel, J. (2002). Child care, women's employment and child outcomes. *Journal of Population Economics*, 15, 527–548.

Waitzkin, H. (1983). *The second sickness: Contradictions of capitalist health care*. New York, NY: Free Press.

———. (2000). *The second sickness: Contradictions of capitalist health care* (2nd ed.). Lanham, MD: Rowman & Littlefield.

Walby, S. (1990). *Theorising patriarchy*. Oxford, UK: Blackwell.

———. (1992). Post-post-modernism? Theorizing social complexity. In M. Barrett & A. Phillips (Eds), *Destabilizing theory: Contemporary feminist debates* (pp. 31–52). Cambridge, UK: Polity Press.

Walby, S., & Greenwell, J. (1994). *Medicine and nursing: Professions in a changing health service*. London, UK: Sage.

Walker, A. (1990). The economic 'burden' of ageing and the prospect of intergenerational conflict. *Ageing and Society*, 10, 377–396.

Walters, V. (1992). Women's views of their main health problem. *Canadian Journal of Public Health*, 83 (5), pp. 371–374.

———. (1994). Women's perceptions regarding health and illness. In S. Bolaria, H. Dickinson (Eds), *Health, illness and health care in Canada*. Scarborough, ON: Nelson Thomson Learning.

Walton, M. (1998). *The trouble with medicine: Preserving the trust between patients and doctors*. Sydney: Allen & Unwin.

Wardlow, H., & Curry, R. (1996). Sympathy for my body. Breast cancer and mammography at two Atlanta clinics. *Medical Anthropology*, 16, 319–340.

Ware, N. (1992). Suffering and the social construction of illness: The delegitimation of illness experience in chronic fatigue syndrome. *Medical Anthropology Quarterly*, 6(4), 347–361.

Wargo, J. (1996). *Our children's toxic legacy: How science and law fail to protect us from pesticides*. New Haven, CT: Yale University Press.

Wathan, C.N., & Harris, R.M. (2006, July 4). An examination of the health information seeking experiences of women in rural Ontario, Canada. *IRInformation Research*, 11. Retrieved from http://informationr.net/ir/11-4/paper267.html

Watkins, E. (2007). The medicalization of male menopause in America. *Social History of Medicine*, 20(2), 369–388.

Waxler-Morrison, N., Hislop, T.G., Mears, B., & Kan, L. (1991). Effects of social relationships on survival for women with breast cancer: A prospective study. *Social Science & Medicine*, 33(2), 177–183.

Wazana, A. (2000). Physicians and the pharmaceutical industry: Is a gift ever just a gift? *Journal of the American Medical Association*, 383, 373–380.

Weber, M. (1968/1921). *Economy and society*. New York: NY: Bedminster.

Weedon, C. (1997). *Feminist practice and poststructuralist theory* (2nd ed). Cambridge, MA: Blackwell.

Weiss, G., & Lonnquist, L. (2006). *The sociology of health, healing, and illness* (5th ed.). New Jersey: Pearson Education Inc.

——— & ———. (2006). The development of scientific medicine. In G. Weiss, & L. Lonnquist, *The sociology of health, healing, and illness* (5th ed.). New Jersey: Pearson Education.

——— & ———. (2009). *The sociology of health, healing, and illness* (6th ed.). New Jersey: Pearson Education Inc.

Wendell, S. (1996). *The rejected body: Feminist philosophical reflections on disability*. New York, NY: Routledge.

———. (1989). Toward a feminist theory of disability. *Hypatia*, 4(2), 104–124.

———. (2001). Unhealthy disabled: Treating chronic illnesses as disability. *Hypatia*, 16(4), 17–33.

Western, M. (2000). Class in Australia in the 1980s and 1990s. In J. M. Najman & J. S. Western (Eds), *A sociology of Australian society* (3rd ed.) (pp. 68–88). Melbourne: Macmillan.

Westra, L., & Lawson, B.E. (Eds). (2001). *Faces of environmental racism: Confronting issues of global justice*. Lanham, MD: Rowman & Littlefield Publishers.

What is homeopathy? (2009). Ontario College of Homeopathic Medicine. Retrieved from www.ochm.ca/what-is-homeopathy.html

White, J.P., & Mulvaney, D.J. (1987). How many people? In D.J. Mulvaney & J.P. White (Eds), *Australians to 1788*. Sydney: Fairfax, Syme and Weldon.

White, K. (2000). The state, the market, and general practice: The Australian case. *International Journal of Health Services*, 30(2), 285–308.

———. (Ed). (2001). *The early sociology of health and illness*, 6 vols. London, UK: Routledge.

White, K., & Willis, E. (1998). Evidence based medicine and the sociology of medical knowledge. Paper presented: *Annual National Conference of the Australian Sociological Association*. Brisbane.

White, R. (2002). Social and political aspects of men's health. *Health*, 6(3), 267–286.

Whitehead, M. (1987). *The health divide: Inequalities in health in the 1980s*. London, UK: Health Education Council.

———. (1992). The concepts and principles of equity and health. *International Journal of Health Services*, 22(3), 429–445.

———. (1995). Tackling inequalities: A review of policy initiatives. In M. Benzeval, K. Judge, & M. Whitehead (Eds), *Tackling inequalities in health: An agenda or action*. London, UK: King's Fund.

———. (1998). Diffusion of ideas on social inequalities in health: A European perspective. Milbank Quarterly, 76, 469–492.

Whitehead, M., & Drever, M. (1997). Health inequalities: Main findings and implications for the future. In M. Drever & M. Whitehead. (Eds), *Health inequalities*. London, UK: Stationery Office.

Whitehead, M., Judge, K., Hunter, D. J., Maxwell, R., & Scheuer, M. A. (1993). Tackling inequalities in health: The Australian experience. *British Medical Journal*, 306, 783–787.

Whitley, R., Kirmayer, L.J., Groleau, D. (2006). Understanding immigrants' reluctance to use mental health services: A qualitative study from Montreal. *Canadian Journal of Psychiatry*, 51(4).

WHO. (n.d.). Definition of health. Retrieved from https://apps.who.int/aboutwho/en/definition.html

———. (1946). Constitution of the World Health Organization. WHO, Geneva.

———. (1978, Sept. 6–12). Alma-Ata declaration. Declaration of Alma-Ata International Conference on Primary Health Care. Alma-Ata, USSR. Retrieved from www.who.int/hpr/NPH/docs/declaration_almaata.pdf

———. (2004). *Suicide rates*. Retrieved from www.who.int/mental_health/media/cana.pdf

———. (2008). World health statistics, 2008. Retrieved from www.who.int/whosis/whostat/EN_WHS08_Full.pdf

Wicks, D. (1995a). Contested femininity: Gender and work at the Sydney infirmary 1868–1875. *Journal of Interdisciplinary Gender Studies*, 1, 89–99.

———. (1995b). Nurses and doctors and discourses of healing. *Australian and New Zealand Journal of Sociology*, 31(2), 122–139.

———. (1999). *Nurses and doctors at work: Rethinking professional boundaries*. Sydney: Allen & Unwin.

Wilkins, R.J., Berthelot, J-M., & Ng, E. (2002). Trends in mortality by neighbourhood income in urban Canada from 1971–1996. *Health Reports*, 13, (supplement), 1–28. Ottawa, ON: Statistics Canada.

Wilkins, R.J., Tjepkema, M., Mustard, C., & Choini're, R. (2008b, Sept.). The Canadian census mortality follow-up study, 1991 through 2001. *Health Reports*, 19, 3. Ottawa, ON: Statistics Canada.

Wilkins, R.J., Uppal, S., Fines, P., Senecal, S., Guimond, E., & Dion, R. (2008a, Mar.). Life expectancy in the Inuit-inhabited areas of Canada, 1989 to 2003. *Health Reports, 19*(1). Ottawa, ON: Statistics Canada.

Wilkinson, M. (2000, May 13). Negative imaging. *Sydney Morning Herald*, p. 40.

Wilkinson, R. (1992). Income distribution and life expectancy. *British Medical Journal*, 304, 165–168.

———. (1996). *Unhealthy societies: The afflictions of inequality*. London, UK: Routledge.

———. (1999). Putting the picture together: Prosperity, redistribution, health, and welfare. In M. Marmot & R. G. Wilkinson (Eds), *Social determinants of health* (pp. 256–274). Oxford, UK: Oxford University Press.

Wilkinson, R., & Marmot, M. (Eds). (1998). *The solid facts: Social determinants of health*. Copenhagen: World Health Organization.

Wilkinson, R., & Marmot, M. (Eds). (2003). *Social determinants of health: The solid facts* (2nd ed.). Copenhagen: World Health Organization. Retrieved from www.epha.org/a/856

Wilkinson, R., & Pickett, K. (2009). *The spirit level: Why more equal societies almost always do better*. London, UK: Allen Lane.

Williams, A.P., Domnick-Pierre, K., Vayda, E., Stevenson, H.M., & Burke, M. (1990). Women in medicine: Practice patterns and attitudes. *Canadian Medical Association Journal*, *143*(3), 194–201.

Williams, A.P., Deber, R., Baranek, P., & Gildiner, A. (2001). From Medicare to home care: Globalization, state retrenchment, and the profitization of Canada's health-care system. In P. Armstrong, H. Armstrong, & D. Coburn (Eds), *Unhealthy times: Political economy perspectives on health and care in Canada* (pp. 7–30). Toronto, ON: Oxford University Press.

Williams, G. (2000). The genesis of chronic illness: Narrative re-construction. In P. Brown, *Perspectives in medical sociology* (3rd ed.). Illinois: Waveland Press Inc.

Williams, G. (2004). The genesis of chronic illness. In M. Bury, & J. Gabe (Eds), *The sociology of health and illness* (pp. 247–255). London, UK: Routledge Press.

Williams, L., & Germov, J. (2004). The thin ideal: Women, food and dieting. In J. Germov & L. Williams. (Eds), *A sociology of food and nutrition: The social appetite* (2nd ed.). Melbourne: Oxford University Press.

Williams, L. S., & McKenzie, F. (1996). *Understanding Australia's population*. Canberra: AGPS.

Williams, R. (1990). *A Protestant legacy: Attitudes to death and illness among older Aberdonians*. Oxford, UK: Oxford University Press.

Williams, S., & Calnan, M. (1996). The 'limits' of medicalization: Modern medicine and the lay populace in 'late' modernity. *Social Science & Medicine*, *42*(12,) 1609–1620.

Willis, E. (1983). *Medical dominance*. Sydney: Allen & Unwin.

———. (1989a). Complementary healers. In G.M. Lupton & J. Najman. (Eds), *Sociology of health and illness: Australian readings* (pp. 259–279). Melbourne: Macmillan.

———. (1989b). *Medical dominance* (Rev. ed.). Sydney: Allen & Unwin.

———. (1994). *Illness and social relations*. Sydney: Allen & Unwin.

———. (1998). Public health, private genes: The social context of genetic biotechnologies. *Critical Public Health*, *8*(2), 131–139.

———. (2004). *The sociological quest* (4th ed.). Sydney: Allen & Unwin.

Willman, D. (2000, June 4). The rise and fall of the killer drug Rezulin. *Los Angeles Times*.

Windsor hospital probes other cases of concern. Retrieved from www.cbc.ca/canada/windsor/story/2010/02/24/windsor-second-mastectomy-100224.html'ref=rss).

Winter, I. (Ed). (2000a). Social capital and public policy in Australia. Melbourne: Australian Institute of Family Studies.

———. (2000b). Major themes and debates in the social capital literature: The Australian connection. In I. Winter (Ed), *Social capital and public policy in Australia* (pp. 7–42). Melbourne: Australian Institute of Family Studies.

Witz, A. (1992). *Professions and patriarchy*. London, UK: Routledge.

Wolf, N. (1991). *The beauty myth*. Toronto, ON: Vintage Books.

Wolsko, P.M., Eisenberg, D.M., Davis, R.B., Ettner, S.L., & Phillips, R.S. (2002). Insurance coverage, medical conditions and visits to alternative medicine providers: Results of a national survey. *Archives of Internal Medicine, 162*(3), 281–285.

Women and Health Care Reform. (2008). Women and private health insurance. Retrieved from www.womenandhealthcarereform.ca/en/publications.html#insurance

Women's Health in Women's Hands Community Health Centre. (2003). Racial discrimination as a health risk for female youth: Implications for policy and healthcare delivery in Canada. Toronto, ON: The Canadian Race Relations Foundation.

Wong, M., & Neill, S. (2000). Physician use of complementary and alternative medicine (CAM) literature. *Complementary Therapies in Medicine, 9*(3), 173–177.

Wordsworth, A. and Armstrong, L. (2009, Spring). Risks of exposure to environmental contaminants during pregnancy. *Women and Environments*, 80/81, 26–28.

Working conditions as a determinant of health. Retrieved from www.phac-aspc.gc.ca/ph-sp/oi-ar/05_working-eng.php

World Bank. (2004). *World development report 2004: Making services work for poor people*. New York, NY: World Bank and Oxford University Press.

World Nuclear Association. (2009). Retrieved from www.world-nuclear.org/info/inf32.html

Wotherspoon, T. (2009). Transformation in Canadian nursing and nurse education. In S. Bolaria, & H. Dickinson (Eds), *Health, illness and health care in Canada* (4th ed.) (pp. 99–121). Toronto, ON: Nelson Education Ltd.

Wright, E.O. (1997). *Class counts: Comparative studies in class analysis*. Cambridge, UK: Cambridge University Press.

Wuest, J., Hodgins, M.J., Malcolm, J., Merritt-Gray, M., & Seaman, P. (2007). The effects of past relationship and obligation on health and health promotion in women caregivers of adult family members. *Advances in Nursing Science*, 30(3), 206–220.

Yalnizyan, A. (2005). *Getting better health care: Lessons from (and for) Canada*. Ottawa, ON: Canadian Centre for Policy Alternatives.

Yalnizyan, A. (2007). *The Rich and the Rest of Us*. Ottawa: ON, Canadian Centre for Policy Alternatives, March.

Yamashita, H., Tsukayama, H., & Sugishita, C. (2002). Popularity of complementary and alternative medicine in Japan: A telephone survey. *Complementary Therapies in Medicine, 10*(2), 84–93.

Yassi, A., & Hancock, T. (2005, Oct.). Patient safety-worker safety: Building a culture of safety to improve healthcare worker and patient well-being. *Healthcare Quarterly*, 8 (Special Issue), 32–38.

York University Centre for Health Studies. (1999). *Complementary and alternative health practices and therapies: A Canadian overview*. Toronto, ON: Prepared for Health Promotion and Programs Branch, Health Canada.

Zawilski, V. (2010). (Ed). *Inequality in Canada* (2nd ed.). Toronto, ON: Oxford University Press.

Zazzera, L.D. (2007, Winter). Marginalization and its connection to stroke in women. *OWHN e-Bulletin*. Retrieved from www.owhn.on.ca/ebulletin,spring2007 .htm#a.

Zborowski, M. (1952). Cultural components in responses to pain. *Journal of Social Issues, 8*(4), 16–30.

Znaimer, M. (2010). Who's zooming who? CARPHealth. Retrieved from http://imakesnews.com/ca/carppromotions/e

Zola, I.K. (1972). Medicine as an institution of social control. *Sociological Review*, 20, 407–584.

———. (2000). Pathways to the doctor: From person to patient. In P. Brown (Ed), *Perspectives in medical sociology* (3rd ed.) (pp. 198–214). Illinois: Waveland Press.

Index

Note: Page numbers in boldface indicate figures.